THE COMPLETE CATALOGUE OF BRITISH CIGARETTE CARDS

THE
COMPLETE
CATALOGUE
OF BRITISH
CIGARETTE CARDS

COMPILED BY
THE LONDON CIGARETTE CARD COMPANY

SECOND EDITION

Webb & Bower

EXETER, ENGLAND

First published in Great Britain 1981 by
Webb & Bower (Publishers) Limited
9 Colleton Crescent, Exeter, Devon EX2 4BY
in association with Limelight Limited
Chudleigh Knighton, Newton Abbot, Devon TQ13 0HD

Second edition 1982

Designed by Brian Ainsworth

British Library Cataloguing in Publication Data
  The complete catalogue of British cigarette
    cards.
    1. Cigarette cards – Great Britain – Collectors and collecting
    I. London Cigarette Card Company
    769.5   NE965.3.G7
    ISBN 0-906671-85-X

Typeset in Great Britain by Keyspools Limited, Golborne,
Warrington, Lancashire.

Printed and bound in Hong Kong by Mandarin Offset
International Limited

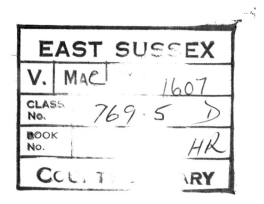

CONTENTS

PART ONE

History and Development—*page 8*

Origins—The Edwardian era—The Great War—Twenties trends—Cartophily gets organized—The Thirties: heyday of cards—The Approach of World War II—Card issues cease—Britain at war—Post-war resumption of card issues—The Fifties and Sixties—The dawn of a new era

Collecting—*page 20*

Why people collect cards—The great rarities—Errors and varieties—Silks and novelties—How to start collecting—Buying cards—Condition—Investment—Literature—Display and storage—Security—Selling your cards

PART TWO—ILLUSTRATIONS

Natural history

Butterflies and moths—Birds—Trees, plants and flowers—Wild animals—Dogs and pets

Sport

Horses and the Turf—Cricket—Football—Golf—Wrestling—General sports and games

Armed forces

Military—Navy

Transport

Aviation—Motoring—Shipping—Railways

Entertainment

Cinema, stage and radio stars

Pre-1919 beauties

Royalty

Famous People

Commemorative issues

The Arts

Music and literature—Famous paintings—Architecture and buildings

Places and views

Heraldry

Flags

Antiques

Tricks and puzzles

Supplement on Railways – *pages 129–160*

PART THREE—THE CATALOGUE

PART ONE

HISTORY AND DEVELOPMENT

Origins

During the seventeenth and eighteenth centuries, tradesmen often produced cards to advertise their wares, among which was snuff. Attractive examples of snuff cards have survived from this period and fairly typical is one which appeared recently in auction. It pictures a man and a woman between whom is the verse 'Gentlemen: A virgin that's old and thin in her shape, the stars have decreed to be your wedded mate. Lady: A man of high birth and wealth you shall marry, and a title to boot so dear Miss do not tarry'. Another feature of early, hand-packaging days was the tobacconist's use of specially printed strips of paper for wrapping smokers' purchases. One such was R. Ellis of High Street, Hastings, whose wrappers depicted twelve different sketches celebrating the Alaskan gold rush to which Mr. Ellis's brother had gone to seek his fortune. Each picture was accompanied by a piece of doggerel such as 'Restored to wealth we tried and more, at length we hit on a golden store, we dug and waded and some gold we bore, from the Diggins'.

With the advent of wrapping machines in the nineteenth century, pieces of plain card were used as protective stiffeners for the contents of the paper packages and by the late 1870s in the USA these inserts were being embellished with advertisements and pictures. Smokers began to collect the cards in order to obtain the full series and the hobby of cartophily was born. It soon became obvious to the original issuers that this was a highly effective method of encouraging brand loyalty, and the practice spread rapidly to other manufacturers. It was one of these American companies, Allen & Ginter, who were responsible for introducing the fore-runner of the first British cigarette cards when they packed with their Richmond Gem brand a pair of oval cards held together by a stud, one section of which was a calendar for 1884 with UK parcel postage rates on the back.

By the 1890s, many of the larger British tobacco companies were issuing cards. Beginning with advertisement cards, they soon progressed to series on particular themes: beauties, soldiers, ships, kings and queens, etc. They were usually coloured lithographs printed to an exceptionally high standard with decorative, but non-descriptive, backs. The first company to issue photographic cigarette cards on a large scale was Ogdens. In 1894 they began their Guinea Gold and Tabs cards and during the next thirteen years many thousands of different cards were issued covering almost every facet of the life of that period, a truly unique visual record.

It was Ogdens who were to become the springboard for an American assault on the British market. In 1901 James 'Buck' Duke, chief of the giant American Tobacco Company, bought Ogdens of Liverpool and set about a programme of price-cutting and bonus schemes. Thirteen of the largest UK manufacturers pooled their resources to meet the challenge, as a result of which the Imperial Tobacco Company was set up. Fierce competition thwarted Duke's masterplan and a year later he sold out to Imperial. During the years which followed, more firms joined Imperial, but each company retained its identity within the group and continued to issue cards in its own right.

The Edwardian era

In the early 1900s there were around 150 different companies issuing cards in Great Britain and Ireland and between them they issued approximately 1800 series in the years up to 1919. The predominance of male smokers is reflected in the subject matter on these early cards: actresses and beauties were extremely popular, as were series on sporting themes. The British Empire was at its zenith and the might of Britain's army and navy was unparalleled. Within this context, armed conflict gave added impetus to military issues, and the Boer War, Boxer Rebellion and the Russo-Japanese War featured prominently. Queen Victoria's death in 1901 had a traumatic effect on the nation and led to a spate of Royalty issues. Major centenaries such as the Battle of Trafalgar were celebrated by special issues such as Wills' *Nelson Series* and Player's *Life on Board a Man of War in 1805 and 1905*. Two great contemporary inventions, the motor car and the aeroplane, inspired the first of many series on these themes. Exploration and discovery caught the public's imagination, hence series devoted to Polar Exploration, Egyptology and Wireless Telegraphy. In this category Wills' *Famous Inventions* provides a fascinating insight into the scientific and technical achievements of the era. The influence that the scouting movement had at this period is evidenced by its extensive coverage on cards. The Edwardian fascination with collecting undoubtedly stimulated some of the many issues on birds' eggs, butterflies, porcelain, etc. The popularity of the stage, especially the music hall, as the principal medium of entertainment is also apparent. And, apart from these themes, hundreds of other series were produced on almost every topic imaginable from architecture to zoology. By 1913 the majority of new issues bore the welcome addition of descriptive backs.

The Great War

The outbreak of the War in 1914 sparked off a great number of patriotic card issues. Many influences were at work: the spontaneous expression of national pride; a desire to help the war effort; an insatiable public craving for news, particularly good news and information; a need to focus antagonistic emotions by vilifying the enemy; to glorify the heroism of our gallant forces; and to demonstrate the supporting role of civilians on the home front. Early in the War, Wills issued a series of miniature

Recruiting Posters published by the Parliamentary Recruiting Committee. Some later issues by this firm, notably *Allied Army Leaders* and *Military Motors*, bore the clause 'Passed by Censor' or 'Passed for Publication by the Press Bureau' as testimony that no secrets were being betrayed. Gallahers put out no fewer than eight series of *Victoria Cross Heroes* in 1915 and 1916. Carreras' *Women on War Work* showed how wives and daughters were coping with the jobs in industry and transport which had previously been male occupations. The same company's *Raemaeker's War Cartoons* cast the enemy as treacherous barbarians. Hill's *Fragments from France* gave a lighter view of life in the trenches. Wills produced their series on the *Gems of Belgian, French and Russian Architecture* at the time when these countries were under Teutonic threat. Dozens of series were devoted to leaders, generals, heroes, uniforms, decorations, medals, weapons, equipment, warships, maps, trophies, drill, training and flags.

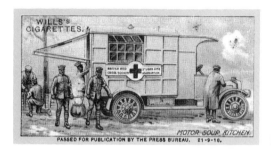

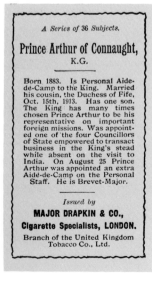

Two series of cards actually became 'war casualties'. Wills had prepared their *Waterloo* series to mark the centenary of the French Army's defeat by Wellington but for political reasons this was never actually issued, and a similar fate befell Wills' second series of *Musical Celebrities* where portraits of suitable Allied artistes were substituted for the eight original German personalities.

By 1917 the German blockade had exacted such a toll on Allied shipping that the resulting shortage of raw materials halted production of cigarette cards, bringing to a close the classic early era of card issues.

Twenties trends

When cards began to be produced once more in the early Twenties, many were merely reissues of earlier series with a timeless appeal. Players, for instance, with their *Cries of London 2nd Series* and *Characters from Dickens*, Churchman with *East Suffolk Churches*, Gallaher with *Boy Scouts*, *Fables and Their Morals*, and *Plants of Commercial Value*. Entirely new issues were soon to follow, but there was a conspicuous lack of series with a military theme. It was a time to forget the horrors of the Great War and more tranquil subjects were the order of the day. The change was even reflected in the materials used; and this was the great period of silk issues. These were especially attractive to women, and Godfrey Phillips even went so far as to issue a series called *Prizes for Needlework*. Many more sets with a feminine bias were to follow during the next two decades—*Feathered Friends*, *Flower Studies*, *Our Puppies*, *Little Friends*, *Your Birthday Tells Your Fortune*, *Our Pets*, *Home Pets*, *Cats*, *Love Scenes from Famous Films*, etc., to quote just a few. Undoubtedly the choice of such subjects

ICE LOCOMOTIVE.

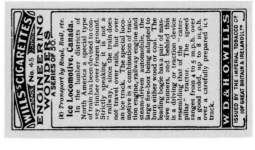

MOUNTAIN PANSY.

SIR AUSTEN CHAMBERLAIN.

was influenced by the fact that an increasing number of women were becoming smokers. Nonetheless, men still formed the largest part of the market, and the majority of issues were prepared with male interests in mind. Sporting themes, particularly football, cricket and boxing, continued to be popular, as did entertainment. Motoring and aviation increased in importance as cars and aeroplanes became part of everyday life. The designs on card backs became less ornate, the descriptions became less stilted and photographs were increasingly used. Many of the old pre-Great War companies were no longer in existence, including one of the most famous names in cartophily, Taddy & Co. This long-established company, noted for the high standard of its issues, ceased trading in 1920 following a strike of cigarette machine operatives. But there were many new firms to fill the gaps, in quantity if not in quality. The Twenties and Thirties were to become the heyday of card issues when almost one hundred different manufacturers produced between them well over 2000 series.

Cartophily gets organized

It was in the late Twenties that the first whole-hearted attempt was made to put cigarette card collecting on a sound footing. There was a hitherto un-filled need for card issues to be catalogued, for information to be recorded, and for a pool of cards to be made available to collectors. And so the London Cigarette Card Company was established by Colonel C. L. Bagnall in 1927, becoming a limited company soon afterwards. It is largely due to the Colonel's organizing ability that the hobby of cartophily, a term coined by him, can function as it does today, bringing pleasure to thousands of collectors the world over. He published the first catalogues, and founded *Cigarette Card News* in 1933. Stocks of cards were purchased by the company and then laboriously sorted into sets and carefully stored. Collectors rapidly discovered that the company's premises in West London, where the firm remained for fifty years until its move to Somerset, were a 'Mecca' from which they could obtain those elusive odd cards to make up sets, to buy complete sets, to browse or to seek advice. The company flourished and grew to employ a large full-time staff. After Colonel Bagnall's death, his daughter Dorothy became Managing Director until her retirement in 1975 when the family link spanning almost half a century ended.

Like good wine, the stocks of cards laid down in the Twenties and Thirties and carefully kept in a controlled environment ever since, are still available for sampling. Today the London Cigarette Card Company functions in much the same way as it always has done. It buys and sells old cigarette and trade cards, buys in bulk stocks of modern issues to be hand-sorted and stored to await future generations of collectors, publishes reference books, annual catalogues, and a monthly magazine, runs auctions and supplies albums and all manner of collectors' aids. Operating entirely as a mail-order concern from its premises in Sutton Road, Somerton, a small town in the heart of Somerset, the company has around five hundred million cards in stock and handles many thousands of orders during the course of a year.

The Thirties: heyday of cards

The late Twenties and early Thirties were a period of great change. Technological developments were making great strides affecting almost every sphere of life. In the cinema, silent movies gave way to the talkies and almost overnight many of the great names who were unable to adapt to the new medium, often because of poor speaking voices or thick foreign accents, disappeared into oblivion. This is well demonstrated by Wills' *Cinema Stars* where the artistes featured in the third series issued in 1931 are quite different from the stars who appeared in the first two series issued three years earlier. The cinema dominated entertainment in the Thirties, and probably more series were issued on this subject than any other, to the virtual exclusion of the stage. Usually the cards were straightforward portraits of film stars, or scenes from films, but Morris were responsible for the most imaginative series, *How Films are Made*. Radio had established itself and was a considerable influence by the early Thirties. Several firms included radio stars in general series, but Wills devoted two complete issues to *Radio Celebrities* and in 1936 Ogdens produced an excellent series on *Broadcasting* in considerable contrast to Phillips' series of the Twenties.

In travel and transport, phenomenal differences can be observed in series issued only a few years apart. Compare Murray's 1929 series *Type of Aeroplanes* with Player's 1936 issue of *International Airliners*, Wills' *Railway Engines* 1924 and their similar series of 1936, Lambert & Butler's 1926 series of *Motor Cars* with that issued in 1934, or even more strikingly with Player's two series of 1936 and 1937, and Wills' two series of *Speed* issued in 1930 and 1938.

In sport, as is to be expected, personalities were constantly changing and this was reflected by the card issues of the period. But certain comparatively new sports were rising in popularity, particularly greyhound racing, speedway and tennis. Great events came and went, many to be marked by special card issues. Numerous series were produced to celebrate the Silver Jubilee of George V, and even more for the Coronation of George VI. Phillips covered the Amsterdam Olympics in 1928. Hill issued a souvenir series on the demise of the Crystal Palace in 1936, Mitchell a series to mark the Empire Exhibition, Scotland, in 1938, and so on. Mitchell were responsible also for a glimpse of what life in the future was imagined to hold in store, *The World of Tomorrow*.

Side by side with these, hundreds of new issues on almost every imaginable theme were being poured out each year. The big companies had special departments employing artists, researchers and photographers for the sole purpose of preparing card issues on a regular basis. Printing presses up and down the country were kept busy producing cards by the million. Just one series, Wills' *Railway Engines* 1936, had a print run of 600 million. Cigarette cards had become almost an industry in their own right.

An idea of the effect that cigarette cards had on people from all walks of life at this period can be gauged from the number of anecdotes which appeared in the press, especially when hard news was scarce. There is the delightful story which appeared in a London evening paper in 1935 about a titled lady who, as she alighted from her Rolls outside Harrods, observed a pedestrian throw a cigarette card towards the gutter and sent her chauffeur to retrieve it. Not, one suspects, merely to keep the street tidy. And there were innumerable tales of schoolboys striking it rich with extraordinary runs of good luck in playground games involving cigarette cards.

The approach of World War II

As the signs of approaching conflict became more intense, so there was a change in the subjects chosen for new card series. There were still plenty of issues featuring film stars, cricketers, footballers, and flowers, but themes with a military flavour took on an increasingly important role. There were those which emphasized Britain's preparedness to defend itself against an enemy onslaught. Carreras' *Britain's Defences* issued in September 1938 is a good example. Some drew attention to the might of the armed services, hinting at the nation's ability to strike back. Player's *Aircraft of the R.A.F.* (August 1938) and *Modern Naval Craft* (February 1939) are in this category. Others sought to educate the public to distinguish between friendly and hostile aircraft—witness Lambert & Butler's 1937 series of *Aeroplane Markings*, and Godfrey Phillips' 1938 series of *Aircraft*. Many sets familiarized the population with the functions performed by the armed services and the sort of life that could be expected after call-up. Churchman issued two fine sets on *The Navy at Work* and *The R.A.F. at Work*. Ardath produced *Life in the Services*, Wills *Life in the Royal Navy*, Gallaher *The Navy*, Pattreiouex *The Navy*, Carreras *Our Navy*, Jackson *Life in the Navy*, all between 1937 and 1939. Lambert & Butler's *Interesting Customs and Traditions of the Navy, Army and Air Force* (January 1939) gave a new angle to the same topic. The desirability of being in good physical shape both as individuals and collectively as a nation, was impressed upon us by Lambert & Butler's *Keep Fit* (November 1937) and Ardath's *National Fitness* (September 1938). In a more general vein, such series as Player's *Military Uniforms of the British Empire Overseas* (1938) and *Uniforms of the Territorial Army* (1939) and Hill's *War Decorations and Medals* (1940) all had a part to play in adding to knowledge and awareness of wartime matters.

Possibly the most useful and informative of all, however, was a series produced by The Imperial Tobacco Company in August 1938. A print-run of hundreds of millions of cards was given saturation distribution in the cigarette brands of Wills, Churchman, Ogdens, Hignett and Mitchell. It was called *Air Raid Precautions* and covered such matters as how to use gas masks and stirrup pumps, how to deal with an incendiary bomb, garden shelters, refuge rooms and window protection. How many lives these cards were to save is open to speculation, but one can only applaud the responsible attitide shown by the issuers.

CATAPULTING AIRCRAFT

BREN GUN

INCENDIARY BOMB COOLING DOWN

A GALLERY OF 1934

A SERIES OF 50

8

ADOLF HITLER

At 45 Dictator of Germany. Before the War he was a house painter; to-day he is the autocratic ruler of 66,000,000 people. One of the founders of the German National Socialist Party (Nazis); eleven years ago he was sentenced to imprisonment for his share in a revolt against the Bavarian Government but was released after a few months. Now he has more power and influence over the destinies of the German people than was ever exercised by Wilhelm II. With the death of Hindenburg in 1934 came Hitler's final step to power, for he combined with the office of Chancellor which he already held, that of Leader (Führer) of the German nation.

ISSUED BY

STEPHEN MITCHELL & SON

BRANCH OF THE IMPERIAL TOBACCO CO. (OF GREAT BRITAIN & IRELAND), LTD.

ADOLF HITLER

ALBUMS FOR CHURCHMAN'S PICTURE CARDS CAN BE OBTAINED FROM TOBACCONISTS AT ONE PENNY EACH

AIR-RAID PRECAUTIONS

A SERIES OF 48

12

INCENDIARY BOMB COOLING DOWN

(Preliminary Fire Extinguishing with Jet from Stirrup Hand Pump)

Much damage may be caused in an air raid by light incendiary bombs. The intense heat and smoke from such a bomb and the fire which it will have started make close approach impossible until the atmosphere has been cooled down and the fire partly extinguished. This is done with a jet of water from a hose not less than 30 ft. long. The stirrup hand pump (illustrated and described on Card No. 16) is recommended for this purpose. The girl in the picture is kneeling, as smoke is not so thick close to the ground. Note Redhill container in foreground (see Card No. 15).

ISSUED BY THE IMPERIAL TOBACCO CO. (OF GREAT BRITAIN & IRELAND), LTD.

W. A. & A. C. CHURCHMAN

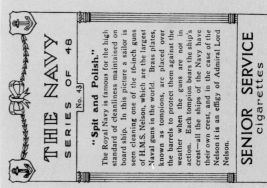

"SPIT AND POLISH"

MODERN TANK

THE NAVY

SERIES OF 48

No. 43

"Spit and Polish."

The Royal Navy is famous for the high standard of cleanliness maintained on board ship. In this picture a sailor is seen cleaning one of the 16-inch guns of H.M.S. Nelson, which are the largest Naval guns in the world. Brass plates, known as tompions, are placed over the barrels to protect them against the weather when the guns are not in action. Each tompion bears the ship's crest—all the ships of the Navy have their own crest, and in the case of the Nelson it is an effigy of Admiral Lord Nelson.

SENIOR SERVICE

cigarettes

MODERN ARMAMENTS

◇

A SERIES OF 50 SUBJECTS FROM ACTUAL PHOTOGRAPHS

◇

LOUIS GERARD

LIMITED

18 BURLINGTON ARCADE

LONDON

W.1.

THE BOATSWAIN'S PIPE.

LIFE IN THE NAVY

A SERIES OF 28.   NO.1.

THE BOATSWAIN'S PIPE

The "Bo'sun's Pipe" or "Whistle" is used by the Boatswain's mate for piping orders to the crew. It is possible to give various calls, employing different notes, with the pipe, just as it is with a bugle. The expression "to pipe" really refers to the act of calling out the order required in conjunction with the use of the "call", but nowadays the entire procedure is generally known as piping.

PETER JACKSON

Cigarettes

217, PICCADILLY. W.

Card issues cease

Cigarette Card News managed to continue publication throughout the War, albeit in abbreviated form; not so, however, the cards themselves. Casualties of the paper shortage, one manufacturer after another ceased producing cards. The magazine records each firm's exit from the ranks of card issuers—January 1940, Ogden's cigarettes 'the issue of cigarette cards has now been discontinued', February 1940, C.W.S. cigarettes 'the Society will cease to issue cards once present stocks are exhausted', and so on.

By the close of the year cigarette cards were discontinued, with just one exception. In 1941 and 1942, the Ministry of Information distributed through Ardath a series of cards headed 'It all depends on me'. Each dealt with a different civilian occupation in

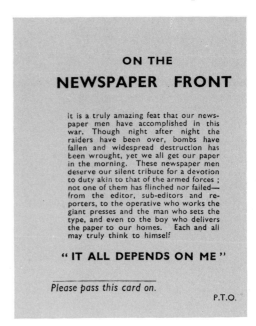

'home front' terms. Of bus, tram and lorry drivers, for instance, it was said 'These men are as brave and as tough as the men of our fighting forces, and they are playing their part in the national war effort just as nobly—all honour to them, and may each one realise from the bottom of his heart the truth of these five words "It all depends on me". Please pass this card on'.

Cartophilists went about their duties as servicemen or civilians confident that, as had happened after the Great War, once hostilities had ended it would be just a question of time before cigarette cards were issued once more. They were to be disappointed.

Britain at war

Wartime life was not all gloom and despondency, the lighter side kept shining through; and the esteem in which cigarette cards were held at that time can be gleaned from the 1940 newspaper reports of a court case. An LNER train driver, Mr William Hagland, offered to stand surety in a case being heard in a Metropolitan Court. When asked to establish his identity and provide evidence as to his good character, he produced from his hat band card no. 19 of Churchman's 1938 series of *In Town Tonight* on which Mr Hagland himself was pictured. The magistrate read aloud the wording on the back of the card, including the information that Mr Hagland was the father of twenty-three children, had completed fifty-two years service with the railway, and had appeared on television. The court had no hesitation in accepting the card as evidence.

Air-raids on London were inflicting death, devastation and the disruption of normal life. But it is interesting to note that the London Cigarette Card Company carried on business as normal despite the fact that many staff and collectors were away from home on active service. Tributes and encouragement poured in. Typical of many was one from Mr S. C. Hall, a reader in Canada. Part of his letter, reproduced in the October 1940 issue of *Cigarette Card News* said 'I sincerely trust you are none the worse for Hitler's raids on London. It must be a terrible experience for everyone, but those of us who are watching from afar are with you, and we hope that the British will give the enemy all that is coming to them. Over here, we have every confidence in the ultimate victory for Britain, but realise too that it is not going to be any walk-over. So good luck from Canada.'

The mood of defiance expressed by cartophilists is exemplified in another extract, this time from the July 1940 issue: 'In this hour, when the Press keeps nagging that we are going to be invaded, two series, Ardath's *Britain's Defenders* and Carreras' *Britain's Defences*, should be prominently displayed in every tobacconist's window. These cards would show that, whilst the newspapers were preoccupied with the trivialities of life, some patriotic manufacturers gave thought to realities. Every card is heartening, as heartening as the thought that if the Germans are nearer to us we are nearer to the Germans.'

Post-War resumption of card issues

If Lambert & Butler were issuing their series of *Common Fallacies* in 1982 instead of 1928, they would probably include one about cigarette cards not being produced after the war. The fact of the matter is that a very large number of cigarette cards have been issued in this country since 1945. The difference is that since the war the number of tobacco issues has been a mere trickle in comparison with the halcyon days of the 1930s.

At least three of the principal branches of the Imperial Tobacco Company had prepared new series of cigarette cards ready for release after the War. Churchman had *World Wonders Old and New*, Players did *Shipping* and Wills printed *Life in the Hedgerow*. None of these was ever officially issued, although some sets slipped through the net in sufficiently large quantities to make them no great rarities. It was left to the tiny Bristol firm of Richard Benson to lead the way in 1946 with a re-issue of their *Old Bristol Series*.

In the immediate post-war period, most commodities were in short supply and paper was no exception. Carreras overcame this problem by hitting upon the ingenious ploy of printing cards on the large and normally blank surface of the cardboard slide inside packets of Turf cigarettes. Beginning with *Film Stars* in 1947, they produced in this way some sixteen different series in blue and white over a period of ten years.

The Fifties and Sixties

In the early Fifties there was a flurry of activity from the minor tobacco companies. The Amalgamated Tobacco Corporation issued about forty different series during the years from 1952 to 1962, the earliest of which appear to have been diverted to the British market following an advertising ban in South Africa where the firm's principal operation was. The Coronation in 1953 prompted the Moorgate Tobacco Company, whose sales were virtually confined to Birmingham and the surrounding area, to issue a set titled *The New Elizabethan Age*, and Phillip Allman produced their *Coronation Series*. Allman also came out with some racy pin-up pictures in the same year, and the Osborne Tobacco Company gave us their series of *Modern Aircraft*. In 1955,

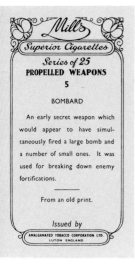

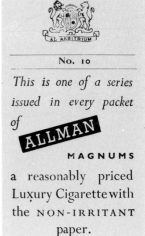

Marcovitch, whose Red and White brand was then enjoying considerable popularity, produced a brief issue. The Co-operative Wholesale Society issued their only post-war tobacco cards in 1957, a series of *Western* (film) *Stars*. May Queen cigarette cards seem to have put in an appearance at around the same time.

The less said about the Sixties the better. This was undoubtedly the darkest period for collectors of new tobacco issues. With the exception of the Amalgamated Tobacco Company's last series, a brief incursion by Dobie with their *Four Square Book* and Carreras with *Send for the Guards*, it seemed that cigarette cards were to suffer the fate of dinosaurs and dodos.

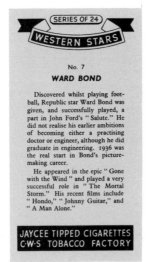

The dawn of a new era

The 1970s began in much the same way. Early in the decade, rather half-hearted attempts by Carreras with their *Military Mug Cards*, Player with their *Basket Ball* cards and Rothmans with a Consulate issue called *Country Living* had very little impact. Then suddenly in 1976 Carreras launched a new brand, or rather revived a pre-war best seller, Black Cat cigarettes. And in every packet came one of their series of fifty *Vintage Cars*. They followed up regularly with new series, *British Birds* and *Military Uniforms* in 1976, *Flowers All the Year Round* and *Kings and Queens of England* in 1977, *Sport Fish* in 1978 and *Palmistry* in 1980.

At around the same time, another major tobacco manufacturer began issuing cards. In 1975 John Player and Sons produced a series of large cards, *The Golden Age of Motoring*, packed with their Doncella cigars. This was a period when there was

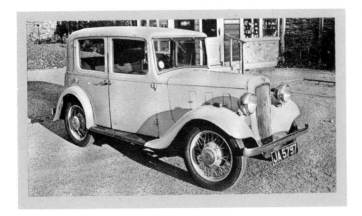
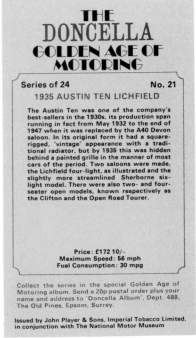

considerable publicity about the harmful effects of smoking, particularly of cigarettes, and sales of small cigars were taking an increasing share of the market. The Doncella brand thrived, and Players followed their first issue with the *Golden Age of Steam* (1976), *The Golden Age of Flying* (1977) and *The Golden Age of Sail* (1978). Having exhausted the tranport theme, Players continued in 1979 with *Napoleonic Uniforms*, followed in 1980 by *History of the V.C.*, and in 1981 by *Country Houses and Castles*. But, most encouraging of all, they extended card issues to their similar Grandee brand with *Top Dogs* (1979), *British Birds* (1980) and *Famous MG Marques* (1981).

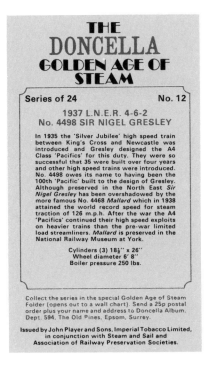

Two other recent developments are worthy of note. Towards the end of 1979, the American giant Liggett and Myers launched in their Chesterfield brand (under the Phillip Morris label in the UK) a set of *Cocktail Cards*, and the old firm of Taddy & Co. was resurrected as a new company which has since issued series of *Motor Cars* and *Railway Engines* of 1930s vintage with their Clown and Myrtle Grove brands.

Today, when the normal avenues of media advertising for tobacco products are becoming increasingly restricted, and the once-popular gift coupon schemes have ended, it is clear that manufacturers will turn to other ways of keeping up their sales. Sponsorship of sporting events undoubtedly brings a considerable publicity dividend, but the success of the Doncella and Grandee brands could point the way to another possibility, that well-tried experiment in brand loyalty which has achieved results at low cost for a hundred years, the inclusion of cigarette cards in every packet.

COLLECTING

Why people collect cards

In the earliest days of card issues people collected them simply because the cards were given away free and they found the pictures attractive. This, of course, still applies today with current series. But the majority of collectors nowadays are interested in cards which have long-since disappeared from the packets, and, like stamp collectors, they tend to have specialized interests.

Firstly, there are the thematic collectors—those who are interested in a particular subject and wish to obtain the pictures and information that relate to it. Almost every subject imaginable has a following, and such is the vast range of card series available that few interests are not covered. The most popular, however, are probably railways, cricket, military matters, football, film stars and motor cars. Not surprisingly, each of these topics has appeared in numerous series over the years, in some cases so frequently that the thematic collector is able to confine his collection to a specialized aspect, for example footballers of the 1920s, cinema stars of the 1930s, and so on.

Others collect the issues of an individual manufacturer regardless of the subject matter; or specialize in a method of printing—early lithography, photogravure, real photographs, etc. Here, for the student of the art of printing, there is a visual record of printing developments during the past hundred years. And it is not only the changes in printing techniques that can be traced, but also fashions in type-faces and styles of graphic ornamentation. The backs of cards vary from the ornate and flowery designs and descriptions of the Victorian era to the more functional appearance of the present-day designs.

Because cards tend to reflect faithfully the age in which they were issued, there are groups of collectors who enjoy collecting cards from just one decade, a monarch's reign, or some other clearly defined period. A broadly-based collection built up in this way would show the royal, political, military, sporting and entertainment personalities of that time, the modes of transport, great events such as coronations and exhibitions, the achievements and discoveries of the generation, and its hopes, aspirations and fears.

The accuracy of both texts and pictures on cigarette cards makes them a useful source of material for historians, researchers and the media. Television companies regularly resort to cards in order to lend authenticity to nostalgia progammes, documentaries and period dramas. Examples of this are the BBC's use of one of Carreras' *Women on War Work* cards on the front cover of *Radio Times* (advertising a series about the role of women during the Great War), and ITV's use of Lambert & Butler's *Dance Band Leaders* for their programmes about the great British bands of the Thirties.

In another category are 'type' collectors: those who collect a single card from a series, rather than a complete set. Sometimes this is because sets are simply not available, as is often the case with particularly rare and expensive cards, but often it is because in this way a person of limited means with an ambitious collecting aim can obtain at least a representative selection of the cards he requires. That is not to imply that cartophily needs to be an expensive hobby. A quick glance through the catalogue section of this book will show that many series more than forty years old and in prime condition can be purchased for between two and five pounds per set. And bearing in mind that sets commonly comprise fifty cards, compare those prices with what you would have to pay for stamps and other collectors' items of equal age and condition.

The great rarities

The great rarities are those cards which are in shortest supply and highest demand. As a general rule, the older the series the fewer cards there are still around in top condition. The number originally printed also affects availability. Some large manufacturers ran off their series by the hundred million, whilst the small firms produced only a few thousand. Certain companies' cards have a special quality— Taddy for instance—and demand for them is disproportionately high. Subject matter, too, has an effect; for example cricketers are more keenly sought after than, say, flowers. The method of printing also creates desirability, with coloured lithographs being more attractive than photographic cards to most collectors. Finally, there are those cards which, for one reason or another, were never officially circulated but of which a few sets have survived.

A handful of series from the earlier (pre-Great War) period of card issues are particularly rare and are priced at more than £100 per card. Many collectors will never come across any of them during a lifetime of cartophily, and as complete sets they hardly ever come on to the market. The record price for a set of cards sold at auction still stands at more than £2,000, the price paid in 1976 for the Taddy set of 20 *Clowns and Circus Artistes*. Today there are many series which if auctioned as a complete set in top condition would each fetch over £1,000. In June 1981, £510 was paid for the earliest known British cigarette card—the record price for a single card.

The catalogue section of this book will reveal those series that are scarcest. Against a few entries there is not even a price shown for odd cards, let alone sets. This means that the series has been recorded and documented at some time during the history of cartophily, but cards are hardly ever seen and are not even to be found among the London Cigarette Card Company's massive stocks. Knowledge of cards is being supplemented all the time. Previously unrecorded cards are being discovered quite regularly, as a quick glance through the 'Discoveries' column of *Cigarette Card News* will reveal. Almost invariably such hitherto undocumented items are placed in auction.

Of the series in the 'unissued' category, Wills' *Waterloo* is probably the most celebrated. Having been prepared to celebrate the centenary of the famous battle, it was not issued for political reasons, but a handful of sets survived. The same firm's series on the *Life of King Edward VIII* was also never issued because of the King's abdication.

Errors and varieties

Unlike philately, where freak stamps are often the most keenly sought after and become highly priced rarities, the errors and varieties that occur on cigarette cards do not attract the cartophilist in the same way and therefore tend to be available at the same price as ordinary cards or at only a modest premium. Considering the enormous number of different series that have been issued, the occurrence of such abnormalities is remarkably small, but they can be grouped into three categories: errors of fact in the picture or text; technical misprints; and alterations made during the currency of a series due to changing circumstances.

Perhaps the most celebrated example of a pictorial error occurs on no. 43 of Player's *Dandies*. The artist portrayed Disraeli at the age of twenty-two with Big Ben in the background. However, when Big Ben was installed in the clock tower at Westminster, Disraeli would have been in his late fifties. As soon as the mistake was discovered, attempts were made to erase the offending tower but it remained as a shadow. In the later printing the whole background was removed. Another well-known blunder crops up on no. 21 of Carreras' *Figures of Fiction* where the negro Uncle Tom has pink feet.

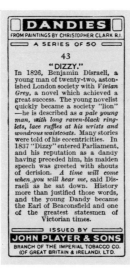

Errors of text can be demonstrated by reference to Player's *British Empire Series*. On no. 7, 'Corroboree' was originally printed as 'Corrohoree', and on no. 10 the caption was at first printed as N.S.W. Postman on 'Skates', changed later to 'Ski'.

All kinds of technical errors can be found on cards. An often quoted example is the mirror-image numeral 4 on some Cope's *Castles* cards. It is not unknown for the printing to become so out-of-register that, in extreme cases, the text on the back of one picture may in fact belong to a different number in the series, or indeed for one side to be blank. Sometimes a colour is entirely missing, or printed slightly out-of-register giving the picture a blurred 3-D effect.

More numerous, however, are the true 'varieties' where the text has been altered during a print-run or before reprinting. Wills' 1936 series of *Household Hints* demonstrates this at no. 43. On the original printing, the description on the back refers to 'cleaning a Thermos flask'. Second thoughts on accuracy caused this to be changed to 'cleaning a vacuum flask'. At no. 16 in the same issue, the original text concerning

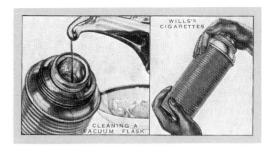 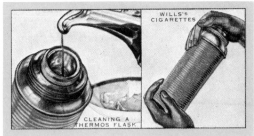

the use of carbon tetrachloride or benzene for treating woodworm was amended to state that these inflammable liquids should be handled carefully. Whether or not this latter alteration was the result of a sharp-eyed safety-conscious member of the smoking public drawing the manufacturer's attention to the potential hazards of these chemicals is not recorded. Quick reaction to changing circumstances can be seen clearly in the text alterations made on no fewer than ten different cards in Player's 1939 issue of *Uniforms of the Territorial Army*. Printing of this series was actually in progress at the outbreak of war, and references to 'the war' were changed to 'the Great War' or to 'the 1914–1918 war'. Military personalities were constantly being promoted in rank, or receiving new decorations, and the cards had to keep pace. Hence Baden-Powell can be found as either a Colonel or a Major-General in Salmon and Gluckstein's *Heroes of the Transvaal War*. Footballers were forever changing clubs, and there are many

instances of the player being quoted in the same card series as representing different teams; for example Ashurst on no. 27 of Gallaher's *Famous Footballers* appears for both Notts County and West Bromwich Albion.

Where a considerable period of time has elapsed between printings, some fairly drastic changes can be seen. A good example occurs in Wills' *Locomotives, Engines and Rolling Stock*. The first printing was in 1901, the second in 1903. In between, Wills had become a part of the Imperial Tobacco Company and the later printing has a clause noting this fact, but several cards also bore different pictures showing newer types of engine. There was an even longer gap between the two printings of Player's series of *Players Past and Present*. On the 1923 reprint, seven years after the original issue, the descriptions on numbers 4 and 6 had been altered to take into account the death of the subjects portrayed—Sir George Alexander and Sir Herbert Tree respectively.

Nor was it unusual for one card to be substituted with a completely different picture. This is commonplace in Ogdens long-running Guinea Gold series. Player's *Gallery of Beauty* from the 1890s contains five alternative portraits. And, of course, there is that previously mentioned casualty of the Great War, Wills' *Musical Celebrities* second series.

Silks and novelties

Straightforward rectangular pieces of cardboard were by far the most common type of cigarette card, but many firms have striven over the years to introduce an element of individuality and surprise to their issues. The result has been not only a wealth of different card shapes and ideas, but also an extraordinary variety in the materials actually used. Into this latter category come fabrics, metals and celluloid.

Amongst the less common paper and cardboard issues are circular cards such as Rothman's *Beauties of the Cinema* and Godfrey Phillips' *Cinema Stars*, and oval cards such as Carreras' two series of 72 *Film Stars* and 72 *Popular Personalities*. Some manufacturers, Drapkin for example, with their *Soldiers and their Uniforms*, and Carreras with *Flags of the Allies*, produced cards die-cut to an outline shape, or push-out cards on which the subject outline had been perforated, such as Ogdens with their 1923 series of *Birds' Eggs* and *Children of All Nations*.

An idea popular with several companies was the sectional series whereby each card formed a portion of a larger picture. Wills used this concept for their 1920s series of *Famous Pictures*, Millhoff for their *Geographia Map Series*, Ogdens for their *Sectional Cycling Map* and *Coronation Procession*, Anstie for half a dozen different sets issued in the mid-Thirties, and Ardath for their *Empire Flying Boat* and *Trooping the Colour*. John Player and Sons came up with a novel departure from their normal issues when in the early Thirties they produced transfers of *Aviary and Cage Birds*, *Boy Scout and Girl Guide Patrol Signs and Emblems*, *Butterflies*, *Derby and Grand National Winners*, *Dogs*, *Poultry*, *Wild Animals* and *Wild Birds*; when wetted the image could be transferred to another surface and this feature made them particularly attractive to youngsters. Godfrey Phillips produced a *Novelty Series*, each card comprising two sections slotted together which, when pulled apart, caused the subject to alter its appearance. The same firm issued postcards in its larger cigarette packs, stamp cards bearing real foreign stamps, and voucher cards exchangeable for gifts. Sarony punched holes in the margins of some of their issues so that they could be fitted into special binders; Carreras produced a miniature English-French dictionary booklet; Players gave out long, thin book-marks depicting famous authors, and Wills, among others, issued calendars.

A wide variety of card games was issued. Miniature playing cards abounded. Carreras introduced the game element with many of their series: *Alice in Wonderland*, *Granpop*, *Greyhound Racing Game*, *Happy Family*, etc. Drapkin had *The Game of Sporting Snap*, Churchman thought of *Contract Bridge*, Copes liked *The Game of Poker* and there were numerous series to do with fortune-telling, horoscopes and palmistry. Most commonly, particularly among early series of actresses and beauties, the playing card was inset at the corner of each picture so that the series could be treated as a normal issue for its subject matter, or used as a set of playing cards.

Cavanders utilized the stereoscopic technique, issuing sets of photographic cards each with a left and a right image which appeared three-dimensional when looked at through a special viewer. A fertile imagination on the Wills payroll created their *Animalloys* series—sectional cards of real animals designed so that the various portions

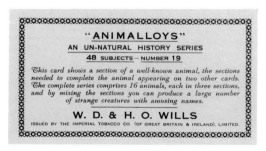

were interchangeable to produce all sorts of weird imaginary beasts. With children very much in mind, some companies issued model series, for example Carreras *Round the World Scenic Models*, Mitchell *Village Models*, and Phillips *Model Railways*. And some companies seem to have developed what might be mistaken for sponsorship in reverse to promote, in a subtle way of course, the attractions of a particular railway company—Murray's *Holidays by the L.M.S.*, Couden's *Holiday Resorts in East Anglia served by the L.N.E.R.*

From an early date, the tobacco companies diversified into the use of fabrics instead of paper. These are invariably grouped together by collectors as silks and canvasses. With silks, the picture could be either embroidered or printed on to the material, and sometimes the fabric was paper-backed to make handling easier. Amongst the embroidered silks, military subjects and flowers are predominant. Anstie were masters of this technique, producing some fine woven examples such as *Regimental Badges* and *The Royal Standard*. Perhaps the best known of all silks are the *Kensitas Flowers*, which were silks embroidered in Eastern Europe under contract to J. Wix and Sons of London, each flower being enclosed in a paper folder giving details of the subject. The firm also produced a special presentation album into which the folders could be inserted.

The great majority of silks, however, were printed rather than embroidered. Godfrey Phillips were by far the most prolific issuers, turning out something in the region of fifty different series between 1910 and 1925. Often these bear the B.D.V. brand initials and cover a variety of subjects: paintings, ceramics, beauties, badges, crests and arms, birds, butterflies, flags, war heroes, etc. Wix distributed large numbers of their *British Empire Flags* and *National Flags*, each enclosed in a transparent paper pocket. R. & J. Lea were one of the better known issuers of paper-backed silks, with popular series of *Butterflies and Moths*, *Old Pottery* and *Regimental Crests and Badges*. B. Morris, Drapkin, Muratti, Murray and several smaller firms are also noted for their paper-backed issues.

Canvasses, or rather a linen fabric glazed to give the appearance of canvas, were the domain of Hill and Muratti who used this material to enhance their *Canvas Masterpieces*, etc.

Carreras produced *Lace Motifs*. Less commonly, metal was used. The International Tobacco Company used thin bronze to cold-stamp their *Famous Buildings and Monuments of Britain* into relief and enclosed the resulting metal plaques in cellophane envelopes with a descriptive text. Earlier, in 1901, Wills had produced a series of ten oval medalets of the *Royal Family and Boer War Heroes* which could be attached to a watch-chain, and in the Thirties Rothmans issued a series of metal charms for attaching to a bracelet. Cohen Weenen combined metal with card to produce a series of metal-framed portraits of celebrities.

In a class of their own were the miniature gramophone records with a cardboard backing issued as a variety series of 25 'Talkie' cigarette cards by the Record Cigarette Company of London.

How to start collecting

For newcomers to the hobby, the sheer variety to choose from may seem a little daunting. A good starting point for a new collector would be to scan the catalogue at the back of this book, making a list of the series which seem 'probables' both for content and price. A good representative selection is actually illustrated in the central section of this book. Alternatively, you might decide to purchase an odd card from each of the series concerned to make sure that they come up to your expectations before buying a complete set. If the amount of money available is somewhat limited, and this applies particularly to young collectors, it is worth considering whether to start with the modern trade issues, of which there are three or four thousand series listed in the L.C.C. Co's Trade Card Catalogue ('trade cards' are those cards issued by companies other than cigarette manufacturers), most of which cost less than a pound a set. Or, for a little over a pound, you can buy a bundle of one hundred assorted trade cards (two cards from each of fifty different series).

A subscription to *Cigarette Card News* is recommended because this magazine will keep you in touch with what is happening in the hobby. Merely by having read this book, you will have some idea about the history of cards, what some of them look like, the range of subjects, and their prices. There is, however, another book of a general nature which would be useful to the beginner, a paper-back by Dorothy Bagnall called *Collecting Cigarette Cards and Other Trade Issues*. Further information about these books and other cartophilic publications will be found later in the literature section.

Buying cards

Many people who buy this book will be collectors of long-standing with substantial holdings of cigarette cards built up over the years to whatever pattern they have found appeals to them most. They may wish to add to their collections by buying complete sets of cards. Alternatively, they may already possess part sets needing odd cards for completion, or may have sets in which some cards have been damaged and need replacing. Almost certainly The London Cigarette Card Company Limited will be able to help. For full details, see 'How to Order Cards' on page 255.

If you are thinking about buying cards in auction, the London Cigarette Card Company stages five or six a year at Caxton Hall in London. The auction catalogues are sent out a month or six weeks in advance, free to subscribers to *Cigarette Card News* (which I shall mention later), or on application. The company's auction department takes great pains to ensure that each lot is fully and accurately described, including the all-important condition of the cards. You do not have to be present in the room in order to take part because collectors can bid by post confident that if successful they will receive goods which match their description. This is not true of all auctions, especially those run by non-specialists who include a few cigarette cards as part of a general sale, not because they intend to deceive but because they do not have the expertise to evaluate condition.

The London Cigarette Card Company's auctions at Caxton Hall are extremely popular cartophilic events. Often the sale includes rare or even previously unknown cards and those present have the opportunity to examine these treasures even if they have no intention of bidding. And, of course, there is always the chance to snap up a bargain because invariably there are lots which are knocked down for as little as one pound. Another aspect which encourages collectors to travel long distances, even from overseas, is the chance to meet fellow-collectors in a relaxed atmosphere where news and ideas can be freely exchanged. In addition to the auction itself, there are hundreds of sets of cards available for direct sale, and the collector is at liberty to browse. A full range of catalogues, reference books, albums, selections of rare odd cards, cards stuck in special albums, and collectors' aids, is also on offer.

Condition

Whether you are buying purely for the joy of collecting, or with investment potential in mind, one factor is of absolutely paramount importance. That is the condition of the cards. The prices which are quoted in the catalogue are the London Cigarette Card Company's selling prices for cards in best condition. This means that the cards should be perfect in every respect.

If you are tempted to buy cards from other collectors or from shops, you are advised to be cautious. Before committing yourself to a purchase you would be wise to examine each card carefully to make sure the set is complete, to satisfy yourself as to condition, and to check our catalogue price to ensure that you are getting value for money. Beware of cut cards—those which have been trimmed to make the edges appear sharp, or cards which have been cut from proof sheets; these are often virtually worthless. Cards stuck in their special albums, like those issued by Players and Wills for adhesive-backed cards in the 1930s, are of considerably less value than cards which have not been stuck in.

Investment

Naturally, prices have increased over the years, partly because of inflation generally, but also because more people are collecting cards now than at any time since the War, and thus altering the balance between supply and demand. On average, prices for cards in 1982 are 140% higher than they were five years ago. Many series are below the norm, some have trebled in value. This leads to another class of collector: those who buy cards for investment. Of course, everybody who collects cards is an investor to some degree. No one wishes to pay more than he has to for anything, and there is a certain satisfaction in knowing that what you possess is more valuable than when it was bought. But, for most collectors, the financial aspect is of secondary importance; the main attraction is the merit of the cards themselves. Nonetheless, with conventional methods of saving and investment often yielding a return which is less than the rise in the cost of living, it is hardly surprising that works of art, antiques, stamps, etc., which have appreciated in value by more than the rate of inflation, have attracted the attention of investors. Cigarette cards are no exception. The growth in card values has been steady rather than spectacular, but it is undoubtedly true that wise buying has in the past proved to be a sound long-term investment. The key words here are 'wise' and 'long-term'. Anybody who thinks he is going to be able to buy cards now and sell them in a few months for a quick profit is going to be disappointed. For a start, the companies whose business it is to deal in cards have to cover their running costs, and so they will buy in at less than the catalogue selling price. Secondly, values increase gradually and sensibly as the years go by; there are not the frantic leaps and deep plunges that are associated with the gold market or the stock exchange.

Literature

There are many cartophilic publications ranging from the general to the specific. A catalogue is available which covers only trade cards; and they too have a long history. In the period since 1945 trade cards have formed the bulk of the new issues, and the trade card catalogue features around 4000 different series of all ages from the late nineteenth century up to the present day.

Shortly to be published is yet another catalogue which covers overseas issues of cigarette cards: European, American, African, Asian and Australian series. The London Cigarette Card Company is also responsible for two handbooks (the H and Ha references in the catalogue section of this book refer to the relevant entries in Handbook Parts I and II respectively). These give cross-references and provide additional information, such as subject listings of un-numbered series, and illustrations of non-descriptive cards. There are also reference booklets, each dealing in detail with the issues of an individual manufacturer or group of manufacturers. Of similar format is the *Directory of British Issuers* and *Glossary of Cartophilic Terms*. There is the *World Index and Handbook Part I* listing tobacco issues of the world (without prices) and the supplementary *World Indices Parts II and III*, all extremely weighty volumes. Dorothy Bagnall's *Collecting Cigarette Cards and Other Trade Issues* traces the history and development of picture-cards with chapters on specific aspects of collecting. Lastly, and by no means least, is *Cigarette Card News and Trade Card Chronicle*, which has been published by us regularly ever since 1933. Posted monthly to collectors in more than thirty countries, the magazine contains articles by expert contributors on various aspects of cartophily, detailed information on new series as they are issued, valuable notes resulting from research by the compilers and by collectors, readers' letters, advertisements and announcements of interest to collectors, special lists including money-saving offers, free catalogues for public and postal auctions, and free sample cards of certain new issues. Full details of how to subscribe, and of how to obtain the books mentioned in this section, will be found in the catalogue section at the end of this book.

Display and storage

As long ago as the turn of the century, Ogdens were supplying specially-made cardboard albums so that collectors could display their 'Guinea Gold' cards two hundred at a time. Other manufacturers, particularly Players and Wills, produced similar hard-back albums of varying capacities, and later most of the large tobacco companies issued paper albums designed to house individual sets of cards. These were generally of either the 'corner slot' variety, with slots cut in the pages into which the corners of cards could be inserted, or the 'slip in' type whereby cards could be slid between the two layers of the page until the picture appeared in the aperture. Both these types of album were far from ideal in that they permitted only one side to be exhibited or, if they were of the 'through window' type, only the central portion of each card was shown. A further disadvantage was that the card surfaces were exposed to handling and marking. Another kind of album popular in the Thirties was the type that was designed for cards to be stuck into. The series for which they were intended had adhesive backs and the descriptive texts were printed alongside the appropriate card-spaces for reference once the cards had been stuck down.

Since the War, modern materials have made the older types of album obsolete. Today there is available a range of loose-leaf binders into which can be inserted leaves to house many different sizes of card. Made from various types of plastic material, each leaf contains pockets into which the cards can be slipped. Once in place, the full area of both the front and back of each card is displayed, and the plastic film obviates the old problem caused by handling. Different sizes of card can be housed in the same album and pages can be added or removed at will for easy rearrangement. Spaces at the margins of the leaves and a pocket on the album's outer spine are useful for inserting notes and index references.

If you intend neither to look at your cards nor to handle them, they may be wrapped in paper for storage in drawers until required. Semi-transparent, high quality 'glascine' paper wrapping strips, ready cut to size, are available in packs of 200 from the London Cigarette Card Company. Do not use rubber bands on cards; over a long period indentations will appear wherever contact is made, and the rubber may also stain your cards.

It is vitally important that cards are stored in the right conditions. Strong sunlight can lead to fading; dust will make the outer surfaces dirty; bookworms or other undesirables will ruin your cards. The worst enemy of all is moisture; it can lead to mildew, buckling, and sticking together. So do not keep your cards in an attic or in a room liable to condensation. Ideally, cards are best kept in a dry room with an even temperature, and, of course, out of reach of young children and pets.

Security

As with all items of value, it is only common sense that you should take steps to ensure the security of your collection. It is not unknown for cigarette cards to be stolen and when this happens details of the traceable rare items are exchanged among dealers so that, if the criminals attempt to sell, the police can be alerted. I am pleased to say that this sytem has proved very effective. There is little that can be done to thwart really desperate crooks, apart from depositing your collection in a bank strongroom, which, of course, would rather spoil the enjoyment of ownership. However, there are other less extreme measures that can be taken to make a collection less vulnerable. Firstly, to adapt the old wartime slogan, 'Careless words cost cards'. To talk openly in the hearing of strangers about your valuable collection is asking for trouble. If your local newspaper wants to publish an article about you and your collection, as they often do, do not let them print your address, because it could be an open invitation to an unwelcome visitor. Secondly, it is a good idea to consult a crime prevention officer at your local police station. His advice is free, and he will be able to tell you how to improve the security of your home. The fitting of special window and door locks is a useful and comparatively low-cost safeguard. If you are going to be away from home for any length of time on business or on holiday, ask the neighbours to keep an eye on the house and tell the police so that they can make periodic checks to ensure that all is well. Thirdly, if the worst does happen, there is some consolation in being adequately insured against your loss. An ordinary household-contents policy will not cover a valuable collection, and you would be wise to contact an insurance broker to obtain competitive quotes before taking out a special policy. Finally, you can help yourself and fellow-collectors by reporting anything suspicious you see or hear, and by telling the police if you are offered cards in dubious circumstances.

Selling your cards

Collectors who wish to change the emphasis of their collection may find that they have cards which they no longer require and therefore wish to sell. The catalogue section of this book will give an indication of their comparative worth. The London Cigarette Card Company are interested in buying cards, but please remember that normally we will accept only those in top condition and that the allowance for odd cards is going to be considerably less than for complete sets because of all the trouble and expense involved in having to sort them into stock. Very rare cards are acceptable in substandard condition. We will also take complete sets stuck in their manufacturers' original special albums, but bear in mind that these are worth less than top class cards which have not been stuck down. Before we buy your cards, we must examine them to assess their worth. Pack them carefully before posting; do not bring them to us personally. On receipt, our experts will inspect all the cards before sending you a form on which is indicated their value to us. If you do not wish to accept the amount shown, we will be happy to send back the cards on payment of the cost of return postage, plus a 50p handling fee to cover part of the administrative expense involved.

PART TWO

Orange Tip

LIME HAWK-MOTH & LARVA

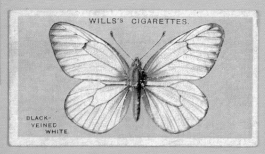

BLACK-VEINED WHITE

COMMON BLUE

BROAD BORDERED BEE HAWK-MOTH

SMALL COPPER

LARGE GARDEN WHITE; FEMALE.

S. America—
Chlorippe lavinia

GOLDEN KNIGHT CIGARETTES

JERSEY TIGER MOTH (enlarged).

Occasional in England. More common in South of Europe. Seen in July. Fond of sunning on thistles, preferring weedy slopes to gardens.

These satin butterfly illustrations are delightful subjects for embroidery and applique. Patterns for a variety of subjects, with instructions, will be sent post free on request, accompanied by empty packet, addressed to R. J. LEA, LTD., "Chairman" Tobacco Factory, Manchester.

R. J. LEA LTD. MANCHESTER.

BUTTERFLIES & MOTHS — THESE PICTURES ARE ISSUED BY **ADKIN & SONS** BRANCH OF THE IMPERIAL TOBACCO CO. (OF GREAT BRITAIN AND IRELAND), LIMITED.

25

LIME HAWK-MOTH.
(*Smerinthus tiliæ*).

This pretty moth appears during the months of May or June, and is commoner in England than it used to be, especially in the South. It is found throughout Europe, and in Siberia. It measures as much as 3 in. across the wings. The caterpillar is rough, has seven oblique stripes on each side, with a horn on the tail, and feeds on the lime and elm trees. The chrysalis is of a dark brown colour, and rough like the caterpillar.

A SERIES OF 25

BRITISH BUTTERFLIES

No. 14
THE ORANGE TIP.
(*Euchloë cardamines*).

This attractive butterfly is fairly common throughout England, Ireland, Wales and southern Scotland. It is usually to be found on the outskirts of woods, along hedgerows, and in flowery lanes during May, June and sometimes in early July. In flight the Orange Tip is quite conspicuous, but when it has taken up its position for the night on a flower-head of hedge parsley or garlic mustard, with its wings folded up, it so closely resembles its background as to be almost indistinguishable. Our picture shows the male which measures about one and three-quarter inches across the wings. The female presents rather a contrast, as it is without the large orange-coloured patch which distinguishes the male.

PLAYER'S CIGARETTES
ISSUED BY **JOHN PLAYER & SONS,** BRANCH OF THE IMPERIAL TOBACCO COMPANY (OF GREAT BRITAIN & IRELAND) LIMITED

WILLS'S CIGARETTES

BRITISH BUTTERFLIES A SERIES OF 50

43

BLACK-VEINED WHITE.
(*Aporia cratægi*).

This fine insect is now extremely scarce in this country, although it was formerly very abundant in many parts of South England, especially in the New Forest and Kent. It appears on the wing during the latter part of June and first half of July, and frequents clover, lucerne, and corn-fields. The eggs are laid in batches varying from 100 to 200 in a batch, on hawthorn, blackthorn, and different varieties of cultivated trees; the caterpillars hibernate and pupate when about two-thirds grown in the following May. The butterfly measures in expanse 2¼ inches.

ISSUED BY THE IMPERIAL TOBACCO CO. (OF GREAT BRITAIN & IRELAND) LTD.

BUTTERFLIES & MOTHS — THESE PICTURES ARE ISSUED BY **JOHN PLAYER & SONS** BRANCH OF THE IMPERIAL TOBACCO CO. (OF GREAT BRITAIN AND IRELAND), LIMITED.

32

Broad-bordered five-spot Burnet.
(*Zygæna trifolii*).

This moth is the most common of the five-spotted Burnets, and is found in damp woods and meadows in June. It is a local insect in Great Britain, though widely distributed in Europe. The brownish chrysalis is enveloped in a yellow silken cocoon, which is usually fixed to a reed, grass stem or twig. The caterpillar is found in May, and feeds on bird's-foot, vetch, and various species of trefoil.

BRITISH BUTTERFLIES Nº I. ISSUE.

No. 11
Common Blue.

Is indigenous to every part of the British Isles. It is double brooded in England, the first brood from May to July, and the second from July to September. In Ireland and Scotland only one flight appears in June or July. The eggs are usually laid on Bird's Foot Trefoil.

GODFREY PHILLIPS,
LONDON, ENGLAND.

BUTTERFLIES AND MOTHS SERIES OF 48. Nº 34.

SMALL COPPER
The Small Copper is a playful and swift-flying butterfly, plentiful almost everywhere in the British Isles. The caterpillar is green, and may be found feeding on the leaves of the Dock, Greater Knapweed, seen in the picture, or Sorrel. There is considerable variation in this species. Many of the butterflies having a good deal of black about them, and the bands on the edges of the wings vary in width.

ISSUED BY **GALLAHER LTD.**
VIRGINIA HOUSE. LONDON & BELFAST

BRITISH BUTTERFLIES SERIES OF 25

No. 5.

LARGE GARDEN WHITE.

The breadth varies from 1¾ in. to 2½ in. The female has three black marks on the upper wing, besides the black appearing at the tip. They are seen in May, June and August, and are very common, being found almost everywhere, but chiefly in vegetable gardens, where the female lays her eggs on cabbages, etc. There are two other British white butterflies very similar, but smaller.

ISSUED BY **ABDULLA & Cº LTD** 173, NEW BONDS! LONDON.W.

BUTTERFLIES A SERIES OF 50

28

FOREIGN BUTTERFLIES:
SOUTH AMERICA.

Chlorippe laurina.

The small group of butterflies known by the name *Chlorippe* is confined to the tropical regions of Central America. The beautiful species illustrated inhabits the wooded country of Colombia, Peru and Bolivia, and is never met with in treeless or cultivated districts. The male, with its brilliant blue colouring, is not uncommon, but the comparatively dull-coloured female is exceedingly rare in collections, probably because its habitat is out of the reach of collectors. The male has a wing expanse of about 3½ inches, the female being somewhat larger.

ISSUED BY **JOHN PLAYER & SONS** BRANCH OF THE IMPERIAL TOBACCO CO. (OF GREAT BRITAIN & IRELAND), LTD.

GOLDEN KNIGHT CIGARETTES

THE BUFF TIP (to size).

Common throughout the British Isles during June and July.

These satin butterfly illustrations are delightful subjects for embroidery and applique. Patterns for a variety of subjects, with instructions, will be sent post free on request, accompanied by empty packet, addressed to R. J. Lea, Ltd., "Chairman" Tobacco Factory, Manchester.

R. J. LEA LTD MANCHESTER

Player's Cigarettes

Goldfinch-Bullfinch Hybrid

STONECHAT

Player's Cigarettes

Bullfinch-Canary Mule

Gallaher's Cigarettes.

COMMON GULL

JACKDAW

OGDEN'S CIGARETTES

LENGTH OF EGG ABOUT 8 IN

ROBIN

Gallaher's Cigarettes

BLACK-CAPPED LORY

JACKDAW

HERON

Nº 12. MOTTLE TUMBLER.

COPES CIGARETTES

SONG THRUSH (Turdus Musicus)

GOLDEN-FRONTED BULBUL

6 JACOBIN.

OGDEN'S CIGARETTES

WHITETHROAT.

PLAIT-BILLED HORNBILL.

BRITISH BIRDS' EGGS
GOLDEN EAGLE. 42 **OGDEN'S CIGARETTES.**

MOORHEN (FEMALE)

Skylark.

SEDGE-WARBLER AND YOUNG

Player's Cigarettes

Red Sussex

BRITISH BIRDS.
RING-OUZEL. 41 **OGDEN'S CIGARETTES.**

GOLDFINCH
AND NEST

BERNACLE GOOSE.

OYSTER CATCHER SITTING.

BLACKCAP

WILLS'S CIGARETTES
A SERIES OF 50
BRITISH BIRDS No. 23

W.D. & H.O. WILLS
BRISTOL & LONDON

WHITETHROAT.
(Sylvia cinerea.)

The lively little Whitethroat, one of the best known of our summer visitors, arrives here in April, and leaves again in September. *Nest:* a frail structure, loosely suspended among the stalks of a clump of nettles (hence the bird is sometimes known as the *Nettle Creeper*). *Length*—5¾ ins. *Eggs*—4 to 5, dirty greenish white, spotted with grey and brown; about ⅜ in. long.

25

C·W·S CIGARETTES
This surface is adhesive. Ask your Co-operative Store for the attractive Album (price one penny) specially prepared to hold the complete series.

BRITISH AND FOREIGN BIRDS. Set of 48.

No. 1.
The Blackbird (Partially Migrant.) Sometimes called the Merle or Black Thrush, we hear its fluting song towards the end of February, the clear and lovely notes calling the clear and lovely notes calling the strawberry and elderberry bed, The food generally consists of snails, slugs, worms, and insects, Kinds of berries are consumed when food is scarce. *Nest* is built low down in the shrubbery or hedgerow, The young are reared chiefly on earth worms. Many Blackbirds nitrate in September and October.

C·W·S Tobacco Factory.

26

CURIOUS BEAKS
A SERIES OF 50.

23
The Plait-billed Hornbill.
(Rhytidoceros undulatus.)

In this species the beak is not one of the extravagant type carried by some of the other Hornbills, but it is none the less very remarkable. It consists of a series of raised horny bars with coloured brown to throw them into relief, the base of the lower mandible, where, however, the buff lines are not raised, In addition, the base of the lower mandible is coloured lemon yellow. The male bird has a broad ring of pink skin round the eye, the throat of the female being coloured blue, The Plait-billed Hornbill inhabits the Malayan forests.

ISSUED BY
JOHN PLAYER & SONS
BRANCH OF THE IMPERIAL TOBACCO C?
(OF GREAT BRITAIN & IRELAND) LT?

27

BRITISH BIRDS
No. 23

SWALLOW
Hirundo rustica

in a series of 50

Craven "Black Cat"

Each spring we welcome the Swallow as it returns from spending the winter in South Africa. Winter in Britain holds little hope for it as it feeds almost entirely on flying insects. It is a bird of open cultivated country particularly where there is open water, or a river, It nests, often in small groups, in a farm or disused building. The saucer-shaped nest is constructed of mud and grass is attached to a wall or beam.

THE HOUSE OF CRAVEN
Proprietors, Carreras Ltd.
Christopher Martin Road, Basildon, Essex.
Registered in England (No. 364618)

28

BIRDS & THEIR YOUNG
A SERIES OF 50

23
MOORHEN
(Gallinula chloropus chloropus)

Length: about 13 in. *Resident:* haunts weedy ponds and rivers, also lakes in public parks. *Diet:* various water weeds, water insects, seeds and grain. *Nest:* (April onwards) platform of various water plants, placed on ground near water in vegetation or low bush. *Eggs:* 6-10, hatched in June; by end of July young more actively alert, are then able to swim and dive, and, with dull olive-brown beaks and heavy, legs dangling, toes catching the water; at annual moult in July and August adults drop all flight feathers at once, and are then unable to fly for a short period.

JOHN PLAYER & SONS
BRANCH OF THE IMPERIAL TOBACCO CO., LTD.

29

BIRDS' EGGS
50 IN SERIES.

GOLDEN EAGLE'S EGG.
(Aquila chrysaëtos.)

The Golden Eagle used to breed in England and Wales, but is now only a resident in the Western Highlands. It is being rapidly exterminated. The nest is a large structure, built of sticks, and placed on some high crag, or tree. Two or three eggs are laid, pale blue-green, or white- in colour, clouded with warm brown, and grey markings. This eagle will sometimes attack a full-grown deer.

SIZE OF EGG.
3½ INCHES.

OGDEN'S
BRANCH OF THE IMPERIAL TOBACCO CO.
(OF GREAT BRITAIN & IRELAND), LTD.

30

WILD BIRDS
A SERIES OF 50

44
SEDGE-WARBLER AND YOUNG.

This small Warbler is found distributed generally over these islands in all marshy districts. It spends the winter months in Northern Africa, and arrives in England towards the end of April. The nest is built in a clump of rank vegetation, or in a hedge at some distance from water. The male sings throughout the day and a considerable part of the night, and is a clever mimic, imitating the notes of the Swallow, Blackbird, Chaffinch and other birds found in its haunts. It is a confiding bird, but will scold loudly any intruder who goes too near its nest.

ISSUED BY
JOHN PLAYER & SONS
BRANCH OF THE IMPERIAL TOBACCO CO
(OF GREAT BRITAIN & IRELAND), LTD

31

BIRDS & EGGS
REPRESENTING

THIS PICTURE IS N?
27
OF A SERIES OF 50

SKYLARK.
Alauda arvensis.

Universal in Great Britain, its song and habits are too well known to need description. Its nest is a cup-shaped depression scratched out of the ground.

ISSUED BY
LAMBERT & BUTLER
BRANCH OF THE IMPERIAL TOBACCO CO. (OF GREAT BRITAIN & IRELAND), LTD.

32

BRITISH BIRDS
50 IN SERIES

RING-OUZEL.
(Turdus torquatus.)

Whilst your own Blackbird is appearing here from the British Isles for the winter, re-maining here from April to September. It is fairly common in hilly and mountainous places, and is the only member of the Thrush family which migrates from the British Isles for the winter, The distinguished by the white crescent lying across the base of the throat. It is food chiefly worms, slugs, insects, and berries. The food in September and October is mainly derived from the moors, The food on the moors being that of worms, insects, slugs, and berries.

OGDEN'S
BRANCH OF THE IMPERIAL TOBACCO CO.
(OF GREAT BRITAIN & IRELAND), LTD.

33

POULTRY
A SERIES OF 50

34

No. 44

RED SUSSEX.

Fanciers who admire Red Fowls can hardly do better than take up this fine British breed. Unlike the Rhode Island breed, they have white legs and skin, and are therefore ideal table birds. Red Sussex Fowls have very broad shoulders and backs, with long breastbones, and viewed from above they have a peculiar flat and square appearance. The cocks weigh up to 9 pounds and the hens about 7½ pounds; the latter are excellent layers of tinted eggs, and splendid mothers.

JOHN PLAYER & SONS
BRANCH OF THE IMPERIAL TOBACCO CO., LTD.

GAME BIRDS AND WILD FOWL
A SERIES OF 50.

35

16
BERNACLE GOOSE.
(Bernicla leucopsis.)

The Bernacle Goose is a winter visitor, the first arriving towards the end of September, and the majority reaching British shores late in October, leaving again in March and April. Its winter haunts are more northerly than the Brent Goose, and it is plentiful on the Hebrides, west of Scotland, and north of Ireland. Greenland, Spitzbergen, and parts of the Arctic, are its breeding grounds. Though not quite such a salt-water bird as the Brent, its food is similar. The name is derived from the old myth that geese were born from ship-barnacles.

ISSUED BY
JOHN PLAYER & SONS
BRANCH OF THE IMPERIAL TOBACCO C?
(OF GREAT BRITAIN & IRELAND) LT?

EGGS, NESTS & BIRDS
N? 1. ISSUE.

36

No. 2.
Gold Finch.

The Gold Finch's nest is beautifully made of white lichen or moss bound together for security with fine roots, and the whole of the interior lined with the silky down of the Coltsfoot, Willow cotton or feathers. She lays from four to five eggs—size, axis 0·75, diam. 0·50 in.. pale bluish or greenish white and spotted with brown.

GODFREY PHILLIPS,
LONDON, ENGLAND.

BIRD PAINTING
A SERIES OF 50   No 25

Blackcap

This bird only visits the British Isles in the spring and summer months, although a few of their members occasionally remain during the winter. The Blackcap's song is very beautiful and even preferred by some to that of the Nightingale. The nest is placed in thick low cover, such as herbage or bushes, often on cultivated ground. Built of hay and roots, lined with hair, it contains five or six eggs of a pale marbled brown with scanty dark spots, but they may have a greenish or bluish cast.

ISSUED BY
GODFREY PHILLIPS LTD.
AND
ASSOCIATED COMPANIES

37

WILD BIRDS AT HOME
SERIES OF 36

No. 18. OYSTER CATCHER SITTING

With black and white plumage, bright red bill and pink legs, the oyster catcher is one of our most striking shore birds, In the seashore which it frequents in parties throughout the winter. During May and June they can be observed standing in regular intervals, the sitting bird having quietly slipped from the nest to join her mate at the first sign of danger. They do not catch oysters, however, but is expert at knocking limpets from the rocks and extracting mussels from their shells as the tide subsides.

ISSUED WITH
BALDRIC
by
R. S. CHALLIS & Co., Ltd.
130, New North Rd., London, N.1.

38

WILLS'S CIGARETTES
No. 15
WILD FLOWERS.
A SERIES OF 50.

BLACK KNAPWEED.
Centaurea nigra.

The "Iron-weed" or "Hard-head," as it is frequently called, is remarkable for its toughness. The hard bracts or "knobs" which form the base of each flower-head are built up with overlapping scales, like the tiles on a roof, each green scale edged with dark brown or black; this gives the bracts a black appearance, and the plant its name Black Knapweed. It is very common, and found growing in meadows and hedge-rows all over the country. It has very tough, sinewy stems, with rough stalkless leaves. Perennial, flowers from June to October; grows from one to two feet high.

39

W.D. & H.O. WILLS
BRISTOL & LONDON.
ISSUED BY THE IMPERIAL TOBACCO Cº
(OF GREAT BRITAIN & IRELAND) LTᴰ

THESE PICTURES OF
USEFUL PLANTS & FRUITS

BRAZIL NUT.
(Bertholletia excelsa.)

This is one of the most extraordinary fruits of South America. The nuts are not borne singly, but are packed with most remarkable exactness, to the number of from twelve to twenty, in a hard capsule, which is nearly round, and so hard and heavy is this great pod, that when ripe, it is dangerous to pass under the trees for no head is sufficiently hard to withstand the fatal blow of the falling Castanha Cabomba, as the Brazilians call them. The tree reaches to a height of 120 feet.

ARE ISSUED BY

40

JOHN PLAYER & SONS
BRANCH OF THE IMPERIAL TOBACCO CO. (OF GREAT BRITAIN AND IRELAND), LIMITED.

CARRERAS
·HIGH-CLASS·
CIGARETTES
A SERIES OF 24 ORCHIDS

Nº 15

MASDEVALLIA COCCINEA.

A beautiful epiphytal orchid inhabiting the southern slopes of the mountains in Colombia, where it is found at elevations from 8,000 feet to 10,000 feet. It is of compact growth, with tufts of leathery, dark green leaves. The flowers are borne upon stems about one foot high. Not difficult to cultivate, providing it is kept in a cool, moist atmosphere, and well shaded from the sun in summer. Introduced in 1869.

CITY ROAD.   LONDON. E.C.I.
43

CACTI
A SERIES OF 25

No. 6
CLEISTOCACTUS BAUMANNII

The stiff, erect stem of this fine cactus is often about 1 metre in height and bears many brightly coloured spines. The orange and scarlet flowers are 6 to 7 cm. long and are freely produced over a fairly extended period. It is popular with collectors because relatively easy to cultivate and can be propagated from seeds and cuttings.

FUMEZ LES FAMEUSES CIGARETTES
"MILLS"
FILTERTIPS

41

Nº 9
A SERIES OF 50
ROSES.
WILLS'S CIGARETTES

QUEEN OF SPAIN.
(Hybrid Tea.)

A rose of robust habit with large, full, and globular flowers, which require a hot summer to be seen at their best. An exhibition rose only, and not suitable for either garden or house ornamentation. It will thrive best in a light loam soil. Awarded the gold medal of the National Rose Society, 1907.

W.D. & H.O. WILLS.
BRISTOL & LONDON.
ISSUED BY THE IMPERIAL TOBACCO Cº
(OF GREAT BRITAIN & IRELAND) LTᴰ

42

ALBUMS FOR WILLS'S PICTURE CARDS CAN BE OBTAINED FROM TOBACCONISTS AT ONE PENNY EACH

GARDEN FLOWERS
A SERIES OF 50
SELECTED AND DESCRIBED BY RICHARD SUDELL, F.I.L.A., F.R.H.S.

17
DELPHINIUM
Variety: Mrs. Townley Parker.

Hardy perennial. Height: 5 feet. Blooms July. Colour: sky blue, white eye. Most colourful and stately plant for the back of the mixed flower border.

Can be raised from seed. Sow in lines in the nursery bed; transplant when large enough to handle, six inches apart, with a foot between the rows, and set out in autumn where they are to bloom. Also increased by cuttings detached from the parent plant in autumn. Needs staking and tying early to avoid breakage. Likes a deep well-cultivated soil and plenty of manure, with a generous dusting of lime before planting. Allow three feet of space to each plant.

W.D. & H.O. WILLS
MANUFACTURERS OF GOLD FLAKE, CAPSTAN, WOODBINE AND STAR CIGARETTES
BRANCH OF THE IMPERIAL TOBACCO CO. (OF GREAT BRITAIN & IRELAND) LTD

44

CARRERAS LTD
CITY ROAD **22** LONDON E.C.I.
ESTD. 1788
WILD FLOWER ART SERIES

WILD DAFFODIL OR LENT LILY flowers in early spring. It can grow happily in grass meadows, as the bulbs are pulled deeply into the ground by their roots, which then get food without interference from the grass roots. Each flower is upright as a bud, but bends towards the sun as it opens.

INSTRUCTIONS.

After collecting this series of 25 cigarette cards and painting in water colours the outlined copy of each picture, send them together with your full name and address to:—

"Wild Flowers,"
Messrs. Carreras, Ltd.,
Arcadia Works, City Road,
LONDON, E.C.I.

On receipt of which you will be credited with 50 coupons available towards any one of the 200 beautiful gifts in our Gift Booklet, and your cards returned.

45

THIS SURFACE IS ADHESIVE. ASK YOUR TOBACCONIST FOR THE ATTRACTIVE ALBUM (PRICE ONE PENNY) SPECIALLY PREPARED TO HOLD THE COMPLETE SERIES

WILD FLOWERS
A SERIES OF 50

33
REST-HARROW
(Ononis arvensis)

In fields and on waste ground, especially near the sea, may be found the tangled Rest-harrow with its delicate rose-pink flowers, which are in bloom from June to August. There are two main varieties, one spreading on the ground and without spines, the other more erect, spiny, and with smaller leaves. The creeping habit of its roots explains the name Rest-harrow; as an old writer puts it "It maketh the oxen whilest they be in plowing to rest or stand still." The flowers are of the butterfly-shape characteristic of the pea family to which it belongs.

W.D. & H.O. WILLS
ISSUED BY THE IMPERIAL TOBACCO CO. (OF GREAT BRITAIN & IRELAND), LTD.

46

Nº 29
A SERIES OF 50
ALPINE FLOWERS
WILLS'S CIGARETTES

ALPINE FLAX.
Linum alpinum.

A beautiful little plant that is not difficult to cultivate, and which flowers in July, when most Alpines have finished. It likes an open situation, with gritty soil containing a little peat. Propagated by seeds sown in spring, or by division during autumn or early spring. Height, 6 inches to 9 inches.

W.D. & H.O. WILLS.
BRISTOL & LONDON.
ISSUED BY THE IMPERIAL TOBACCO Cº
(OF GREAT BRITAIN & IRELAND) LTᴰ

47

STRUGGLE FOR EXISTENCE
A SERIES OF 25

No. 9
Hard Drinkers.
Marsh Marigold.

Plants which "perspire" profusely, need to *take in* much water. Hard Drinkers have usually wide-spread, thin leaves, quickly flagging should water-supplies be cut off. Marsh Marigolds are called Drunkards by some people! A shoot with its cut end fixed through a cork into a narrow glass tube or bottle containing water, will soon show its hard drinking by the change in level of the water.

ISSUED BY

JOHN PLAYER & SONS
BRANCH OF THE IMPERIAL TOBACCO Cº (OF GREAT BRITAIN & IRELAND) LTᴰ

48

GARDEN FLOWERS
SERIES OF 48   Nº 45

STOCKS

Stocks are among the most charming and fragrant of garden plants, growing mostly as half-hardy biennials in shades of white, red, blue and purple. The seeds may be sown out of doors in April and will flower late in the summer, or alternatively they may be raised in heat in the early spring. The soil for planting out should be rich and deep, and the plants should be set about one foot apart each way.

ISSUED BY

GALLAHER LTᴰ
VIRGINIA HOUSE, LONDON & BELFAST

49

CWS GRAND PRIOR.
A WONDERFUL CIGARETTE
CWS · ENGLISH · ROSES
FIRST SERIES 24 · Nº 11

NOBLESSE.
(Hybrid Tea.)

A most beautiful rose of exquisite tints. Colour apricot primrose-yellow, the outer petals flushed with deep pearly pink and rose. Very free flowering on strong growth, with good foliage. Not quite full enough, but its delicate tints are unrivalled.

CWS ANGLIAN MIXTURE
For REFINED PALATES.

50

CRAVEN
Black Cat

No. 30   *in a series of 50*
FLOWERS
all the year round

FUCHSIA – 'Mrs. Popple'
Flowers June—October

There are many hundreds of different varieties of fuchsias, some half-hardy and others hardy. The hardy fuchsias are among the easiest shrubs to grow and Mrs. Popple, with its purple and red flowers, is one of the finest. The flowers are produced from early July until October. The plants are best pruned back to ground level in March each year. This can be followed by feeding with garden fertilizer and top dressing with compost or peat.

THE HOUSE OF CRAVEN
Proprietors: Carreras Ltd.
Christopher Martin Road, Basildon, Essex
Registered in England (No. 384818).

51

MASDEVALLIA COCCINEA

BLACK KNAPWEED.

The Queen of Spain

ALPINE FLAX.

REST-HARROW.

WILD DAFFODIL

DELPHINIUM
Variety : MRS. TOWNLEY PARKER

NOBLESSE

STOCKS

MARSH MARIGOLD

PAPER FOR MARKING LEVEL OF WATER

HARD DRINKERS.

WILL'S CIGARETTES

SCOTS PINE OR SCOTS FIR

WILLS'S CIGARETTES.

LAVENDER.

THE LANGUAGE OF FLOWERS.
PURPLE LILAC FIRST EMOTIONS
OF LOVE

Nosegay Cigarettes
W.&F. Faulkner Ltd London.S.E.
COPYRIGHT

FLOWERS
TO GROW.

SCABIOSA CAUCASICA

HOLLYHOCK.

VANILLA PLANIFOLIA

TEN-WEEK STOCKS

WILLS'S CIGARETTES.

WHITE BEAM.

VINE

KING-CUP

RAGGED ROBIN

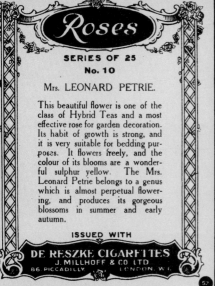

Roses

SERIES OF 25
No. 10

Mrs. LEONARD PETRIE.

This beautiful flower is one of the class of Hybrid Teas and a most effective rose for garden decoration. Its habit of growth is strong, and it is very suitable for bedding purposes. It flowers freely, and the colour of its blooms are a wonderful sulphur yellow. The Mrs. Leonard Petrie belongs to a genus which is almost perpetual flowering, and produces its gorgeous blossoms in summer and early autumn.

ISSUED WITH

DE RESZKE CIGARETTES
J. MILLHOFF & CO LTD.
86. PICCADILLY   LONDON. W.1

52

Wills for Quality

TREES
A SERIES OF 40

36
SCOTS PINE or SCOTS FIR
Pinus sylvestris   *Coniferae*

The Scots Pine is native in North Scotland where it forms a continuation of the coniferous forests of Northern Europe. It reaches a height of 150 feet, with brownish, fissured scaly bark. The needles are rather twisted and borne in pairs on dwarf shoots which fall after three years. The male and female cones occur on the same tree; the small, egg-shaped, male cones (B) are in dense spikes at the base of the year's shoots, while one to three female cones (A) form near the tips. After fertilization, the female cones are pendant (c) and the ends of the scales thicken and become tightly packed. The winged seeds (E) are liberated from the cones (D) after eighteen months. The timber (yellow deal) is used for packing-cases and mine props.

W.D. & H.O. WILLS
ISSUED BY THE IMPERIAL TOBACCO CO.
(OF GREAT BRITAIN & IRELAND), LTD.

53

Nº 21
"OLD ENGLISH GARDEN FLOWERS"

WILL'S'S CIGARETTES

LAVENDER.
Lavandula spica.

A hardy, low-growing evergreen shrub, valued chiefly for the scent of its flowers. Will thrive in almost any good garden soil, but prefers one of a sandy character overlying chalk. Propagation by cuttings of young shoots taken in September and planted in sandy soil in a cold frame. Cuttings must have free ventilation during fine weather.

W.D. & H.O. WILLS,
BRISTOL & LONDON.

ISSUED BY THE IMPERIAL TOBACCO Cº
(OF GREAT BRITAIN & IRELAND) LTᴰ

56

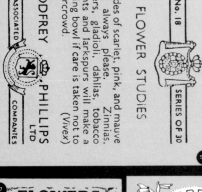

GODFREY PHILLIPS LTD
AND ASSOCIATED COMPANIES

FLOWER STUDIES

No. 18
SERIES OF 30

Shades of scarlet, pink, and mauve will always please. Zinnias, asters, gladioli, dahlias, tobacco plants and larkspurs will make a telling bowl if care is taken not to overcrowd.
(Vivex)

54

55

FLOWERS
A SERIES OF 50
DESCRIBED BY EDITOR
"AMATEUR GARDENING"

No. 46
TEN-WEEK STOCKS.

These, unlike the Brompton stock, which is biennial, is only annual in duration, and will flower in about ten weeks from the time of seed sowing. It is possible to raise seedlings outdoors from sowings made in a sheltered place during May or early June. More usual practice is to sow in a greenhouse or frame in early spring, prick out the seedlings, and harden them off for planting outdoors in May. It is advisable to retain all small seedlings, as these frequently produce the best double flowers.

CARRERAS LTD
(ESTD 1788)
ARCADIA WORKS, LONDON, ENGLAND
KEEP THIS ATTRACTIVE SERIES IN THE
CARRERAS "SLIP IN" ALBUM, ON SALE AT
ALL TOBACCONISTS PRICE ONE PENNY

57

CARRERAS
HIGH CLASS
CIGARETTES
A SERIES OF 24 ORCHIDS

Nº 20

Vanilla Planifolia.

This orchid is best known as the source of Vanilla, which is so extensively used for flavouring in confectionery, etc. Vanilla is prepared from the seed-pods, which have to be gathered before they are quite ripe, and then gradually dried. It is a native of the hot, moist woods in South-east Mexico, but is cultivated largely in the West Indies, Java, Mauritius and other tropical countries. The plant is of a climbing habit, the flowers two inches across and the pods from six inches to nine inches long.

CITY ROAD   LONDON. E C 1

58

OLD FAVOURITES
SERIES OF 25

No. 12.

HOLLYHOCK.

These are particularly picturesque in old-world gardens, whether their background be the dark green of shrubberies, or the mellow warmth of old brick walls. The flaunting pink, red, white or yellow flowers are borne in late Summer, and the double forms are rosette like. It is usually necessary to grow fresh plants from seed every two years, as the leaves are attacked by a fungous disease causing rust-coloured powdery spots, and thus spoiling the plant.

ISSUED BY
ABDULLA & Cº LTᴰ
173, NEW BOND Sᵗ LONDON. W.

R·J·LEA'S CIGARETTES

The best Perennials.

Nº 14 SCABIOSA CAUCASICA

There are not many other hardy border plants that bear such beautiful grey-blue flowers as this variety. Flowering period extends from the end of June till the beginning of October. Almost any garden soil will suit, but the flowers are produced in greater numbers and of more substance if they are in deeply dug ground enriched with manure. The plants may be raised from seeds sown in Spring or from slips off old clumps. Height 2 to 3 feet.

60

MANCHESTER

OUR SPECIALITY
ANGLIAN MIXTURE
TOBACCO

WAYSIDE FLOWERS
SERIES OF 48

No. 40.
Ragged Robin.
Lychnis Flos-cuculi.

Rose of Heaven and Meadow Pink are local names for this delicate-looking plant, but neither seems so appropriate as Ragged Robin. The ragged-looking flowers are over 1 in. in diameter, and each of their five petals is cut into four lobes. The flowers make their first appearance at the end of May.

C.W.S
TYNTAL PLUG
THE UNIVERSAL FAVOURITE

61

WILD FLOWERS
SERIES OF 48. Nº 45

KING-CUP

The splendid King-cup will be found flowering in wet ground throughout the spring and often well on into the summer too. It is a very bright and attractive flower and the large glossy leaves expand to a great size when the bloom is dead. A common English name for it is the Marsh Marigold, while in Scotland it is known as the Luckan Gowan. It is somewhat poisonous, and should be treated with care.

ISSUED BY
GALLAHER LTᴰ
VIRGINIA HOUSE, LONDON & BELFAST

62

PLANTS OF COMMERCIAL VALUE
SERIES OF 100

VINE

Vitis vinifera, of the Vine family, is the Grape Vine. Native of the Caspian region. Introduced into England by the Romans. Chief wine-producing districts—the Rhine Provinces, France, Spain, and Portugal. Also now—South Africa, Australia, California. Currants and raisins are dried grapes.

Nº49
ISSUED BY

GALLAHER LTᴰ
BELFAST & LONDON.

63

WILLS'S CIGARETTES
7
FLOWERING TREES & SHRUBS
A SERIES OF 50.

64
White Beam.
Pyrus Aria.

Occurs locally, especially on chalk soils, on borders of woods; usually as a bush-like tree, but occasionally attains to a height of 40 feet. *Bark* smooth when young, dotted in transverse lines. *Branches* usually tend upwards. *Twigs* stout, brown to grey. *Leaves* vary in shape, usually broadly oval, edges coarsely toothed or lobed, under side downy and white. *Flowers* appear in May or June, white, about ½" in diameter, arranged in loose flat-topped clusters. *Fruit* scarlet, dotted with brown, nearly round, ½" in diameter; sometimes known as Chess-apples. Sharp and rough at first, but edible when matured.

W.D. & H.O. WILLS
BRISTOL & LONDON.
ISSUED BY THE IMPERIAL TOBACCO Cº
(OF GREAT BRITAIN & IRELAND) LTᴰ

Wills for Quality
GARDEN FLOWERS
A SERIES OF 50

34

Pansies.

The delightful little pansy (from the French *pensée*) has for long been associated with tender thoughts. *Love-in-Idleness, Heartsease* and *Jump-up-and-Kiss-me*, are names which indicate the affectionate regard in which the pansies were held in times past. They are easy to grow; in spring or autumn they should be planted firmly 6 in. to 9 in. apart in well-drained loam enriched with a lit'le manure. Seed should be sown in heat in February and if the young plants are hardened and planted out in April they will flower the same year. In taking cuttings strong shoots which have not flowered should be placed in boxes of sandy soil and wintered in a frame.

W.D.& H.O.WILLS

ISSUED BY THE IMPERIAL TOBACCO CO (OF GREAT BRITAIN & IRELAND). LTD

65

ANNUALS
A SERIES OF 50

No. 37

SCABIOUS

(SWEET SCABIOUS).

These lovely flowers are invaluable for vases and table decoration, and although strictly speaking the Scabious is a hardy perennial, it is best treated as a hardy or half-hardy annual. Seed can be sown where it is to flower early in April, and lightly covered. Open sunny positions are the best, and seedlings should be thinned to about 10 in. apart. Alternatively, for early flowering, sow the seed under glass in March, and transplant to the open garden in May. Colours vary from pure white to deep maroon. Mixed strains will provide a galaxy of rich and delicate shades, or selected colours may be purchased.

ISSUED BY

GODFREY PHILLIPS LTD
AND
ASSOCIATED COMPANIES

66

Wills for Quality
ROSES
A SERIES OF 40

17

J. G. GLASSFORD

(Hybrid Tea)

Introduced 1921

Bright scarlet

This Rose has a great advantage over other dark crimson varieties in that it is not affected by weather changes. The blooms are perfectly formed and carried erect on stiff stems. Foliage is free of disease. A good variety for exhibition or garden purposes. If wanted for exhibition, prune the third week in March hard to two eyes, but to four eyes if grown for garden decoration. Awarded a Gold Medal of the National Rose Society.

W.D.& H.O.WILLS

ISSUED BY THE IMPERIAL TOBACCO CO (OF GREAT BRITAIN & IRELAND), LTD.

67

68

WILLS'S CIGARETTES
26
FLOWER CULTURE IN POTS
A SERIES OF 50.

HELIOTROPE or CHERRY PIE.

This exquisitely fragrant flower is often grown on pillars or walls in conservatories. In February the shoots of old plants should be well cut back. When growth begins, repotted in a *compost* of loam, leaf-mould, and silver sand in equal parts. Water carefully until flowers form, then keep roots moist, and apply liquid manure weekly. Nip off points when shoots are a few inches long to encourage bushy growth. Prune and re-pot annually. Cuttings of young shoots may be rooted in spring in sandy soil in propagating frame.

W.D.& H.O.WILLS
BRISTOL & LONDON.

ISSUED BY THE IMPERIAL TOBACCO Cº (OF GREAT BRITAIN & IRELAND) LTº

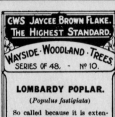

CWS JAYCEE BROWN FLAKE. THE HIGHEST STANDARD.

WAYSIDE · WOODLAND · TREES
SERIES OF 48. - Nº 10.

LOMBARDY POPLAR.

(Populus fastigiata)

So called because it is extensively grown in Lombardy, but its original home is the Himalayas. It grows very rapidly at first, to about 130 feet in height on moist but not marshy soil. The trunk has a furrowed bark and is somewhat fluted in older individuals. Its wood is used for cheap boxes and packing-cases.

CWS RAYDEX MIXTURE FOR REFINED PALATES.

69

Wills for Quality
GARDEN FLOWERS NEW VARIETIES
A SERIES OF 40
SELECTED AND DESCRIBED BY RICHARD SUDELL, F.I.L.A., F.R.H.S.

11

DELPHINIUM

Variety: DUCHESS OF PORTLAND

Perennial. Height: 5 feet or more, according to nature of soil. Habit: erect. Flowers July. Good for cutting. Most effective used in masses at the back of a wide mixed flower border.

Plants will bloom for several years in the same position and need a deeply-dug, fairly rich soil to get the best results. The plants are increased by division of the roots, or by cuttings. Slugs are the worst enemy, but are easily kept at bay by patent slug killers or a mixture of soot and lime dusted around the plants. Staking is necessary for such tall blooms. Stout canes are the most useful, and should just reach the first flowers on the spike, thus being concealed among the foliage.

W.D.& H.O.WILLS

ISSUED BY THE IMPERIAL TOBACCO COMPANY (OF GREAT BRITAIN & IRELAND), LIMITED.

70

71

WILD FLOWERS.
A Series of 25 Designs.
No. 8.

THE VIOLET.

The Violet flowers in early summer in hedges and on banks. The fifth petal is the largest, the narrow end of which is shaped like a round tube, and stands out beyond the sepals like a spur. Inside the tube are the stamens which form a ring round the seed vessel. There are five green sepals, having sharp points, and the lower end slightly swollen. The leaves, which grow close to the ground, are heart-shaped, and have short stalks.

Issued by
E. ROBINSON & SONS LD.
STOCKPORT.

72

CHAIRMAN CIGARETTES

No. 30   **FREE**   No. 30
Collectors returning 200 inner portions of Chairman or Chairman Juniors packets to R. J. Lea, Ltd. will receive a pair of pictures of Rose Gardens, suitable for framing. If only one is required, send 100 inners.

ROSES.
A Series of 50.

CHARLES E. SHEA, H.T.
Elisha J. Hicks, 1916.

Colour clear pink. The blooms are very large, and carried on long stiff stems. Fragrant. A good vigorous growing free blooming Rose for any garden. Prune moderately.

Chairman JUNIORS
R. J. Lea, Ltd., Stockport

Wills for Quality
FLOWERING SHRUBS
A SERIES OF 30

18

SHRUBBY MAGNOLIA
(Magnolia parviflora)

A large deciduous shrub, usually wider than it is high, the Shrubby Magnolia grows wild in Japan and Korea. Its leaves are about 6 inches long and 4 inches wide, dark green above, bluish grey beneath. As with all magnolias, the flowers come singly (i.e. one on each stalk), and they expand successively during June and July. Of cup-like shape, they are pure white, fragrant, and from 3 to 4 inches wide, being borne on rather long stalks and standing erect. A ring of rosy crimson stamens adds much to their beauty. The handsome fruits are conical, about 2 inches long and carmine. A very hardy and beautiful shrub which may be grown in soil of either a loamy or peaty nature.

W.D.& H.O.WILLS

ISSUED BY THE IMPERIAL TOBACCO CO. (OF GREAT BRITAIN & IRELAND), LTD.

73

BRITISH TREES & THEIR USES
A SERIES OF 25

15
The Hornbeam.
(Carpinus betulus).

A native of the southern and midland counties of England and of Wales, where it is common in woods and hedgerows. Under favourable conditions the Hornbeam grows to 70 ft., though usually it is much smaller. In some respects it resembles the Beech, the leaves are however, broader at the base and hairy on the underside, not glossy like Beech-leaves. The flowers are catkins, and the characteristic fruits hang in clusters. The close-grained, yellowish-white 'horny' wood is used for cogs and screws for machinery (3), mallets and similar tools (2), and lasts (1). It makes excellent fuel (4).

LAMBERT & BUTLER

ISSUED BY THE IMPERIAL TOBACCO Cº (OF GREAT BRITAIN & IRELAND) LTº

74

75

WOODLAND TREES SERIES
Nº 38
100 IN SET

THE JUNIPER TREE.

Manifests itself both as a tree and shrub, as a tree it attains a height of 30 to 40 ft., as a shrub, 10 or 12 ft., diversified in shape. The narrow evergreen leaves are awl-shaped, terminating in a sharp point. Male flowers are yellow in colour, the sexes are on different trees. The berry is green during its first year; by the following Autumn it is blue-black, covered with "bloom."

ISSUED BY

GALLAHER LTD.
BELFAST AND LONDON.

HIDDEN BEAUTIES
A SERIES OF 25

12
Wonderful Flower-Dust.

A little puff of flower-dust (pollen), shaken from ripe catkins, includes hundreds of pollen-grains. Obviously then, we should see *one pollen-grain*. Seen under the microscope, however, even a single pollen-grain may surprise us. Pollen-grains of different flowers are found to be very unlike. Those with spikes (as Hollyhock) and with threads (as Clarkia), are well fitted to be carried on winged insects that have visited the flowers in search of food.

ISSUED BY
JOHN PLAYER & SONS
BRANCH OF THE IMPERIAL TOBACCO Cº (OF GREAT BRITAIN & IRELAND) LTD

76

J. G. GLASSFORD

PANSIES.

DELPHINIUM   Variety: DUCHESS OF PORTLAND

POPLAR.

HELIOTROPE.

SHRUBBY MAGNOLIA

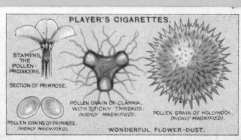

STAMENS, THE POLLEN-PRODUCERS.

SECTION OF PRIMROSE.

POLLEN GRAIN OF CLARKIA, WITH STICKY THREADS. (HIGHLY MAGNIFIED.)

POLLEN GRAIN OF HOLLYHOCK. (HIGHLY MAGNIFIED.)

POLLEN GRAINS OF PRIMROSE. (HIGHLY MAGNIFIED.)

WONDERFUL FLOWER-DUST.

FRUIT   JUNIPER TREE
Cigarettes.

THE HORNBEAM.

PLAYER'S CIGARETTES

RHESUS MACAQUE AND YOUNG

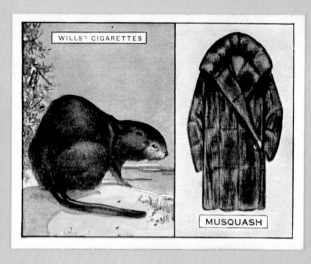

WILLS'S CIGARETTES

MUSQUASH

Great Ant-Eater.

ADKIN'S CIGARETTES.

Gnu of S. Africa.

WILLS'S CIGARETTES

Hignett Bros & Co. Ltd LIVERPOOL.

RHINOCEROS.

BUTTERFLY CIGARETTES.

HYÆNA

PLAYER'S CIGARETTES

OTTER

CARACAL

CIGARETTES.

MACKENZIE'S

The Rhinoceros.

Card 77

MUSQUASH.

The Musquash or Musk-rat is common through-out North and South America.

It makes its home on the banks of slow-running streams and swamps, and lives chiefly on roots of aquatic plants, but it will eat practically anything.

In farmed centres the Musquash houses give the swamps the appearance of a hayfield when heaped in cocks.

In the mating season the male indulges in desperate fights for his inamorata, and having secured her, he keeps her.

The Musquash loves fighting, and will combine with its friends to defeat a common enemy.

The Canadian variety has a deeper fur than the Southern Musquash, but the latter has a tougher pelt. It is used in natural and dyed states. When dyed black and machined to imitate Seal it is often known as Hudson Seal.

Its wearing qualities are of the best, and it is used both for coats and trimmings.

77

Card 78

RHESUS MACAQUE AND YOUNG

The Rhesus Macaque is one of the hardiest of all monkeys, and frequently breeds in this country. A native of India, it is equally immune to great heat or severe cold. The baby, as shown in the picture, is very like the parent, though with a proportionately shorter tail and larger head. Like the human infant, it is at first very helpless and clings tightly to the maternal breast. As it gains strength, however, it gradually changes this position for a seated posture on the maternal hip, and is finally allowed to ride on its mother "jockey fashion." Its upbringing is carried out on strict lines, all its solid food being at first tasted by the mother before being passed to the baby.

78

Card 79

79

Card 80

RHINOCEROS. One horned species found only in East Indies; two horned in Asia and Africa. There are six species large & clumsy thick skins. Live skin used by natives as shields. The two horned African is still in heart of day, going to feeding places morning and evening.

80

Card 81

81

Card 82

GNU.

(Connochætes taurina.)

These ungainly-looking animals are wonderfully quick, and so extremely wary, that fewer are killed by hunters than any other antelopes. They perform the most extraordinary evolutions, wheeling in circles, capering and gambolling around the hunter, stopping suddenly to look at him, then bounding away across the plain. They are found in the open country of S. and E. Africa, north of the Orange River. Height 4½ feet at shoulder. Horns 19 inches long.

82

Card 83

STRIPED HYÆNA
(Hyæna Striata)

In the Wolves' and Foxes' Dens, these savage and powerful brutes are to be found. It is to be met with from India to Northern Africa, where it frequents open, hilly or sandy districts. In inhabited districts the animal is much dreaded on account of its grave-robbing propensities. Its jaws are so powerful that it can crush the shin bone of an ox as readily as a dog breaks that of a fowl.

83

Card 84

13

OTTER
(Lutra lutra)

The Otter belongs to a family of Carnivores (Mustelidæ) which also includes the Badgers, Stoats and Weasels. It is distinguished by its uniformly brown coloured upper parts, flat head, long body, tapering tail, short limbs and webbed feet. Adult males measure from 40 to 50 inches in total length and weigh from 20 to 25 lb., although as much as 40 lb. is on record. It swims and dives with facility, propelling itself with the tail as a rudder. It is found in most of the large streams and rivers of Great Britain and Ireland, and sometimes frequents the sea-shore.

84

Card 85

ANIMAL STUDIES

CHEETA

The Cheeta, or Hunting Leopard, is found in Persia, Transcaspia, Palestine, Africa and India. In the last-named country it is tamed and trained by the native princes to hunt the antelope.

85

Card 86

THE ZOO.   No. 10.

Series of 50.

RHINOCEROS.
Rhinoceros Unicornis.

Are of six species and inhabit Asia and Africa. Are surly and ill tempered and have particularly keen scent organs. The so-called horn is a mass of fibres matted together, and is not connected with the skull. Some have one horn and others two.

86

Card 87

Caracal.
Felis caracal.

This cat is similarly coloured to the lion and puma, but is of course a much smaller edition. Its chief characteristic is the lynx ear-tufts which are black. It is found in India, Arabia and Africa where it lives among grass and bushes. It feeds upon small mammals, though it will kill animals up to the size of gazelles and small deer. In some parts of India it has been trained to hunt and kill after the manner of the cheetah.

87

ZOO STUDIES
A SERIES OF 50

33

PENGUINS

Penguins are essentially birds of the Antarctic, none being found north of the Cape of Good Hope. They are flightless, and essentially fish eaters, obtaining their prey by swimming under water. In this they are aided by their great weight and powerful wings, the birds literally flying under water at an amazing speed. The feet serve as a rudder and, whilst ashore, the tail acts as a "shooting stool." As a rule only two eggs are laid at a time, these being incubated by the parents in turn. The King Penguin of South Georgia, which stands a yard high, lays one egg only, which it hatches between its instep and the heavily-padded abdomen.

HIGNETT BROS. & CO.
ISSUED BY THE IMPERIAL TOBACCO CO.
(OF GREAT BRITAIN & IRELAND), LTD

88

FAUNA OF RHODESIA
A SERIES OF 25

10

The Giraffe.
(Giraffa capensis.)

Harmless, beautiful, mute and almost helpless—the Giraffe stands a solitary and pathetic figure upon the brink of extinction. A easy prey to the hunter and to collectors for menageries. A good Bull may attain a height of nearly 18 ft. The Giraffe is not easy to stalk, because of its mottled hide and its habit of standing quite motionless amongst the low trees upon which it browses. In open country a man mounted on a moderately fast pony can run a Giraffe to a standstill—and then nothing but the hunter's sense of sportsmanship can save the animal from destruction.

ISSUED BY
LAMBERT & BUTLER
BRANCH OF THE IMPERIAL TOBACCO CO.
(OF GREAT BRITAIN & IRELAND), LTD.

89

WILD ANIMALS' HEADS
FROM PAINTINGS BY ARTHUR WARDLE
A SERIES OF 50

35

The Lion.
(Felis leo).

The "King of Beasts" owes his title to the magnificent flowing mane which adorns his head and shoulders, which is, however, only developed in profusion in captivity. His tawny coat, varying from yellow to greyish-brown, harmonizes with the sands and dried grasses of his favourite haunts. Formerly inhabiting the whole of Africa, Lions have been exterminated in many parts, and are now most abundant in the eastern provinces. They are also found in Iraq, Persia and India. The roar of the Lion terrorizes other beasts; they leave their lairs and thus fall an easy prey to the nocturnal prowler.

ISSUED BY
JOHN PLAYER & SONS
BRANCH OF THE IMPERIAL TOBACCO CO.
(OF GREAT BRITAIN & IRELAND), LTD.

90

ANIMALS OF THE COUNTRYSIDE
A SERIES OF 25

No. 19

HARVEST MICE

The harvest mouse is the smallest of the mouse family, and being so small makes it exceedingly light. this enables it to climb a cornstalk and feed on the grain seeds. Seeds and grain are its main diet but it also eats worms and insects.

FUMEZ LES FAMEUSES CIGARETTES
"MILLS" FILTERTIPS

92

NATURAL HISTORY
A SERIES OF 50

17

Eland.
(Taurotragus oryx).

The Eland or Impoofo is the largest of the Antelopes, a fully grown adult bull standing nearly six feet at the shoulders and weighing from half to threequarters of a ton. Formerly common over the whole of Central, S. and E. Africa, it is now rare except in the Transvaal, Nyasaland, Rhodesia, Zululand, and E. Africa generally. Both bulls and cows have the spiral horns characteristic of this species, those of the female being longer and more slender. The Eland appears to be able to live for weeks without drinking; it is, however, a voracious eater.

ISSUED BY
JOHN PLAYER & SONS
BRANCH OF THE IMPERIAL TOBACCO CO.
(OF GREAT BRITAIN & IRELAND), LTD

93

PREHISTORIC ANIMALS
A SERIES OF 25

94

16

PHORORHACOS.

When the remains of this curious bird were discovered in 1887, they were at first identified as those of a mammal, but a few years later were recognised as belonging to a bird, *Phororhacos*, the head of which must have been larger than that of any living bird. Some six species are now known, ranging in size from small varieties measuring about 3 ft. high at the middle of the back, up to giants standing some 7 or 8 feet in total height. *Phororhacos*, which was probably carnivorous, could not fly, and must have run down its victims.

ISSUED BY
EDWARDS, RINGER & BIGG
BRANCH OF THE IMPERIAL TOBACCO Cº
(OF GREAT BRITAIN & IRELAND), LTª

WILD ANIMALS
SERIES OF 48. Nº 13

THE CAPPED LANGUR
The Capped Langur, pronounced and sometimes spelt "Lungoor," lives in Assam, North-East India and Burma and is one of India's Sacred Monkeys which it is sacrilege to kill. It derives its name from the "cap" of darker hair on the crown of its head. The long whip-like tail is a distinctive feature in all langurs. This monkey is a most human and affectionate mother and in Zoos is proud of displaying its offspring.

ISSUED BY
GALLAHER LTD
VIRGINIA HOUSE, LONDON & BELFAST

95

Wild Animals
A SERIES OF 25

No. 4
WILD PIG

This animal is a member of the even-toed ungulates (hoofed mammals). There are several species of wild pig; all having powerful tusks. They live in Central and Western Asia and Northern Africa. In herds they do much damage to crops.

FUMEZ LES FAMEUSES CIGARETTES
"MILLS" FILTERTIPS

96

WHIPSNADE ZOO

A SERIES OF 25 SUBJECTS

Issued with
MORRIS'S HIGH GRADE CIGARETTES

Nº 17

IN THE NEW ZOOLOGICAL PARK AT WHIPSNADE, BEDFORDSHIRE

Here, wild animals roam in natural surroundings and in seeming freedom. An estate of 500 acres, divided into extensive paddocks and yet giving security to the public. This is the largest Zoo in the World

The area of this wonderful showground is fifteen times greater than that of Regents Park Zoo. America has its Yellowstone Park, but this is not a zoo, it is a reservation for birds and animals native to that particular locality; there are no hippos, elephants, emus, ostriches, wallabies or camels such as we have here. Our illustration is that of the Camel, usually associated with the sandy desert.

B. MORRIS & SONS LTD LONDON E.1.

97

"ZOO" SERIES.
25 in Series.

No. 14.

The Gelada Baboon.

Baboons, a very destructive species of Ape, unite both for attack and defence; the males of a whole pack have been known to charge an intruder, and they account for many dogs and cattle, as a bite from their powerful jaws will cripple most animals. They are naturally intelligent and but for their ferocious temper could be trained to usefulness. The Gelada Baboon is found in the hills of Abyssinia.

Issued by
RICHARD LLOYD & SONS,
Branch of Cope Bros. & Co., Ltd..
LONDON & LIVERPOOL

98

99

LIFE AT WHIPSNADE ZOO

A Series of 54. No. 11.

SAM AND HIS TYRE.

There is no better toy than an old motor tyre says Sam, one of the Polar bears at Whipsnade Zoo, for it can be bowled along like a child's hoop, flung aloft and caught again, and gives its lucky owner huge joy as he plays with it in a score of ways. Moreover, this particular tyre enabled the photographer to get a fine snapshot of Sam in a pose that shows not only his great body, immensely strong paws and his beautiful jacket, but his intelligent face and those eyes that seem so alert to all that is taking place before them.

BANDMASTER
MAJOR DRAPKIN & CO.
92, MIDDLESEX ST. LONDON, E.I

COPE'S CIGARETTES
WILD ANIMALS & BIRDS

2 TIGER

The Tiger is the only animal which challenges the Lion's sovereignty, as it equals him in size, strength, activity, and excels him in elegance of form, grace in movement, beauty of his fur, and, possibly, courage. The Tiger is a splendid swimmer, and takes to the water quite readily, whether in search of prey or to escape the hunter.

COPE BROTHERS & CO LTD
LIVERPOOL & LONDON

100

ANIMALS & BIRDS OF COMMERCIAL VALUE
A SERIES OF 100

1 ALPACA

The Alpaca, or Paco, of Peru, forms a species or variety of Llama, but smaller, and inhabits the mountainous tracts of Peru and Chili. It is bred and domesticated for the sake of its long, silky wool. In colour the general hue is white, but varies to grey or even white, and sometimes black. Alpaca wool is chiefly manufactured at Bradford in Yorkshire, for dress materials, Indian blankets, ponchas, and rugs.

Nº 60

ISSUED BY
GALLAHER LTD
BELFAST & LONDON.

101

Bactrian Camel

PLAYER'S CIGARETTES.

LION.

LAMBERT & BUTLER'S CIGARETTES.

GIRAFFE.

HIGNETT'S CIGARETTES

PENGUINS

CAPPED LANGUR & BABY

RINGER'S CIGARETTES.

PHORORHACOS.

PLAYER'S CIGARETTES.

ELAND.

SAM AND HIS TYRE

BABOON

CAMEL

Gallaher's Cigarettes

ALPACA

COPE'S CIGARETTES

TIGER

SCOTTISH TERRIER

ROUGH-COATED COLLIE.

RINGER'S CIGARETTES

14

PLAYER'S CIGARETTES

GLORIOUS EVENT

PLAYER'S CIGARETTES

GORDON SETTERS

RINGER'S CIGARETTES.

RABBITS.—1.

Ch. Rebel Maid of Gadeland

DUTCH AND OLD ENGLISH RABBITS

Ogden's Cigarettes

Yorkshire Terrier

FAULKNER'S CIGARETTES

THE GOLD FISH

COPE'S CIGARETTES.

BORZOI (RUSSIA)

DOGS

41

POMERANIAN.

A Series of 50 Copyright Designs from Original Paintings Issued Solely by

TADDY & CO.

WITH THEIR CIGARETTES.

TADDY & CO LONDON.

113

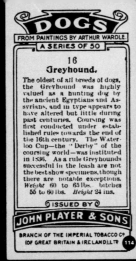

DOGS

FROM PAINTINGS BY ARTHUR WARDLE

A SERIES OF 50

16
Greyhound.

The oldest of all breeds of dogs, the Greyhound was highly valued as a hunting dog by the ancient Egyptians and Assyrians, and in type appears to have altered but little during past centuries. Coursing was first conducted under established rules towards the end of the 16th century. The Waterloo Cup—the "Derby" of the coursing world—was instituted in 1836. As a rule Greyhounds successful in the leash are not the best show specimens, though there are notable exceptions. *Weight* 60 to 65 lbs. bitches 55 to 60 lbs. *Height* 24 ins.

ISSUED BY

JOHN PLAYER & SONS

BRANCH OF THE IMPERIAL TOBACCO CO (OF GREAT BRITAIN & IRELAND), LT.

114

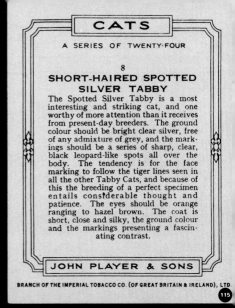

CATS

A SERIES OF TWENTY-FOUR

8

SHORT-HAIRED SPOTTED SILVER TABBY

The Spotted Silver Tabby is a most interesting and striking cat, and one worthy of more attention than it receives from present-day breeders. The ground colour should be bright clear silver, free of any admixture of grey, and the markings should be a series of sharp, clear, black leopard-like spots all over the body. The tendency is for the face marking to follow the tiger lines seen in all the other Tabby Cats, and because of this the breeding of a perfect specimen entails considerable thought and patience. The eyes should be orange ranging to hazel brown. The coat is short, close and silky, the ground colour and the markings presenting a fascinating contrast.

JOHN PLAYER & SONS

BRANCH OF THE IMPERIAL TOBACCO CO. (OF GREAT BRITAIN & IRELAND), LTD.

115

DOGS

A SERIES OF 50.

18
Mastiff.

The Romans, when they invaded these Islands, found the natives possessed of a powerful race of dogs from which the Old English Mastiff is descended. Many of the dogs were taken back to Rome to take part in the sports of the Amphitheatre. The laws of Henry III. provided for farmers, etc., to keep Mastiffs for the defence of their homes. The Mastiff is a large, massive, powerful, symmetrical dog—a combination of grandeur, good nature, courage and docility. *Colour* apricot or silver fawn and dark brindle. *Height* at shoulder 30 ins. *Weight* 150 lbs.

JOHN PLAYER & SONS

BRANCH OF THE IMPERIAL TOBACCO CO (OF GREAT BRITAIN & IRELAND), LT.

116

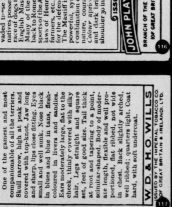

DOGS

A SERIES OF 50

38

BEDLINGTON TERRIER

One of the gamest and most companionable of all the terriers. Skull narrow, high at peak and covered with top-knot. Jaw long and sharp, lips close fitting. Eyes small and well sunk. Nose flesh-coloured in blues and blue in tans, flesh-coloured in livers and sandies. Ears moderately large, flat to the cheek, thinly covered with silky hair. Legs straight and square set, feet of good size. Tail thick at root and tapering to a point, scimitar-shaped. Body of moderate length, flexible and well proportioned, flat ribbed, not wide in chest. Back slightly arched, well filled; quarters light. Coat hard, with well undercoat.

THIS SURFACE IS ADHESIVE, ASK YOUR TOBACCONIST FOR (OR ONE PENNY) THE PROTECTIVE ALBUM (PRICE ONE PENNY) SPECIALLY PREPARED TO HOLD THE COMPLETE SERIES

ISSUED BY

W.D.& H.O. WILLS

BRANCH OF THE IMPERIAL TOBACCO CO (OF GREAT BRITAIN & IRELAND), LTD.

117

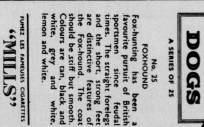

DOGS

A SERIES OF 25

No. 25
FOXHOUND

Fox-hunting has been a favourite pursuit of British sportsmen since feudal times. The straight forelegs and the short, strong feet are distinctive features of the Fox-hound. The coat should be stiff but smooth. Colours are tan, black and white, grey and white, lemon and white.

"MILLS"

FILTERTIPS

FAMEUX LES FAMEUSES CIGARETTES

119

121

DOGS

FROM PAINTINGS BY ARTHUR WARDLE

A SERIES OF 50

44

Wire-haired Fox Terrier.

The Wire-haired Fox Terrier is a cousin of the Smooth-coated variety, and, except for the coat, the accepted standard of points of the two varieties is identical. The two kinds are often interbred, litters sometimes including representatives of both. The Wire-haired Fox Terrier should have a sharp, alert expression, V-shaped ears, dark eyes, a long head and strong foreface. His coat should be hard, wiry and harsh to the touch; silky or woolly hair is a great fault. Colours: white should predominate, with black or tan markings; liver, brindle, or blue markings are objectionable. Height: 14 in. Weight: 18 lb.

ISSUED BY

JOHN PLAYER & SONS

BRANCH OF THE IMPERIAL TOBACCO CO (OF GREAT BRITAIN & IRELAND), LTD.

DOGS

SECOND SERIES OF 48. No. 34

DINGO

The Dingo is the wild dog of Australia, believed to have been introduced there hundreds of years ago by the natives. Since the immense multiplication of rabbits in Australia, the numbers of the Dingo have also greatly increased, and they have become a serious menace to the sheep. There are tame Dingoes as well as wild ones, however. They are not a cultivated breed over here, but Dingoes are sometimes seen at the big dog shows.

ISSUED BY

GALLAHER LTD.

VIRGINIA HOUSE, LONDON & BELFAST

122

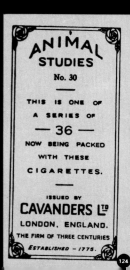

PLAYER'S CIGARETTES

SHORT-HAIRED SPOTTED SILVER TABBY

PLAYER'S CIGARETTES.

GREYHOUND.

THE CALM BEFORE THE STORM

PLAYER'S CIGARETTES.

MASTIFFS.

WILLS'S CIGARETTES

BEDLINGTON TERRIER

JOB CIGARETTES
IRISH TERRIER.

PLAYER'S CIGARETTES

WIRE-HAIRED FOX TERRIER

PUTTING ON WEIGHT

DINGO

OGDEN'S CIGARETTES.

H. BLADES.

PLAYER'S CIGARETTES

C. SMIRKE.

KINNEARS
HANDICAP
Cigarettes

ALLSOPP.

F. RICKABY

Won by a short head.
1¼ lengths between
2nd and 3rd.

The Cesarewitch.
ROSE PRINCE 1. TERESINA 2. CEYLONESE 3.

Miwani (broke down close
home) was 4th. Tharros
5th. Sailor Son 6th.

Ceylonese   Miwani   Teresina   Tharros Sewing Machine RosePrince   Sailor Son

WILLS'S CIGARETTES

"SNAKE LIGHTNING"   JOCKEY: T. HAWCROFT

PLAYER'S CIGARETTES

THE ACTIVE VANNER

FRANKLYN'S CIGARETTES.

TAKING A FENCE.

W & F. FAULKNERS CIGARETTES

TAMAR

RACING CARICATURES
SERIES OF 40

34

Charles Smirke
advanced rapidly to fame in the season of 1923. Apprenticed to Mr. Stanley Wootton at Epsom, he showed marked ability in the saddle, and soon became one of the most popular light-weights. He rode his first 40 winners in exceptionally quick time, among them being Daughter-in-Law in the Derby Cup. In the following year he could no longer claim the apprentice allowance, but this did not interfere with his success, and early in the season he showed that he would be a formidable competitor for the jockey championship. He is wonderfully strong for his size, and rides with great intelligence.

TURF CIGARETTES

Big Events on the Turf.
Series of 12.
11.—The Cesarewitch Stakes (H'cap.)
Value £1,885.
2 miles 2 furlongs.
Run at Newmarket, October 17th, 1923.
Time 3 mins. 48 secs.

The triumph of Rose Prince was a great day for America, for owner, trainer and jockey, all hail from the other side of the Atlantic. It was only after a thrilling struggle, however, that the victor got the better of Teresina by a matter of inches. Archibald allowed his mount plenty of time to settle down, but at the mile post, Rose Prince was going somewhat lazily, so the jockey brought out his whip. Then it was that Rose Prince speedily took hold of his bit, and by the time the Bushes were reached, he was in a position to challenge. At the bottom of the hill, Rose Prince went out to win his race. Teresina stuck to him very determinedly, however, and it was only by a short head that the French-bred horse succeeded. He was all out at that, too, for Teresina gave a very game display.

129

In the London streets one cannot fail to admire the grand show made by the heavy Active Vanners, the property of various business houses which still take pride in their stables. Unfortunately, the number employed is gradually diminishing. Carefully selected for their combination of strength, quality and action, they gladden the eye as they bowl along at a lively pace with big loads. Their good breeding is seen at a glance; indeed, many of them would not be out of place at a Coaching Club meet. One cannot refrain from regretting that these fine steppers are disappearing year by year from the duties they discharge with such distinction, though at the London Van Horse Parade at Regent's Park 536 horses were paraded in 1937.

RACEHORSES & JOCKEYS, 1938
A SERIES OF 40

26

"SNAKE LIGHTNING"
Jockey: T. HAWCROFT

This colt proved himself a good stayer in 1938 when running a dead-heat with *Naval Display* for the Goodwood Stakes of two miles three furlongs. Earlier in the season, with T. Hawcroft up, he won over two miles at Kempton Park and over a mile-and-a-half at Lingfield. He was bred by his owner, Sir Harold Gray, and is a chestnut by *Sea Serpent* (a son of *Golden Myth*, who won the Irish St. Leger of 1931) out of the *Bachelor's Double* mare *Daytime*. In his first season he ran three times without success and in the following year he carried off the Lingfield Handicap as well as a race at Lewes. Mr. Victor Gilpin trains him at Michel Grove, Sussex.

PROMINENT RACEHORSES OF 1933

A SERIES OF 50

36

"NITSICHIN"

Bay mare (1928) by *Achtoi-Latium*.
Breeder : MAJOR V. H. PARR.
Owner : MR. D. S. KENNEDY.
Trainer : P. THRALE at West Horse-ley, Surrey.

Bought by her present owner as a Yearling for 380 guineas, this grand staying mare had won £8,182 in stakes for him up to the end of 1933. Her most important success was in the Cesare-witch of 1932, which, with M. Beary up, she easily won under 8 st. 9 lb., starting second favourite at 10 to 1. She has carried off two London Cups at Alexandra Park, the Irish Oaks, and the Jockey Club Cup at New-market.

ISSUED BY
OGDEN'S
BRANCH OF THE IMPERIAL
TOBACCO CO. (OF GREAT
BRITAIN & IRELAND), LTD.

134

ISSUED BY
OGDEN'S
BRANCH OF THE IMPERIAL
TOBACCO CO. (OF GREAT
BRITAIN & IRELAND), LTD.

RACEHORSES

A SERIES OF 50.

36

VELOCITY.

Owned by Mrs. H. V. Jackson, and purchased for her from an Irish farmer for £130, *Velocity* was successful in the Castle Irwell Handicap and Don-caster Cup, also winning the last race of the flat season at Manchester.

In 1926 he won the Cambridgeshire of 1925, when he was sent to be trained very big, so up for his party when he was, by *Fairway* out of *Pintadeau*, and indeed very English, and landed every penny in a *tricroset*. He was bred by Lord Barnby, and his owner, Lord Chatris Hill, Stockbridge, by H. S. Persse. As a two-year-old he ran at first unnamed.

135

NOTE.—THIS SURFACE IS ADHESIVE.
ASK YOUR RETAILER FOR
THE ATTRACTIVE ALBUM SPECIALLY
PREPARED TO HOLD THE COMPLETE SERIES

DERBY ENTRANTS
1926.

A SERIES OF 25.

23

Review Order.

LORD BARNBY'S COLOURS.

Review Order is a chestnut colt by *Grand Parade* winner of the Derby, *&c.*, out of *Sanfoin* mare *&c.*, &c. He was bred by his owner, Lord Barnby and his owner, Lord Barnby, is an owner who has been a good many years connected with the Turf. As a two-year-old he ran in the Molecomb Stakes at Goodwood, and the Rous Memorial Stakes at New-market. He was third in three of his eight races but unplaced once. He won £5,090 in stakes.

ISSUED BY
OGDEN'S
BRANCH OF THE IMPERIAL TOBACCO CO.
(OF GREAT BRITAIN & IRELAND), LTD.

138

FAMOUS
IRISH-BRED HORSES

A SERIES OF 25

24

"KELLSBORO' JACK."

Bay gelding by *Jackdaw-Kells-boro' Lass*, by *Oppressor*. Breeder: Mr. Hely-Hutchinson. Owner: Mrs. Ambrose Clark. Trainer: I. Anthony. *Kellsboro' Jack* was seven years old when he won the 1933 Liverpool Grand National Steeplechase (£7,345) for Mrs. Ambrose Clark, an American patroness of the Irish and British Turf. The gelding was bred by Mr. Carlos and purchased by Mr. Ambrose Clark who, having had ill-fortune with so many of his horses, offered to give *Kellsboro' Jack* to his wife. She objected to the ownership of "a gift horse" and insisted on paying £1 for his possession. *Kellsboro' Jack* thus has the distinction of being the world's greatest winner of the lowest-priced steeplechase. In 1936 he won the Champion Steeplechase at Liverpool.

JOHN PLAYER & SONS
BRANCH OF THE IMPERIAL TOBACCO CO.
(OF GREAT BRITAIN & IRELAND), LTD.

139

DERBY ENTRANTS
1929.

A SERIES OF 50

39

PHILAMOR.

Owner: Mr. W. T. Sears.
Colours:
CERISE, BLACK HOOP ON BODY,
BLACK CAP WITH GOLD TASSEL.
This colt cost 8,500 guineas as a yearling. He is trained at Newmarket by Felix Leach, Junr., who was only able to bring him out once as a two-year-old. That was in the Prince of Wales's Stakes at York, in which he was un-placed. *Philamor* is a brown colt by *Son-in-Law* out of *Love-oil*. He is half-brother to *Legatee* (who was unbeaten as a three-year-old), and *Saracen*, winner of the Manchester November Handicap.

ISSUED BY
OGDEN'S
BRANCH OF THE IMPERIAL TOBACCO CO.
(OF GREAT BRITAIN & IRELAND), LTD.

142

DERBY ENTRANTS
1928.

A SERIES OF 50

45

"The Hermit II."

(OWNER: MR. A. K. MACOMBER.)

The property of an American whose colours are familiar in England, this bay colt by *McEnbing* out of *Halpine* was placed at the top of the Free Handicap with *Fairway* and *Brûland*. He is trained at New-market by S. H. Darling, who gave him his first race in the First October Meeting. He gained a runaway victory and achieved another comfortable success in the Prendergast fortnight later. He failed, however, to concede 15lb. to *Felso* in the Moulton Stakes.

ISSUED BY
OGDEN'S
BRANCH OF THE IMPERIAL TOBACCO CO.
(OF GREAT BRITAIN & IRELAND), LTD.

141

HORSEMANSHIP

A SERIES OF 50

10

HOW TO HOLD A
DOUBLE BRIDLE

The hands are held in an odd position for the purpose of demonstration. The following points, illustrated in our picture, should be noted: (a) It is usual for the position of the curb and bridoon reins to be reversed. Only the experienced should emulate this picture, owing to the pressure on the outside rein. (b) The curb rein (2 and 4) is round the little finger and the bridoon rein (1 and 3) round the third finger, the little finger being the most sensitive to any movement of the horse's mouth. (c) The two reins are passed up, if any, into the palm of the hand over the index finger, and held in place by the thumb.

ISSUED BY THE IMPERIAL TOBACCO CO.
LAMBERT & BUTLER
LTD.

143

RACING SCENES
SERIES OF 48   No 24

"NECK AND NECK"

Our picture shows two horses in training galloping neck and neck on the New-market Heath. There are several recognised training gallops on the public heath, which has been the centre of thoroughbred racing in Eng-land for over 300 years. The special character of the soil keeps the turf in splendid condition, being porous enough to absorb the heavy rains and mossy enough to retain some moisture in very dry weather.

ISSUED BY
GALLAHER LTD
VIRGINIA HOUSE LONDON & BELFAST

144

145

DERBY WINNERS

SERIES OF 50
No 30

SIR HUGO.

Owner—The late Earl of
Bradford.

Jockey—F. Allsopp.

He won the Derby of 1892, and might be described as quite a moderate animal, but beyond this victory he did very little else. In the race for the Derby he was running a brilliant mare (La Fleche) evidently thought he had the race in hand, and her defeat caused the utmost consternation amongst sporting people.

SMITH'S
ALBION GOLD FLAKE
CIGARETTES

146

H. WATTS.

G. RICHARDS

OGDEN'S CIGARETTES

MR. D. S. KENNEDY'S COLOURS

"NITSICHIN"

Ogden's Cigarettes.

VELOCITY.

Player's Cigarettes

Mr. C. Davis, His Majesty's Huntsman

OGDEN'S CIGARETTES.

LORD BARNBY'S COLOURS

REVIEW ORDER

PLAYER'S CIGARETTES

"KELLSBORO' JACK"

OGDEN'S CIGARETTES.

PHILAMOR.

OGDEN'S CIGARETTES

"THE HERMIT II."

"NECK AND NECK"

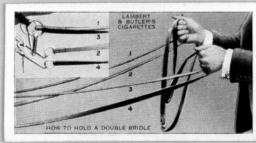

LAMBERT & BUTLER'S CIGARETTES

HOW TO HOLD A DOUBLE BRIDLE

F. & J. SMITH'S CIGARETTES.   1892.

LORD BRADFORD

F. ALLSOPP.

SIR HUGO.

PLAYER'S CIGARETTES

D. G. BRADMAN

H. ENTHOVEN
CAMB. UNIVERSITY

HAROLD LARWOOD

PLAYER'S CIGARETTES

A. H. H. GILLIGAN (SUSSEX)

CHURCHMAN'S CIGARETTES

B. H. VALENTINE

OGDEN'S CIGARETTES

C. WASHBROOK

H. SUTCLIFFE
YORKSHIRE

WILLS'S CIGARETTES.

E. ARNOLD (WORCESTERSHIRE).

WILLS'S Cigarettes.

MR. C. McGAHEY,
ESSEX

ROBERT ABEL.
SURREY

PLAYER'S CIGARETTES

T. B. MITCHELL (DERBYSHIRE)

CHURCHMAN'S CIGARETTES.

YORKSHIRE.

G. C. WHITE.

CRICKET TERMS.

"Leg stump"

GRENADIER CIGARETTES
W. & F. Faulkner Ltd. London, S.E.

PLAYER'S CIGARETTES

P. HOLMES, YORKSHIRE

No. 24

CRICKET, TENNIS & GOLF CELEBRITIES
A Series of 50

THIS SURFACE IS ADHESIVE

HAROLD LARWOOD
(Nottinghamshire)

The famous Notts. bowler, he first appeared in a Test Match v. Australia, at Lord's, in 1926. Took 18 wickets in the Tests in Australia, 1928-29, and 33 in the 1932-33 series. Hit up 98 in the fifth Test in the Commonwealth two winters ago. Larwood takes a long run when delivering his "expresses" and is one of the fastest bowlers in the world to-day. Was second in the 1934 averages, with 82 wickets at an average of 17.25.

ISSUED WITH
ARDATH CORK
CIGARETTES

147

Cricketers Series

Nº 24.

H. J. Enthoven,
Cambridge University,

Is captaining his Varsity during 1926, and is a splendid all-round cricketer. Described as the most improved cricketer in England, he increased his bowling average from 17 to 50 wickets for 22·14 each during 1925, and his batting average from 24 to 51·93. In the Inter-Varsity match at Lord's he scored 104 in 1924 and 129 in 1925, and played for the Gentlemen against the Players in the latter year.

SMOKE
TRAWLER, CRITIC,
CLUB MEMBER
CIGARETTES.

J. A. PATTREIOUEX
MANCHESTER

148

THIS SURFACE IS ADHESIVE. ASK YOUR TOBACCONIST FOR THE ATTRACTIVE ALBUM (PRICE ONE PENNY) SPECIALLY PREPARED TO HOLD THE COMPLETE SERIES

CRICKETERS 1938
A SERIES OF 50

38

D. G. BRADMAN
(New South Wales, South Australia and Australia)

Don Bradman has been outstanding in the cricket world since his astonishing successes in England during the 1930 tour, when he made 1,000 runs before the end of May—the only Australian ever to achieve this feat—scored a century on his first Test appearance in England; completed three double centuries in the Test series, including the record 334 at Leeds, and reached the highest aggregate for one series of Tests (974). Against England his average is 89·63, and he holds the world's first-class cricket record of 452 not out against Queensland. He is a marvellous fieldsman. Revisits England as Australia's captain. Born August 27th, 1908.

JOHN PLAYER & SONS
BRANCH OF THE IMPERIAL TOBACCO CO.
(OF GREAT BRITAIN & IRELAND) LTD.

149

150

A SERIES OF 50

FAMOUS CRICKETERS

INCLUDING
THE S. AFRICA TEST TEAM

No. 43. FRANKLIN, H. W. F.
(Essex.)

A forcing batsman, with good driving power on the off-side. Scored 319 runs, average 21·26, in 1922, and 266 runs, average 22·16, in 1923. Made a splendid 106 against Middlesex at Leyton in 1923, being his first century for his County, he and Douglas adding 160 runs in just over two hours.

ISSUED WITH
'SUNRIPE' CIGARETTES
WHICH STAND ALONE FOR SIZE AND TONE

CARRERAS
HIGH-CLASS CIGARETTES

H. SUTCLIFFE
(England and Yorkshire)

A grand opening batsman who maintains a high degree of consistency, he has taken part in the last five series of Test matches. In his first tour he secured an average of 81.55, a really remarkable achievement. He has also been concerned in eleven century first-wicket partnerships with J. B. Hobbs against Australia, and obtained eight individual scores of 100 or over

A Series of Cricketers No. 20

ARCADIA WORKS
LONDON·ENGLAND

151

PROMINENT CRICKETERS OF 1938
A SERIES OF 50

32

C. WASHBROOK
(Lancashire and England)

Cyril Washbrook, who was born at Barrow on January 6th, 1915, has now established himself as Lancashire's opening batsman. When eighteen years of age he hit up 202 not out in his first match for the Lancashire Second Eleven. This innings earned him immediate promotion to the First Eleven, and in his second game for the County, against Surrey, he made 152. Although, in 1937, he did not find a regular place in the eleven until late in June, Washbrook scored 1,546 runs, average 42·94, with three centuries in four innings. He is an attractive all-round batsman, and also fields brilliantly in the deep.

ISSUED BY
OGDEN'S
BRANCH OF THE IMPERIAL TOBACCO CO
(OF GREAT BRITAIN & IRELAND) LTD.

152

CRICKETERS
A SERIES OF 50

45

B. H. VALENTINE
(Kent and England)

A Cambridge Blue, Valentine shows his Repton training in dashing off-side play. If over-venturesome, he is most attractive to watch when, thanks to quick footwork, he punishes good-length bowling with full-blooded drives. He excelled with 1,738 runs in 1933 and, when touring India in the winter of 1933–34, made 136 in the first Test match at Bombay. He often captains Kent, and superb fielding makes him a splendid leader. In the deep he brings off amazing catches by speedy running and accuracy in judging the flight of the ball. Valentine is a soccer Blue and a Corinthian.

ISSUED BY THE IMPERIAL TOBACCO CO.
W.A.& A.C.CHURCHMAN
(OF GREAT BRITAIN & IRELAND), LTD.

153

154

CRICKETERS 1930
A SERIES OF 50

16

A. H. H. Gilligan.
(Sussex.)

The youngest of three brothers who at Dulwich College excelled at both cricket and rugby football, Harold Gilligan is the new captain of Sussex. When injuries crippled Arthur last summer, Harold undertook the duty and for the same reason the M.C.C. called upon him to lead the team in Australasia. Harold Gilligan seems gifted for the office. After he accepted the post Sussex won four of their remaining six county matches, the other two being drawn. A dashing bat, Harold Gilligan excels in drives and forcing strokes. He fields brilliantly at cover point, and, aged 34, is at his best.

ISSUED BY
JOHN PLAYER & SONS
BRANCH OF THE IMPERIAL TOBACCO CO.
(OF GREAT BRITAIN & IRELAND), LTD.

CRICKETERS, 1934
A SERIES OF 50

19

T. B. MITCHELL
(Derbyshire and England)

Thomas Bignell Mitchell reached Test rank when, at the age of 31, he helped to beat Australia in the fourth and deciding encounter which won England the Ashes under D. R. Jardine in February, 1933. The need to wear spectacles does not handicap Mitchell's smartness in the field, and he can hold hot catches off his own slow leg-break bowling. He progressed from 113 wickets in 1929 to 142 last season, average 19, and has assisted materially in making Derbyshire one of the best County sides. Mitchell goes in last and is modest about his batting.

ISSUED BY
JOHN PLAYER & SONS
BRANCH OF THE IMPERIAL TOBACCO CO.
(OF GREAT BRITAIN & IRELAND), LTD.

155

A Series of over
250 SUBJECTS
being issued

SWEET CROP
SMOKING MIXTURE

a most
DELICIOUS SMOKE
always reliable ·
in packets.

COHEN, WEENEN & CO.
···· LONDON ····

156

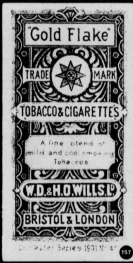

"Gold Flake"

TRADE MARK

TOBACCO & CIGARETTES

A fine blend of mild and cool smoking Tobaccos

W.D. & H.O. WILLS

BRISTOL & LONDON

Cricketer Series 1901 Nº 4?

157

CRICKETERS

28

WILLS'S CIGARETTES

E. ARNOLD.
(Worcestershire England.)

One of the best all-round cricketers in England. He was first chosen for the Players v. Gentlemen in 1899, and in later years he has usually been included in representative matches. As a member of the famous M.C.C. team that visited Australia in 1903, he bowled consistently well throughout the tour. He has four times taken over 100 wickets in a season, and scored 1,000 runs in a season. Excellent in the field.

W.D. & H.O. WILLS
BRISTOL & LONDON

ISSUED BY THE IMPERIAL TOBACCO Cº
(OF GREAT BRITAIN & IRELAND) Lᵗᵈ

ALBUMS FOR THESE PICTURE CARDS CAN BE OBTAINED
AT 1/- EACH FROM ALL TOBACCONISTS

158

159

CRICKETERS CARICATURES BY "RIP"
A SERIES OF 50

20

P. Holmes,
YORKSHIRE.

Holmes, with Sutcliffe, is one of the most famous first-wicket batsmen of the world, rivalling even Brown and Tunnicliffe, Duff and Trumper, or Hobbs and Rhodes. Last season, but for Hobbs's extraordinarily fine scoring, Holmes would have been the batsman of the year. Critics who saw his record innings of 315 at Lords were of opinion that even Hobbs had never excelled it. Is a very fine field in the country, and above the average as a wicket-keeper. Went to the W. Indies with the M.C.C. team last year, and played for England in 1921.

ISSUED BY
JOHN PLAYER & SONS
BRANCH OF THE IMPERIAL TOBACCO Cº
(OF GREAT BRITAIN & IRELAND) Lᵗᵈ

160

161

SERIES OF 50

Nº 37

CRICKETERS

G. C. WHITE.

Gordon C. White (Transvaal), born in 1882, was one of the few players who fell below their Colonial reputations in the 1907 tour of the South Africans in England, when he only passed the century once (162 not out), late in August, against Gloucestershire, at Bristol. He had the reputation of being the best bat in the team, but failed in the Test matches, and finished eighth in the averages.

SMITH'S ORCHESTRA CIGARETTES

FAMOUS CRICKET COLOURS
SERIES OF 25

22

YORKSHIRE.

The quaint design of the "White Rose of York" worn by the Yorkshire eleven is one of the most familiar badges seen on the cricket field. The club colours are light-blue, dark-blue and gold. Formed in 1863, Yorkshire has always possessed one of our most powerful sides. Up to the end of 1925, the championship of the First Class Counties had been won 14 times, the first occasion having been in 1893. The tremendous cricketing strength of the County may be gauged from the figures given in the 1927 edition of "Wisden"—out of 1,090 matches played, no less than 572 have been won, and only 177 lost.

W.A. & A.C. CHURCHMAN
ISSUED BY THE IMPERIAL TOBACCO CO.
(OF GREAT BRITAIN & IRELAND) LTD.

162

SCOTTISH FOOTBALL SNAPS
A SERIES OF 50

2

ANDREW ANDERSON
(Heart of Midlothian)

Hearts' right back is one of the outstanding personalities in a very brilliant team. He was rightly regarded as having few equals in season 1934-'35, and was the unanimous choice of the selectors for all international matches. He is a cool, deliberate player, quick to make up his mind, sure in the tackle, and a steady kicker. At his best on big occasions, Andrew Anderson made his fame secure by a great display in his initial international against England at Hampden Park in April 1933. He has been with Hearts for over four years, having been secured in face of keen competition from Baillieston at the end of the Intermediate dispute.

ISSUED BY
STEPHEN MITCHELL & SON
BRANCH OF THE IMPERIAL TOBACCO CO.
(OF GREAT BRITAIN & IRELAND) LTD.

163

FOOTBALLERS
1928-9
2ND SERIES 51-75

61

W. J. Kirton.
(Coventry City.)

Kirton has had a long and notable career. Formerly with Leeds City, he went to Aston Villa in 1920. In his first season at Villa Park he secured a Cup Winner's medal, scoring the only goal in the Final with Huddersfield Town at Stamford Bridge, when an extra half hour was played for the first time in the history of the Final. He was in the Villa Team beaten by Newcastle in the Cup Final at Wembley in 1923-24. Kirton was capped for England v. Ireland in 1922. Joined Coventry this season. Height 5 ft. 6½ in. Weight 11 st. 11 lb.

ISSUED BY
JOHN PLAYER & SONS
BRANCH OF THE IMPERIAL TOBACCO CO.
(OF GREAT BRITAIN & IRELAND), LTD.

164

FOOTBALL CARICATURES
A SERIES OF 50

41

E. HERBERT
(Hull)

Ernest Herbert, one of the best discoveries as a stand-off half in recent years, is twenty years of age, 5 ft. 8¼ in. in height, and weighs 11 st. 9 lb. He joined Hull in Feb. 1934 from the Ossett Rugby Union club, and in the following season scored fifteen tries in thirty-nine matches, as well as one for Yorkshire against Lancashire. He has played a big part in the club's recent revival. His father was a Durham forward in the nineties, and his brother is the present Wakefield Trinity half-back. Both brothers were born in Wakefield.

HIGNETT BROS. & CO.
ISSUED BY THE IMPERIAL TOBACCO CO.
(OF GREAT BRITAIN & IRELAND), LTD.

165

166

FOOTBALL CARICATURES BY 'MAC'
A SERIES OF 50

13

Harry Foxall.
(Portsmouth.)

Harry Foxall, the tall, untiring and angular captain and centre-half, has been for five seasons the linch-pin of the Portsmouth team. He helped to put the "motion" in promotion when they rose to the First Division. Born at Old Hill, near Birmingham, he played his first grown-up football for Cradley Heath. A younger brother, Arthur, was a popular figure in the ranks of Kidderminster harriers. Foxall reaped useful experience with the Welsh clubs, Pontypridd and Merthyr, on his way to Frattou Park.

ISSUED BY
JOHN PLAYER & SONS
BRANCH OF THE IMPERIAL TOBACCO C⁰
(OF GREAT BRITAIN & IRELAND) LTD

167

ASSOCIATION CUP WINNERS
A SERIES OF 50

10

Preston North End, 1889.

The crowd of over 25,000 people who assembled at the Oval to witness this Final were treated to one of the finest exhibitions of polished football ever seen. The passing of Preston North End was like clock-work, their defence superb. In the first half Dewhurst opened the scoring, Ross increasing the total shortly afterwards. With the change of ends the Wanderers were expected to do much better, but they played a losing game from beginning to end, and when Thomson scored the third goal for Preston, it was a fitting climax to a game in which the Wolverhampton eleven were outclassed in every department. Result: Preston North End 3 goals. Wolverhampton Wanderers Nil.

ISSUED BY
JOHN PLAYER & SONS
BRANCH OF THE IMPERIAL TOBACCO CO.
(OF GREAT BRITAIN & IRELAND), LTD.

FOOTBALLERS IN ACTION
SERIES OF 50

No. 22

TOTTENHAM v. HUDDERSFIELD TOWN

An incident in the League game between Tottenham Hotspur and Huddersfield Town at White Hart Lane. James Smith, the Hotspur goalkeeper, has jumped to catch a ball that looked like passing over his head whilst friend and foe look on in admiration of a brilliant save.

ISSUED BY
GALLAHER LTD.
BELFAST & LONDON.

168

---

66 SUBJECTS.

WILLS'S "CINDERELLA" CIGARETTES.

In Packets containing
5 CIGARETTES,
Price 1d.

THESE CIGARETTES ARE
BRITISH MADE
BY
BRITISH LABOUR
WITH
BRITISH CAPITAL

Issued by the
Imperial Tobacco Co., Ltd.

169

ASSOCIATION FOOTBALLERS
2ND SERIES OF 50

30

A. McNAB
(West Bromwich Albion)

An outstanding member of West Bromwich Albion, a team in which the appearance of a Scotsman has always been exceptional, Alexander McNab was born in Glasgow and before becoming a professional footballer worked as a grocer. While playing with the junior club, Pollok, he signed on for Sunderland in 1932, going to Roker Park as a left-wing forward. Later he moved to left-half and it is in this position that he has won distinction. He played a notable part in the Cup Final of 1937, when Sunderland defeated Preston North End, and in 1939 he was chosen to play for Scotland against England. He joined West Bromwich Albion in season 1937/38.

W. A. & A. C. CHURCHMAN
BRANCH OF THE IMPERIAL TOBACCO CO.
(OF GREAT BRITAIN & IRELAND) LTD.

170

No. 32

A Series of 50 FAMOUS FOOTBALLERS

ARDATH ALBUMS ARE ON SALE AT TOBACCONISTS, PRICE 1d.

J. McGRORY
(Glasgow Celtic)

Centre - forward. Became prominent just after the War. Had a short spell with Clydebank, then joined Celtic. Scored 8 out of 9 goals v. Dunfermline, January 14th, 1928. Scottish League Championship Medal 1926. Scottish Cup Medals 1925-31-33. Scottish International v. England (2) Wales, Ireland (4). Born Glasgow.

ISSUED WITH
ARDATH CORK and STATE EXPRESS 333 CIGARETTES

171

FOOTBALL CLUB CAPTAINS
A SERIES OF 50

19

A. ROWE
(TOTTENHAM HOTSPUR)

Rowe is one of the many young players Tottenham Hotspur have trained from boyhood. Serving his apprenticeship as a centre-half in the nursery at Northfleet he was promoted to the Tottenham team in 1931-32 and he played a notable part in the revival of the club, assisting them to regain their place in the First Division in the following season. He has appeared once for England, being the pivot of the team which defeated France on the Tottenham ground in 1933 by four goals to one. As a centre-half he cleverly combines attack with defence.

HIGNETT BROS. & CO.
ISSUED BY THE IMPERIAL TOBACCO CO.
(OF GREAT BRITAIN & IRELAND), LTD.

172

SERIES OF 150 FOOTBALLERS
No 90

JAMES BLAIR.

A youthful but experienced back, who plays the game all the time and should soon gain the highest honours in the world of football. Reliable at either right or left, and can be safely entrusted with any position.

SMITH'S "PINEWOOD" CIGARETTES

173

INTERNATIONAL CAPS

No. 5 of a Series of 50

C. JONES
(Birmingham)

Centre-forward. Born Oswestry, N. Wales. Started his professional career with Oswestry and after a short trial was turned down on account of being too frail. Secured another chance with Wrexham, and following an amateur period with the Welsh club was signed on professional forms. In 1934-35 season Birmingham obtained his signature at a fee of £1,250. Represented Wales against Ireland in 1935.

THIS SURFACE IS ADHESIVE

GODFREY PHILLIPS LTD.
AND ASSOCIATED COMPANIES

174

CARRERAS
QUALITY CIGARETTES

A. BLACK
(Leicester City)

Was a Scottish junior with Bathgate, and joined Leicester City in 1920. Has an exceptional record of service, having played in over 500 matches and received two benefits, with a reputation for being a consistent and forceful right-back. Won the D.C.M. during the War, while serving with the Argyll and Sutherland Highlanders.

SERIES OF 75   N⁰ 40

ARCADIA WORKS LONDON · ENGLAND

175

FAMOUS FOOTBALLERS
A SERIES OF 50

No. 4.

PERCY GROSVENOR
(Left Half Back)
Leicester City.

Born Evesham. Height 5 ft. 10½ ins., weight 11 st. 7 lbs. Signed by Leicester City from Dudley Junior Club. Developed into one of the soundest wing halves in the country, and he uses his height to good effect in defending the goal, but it is in his good ability in initiating attacks that he really shines.

ISSUED BY
R. & J. HILL. LTD.
Proprietors of
HY. ARCHER & CO.
London & Birmingham

176

177

PLAYER'S CIGARETTES

HARRY FOXALL

HIGNETT'S CIGARETTES

E. HERBERT (HULL)

PLAYER'S CIGARETTES

W. J. KIRTON (COVENTRY CITY)

MITCHELL'S CIGARETTES

A. ANDERSON (HEARTS)

CHURCHMAN'S CIGARETTES

A. McNAB (WEST BROMWICH ALBION)

Football Series No. 21.

M. Sanders, Barrow-in-Furness.

Gallaher's Cigarettes.

PLAYER'S CIGARETTES

HOWARTH · HOLMES · Dr. MILLS-ROBERTS · DRUMMOND · GRAHAM · RUSSELL · GORDON · DEWHURST (F.) · ROSS · GOODALL · THOMSON

ASSOCIATION CUP WINNERS
PRESTON NORTH END, 1889

C. JONES

J. BLAIR
CLYDE F.C.

HIGNETT'S CIGARETTES

A. ROWE (TOTTENHAM HOTSPUR)

J. McGRORY

FOOTBALL TERMS.

FULL BACK
GRENADIER CIGARETTES
W. & F. Faulkner Ltd. London, S.E.
COPYRIGHT.

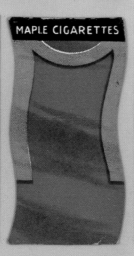

MAPLE CIGARETTES

P. GROSVENOR
LEICESTER CITY

CARRERAS CIGARETTES

A. BLACK
LEICESTER CITY (1ST DIV.)

S. COWAN

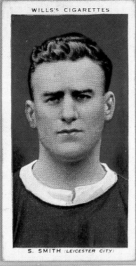

WILLS'S CIGARETTES

S. SMITH (LEICESTER CITY)

J. J. WILLIAMS

CHURCHMAN'S CIGARETTES

J. E. FORREST

W. MINTER (Spurs).

WILLS'S CIGARETTES

JOHN ROBERTS

OGDEN'S CIGARETTES.

J. E. RAPHAEL.

PLAYER'S CIGARETTES

W. GILLESPIE

MITCHELL'S CIGARETTES

P. STEELE
(DUNFERMLINE ATHLETIC)

OGDEN'S CIGARETTES.

RICHMOND.

F. & J. SMITH'S CIGARETTES

BIRMINGHAM.
H. HAMPTON.
Now with Newport County.

PROMINENT FOOTBALLERS.

F. PIERCY,
WEST HAM UNITED.

GALLAHER'S CIGARETTES.

ALEX. RAISBECK,
PARTICK THISTLE, 1909-10.

D. M'GARRY

J. T. PALETHORPE

HIGNETT'S CIGARETTES

BIRMINGHAM

RUGBY INTERNATIONALS
A SERIES OF 50

20

J. E. FORREST
(Glasgow Academicals and Scotland)

J. E. Forrest, a wing-three-quarter, was capped for Scotland against England in 1935, but his only other experience of international play was in 1932. That year he played for his country against the "Springboks," who, touring the British Isles, lost only one game (against a Leicestershire and East Midlands XV) out of 26. Forrest has been a powerful member of the Territorial Army team in their annual games with the Army. He is sound in defence, and with his speed and audacity needs a lot of catching. The illustration shows the Glasgow Academicals' colours.

W. A. & A. C. CHURCHMAN
ISSUED BY THE IMPERIAL TOBACCO CO. (OF GREAT BRITAIN & IRELAND), LTD.

179

POPULAR FOOTBALLERS
Nº 2

J. J. WILLIAMS
(Huddersfield Town)

Born at Aberdare, 23 years ago, John James Williams gained experience with Aberaman and Llanelly before he was signed by Huddersfield Town in November, 1932. Standing 5 ft. 5½ ins., the Town's outside right weighs 10 stones.

Since the front of this card was printed, Williams has been transferred to Aston Villa.

A SERIES OF 48
ISSUED BY
CARRERAS LIMITED
ARCADIA WORKS, LONDON, ENGLAND.

KEEP THESE CARDS IN THE CARRERAS "SLIP-IN" PICTURE CARD ALBUM OBTAINABLE FROM ALL TOBACCONISTS (PRICE ONE PENNY)

180

THIS SURFACE IS ADHESIVE. ASK YOUR TOBACCONIST FOR THE ATTRACTIVE ALBUM (PRICE ONE PENNY) SPECIALLY PREPARED TO HOLD THE COMPLETE SERIES

ASSOCIATION FOOTBALLERS
A SERIES OF 50

39

S. SMITH
(Leicester City)

Born in the colliery village of Whitburn, which has given many notable players, Septimus Smith is the younger brother of Jack and William, who have won distinction with Portsmouth. He joined Leicester City, and first appeared in the League side at Huddersfield in 1929. Originally he was an inside forward, but although still occasionally appearing in the front line, his usual place is at right-half where he is notable for his speed and fine resource in attack. Until 1935 he had not received international recognition, but in the Jubilee match between England and Scotland on Aug. 21st, he played a magnificent game in place of Bray (retired injured) in the second half.

W. D. & H. O. WILLS
ISSUED BY THE IMPERIAL TOBACCO CO., LTD.

181

FAMOUS FOOTBALLERS
Nº 45

S. COWAN
(Manchester City)

S. Cowan crowned his football career when he captained the winning Manchester City team in the F.A. Cup Final in 1934. Born in Chesterfield, he played for Denaby United and Doncaster Rovers before Manchester City secured him in 1924, as centre-half. Has played in three Cup Finals and is English International.

Has now been transferred to Bradford City.

A SERIES OF 48
ISSUED BY
CARRERAS LIMITED
ARCADIA WORKS, LONDON ENGLAND

182

FOOTBALLERS, CARICATURES BY "RIP."
A SERIES OF 50

14

William Gillespie.
(Sheffield United.)

One of Ireland's greatest footballers. He is the captain of Sheffield United, and had the honour of leading his team to victory in the cup final of 1925. Born in Londonderry, he joined Leeds City in 1910, and was transferred to the Sheffield Club in the following year. He had the misfortune to break a leg in 1914, and the injury probably robbed him of another cup winner's medal. Gillespie has played in 20 matches for Ireland, and as an inside left he is unsurpassed.

ISSUED BY
JOHN PLAYER & SONS
BRANCH OF THE IMPERIAL TOBACCO CO. (OF GREAT BRITAIN & IRELAND), LTD

183

48

FAMOUS FOOTBALLERS
50 IN A SET.

J. E. RAPHAEL.

Raphael, the Old Merchant Taylor, opportunist and individualist, is probably the most criticised threequarter England possesses. He is a player of moods; his best is brilliant, his worst indifferent. He plays a lone hand cleverly at times, and is an adept at bursting through with an electric dash. Gained his "Blue" at Oxford, and has played for England many times.

ISSUED BY
OGDEN'S
BRANCH OF THE IMPERIAL TOBACCO CO. (OF GREAT BRITAIN & IRELAND), LTD.

184

Wills for Quality

RUGBY INTERNATIONALS
A SERIES OF 50

38

John Roberts.
Cardiff, Cambridge University and Wales.

John Roberts has a remarkable record for versatility in three seasons of first-class Rugby. Capped for Wales in 1927, he played as a centre threequarter till he was tried on the left wing with such success that he kept his position. As a Cambridge Blue he played at full-back against Oxford in 1927 and 1928. The opposition in the latter match included his younger brother, W. Roberts, Oxford's stand-off half, and both brothers played for Wales against England a little later. John Roberts is a strong, determined player, difficult to stop. In defence he kicks and tackles well.

W. D. & H. O. WILLS
ISSUED BY THE IMPERIAL TOBACCO CO. (OF GREAT BRITAIN & IRELAND), LTD.

185

For your Cigarettes to be Handfilled, with the Sand and Dust extracted, see that the name of

JONES BROS., Tottenham,

is on the Packet.

186

"IMPERIAL" TOBACCO.

A ripe, full flavoured Pipe Tobacco, fine cut. In a good well-seasoned briar or a well-coloured meerschaum it will be found an admirable tobacco.

In 1 oz. & 2 oz. Tin Foil Packets, or ¼, ½ and 1 lb. Air-Tight Tins.

TADDY & CO.,
LONDON.

These cards are issued with Taddy's 'MYRTLE GROVE' MEDIUM Cigarettes.

187

FOOTBALL CLUB RECORDS.
A SERIES OF 50.—No. 24

BIRMINGHAM.

ENGLISH LEAGUE, DIV. I.
RECORD 1921-2.

	Home.	Away.
Arsenal	L 0—1	L 2—5
Aston Villa	w 1—0	D 1—1
Blackburn Rov.	w 1—0	D 1—1
Bolton Wander.	D 1—1	w 2—1
Bradford City	w 1—0	w 2—1
Burnley	L 2—3	L 1—3
Cardiff City	L 0—1	L 1—3
Chelsea	w 5—1	w 2—1
Everton	D 1—1	L 1—2
Huddersfield T.	L 0—2	L 0—1
Liverpool	L 0—2	L 0—1
Manchester City	w 3—1	L 0—1
Manchester Unit.	L 0—1	D 1—1
Middlesbrough	w 4—3	D 1—1
Newcastle United	L 0—4	w 1—0
Oldham Athletic	w 3—0	w 1—0
Preston N. End	L 0—2	D 2—2
Sheffield United	w 2—1	w 2—1
Sunderland	w 1—0	L 1—2
Tottenham H.	L 0—3	L 1—2
West Brom. Alb.	L 0—2	L 1—2

Total played, 42; W., 15; L., 20; D., 7. Goals for, 48; against, 60. Points, 37. Position, 19th.

Issued by The Imperial Tobacco Co. (of Great Britain & Ireland), Limited.

188

22

FOOTBALL CLUB COLOURS
50 IN A SET.

RICHMOND R.F.C.

The Richmond Rugby Club was formed some 45 years ago, and the wearers of the maroon, yellow and black maintain all the sporting traditions of the old club, which plays on the splendid Richmond Athletic Ground in Surrey, where the 'Varsities and the pick of the English amateur teams are annually met. The club numbers about 300 members, and runs four teams.

ISSUED BY
OGDEN'S
BRANCH OF THE IMPERIAL TOBACCO CO. (OF GREAT BRITAIN & IRELAND), LTD.

189

THIS SURFACE IS ADHESIVE. ASK YOUR TOBACCONIST FOR THE ATTRACTIVE ALBUM (PRICE ONE PENNY) SPECIALLY PREPARED TO HOLD THE COMPLETE SERIES

SCOTTISH FOOTBALLERS
A SERIES OF 50

40

P. STEELE
(Dunfermline Athletic)

P. Steele is a steady goalkeeper, whose custodianship considerably helped the Fifers back into the First League. He does his work in a quiet effective way without the inclination to showmanship which affects so many goalkeepers. Steele, who used to be with Leith Athletic, has given the Fife club fine service in the position. A remarkable feature of Steele's play is the tremendous length he gets into his clearing kicks.

ISSUED BY
STEPHEN MITCHELL & SON
BRANCH OF THE IMPERIAL TOBACCO CO. (OF GREAT BRITAIN & IRELAND), LTD.

190

A.F.C. NICKNAMES
A SERIES OF 50

4

BIRMINGHAM

The Club was originally known as Small Heath Alliance, and in 1888 they adopted "limited liability" and became The Small Heath Football Club Ltd., familiarly known as the "Heathens." When this nickname was no longer applicable they became simply the "Blues" because of their blue jerseys. The club is, however, always depicted as a negro. They were the first winners of the Second Division Championship in 1892-3, and although they fell back into this competition they have held senior rank since 1921. In 1930-31 they reached the final of the Cup competition and lost by the odd goal of three to West Bromwich Albion.

ISSUED BY
HIGNETT BROS & CO
BRANCH OF THE IMPERIAL TOBACCO CO. (OF GREAT BRITAIN & IRELAND) LTD

191

ENGLISH & SCOTTISH FOOTBALL STARS
A SERIES OF REAL PHOTOGRAPHS

No. 25.

J. T. PALETHORPE,
ASTON VILLA A.F.C.

Played for Sheffield Wednesday during the season 1934/35 and in 20 matches scored 8 goals. Born at Leicester. Took part in the 60th Cup Final at Wembley 1935, when he scored one goal playing Centre Forward.

ISSUED BY
JOHN SINCLAIR Ltd
NEWCASTLE-ON-TYNE

192

No. 40.

D. M'GARRY
(Greenock Morton, Outside Left)

Dan proved himself one of the most dangerous goal-scoring wingers in the country in season 1936-37. His snappy shooting was a feature of the Second Division, and helped his club to the First. Yet he is now on his second venture into senior football. He joined Dunfermline Athletic after spells with Port-Glasgow Juniors and Arthurlie Juniors, but failed to hit it off, and was re-instated as a junior. Still Morton fancied him, and Dan has certainly justified their faith. Height: 5 ft. 6 ins. weight: 10 st. 9 lbs. A native of Howwood.

Topical Times Photo.

SCOTTISH SERIES
ISSUED BY
JOHN SINCLAIR Ltd
NEWCASTLE-ON-TYNE

193

Association Football Club Colours

PARTICK THISTLE

Connection with the First Division of the Scottish League dates back to 1897-8, and they have not been over-successful in the search for points. In Scottish Cup Ties they also have yet to make their mark.

ISSUED BY
GALLAHER LTD.
BELFAST AND LONDON

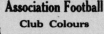

Series of 100. No. 11

194

PROMINENT GOLFERS
A SERIES OF 50

28

Roland Mackenzie.

A high place among American amateur golfers of Scottish extraction is held by Roland Mackenzie, of Washington. He was only nineteen when he helped the U.S.A. to beat Britain in the Walker Cup match of 1926 at St. Andrews. He repeated the visit in '30, and again was on the winning side at Sandwich. Mackenzie failed as a challenger for the British Amateur Title, both in '26 and '30, but he holds a fine record on his own side of the Atlantic. He has a beautiful style, and drives a long ball without any preliminary fuss. He should be a champion once he has tightened up his short game.

W. A. & A. C. CHURCHMAN

ISSUED BY THE IMPERIAL TOBACCO CO. (OF GREAT BRITAIN & IRELAND), LTD.

195

FAMOUS GOLFERS
A SERIES OF 27
REAL PHOTOGRAPHS.

No. 11.

MISS DIANA ESMOND
ST. CLOUD, FRANCE.

Winner of the Girls' Championship, Stoke Poges, 1926, her sister Sybil reaching semi-final. Played in "Eve's" Autumn Foursomes, 1926-27. Daughter of Mr. Edward Esmond, the well-known race-horse owner

ISSUED WITH

"De Reszke"
The Aristocrat of
CIGARETTES
J. MILLHOFF & Co. Ltd. LONDON ENGLAND

196

GOLF
A SERIES OF TWENTY-FIVE

9

DRIVE
HENRY COTTON

Henry Cotton (Ashridge) takes great care in addressing the ball for a drive (Fig. 1). His stance is with the feet fairly close. The right shoulder is drooping and his head is to the right of the ball. He takes the club back slowly with the left hand in control. In the down-swing there is a pronounced delayed action of the wrists. These do not uncock until late, when they speed up the club-head just before and during impact. There is a decided turnover of the right forearm early during the follow-through, with the right arm straight (Fig. 2). An outstanding feature of Cotton's drive is his control of the left side. In the down-swing the left hip is pivoted round further than is usual. At impact the left leg is rigid, with left foot in firm contact with the ground, although inside of the foot is eased.

JOHN PLAYER & SONS

197

CAN YOU BEAT BOGEY AT ST. ANDREWS?
SERIES OF 55   CARD NO. 51

MR. RABBIT'S ROUND— 17TH HOLE.

Mr. Rabbit relapsed again here. He hit the drive of his life right over the sheds and that unsettled him. He hooked his second into the Scholar's bunker, smote hard and went right over the green into the road and close to the wall. Here he tried to play a racket shot off the wall. Three. The ball nearly hit him in the stomach and bounded into the Road bunker. Four. Stayed there—five. Nearly into the Road again—six. Two putts. **8.**

Bernard Darwin

For Particulars of a Competition in connection with this card, see the inset enclosed with this packing.

W. A. & A. C. CHURCHMAN,
IPSWICH.

Issued by The Imperial Tobacco Company (of Great Britain and Ireland), Limited

198

---

the course?" and went there. Result—his second was kicked away by the ridge and he angrily took five. Mr. Tiger, more docile, drove well to the right. This made the hole longer but he got the opening to the green and so a four "I can't get up either way" said philosophical Mr. Rabbit. So he hit two of those and one of them and got his five, "Which I think" he remarked "gives me the hole with my stroke, eh Everyman?"

Bernard Darwin

SERIES OF 36   HOLE No. 9 (INLAND)
* See enclosed slip for explanation of this series of cards

W. A. & A. C. CHURCHMAN, IPSWICH.
Issued by The Imperial Tobacco Company (of Great Britain and Ireland), Limited

199

FAMOUS GOLFERS
SERIES OF 12

No. 2
JAMES BRAID

has won the Open Golf Championship upon five occasions—1901, '95, '06, '08, '10—these successes being scored in the remarkably short space of nine years. He was born on 6th February, 1870, at Earlsferry, a little village on the coast of the Firth of Forth, and he started work as a joiner. Soon after reaching London to work in a club-making establishment he turned professional. Possessed of great height and strength, Braid, at the zenith of his fame could hit the ball a prodigious distance, and when he won his championship at Prestwick in 1908 he played a remarkable shot from a thick clump of gorse, digging the ball out of the gorse with such effect that he played it on the green and the clump of gorse with it. He is now largely engaged in designing golf courses.

W. A. & A. C. CHURCHMAN

ISSUED BY THE IMPERIAL TOBACCO COMPANY (OF GREAT BRITAIN & IRELAND), LIMITED.

200

GOLF STROKES SERIES issued with:

MORRIS'S HIGH-GRADE CIGARETTES.

No. 2.

TOP OF SWING,
BRASSIE OR DRIVER.

Weight evenly distributed between both feet. Pressure on ball of left foot from knee. Club in horizontal position, left arm fairly straight, and both wrists under shaft. Right elbow away from body but pointing down.

B. MORRIS & SONS LTD. LONDON.

201

202

B 23   **FULL DRIVE**

Demonstrated by

ARCHIE COMPSTON

This is one of a series of fifty instructive slow-motion photographs packed with John Cotton tobacco and cigarettes. When fastened together by a rubber band they make a complete "flicker" of two golf shots.

JOHN COTTON LTD., EDINBURGH.

204

MARSUMA
PURE VIRGINIA
CIGARETTES
SERIES OF 50 PICTURES

48. E. BLACKWELL.

This is a fine finish of one of, if not the longest driver playing golf to-day. He holds the record. Comparing his footwork with that of the Champions shown in this series, there is seen at once a vast difference in the position of the feet and balance. H. Vardon and James Braid especially swing against the left leg which is very firm at the finish and the left toe does not face the hole as in Blackwell's case. It simply shows there is no royal road to long driving, tho' there may be consistent driving.

MARSUMA Co

CONGLETON.

205

GOLF STROKES

No. 23.

J. H. TAYLOR.
GRIP AT TOP OF SWING.

An important point to remember is that at the top of the swing the club should be under complete control and the right hand, which until now has exerted a loose hold on the shaft, should automatically tighten its grip just before the moment of impact.

COPE BROS. & Co. Ltd.
LIVERPOOL & LONDON

203

FAMOUS GOLFERS
SERIES OF 50

49

Roger H. Wethered who was amateur golf champion in 1923, was born 3rd January, 1899. Possessed of great height and wrists of steel, he can clip his iron shots as far as most golfers can drive. He won the Long Driving Competition in 1921, with an aggregate for three drives of 809 yards 1 inch. Wethered has many long driving feats to his credit. In the Amateur Championship at Prestwick, May, 1922, in the third round he drove hole-high at the right-hand green. From tee to hole the distance was 280 yards of hard operated against the ball remaining in the air. *(See also No. 48.)*

W. A. & A. C. CHURCHMAN

ISSUED BY THE IMPERIAL TOBACCO C° (OF GREAT BRITAIN & IRELAND)...

206

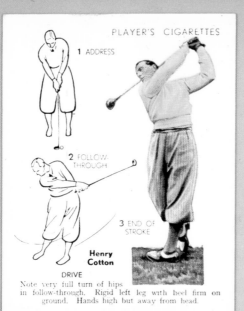

PLAYER'S CIGARETTES

1 ADDRESS

2 FOLLOW THROUGH

3 END OF STROKE

Henry Cotton

DRIVE

Note very full turn of hips in follow-through. Rigid left leg with heel firm on ground. Hands high but away from head.

MISS DIANA V. ESMOND

CHURCHMAN'S CIGARETTES

R. MACKENZIE

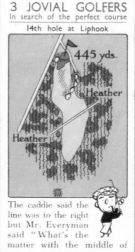

3 JOVIAL GOLFERS

In search of the perfect course

14th hole at Liphook

445 yds.

Heather

Heather

The caddie said the line was to the right but Mr. Everyman said "What's the matter with the middle of

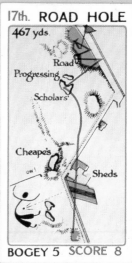

17th. ROAD HOLE

467 yds.

Road

Progressing

Scholars'

Cheape's

Sheds

BOGEY 5   SCORE 8

CHURCHMAN'S CIGARETTES.

J. BRAID.

W. Auchterlonie, Open Champion.

Ogden's Guinea Gold Cigarettes

GOLF STROKES

By ARTHUR G. HAVERS.

"Kenilworth" CIGARETTES.

COPE'S

J. H. TAYLOR.
GRIP AT TOP OF SWING.

CHURCHMAN'S CIGARETTES.

R. H. WETHERED.

A 28   FULL No. 1 IRON SHOT

Demonstrated by

ARCHIE COMPSTON

This is one of a series of fifty instructive slow-motion photographs packed with John Cotton tobacco and cigarettes. When fastened together by a rubber band in correct numerical order, these make a complete "flicker" of two golf shots.

JOHN COTTON LTD., EDINBURGH

Left hand lead at head.

FRANKLYN'S CIGARETTES.

PLAYER'S CIGARETTES.

WRESTLING. Cumberland and Westmorland Style.

CHURCHMAN'S CIGARETTES

MAX SCHMELING

33. RIGHT HOOK TO JAW.

OGDEN'S CIGARETTES.

GUNNER JAMES MOIR.

OGDEN'S CIGARETTES.

MATT WELLS.

OGDEN'S CIGARETTES.

HARRY MASON.

COPE'S

TOMMY BURNS

CIGARETTES

No. 17

THE DIXIE KID.

James J. Corbett

OGDEN'S
CIGARETTES

18.—Billy Matthews.

FAMOUS BOXERS

JACK DEMPSEY

CHURCHMAN'S CIGARETTES

HENRY ARMSTRONG

BOXING LESSONS

AVOIDING PUNISHMENT AT INFIGHTING

COPE BROS. & Cº LTD

TENNIS

A SERIES of 50

25

LOW BACKHAND DRIVE
MISS DOROTHY ROUND

Miss Dorothy Round, Great Britain's leading woman player, gets well down to a low ball on the backhand. Body is turned back during run across court, and racket taken round body by a bend of elbow. Wrist is firm and racket head raised. At start of swing, as right foot comes to ground, with knee bent and body lowered, forearm and racket are dropped down to ball level, racket coming forward with a flat swing, and ball being met in advance of body. Racket face is angled back very slightly to give loft to ball.

JOHN PLAYER & SONS
BRANCH OF THE IMPERIAL TOBACCO CO.
(OF GREAT BRITAIN & IRELAND), LTD.
223

224

SPORTS ALPHABET

A SERIES of 25

Sketches by
JOHN HASSALL
and
FRANK REYNOLDS

with verses by
Roland Carse

"Monax"
CIGARETTES
10 for 3ᵈ

A & J. COUDENS, LTD.
St. Pauls Crescent, London, N.W.1.

225

MEN OF THE MOMENT IN SPORT

SERIES OF 50

20

J. B. HOBBS.
(Surrey and England.)

"Jack" Hobbs, the greatest English batsman since W. G. Grace, has made more centuries in first-class cricket than any other player. His best score was 316 not out for Surrey against Middlesex at Lord's in 1926. In the '25 season, he scored 3,024 runs for an average of 70.32, and hit up the record number of 16 centuries during the summer. Hobbs has toured Australia and S. Africa with English teams, and has played in more Test matches than any other man. He is famed also for his fielding at cover-point, where he saves as many runs as he makes in an innings. He was born in 1882.

W. A. & A. C. CHURCHMAN
ISSUED BY THE IMPERIAL TOBACCO CO.
(OF GREAT BRITAIN & IRELAND) LTD.

226

INTERNATIONAL CAPS AND BADGES

A Series of 25.

9

England. Rugby League.

The roses stand for Yorkshire and Lancashire, the stronghold of the Rugby League. International Matches are played against "Wales" sides, selected from League players of Welsh qualification; and against Touring Teams from the dominions. In 1895 several Northern Clubs in Yorkshire, Lancashire, and Cheshire, left the Rugby Union and formed the Northern Union, this title being changed in 1922 to the "Rugby League." The Rugby Football Union is strictly amateur; while the League permits professionalism, though this is by no means universal.

ISSUED BY
HIGNETT BROS & Co.
BRANCH OF THE IMPERIAL TOBACCO Cº
(OF GREAT BRITAIN & IRELAND), LTᴰ

LAWN TENNIS

SERIES OF 50

12

H. Cochet.

Henri Cochet, born 1901, is one of the "Four Musketeers" of French lawn tennis, the other three being Lacoste, Borotra and Brugnon. In 1922 won French Covered Court Championship and the world's title (covered courts) at St. Moritz ; in the same year he represented his country at International matches. In 1926 Cochet won the French Championship, beating among others, V. Richards, and Lacoste. In 1927 he had his greatest triumph, winning the Wimbledon Championship after beating W. T. Tilden and Borotra. A wonderful stayer, Cochet has been called the "best fifth set player in the world."

W. A. & A. C. CHURCHMAN
ISSUED BY THE IMPERIAL TOBACCO CO.
(OF GREAT BRITAIN & IRELAND), LTᴰ.
227

228

SPORTS & GAMES IN MANY LANDS

SERIES OF 25

7

Pelota, France.

This game, popular in the Basque provinces of France, is also played in Spain. Well-known Pelota players are regarded with affection in the Basque country and they command high wages. The game is played with a hard rubber ball against a front wall (*fronton*), and one or two side walls. A pelota player wears a strong basket-work gauntlet, shaped like a sickle, strapped to his wrist. This enables him to hurl the ball with tremendous force against the wall. On the rebound the ball must be taken by an opposing player and returned to the wall ; should he fail to do so a point is scored and a fresh start made.

W. A. & A. C. CHURCHMAN
ISSUED BY THE IMPERIAL TOBACCO CO.
(OF GREAT BRITAIN & IRELAND), LTᴰ.

SPORTING TROPHIES

SERIES OF 25

21

The Elcho Shield.
(Rifle Shooting.)

This Challenge Shield—a magnificent specimen of repoussé iron work, valued at £2,000—was presented in 1862 by the late Lord Elcho (Tenth Earl of Wemyss and March). It is shot for at Bisley each year by teams of eight representing England, Scotland, and Ireland. The trophy is kept for the year in some conspicuous place in the winner's country (In England, the Guildhall). Match rifles are used ; 15 shots each man at 900, 1,000, and 1,100 yards. Post-war winners :
1920, 1921, Scotland.
1922, 1923, England.
1924, Scotland.
1925, 1926, England.

W. A. & A. C. CHURCHMAN
ISSUED BY THE IMPERIAL TOBACCO Cº
(OF GREAT BRITAIN & IRELAND) LTᴰ
229

SPEED CHAMPIONS

A SERIES OF 30.

No. 10

Miss M. B. Carstairs.

On November 25th, 1928, Miss Carstairs, in an official test of six runs over a measured knot course in the River Medina at Cowes, established a new world's speed record for her class of boat of 39.26 knots per hour. The photo shows Miss Carstairs, who has recently been racing in U.S.A., at the wheel of her new motor-boat.

ISSUED BY
GODFREY PHILLIPS Lᵀᴰ
112, Commercial Sᵗ.
LONDON, E.
230

SPORTS & PASTIMES

A SERIES OF 25 ISSUED WITH
"BOW BELLS"
VIRGINIA CIGARETTES

No. 3.

Ski-Jumping in Norway.

Travelling on Ski (pronounced She) over the frozen snow, is customary in Norway and Sweden. They are wooden runners, about 8-ft. long, and 4-in. broad, firmly fastened under the feet. At the Winter Sports, held in Scandinavia and Switzerland, many brilliant feats of "ski-jumping" are performed.

T. H. COLLINS,
TOBACCO MANUFACTURER,
Ravensdale Mills,
MANSFIELD
231

LAWN TENNIS STROKES

232

No. 6.

VINCENT RICHARDS.
(U.S.A.)

Fore-hand Volley.

Player making stroke while on the run and advancing towards the net. Note perfect balance of body, eyes intent on ball.

For Pipe Smokers
"HIGH CARD"
FLAKE
AND
"ESCUDO"
Navy de Luxe

COPE BROS. & Cº LTᴰ

233

SPORTING CELEBRITIES

No. 28

T. BRADSHAW, Liverpool.

The biggest member of Football's Biggest Team. Over 13st. and 6ft. 2ins. high. Product of Scottish Junior Football ; first made his name with Bury and attained such heights of brilliance that Liverpool paid £8,000 for his transfer in January, 1930. Formerly one of the greatest constructive half backs in the game, but in order to fall in with modern standards of Centre Half play, has now become a rock-like barrier to opposing attacks by his stirring Third Back play. Unlike most big men, Bradshaw does not rely on weight alone, his clever footcraft and shrewd moves being a delight to watch. Capped for Scotland v. England, 1928.

These interesting Photographs are issued with
TRAWLER CIGARETTES 10 for 4ᵈ
CRITIC CIGARETTES 10 for 5ᵈ
ALSO
KING LUD TOBACCOS AND CIGARETTES

234

SPORTS TROPHIES SERIES.

Nº 20.

Cycling

Challenge Cup.

This is a silver bowl, of plain and chaste design, presented by H.M. The King to the Norfolk and Norwich Amateur Cycling Club in 1922. It is raced for each year at local charity sports.

SMOKE
TRAWLER·CRITIC·CLUB MEMBER
CASKET CIGARETTES

J.A.PATTREIOUEX
MANCHESTER

SPORTING PERSONALITIES

SERIES OF 48. Nº 27

Mr. D. HORN

Dennis Horn will always be remembered as one of the most outstanding English track cyclists. He won success as a cyclist in various parts of the world, although his name is always associated with the Herne Hill track, where he broke many records, the most impressive of which was the 25-mile record in 1934, his time being 58 minutes, 34⅘ seconds. Himself a clever exponent of ice skating, his brother Cyril achieved fame as Amateur Skating Champion.

ISSUED BY
GALLAHER LTD
VIRGINIA HOUSE, LONDON & BELFAST
235

CYCLING

A SERIES OF 50
BY THE EDITOR OF "CYCLING"

48

TRACK RACING POSITION

The position of a track rider is planned to enable him to jump suddenly from a walking pace to 40 m.p.h., and the handlebars are deeply dropped in order to streamline the body as much as possible. The full benefit of the careful adjustment of saddle and handlebars is therefore only secured when a rider is absolutely "flat out." Each rider's position varies according to his physical and muscular characteristics, but normally the peak of the saddle is over the bottom bracket, and the handlebars a few inches higher than the front wheel. Crank length is also a factor to be considered by the expert track rider when finding his ideal position. The rider depicted is W. W. Maxfield, British Empire 10-mile champion.

JOHN PLAYER & SONS
BRANCH OF THE IMPERIAL TOBACCO CO.
(OF GREAT BRITAIN & IRELAND), LTD.
236

37

WILLS'S CIGARETTES

HURLERS

A SERIES OF 50.

M. MURPHY.
(Limerick.)

Possessing as he does an unerring positional instinct, and an icy coolness in critical moments, this herculean young Ireland representative is ideally equipped for the arduous task of guarding the bearna baog hail. His skill and resource between the sticks contributed considerably to his county's All-Ireland triumphs in 1918 and 1921. Mick also played on the Munster selected against Leinster in the Inter-Provincial finals. Height 5 ft. Weight 12 st. 6 lb.

W. D. & H. O. WILLS
ISSUED BY THE IMPERIAL TOBACCO Cº
(OF GREAT BRITAIN & IRELAND) LTᴰ
237

CHAMPIONS

2ᴺᴰ SERIES OF 48. Nº 5

G. P. ("PAT") HUGHES

Scarcely touched a tennis racket until he was twenty-one, and is now one of the "three musketeers" of English tennis. Is perhaps a greater doubles than a singles player, and partnered by the formidable Fred Perry, has represented Great Britain in the Davis Cup for the last three years. He helped to win back that trophy for England in 1933, after twenty-one years. Has been very successful on foreign soil, and in 1931 won all three events in the Italian Championships, beating the great Henri Cochet in the singles.

PARK DRIVE
CIGARETTES
Gallaher Ltd.
VIRGINIA HOUSE
LONDON & BELFAST
238

HIGNETT'S CIGARETTES.

1923-24

ENGLAND. RUGBY LEAGUE

CHURCHMAN'S CIGARETTES.

MEL

J. B. HOBBS.

J.—JUMPING.

The Jumper's a jumpy
  enthusiast who
Has a frantic ambition to
  shine
In performing a trick
  Of just clearing a stick,
With the chance of a bruise,
  or a sprain, or a rick,
And the risk of contusing
  his spine.

PLAYER'S CIGARETTES

2   1

Miss
Dorothy
Round

LOW   3
BACKHAND DRIVE
Stroke made to low bounding ball.
Note bent knees and body, right
shoulder lowered to bring racket
head behind ball without dropping
wrist.   Ball hit in front of body.

CHURCHMAN'S CIGARETTES.

THE ELCHO SHIELD.
(RIFLE SHOOTING.)

CHURCHMAN'S CIGARETTES.

PELOTA,
FRANCE.

CHURCHMAN'S CIGARETTES.

H. COCHET.
(FRANCE.)

QUALITY CIGARETTES.

CYCLING. THE CHALLENGE
CUP PRESENTED BY
H.M. THE KING.

FOOTBALL - T. BRADSHAW, LIVERPOOL

LAWN TENNIS STROKES

VINCENT RICHARDS (U.S.A.).
FORE-HAND VOLLEY.

COPE BROS. & Co. LTD.

SKI JUMPING IN NORWAY.
SPORTS & PASTIMES SERIES No. 5.

G. P. HUGHES

WILLS'S CIGARETTES.

M. MURPHY,
(LIMERICK.)

PLAYER'S CIGARETTES

TRACK RACING POSITION

Mr D. HORN

L. OSBORNE,
HULL KINGSTON ROVERS.

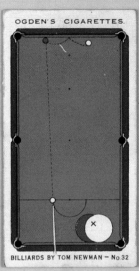

OGDEN'S CIGARETTES.

BILLIARDS BY TOM NEWMAN — No. 32

WILLS'S Cigarettes

ENGLAND, Sea Fishing.

PAAVO NURMI

C. A. Bradley.

OGDEN'S CIGARETTES

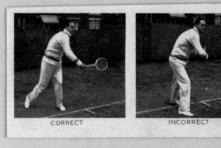

CORRECT   INCORRECT

OGDEN'S CIGARETTES

"WELL MARKED!"

HIGNETT'S CIGARETTES

THE DOUBLE ARM BACK STROKE
ARM ACTION—5TH POSITION

EGYPTIANS PLAYING DRAUGHTS. 1600 B.C.

VIC HUXLEY
NO. 7 OF A SERIES OF 50

Turn over & "Spot the Winner"

GALLAHER'S

CIGARETTES

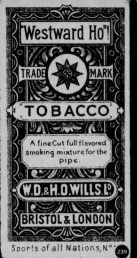

"Westward Ho"!

TRADE MARK

TOBACCO

A fine Cut full flavored smoking mixture for the pipe.

W.D. & H.O. WILLS Ltd.

BRISTOL & LONDON

Sports of all Nations, No. | 239

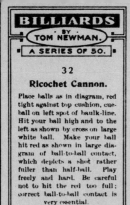

BILLIARDS

BY TOM NEWMAN.

A SERIES OF 50.

32

Ricochet Cannon.

Place balls as in diagram, red tight against top cushion, cue-ball on left spot of baulk-line. Hit your ball high and to the left as shown by cross on large white ball. Make your ball hit red as shown in large diagram of ball-to-ball contact, which depicts a shot rather fuller than half-ball. Play freely and hard. Be careful not to hit the red too full; correct ball-to-ball contact is very essential.

ISSUED BY

OGDEN'S

BRANCH OF THE IMPERIAL TOBACCO CO. OF GREAT BRITAIN & IRELAND, LTD.

240

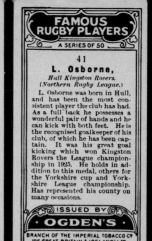

FAMOUS RUGBY PLAYERS

A SERIES OF 50

41

L. Osborne,

Hull Kingston Rovers. (Northern Rugby League.)

L. Osborne was born in Hull, and has been the most consistent player the club has had. As a full back he possesses a wonderful pair of hands and he can kick with both feet. He is the recognised goalkeeper of his club, of which he has been captain. It was his great goal kicking which won Kingston Rovers the League championship in 1925. He holds in addition to this medal, others for the Yorkshire cup and Yorkshire League championship. Has represented his county on many occasions.

ISSUED BY

OGDEN'S

BRANCH OF THE IMPERIAL TOBACCO C? (OF GREAT BRITAIN & IRELAND,) L?

241

OLYMPIC Champions

AMSTERDAM

1928

A SERIES OF 36

N? 5

This picture shows the finish of the 800 metres race won by D. G. A. Lowe (England) who set up a new Olympic record in 1 m. 51 4/5 sec.

ISSUED BY

GODFREY PHILLIPS Lᵀᴰ

112 COMMERCIAL Sᵀ LONDON E

242

LAWN TENNIS

A SERIES OF 25

No. 7

SERVICE. (Position 4.)

Correct.

This illustrates finish of service. The body has twisted to the left, all weight being on left foot.

Incorrect.

The server is in serious trouble. "Oh, no," you think, "no one would serve like that." But many people do, not in so accentuated a manner, but they are still, so to speak, coming up and the result is that they are pulling up the weight of their body when they should be putting every ounce of it into the shot.

Extract from Rules of Lawn Tennis.

SERVICE.

The server shall stand with both feet behind (i.e., further from the net than) the base-line, and within the imaginary continuation of the centre mark and side line.

(b) The object in service is to change the position of the ball with the racket from the position in which it is at the commencement of the service to the position in which it leaves the server's racket.

(c) The service is delivered when the server's racket is carried back ... (the ball must be struck before it touches the ground at the same time).

ISSUED WITH

GODFREY PHILLIPS CIGARETTES

243

244

FAMOUS DIRT-TRACK RIDERS

A SERIES OF 25

15

Jim Kempster.

Although he only started riding a few months ago, "Smiling Jim Kempster" is regarded as one of the greatest of English riders. He is Captain of the Wimbledon Speedways Club and trainer of many coming riders. Among his most notable successes are the winning of a Match Race with Squire Elder, the great American star, and the winning of the Gold Helmet scratch race when opposed to the two Australian champions Frank Arthur and Vic Huxley. After the latter race he was carried shoulder high round the field.

ISSUED BY

OGDEN'S

BRANCH OF THE IMPERIAL TOBACCO CO. (OF GREAT BRITAIN & IRELAND,) LTD.

PACKETS OF

OGDEN'S TAB CIGARETTES

Contain Photos. of

LEADING ATHLETES.

C. A. Bradley.

Established a record by winning the Amateur Sprint Championship four years consecutively 1892 to 1895.

BRITISH MADE BY BRITISH LABOUR.

245

SPORTING CHAMPIONS

a series of 36

N? 13

Paavo Nurmi

Nurmi's masterful style and his wonderful speed have made him one of the finest runners the world has ever known. On January 6th 1927 while running at Madison Square Garden he lowered three world records the same evening. Holds world records for 3000 and 5000 metres.

Issued By

GODFREY PHILLIPS LTD

112 Commercial St. London. E.

PRINTED IN FRANCE

246

HOW TO SWIM

A SERIES OF 25

36

The Double Arm Back Stroke;

Arm Action: Fifth Position.

The start of the arm pull is made with the arms just below the surface in advance of the head, and with the body and legs held in a straight line. The pull is commenced by turning the hands from the palms-upwards position to a palms-outwards position to enable the cupped hands to press against the water throughout the pull. The arms are straight from shoulder joints to wrists to give them firm leverage as they are pulled strongly just below water level, until brought against the thighs (still held straight) for a pause of two seconds.

ISSUED BY

HIGNETT BROS. & CO.

ISSUED BY THE IMPERIAL TOBACCO CO. (OF GREAT BRITAIN & IRELAND,) LTD.

247

249

SPORTS

SERIES OF 25

No. 7

RUGBY FOOTBALL.

The handling code of football, there being two kinds, as played by Amateurs and Professionals, differing slightly, the former having 15 players and the latter two less. Scoring is controlled by shots at goal, which must go over the bar and between the uprights, and a try, which is grounding the ball behind the goal line. In the latter case, additional points may be scored from a goal kick. Speed and correct handling of the oval ball are great assets.

ISSUED BY

GODFREY PHILLIPS Lᵀᴰ

112 Commercial St London. E.

248

ORIGIN OF GAMES

DRAUGHTS

A similar game was known in Ancient Egypt, and some of the pieces used have been found in tombs so early as 1600 B.C. An Egyptian vase also shows a lion and an antelope playing at draughts. Plato ascribes the invention of the game to Thoth, the Egyptian, and Homer represents Penelope's suitors as playing it. The Greeks played the game in one form with 5 men and another with 4 men and .25 squares and in another form with 5 men and 16 squares. Practised by the Norsemen in the 11th century.

ISSUED BY

NICOLAS SARONY & Co.

NEW BOND STREET LONDON W

"SPORTS" SERIES.

100 DESIGNS.

No. 88. HOCKEY. (A Tussle.)

The players are here seen holding each others stick from striking the ball. These tussles usually end in one of the other players coming up and taking the ball.

Issued by

GALLAHER, LTD.

BELFAST & LONDON.

250

251

CELEBRITIES OF SPORT

A SERIES OF 50

No. 4

MISS JEAN NICHOLL

Jean Nicoll is a sixteen-year-old lawn tennis prodigy; so good is she that she took Kay Stammers to three sets in the semi-final of the 1939 Melbury Tournament, and nearly beat her. She won the Middlesex Girls' Singles Junior Lawn Tennis Championship in 1938: her brother won the Boys' singles, and between them they carried off the doubles event. Jean is also an able exponent of Table Tennis, and won the women's English singles championships, junior and senior, in the 1939 competition. She is also a first-class swimmer and golfer.

ISSUED BY

R. & J. HILL, LTD.

LONDON, E.I.

252

GODFREY PHILLIPS LTD AND ASSOCIATED COMPANIES

TO FIND WINNER

CHOOSE YOUR HORSE, THEN MOISTEN WINNING POST WITH FINGER OR END OF WET MATCH

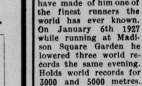

BROWN

GREEN

YELLOW

BLUE

RED

Card 253

A SERIES OF 25

COUNTRY SPORTS.

No. 19

RABBIT-SHOOTING.

In addition to guns, the sportsman must also take ferrets, a long, narrow spade (termed a "draining-tool"), and perhaps a dog or two, not forgetting the usual jar of beer. The dogs should be used to the game and accustomed to working with a ferret, otherwise they may spoil sport or stop an accidental charge of shot themselves. The rabbit burrows are approached in silence, for if the inmates are scared they become hard to bolt. Guns having been placed and the dogs being well in hand a ferret is popped into a burrow. A silent wait may be quickly rewarded by swift sport when the rabbits begin to bolt. A flash of brown fur and a bobbing white scut—then, if shots are not quick, bunny is down another hole. Some sportsmen favour a line ferret; i.e. a ferret with a long line attached to a collar.

PLAYER'S CIGARETTES.

ISSUED BY

JOHN PLAYER & SONS

BRANCH OF THE IMPERIAL TOBACCO COMPANY
(OF GREAT BRITAIN & IRELAND), LIMITED.

253

Card 254

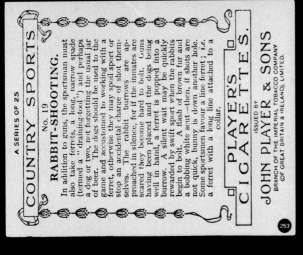

Wills for Quality

LAWN TENNIS, 1931

A SERIES OF 25

No. 15

Mrs. T. A. Lakeman.

(Miss Joan Fry.)

As Miss Joan Fry, Mrs. Lakeman provided a sensation by reaching the Wimbledon Singles Final in 1925, but was then beaten in a plucky fight by Mdlle. Suzanne Lenglen. She was in the Wimbledon Semi-final in 1927; and in 1930 was beaten in the third round by Mdme. Mathieu of France, having previously been a triple winner in the Great Britain Hard Court Championships. She has made numerous appearances in Wightman Cup-ties and other international events. In the Singles game she relies mainly on base-line play and her retrieving powers, but is excellent at the net in Doubles. She was born in Staffordshire in 1906.

W.D. & H.O. WILLS

ISSUED BY THE IMPERIAL TOBACCO COMPANY
(OF GREAT BRITAIN & IRELAND), LIMITED.

254

Card 255

ALBUMS FOR CHURCHMAN'S PICTURE CARDS CAN BE OBTAINED FROM TOBACCONISTS AT ONE PENNY EACH

KINGS OF SPEED

A SERIES OF 50

15

"B. BIRA"

Prince Birabongse, better known as "B. Bira," is the son of the late Prince Bhanurangse of Siam. On the motor-racing tracks they call him "Blue Lightning," a tribute to his skill as a fast driver and the fact that he affects pale blue not only as the colour scheme for his cars, but also for the uniforms of everyone associated with him. Two of his 1958 successes were the Nuffield Trophy Race at Donington and the British Racing Drivers' Club's 192-mile Road Race at Brooklands. "B. Bira" is as good a sculptor as he is motorist, and has exhibited at the Royal Academy.

W.A. & A.C. CHURCHMAN

BRANCH OF THE IMPERIAL TOBACCO CO.
(OF GREAT BRITAIN & IRELAND), LTD.

255

Card 256

THIS SURFACE IS ADHESIVE. ASK YOUR TOBACCONIST FOR THE ATTRACTIVE ALBUM (PRICE ONE PENNY) SPECIALLY PREPARED TO HOLD THE COMPLETE SERIES

TRICK BILLIARDS

BY A. NEWMAN-MOND

A SERIES OF 50

45

POTTING TWO BALLS ALONG THE CUSHION.

Two balls are placed touching each other and touching the cushion. They are midway along the cushion. The cue-ball is a foot from one of the red balls and is also touching the cushion. The object is to pot the two reds in one stroke. This will be found very difficult even when high pace is used. To accomplish this trick, merely place another ball directly in front of the cue-ball as shown by the dotted circle in the diagram. The extra weight does the trick.

ISSUED BY

OGDEN'S

BRANCH OF THE IMPERIAL TOBACCO CO.
(OF GREAT BRITAIN & IRELAND), LTD.

256

Card 257

SPORTING EVENTS AND STARS

SERIES OF 96.

No. 2

DON BRADMAN, Australia.

The amazing human Run-scoring Machine and greatest breaker of bowlers' hearts and established records in the game to-day. Born August 27th, 1908. At the age of 20, playing in Australia's greatest Derby State game for New South Wales versus Victoria at Sydney, he electrified the world by playing a cyclonic innings of 340. The following year, also at Sydney, he amassed a colossal total of 452 not out in one innings against Queensland, which has stood since as the world's record highest score. Leeds is apparently the great "Don's favourite wicket in England, and his two great Test Match scores are household topics throughout Yorkshire—333 versus England in 1930, and 304 versus England in 1934. He also holds the highest Test score in Australia—299 versus South Africa in 1931-32—and, in fact, no record is outside the compass of this wonder batsman.

These Interesting Photographs are issued with the following Cigarettes :-

SENIOR SERVICE ... 10 for 6d
JUNIOR MEMBER ... 20 for 1/4
ILLINGWORTH'S No 10 ... 25 for 1/-

257

Card 258

A SERIES OF THIRTY

7.

SPORTING CUPS & TROPHIES

ROYAL HUNT CUP.

A tall silver cup and cover, with boldly treated decoration of demi-female figures, which hold in their hands festoons of laurel pendant from the handles which are composed of tied reeds. The length of the course is 7 furlongs, 166 yards, and the race is run in the middle of June, under "weight for age" rules.

ADKIN & SONS

BRANCH OF THE IMPERIAL TOBACCO CO (OF GT. BRITAIN & IRELAND) LTD.

258

Card 259

OLD SPORTING PRINTS

A SERIES OF 25

19

J. Goodman.

(Preparing to Start.)

Drawn by Tom Jones.
Published 1820.

It is recorded that "this celebrated runner beat the noted Dick Defoe and also Dank of York." In the early days runners started from an upright position, but in modern footraces sprinters invariably adopt the crouching attitude which gives a quicker start. A better start is also obtained by the use of the pistol instead of the dropping of a handkerchief which in former days was the usual signal for the runners to start.

ISSUED BY

STEPHEN MITCHELL & SON

BRANCH OF THE IMPERIAL TOBACCO CO (OF GREAT BRITAIN & IRELAND) LTD.

259

Card 260

CHAMPIONS OF 1936

A SERIES OF 50

22

LEEDS R.F.C.

Rugby League Cup Winners

Leeds won the Northern Rugby League cup at Wembley for the first time, defeating Warrington in the final. It was notable that their success was the fourth victory in four finals, and therefore whenever they have qualified for the deciding match they have always won, though 26 years ago when Hull were their opponents they only succeeded after a replay. They defeated Hull again in 1923 and their third triumph was against Swinton in 1932. In season 1935-6 Leeds played only one tie at home, but in five matches they scored 64 points to 21, beating Warrington in the final by three goals, four tries, 18 points to 4 goals, 2 points.

ISSUED BY

OGDEN'S

BRANCH OF THE IMPERIAL TOBACCO CO., LTD.
(OF GREAT BRITAIN & IRELAND)

260

Card 261

A Series of 25

SPORTS

Smoke

"Prize Crop"

Cigarettes

ISSUED BY THE

STEPHEN MITCHELL & SON

BRANCH OF THE IMPERIAL TOBACCO CO. (OF GREAT BRITAIN & IRELAND), LTD.

261

Card 262

SPORTING CELEBRITIES IN ACTION

A Series of Thirty-six Actual Photographs.

No. 14.

J. RICHARDSON.

The popular giant forward of the New Zealand (All Blacks) Rugby Team. He is regarded as one of the world's best forwards. He stands over 6 ft. in height and weighs about 15 stone. He captained the All Blacks team in the International match in England in 1925.

Issued by

MAJOR DRAPKIN & CO.

Branch of United Kingdom Tobacco Co. (1929) Ltd., LONDON.

262

Card 263

32

F & J. SMITH'S

W. A. BARRY

Is one of the strongest scullers England ever produced. His stamina in his matches has been wonderful and has won him many victories. On September 25th, 1898, Barry beat G. Towns, of Australia, for the Championship, over the Putney to Mortlake course, but a year later, over the same course, Towns proved the victor. Towns has since beaten Jake Gaudaur.

"CUP TIE" CIGARETTES

3d Per Packet of 10

263

Card 264

DIRT TRACK RIDERS

SERIES OF 50. No 29.

L. H. Boulton.

Born twenty-five years ago at Stoke-on-Trent. One of to-day's most promising stars. A very dashing rider, with great abilities as regards dirt tracks. In the 1928 season he showed he could waltz round the cracks without much trouble, when all was well with machine and track. Went to Liverpool Charity Broadside and won two Gold Cups outright, having beaten some noted English cracks in obtaining these trophies. A Douglas machine enthusiast, and rides at White City, Manchester.

J. A. PATTREIOUEX LTD.

MANCHESTER

SMOKE
TRAWLER, CRITIC, CLUB MEMBER,
CASKET CIGARETTES.

264

Wills's Cigarettes

H.H. Harris Mrs. C. A. Lakeman

PLAYER'S CIGARETTES.

RABBIT-SHOOTING.

CRICKET - DON BRADMAN. AUSTRALIA

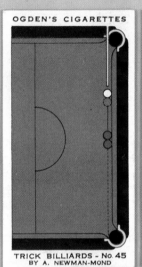

OGDEN'S CIGARETTES

TRICK BILLIARDS - No. 45
BY A. NEWMAN-MOND

CHURCHMAN'S CIGARETTES

"B. BIRA"

J. Goodman

Adkin's Cigarettes

ROYAL HUNT CUP
ASCOT 1912

ROYAL HUNT CUP.

OGDEN'S CIGARETTES

LEEDS R.F.C.

L. H. BOULTON.

BARRY.

MITCHELL'S CIGARETTES.

ARCHERY.

♠ — Q, 8, 3.
♥ — Q, 5, 2.
♦ — K, 8.
♣ — A, K, 7, 4, 3.

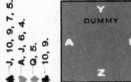

```
        Y
      DUMMY
   A         B
        Z
```

♠ — J, 10, 9, 7, 5.   ♠ — K, 6.
♥ — A, J, 6, 4.   ♥ — 10, 9, 7.
♦ — Q, 5.   ♦ — J, 10, 9, 3, 2.
♣ — 10, 9.   ♣ — Q, 8, 6.

♠ — A, 4, 2.
♥ — K, 8, 3.
♦ — A, 7, 6, 4.
♣ — J, 5, 2.

AN IMPORTANT POINT OF PLAY.

Z deals and bids "One No Trumps." All pass. A leads the Jack of Spades, Y plays the 3, B the King. How should Z play the hand?

SALMON & GLUCKSTEIN LTD

Kiss-Canon.

WILLS'S CIGARETTES.

R. M. N. TISDALL.

OGDEN'S CIGARETTES.

YORKSHIRE AMATEUR BOWLING ASSOCIATION.

25 Poker Hands   No. 11

"A STRAIGHT"

A STRAIGHT is five cards of two or more suits in sequence. With two Straights the highest sequence wins

Issued by
COPE BROS. & CO. LTD., LIVERPOOL
RICHARD LLOYD & SONS, LONDON

PUTTING THE WEIGHT.

PLAYER'S CIGARETTES

MORIAN HANSEN

OGDEN'S CIGARETTES.

WILLS'S CIGARETTES

R. N. CASE

J. GREEN

Ogden's Guinea Gold Cigarettes

CHURCHMAN'S CIGARETTES

♠ — A, K, 5.
♥ — 6, 3, 2.
♦ — A, Q, 6.
♣ — A, Q, 5, 4.

```
       N
   W       E
       S
```

♠ — 3, 2.   ♠ — Q, J, 10.
♥ — 10, 7, 5, 2.   ♥ — A, K, Q, J, 9, 5, 4.
♦ — 9, 8, 7, 5, 3.   ♦ — —.
♣ — 3, 10, 9, 7.   ♣ — 4, 8, 2.

♠ — 9, 8, 7, 6, 4.
♥ — 8.
♦ — K, J, 10, 3.
♣ — K, 6, 3.

NUMBER TWENTY-EIGHT
A VERY SOUND INFORMATIVE DOUBLE

Score: Game all; E–W 40 up; N–S Love, third game.

A Contract player must always be alive to the fact that any double of One No Trump, or of One, or Two of a suit, is definitely informative, provided the doubler's partner has not made a bid. An informative Double is seldom justifiable upon less than about three and a half tricks. The doubler's partner may, if strong enough, make a business pass, with
(over)

Gallaher's Cigarettes

MRS. COLEGATE

276

MILITARY UNIFORMS OF THE BRITISH EMPIRE OVERSEAS

A SERIES OF 50   NO. 26

INDIAN STATES FORCES: ALWAR STATE FORCES

The Alwar State Forces, of which our picture shows the Commandant in Full Dress, consist of two troops of Lancers and one active and one training battalion of Infantry. The forces of the Indian Princes which are classed as Indian States Forces are organized on the same lines as the corresponding units of the regular Indian Army. The active units of the Alwar Forces served in the Great War, the Lancers on the North-West Frontier and in Afghanistan, and the Infantry battalion in Egypt and Palestine. Alwar, which is situated in Rajputana, has a population of three quarters of a million.

JOHN PLAYER & SONS

BRANCH OF THE IMPERIAL TOBACCO CO. (OF GREAT BRITAIN & IRELAND), LTD.

278

279

GRENADIER GUARDS

"BLENHEIM, RAMILLIES," "OUDENARDE," "MALPLAQUET," "DETTINGEN, LINCELLES," "CORUNNA," "BARROSA," "PENINSULA, WATERLOO," "ALMA," "INKERMAN," "SEVASTOPOL," "EGYPT, 1882," "TEL-EL-KEBIR," "SUAKIN, 1885," "KHARTOUM," "SOUTH AFRICA, 1899."

JOHN PLAYER & SONS, LTD.
CASTLE TOBACCO FACTORY, NOTTINGHAM.

Nº 27 MILITARY SERIES OF 50 REGIMENTS

BRITAINS DEFENCES

A SERIES OF 50

NO. 35

"ALL ABOARD".

This picture shows the crew of a giant bomber getting ready to take off. The machine is a Fairey "Hendon", a twin-engined monoplane with a wing span of nearly 102 feet and a length of over 60 feet. The pilot is located forward of the leading edge of the wings, the gunner-bomber's cockpit is in the nose, and the two machine-gunners' places are, one at the extreme tail and the other midway between nose and tail.

CARRERAS LTD
(ESTD. 1788)

ARCADIA WORKS, LONDON, ENGLAND KEEP THIS ATTRACTIVE SERIES IN THE CARRERAS "SLIP IN" ALBUM. ON SALE AT ALL TOBACCONISTS (PRICE ONE PENNY).

280

281

WAR DECORATIONS & MEDALS

A SERIES OF 90.

59

The Commemorative Medal, (1915-18), Italy,

was decreed by H. M. King Victor Emmanuel III on the 29th July, 1920, and granted to all soldiers; to workers under military orders and similar bodies; and to the members of the Auxiliary Corps, such as the Red Cross, the Sovereign Military Order of Malta, etc., who had taken part in the campaigns of 1915-18, for one or more years; and to those who had been authorised to wear the badge for the labours of war, according to the Royal Decree of the 21st May, 1916, and who had served four months in the war zone.

ISSUED BY

JOHN PLAYER & SONS

BRANCH OF THE IMPERIAL TOBACCO Cº (OF GREAT BRITAIN & IRELAND), LTº

MILITARY HEAD-DRESS

A SERIES OF 50

22

15th The King's Hussars;
Officer's full dress shako, 1834.

All Hussar Regiments, except the 15th, wore a bell-shaped shako of black feather. The 15th Hussars had a shako of scarlet cloth, with scarlet cloth top. The upper portion of the shako was bound with 2-inch gold regimental lace, the rosette in front being of similar material. The shako had gold lines with flounders and bullion tassels. The gilt chin scales were fastened to the sides of the shako by lions' heads, and the plume was a drooping one of dark green cock's tail feathers.

ISSUED BY
JOHN PLAYER & SONS

BRANCH OF THE IMPERIAL TOBACCO Cº (OF GREAT BRITAIN & IRELAND), LTº

282

LIFE IN THE SERVICES

A SERIES OF 50   NO. 3

ROYAL NAVY
PHYSICAL TRAINING— ASHORE

Stripped to the waist, these young sailors are watching their instructor demonstrating on the vaulting horse at H.M.S. *Ganges* Training Establishment, Shotley, Suffolk. Here there are large instructional staffs of officers and petty-officers, and physical training is a welcome part of the daily routine. A boy usually spends about a year in one of these "schools" before going to sea. Particularly intelligent boys pass into the Advanced Class and are given a special course of training to fit them for early advancement in the Service.

ARDATH TOBACCO CO., LTD.
Manufacturers of
STATE EXPRESS
and ARDATH CIGARETTES

283

284

PAST & PRESENT
SERIES "B" (Nos. 25-48)

WEAPONS OF WAR
No. 47

PIKE
(Past)

The Pike, Halberd, Bill, Partisan or Gisarm, as its different forms were called, is a weapon with a long history, during which it assumed yet more shapes than it had names. Its greatest use was to enable foot-soldiers to deal with a mounted enemy, who could be pushed off a horse, or pulled off with the hooked blade. Pikes grew to be longer and longer, and in Cromwell's day they were eighteen feet long. At this period pikemen stood behind the musketeers, and protected them while they operated their cumbersome muskets. (See No. 48.)

TEOFANI & Cº LTº

BRANCH OF THE ASSOCIATED TOBACCO MANUFACTURERS (GREAT BRITAIN) LTD.

SOLDIERS OF THE KING

A SERIES OF 36

19

GOVERNOR-GENERAL'S BODYGUARD (CANADA)

This famous Dragoon Bodyguard was organised in 1855 as part of the general militia of the Dominion, but actually the formation is much older: it is the senior corps in the Dominion. Their fine fighting record includes important engagements in the North-West, South Africa (1900), and the Great War (1914-18), where victorious Canadian achievements included the famous battle of Vimy Ridge, regarded by historians as the greatest accomplishment by Canada. His Excellency the Governor-General of the Dominion of Canada is Honorary Colonel, and the regiment is allied to The Queen's Bays (2nd Dragoon Guards) of the British army.

GODFREY PHILLIPS LTD.
and Associated Companies

285

BRITISH ORDERS OF CHIVALRY & VALOUR

A Series of 25
Card No. 4

MOST ILLUSTRIOUS ORDER OF ST. PATRICK

This Irish order of knighthood was founded in 1783 by King George III., after Ireland had obtained legislative independence, and now consists of the Sovereign, the Lord Lieutenant of Ireland, and 22 Knights of one class only, with certain extra and honorary knights. The Chapel is in St. Patrick's Cathedral, Dublin, and the motto "Quis Separabit?" (Who shall separate?) The ribbon is light sky blue, and knights may be distinguished by the letters K.P. The Star of the Order of St. Patrick is worn as a regimental badge by the Irish Guards.

This surface is adhesive

THE "GREYS" CIGARETTES

286

287

THE GREAT WAR SERIES

100 IN SET   Nº 79

HAND GRENADES IN THE TRENCHES.

A curious revival in the recent war has been the use of hand grenades. The up-to-date hand grenade may be thrown by hand (with a range of fifty yards) or fired from a rifle (with a range of 300-500 yards). The Grenadier Guards are so called because they used this weapon over one hundred and fifty years ago.

ISSUED BY
GALLAHER LTD.
BELFAST & LONDON.

A SERIES OF FIFTY WAR PORTRAITS

27

GEN. SIR ARCHIBD. HUNTER, D.S.O.

Born 1856. Served Egypt, 1885. Wounded Battles of Ginniss, 1885, and Toski, 1889. Govr. Omdurman, 1899. S. Africa, 1900-1901. Govr. and Com.-in-Chief, Gibraltar, 1910-13.

FORMAN NOTTS

"SILVER PELICAN,"
The Ideal Tobacco,
6d. per ounce.

TETLEY & SONS.
— LEEDS. —

288

INFANTRY TRAINING

A SERIES OF 50

No. 32.

When a soldier passes an officer he will salute with the hand further from the officer on the third pace before reaching him. The hand is brought up to the salute, the head being turned to the person saluted.

ISSUED BY
OGDEN'S

BRANCH OF THE IMPERIAL TOBACCO Cº (OF GREAT BRITAIN & IRELAND) LTº

289

These Pictures
ARE PACKED
IN THE
BRANDS
OF
Cigarettes
Manufactured by

OGDENS LTD.

Tobacco
Manufacturers

LIVERPOOL
ENGLAND

290

M. 652.

GODFREY PHILLIPS & SONS

CIGARETTE & TOBACCO MANUFACTURERS

LONDON, ENGLAND

291

AIR RAID PRECAUTIONS

A SERIES OF 50

29

THE CIVILIAN RESPIRATOR— HOW TO REMOVE IT

The picture shows the RIGHT way to take off a Civilian Respirator. This should be done by slipping the head harness forward from the back of the head. It is important that the respirator should be taken off in this way. The WRONG way to take it off is by taking hold of the metal box containing the filters and pulling the face-piece off the chin. By this method there is a danger of bending and cracking the transparent window. If this window is cracked, the respirator is useless.

W.D. & H.O. WILLS

MANUFACTURERS OF GOLD FLAKE, CAPSTAN, WOODBINE AND STAR CIGARETTES

BRANCH OF THE IMPERIAL TOBACCO CO (OF GREAT BRITAIN & IRELAND) LTD.

292

OFFICERS FULL DRESS

A SERIES OF 36

15

ROYAL ARTILLERY

This Corps is an amalgamation of the Royal Field and Royal Garrison Artillery, which took place in 1925. The Gunners' mottos are: "Ubique" (Everywhere), and "Quo Fas et Gloria Ducunt" (Where Duty and Glory Lead). "Trains of Artillery" formed part of an army in the field far earlier than the corporate existence of the permanent establishment on May 26th, 1716. The Royal Artillery have a long roll of honours won all over the world.

THIS SURFACE IS ADHESIVE

UNITED KINGDOM TOBACCO COMPANY (1929) AND ASSOCIATED COMPANIES

293

PLAYER'S CIGARETTES.

COMMEMORATIVE MEDAL,
ITALY.

Player's Cigarettes

GRENADIER GUARDS.

PLAYER'S CIGARETTES

ALWAR STATE FORCES

GOVERNOR-GENERAL'S BODY-GUARD (CANADA)

PIKE

PHYSICAL TRAINING—ASHORE

PLAYER'S CIGARETTES.

15TH THE KING'S HUSSARS;
Officer's full dress shako, 1834.

SALUTING
TO
THE SIDE

(WITHOUT ARMS)

WAR SERIES

GENERAL
SIR A. HUNTER, D.S.O.,
British Army.

Gallaher's Cigarettes

HAND GRENADES IN THE TRENCHES

ORDER OF ST. PATRICK

ROYAL ARTILLERY

WILLS'S CIGARETTES

THE CIVILIAN RESPIRATOR—
HOW TO REMOVE IT

PHILLIPS CIGARETTES

Officer, WEST KENT
(Queen's Own) IMPERIAL
YEOMANRY, Scouting
Drill Order, Khaki.

6
♣

Punjaub Mountain Battery.

THOMSON & PORTEOUS

HANDS ACROSS THE SEA

COPYRIGHT
DOBSON, MOLLE & C? L?? EDINBURGH & LONDON

N? 3.

DISTINGUISHED SERVICE ORDER.

KING EDWARD VII

AS HONORARY COLONEL OF THE
1ST PRUSSIAN DRAGOON GUARDS.

Player's
Cigarettes

FARQUHARSON

BLACK CAT
CIGARETTES

COPYRIGHT "LAND & WATER"

"VOX POPULI SUPREMA LEX"

NICHOLLS' CIGARETTES.

ITALY - St Maurice & St Lazarus.

Corunna. 1809.

RALLY ROUND THE FLAG

WE MUST HAVE MORE MEN

BADGES & FLAGS
of BRITISH REGIMENTS.

"Grenadier Guards."
PLAYER'S CIGARETTES.

PLAYER'S
CIGARETTES.

1642.
Time of Battle of Edgehill.

KING'S ROYAL RIFLE CORPS
Officer. (About 1841)

Player's Cigarettes.

BALLOON DRILL

**HEROES OF THE
TRANSVAAL WAR**

Maj Gen Baden Powell.

SALMON & GLUCKSTEIN L??

PLAYER'S CIGARETTES

4TH BN. THE QUEEN'S OWN
CAMERON HIGHLANDERS. 1905.

PLAYER'S CIGARETTES.

BLACK
WATCH.

Officer, 42nd Foot. 1825.

HISTORY OF ARMY UNIFORMS
A SERIES OF 50

No. 7

The King's Carabiniers (1742). 3rd Carabiniers (Prince of Wales's Dragoon Guards).

The 9th Horse was raised in 1685, and at one time bore the name of "The Queen Dowager's Cuirassiers". As a reward for gallantry William III bestowed upon it the title of Carabiniers or King's Carabiniers, but no difference appears to have been made in precedence or equipment, probably this was inspired by the famous corps of carabiniers in the French army. In 1745 the regiment became the 3rd Irish Horse, and 1788 saw another name change to the 6th Dragoons or Carabiniers, with a uniform alteration also, as facings became white.

CARRERAS LTD
(ESTD. 1788)
ARCADIA WORKS, LONDON, ENGLAND
KEEP THIS ATTRACTIVE SERIES IN THE CARRERAS "SLIP IN" ALBUM, ON SALE AT ALL TOBACCONISTS (PRICE ONE PENNY).

310

TADDY & Cos Cigarettes

311

36

THE MASCOT OF THE ROYAL WARWICKSHIRE REGIMENT

Many regiments of the British Army are the proud possessors of mascots, which are often in evidence at ceremonial parades. The Royal Warwickshire Regiment boasts a black buck, the choice of this animal being no doubt determined by the fact that an antelope is incorporated in the regimental badge. The custom of keeping mascots has long been countenanced in the British Army, and other famous examples are the Irish wolfhound of the Irish Guards (see Card No. 33) and the goat of the Royal Welch Fusiliers. The Argyll and Sutherland Highlanders have a pony as their regimental mascot.

LAMBERT & BUTLER
BRANCH OF THE IMPERIAL TOBACCO CO
(OF GREAT BRITAIN & IRELAND). LTD.

312

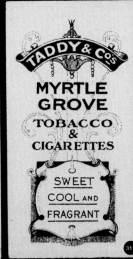

TADDY & Cos
MYRTLE GROVE
TOBACCO & CIGARETTES

SWEET COOL AND FRAGRANT

313

ARMY BADGES
SERIES OF 48. No 21

THE KING'S OWN YORKSHIRE LIGHT INFANTRY

Light Infantry regiments were originally employed as skirmishers, marching 140 to the minute instead of 120, and being more lightly equipped. The honour of being converted into a Light Infantry regiment was conferred on the 51st Foot in 1809, and this regiment, which had been raised by the Lord Lieutenant of West Riding in 1756, was afterwards named The King's Own Yorkshire Light Infantry. Sir John Moore was an officer in the regiment.

ISSUED BY

GALLAHER LTD
VIRGINIA HOUSE, LONDON & BELFAST

314

F & J. SMITH'S

Driver Glassock of the Q Battery Royal Horse Artillery gained the Victoria Cross for his share in saving the guns at Koorn Spruit. Lord Roberts formed the opinion that the conduct of all ranks of Q Battery was conspicuously gallant and daring, he therefore decided that a representative of each rank, one officer, one non-commissioned officer, and two gunners or drivers should receive the much-prized decoration. Harry Glassock was one of the fortunate drivers selected.

ISSUED BY
CUT NAVY
MILD. MEDIUM & FULL

315

2ND SERIES. 51 TO 150. No. 102

ARMY, CORPS & DIVISIONAL SIGNS
1914-1918

3rd (Indian) Corps.

Like that of the 9th Corps (see card No. 87), this sign was founded on the crest of the Corps Commander, Lieut.-Gen. Sir Raleigh Egerton, K.C.B., K.C.I.E. The Egerton crest is three arrows as in the sign, but of gold with black points and feathers, tied with a red ribbon. The arrows in the sign were shown in red (the three being symbolical of the Corps' number), and on the ribbon were two of the battle honours of the Corps during its fighting in Mesopotamia—"Shumran" (see the 14th Indian Division, card No. 105), and "Diyalah" (the crossing of the Diyalah River a few miles below Baghdad, by the 13th [Western] Division in March 1917).

ISSUED BY
JOHN PLAYER & SONS
BRANCH OF THE IMPERIAL TOBACCO CO
(OF GREAT BRITAIN & IRELAND) LTD

316

THE GREAT WAR
VICTORIA CROSS HEROES
1ST. SERIES OF 25
No 18

PRIVATE H. H. ROBSON, V.C.
(2nd Batt. Royal Scots)

won this honour for acting with conspicuous gallantry near Kemmel on Dec. 14th, 1914, in rescuing a wounded N.C.O. Later he attempted a second rescue under fire, and although immediately wounded, continued his effort until a second bullet disabled him.

ISSUED BY
GALLAHER LTD
BELFAST & LONDON

317

No. 23
ALLIED ARMY LEADERS
WILLS'S CIGARETTES
A SERIES OF 50
PASSED FOR PUBLICATION BY THE PRESS BUREAU, 20.12.16

Gen. Sir H. S. Rawlinson, K.C.B.

Gen. Sir Henry Rawlinson was born 1864, and educated at Eton and Sandhurst. He entered King's Royal Rifles, 1884; served in Burma campaign; in Omdurman campaign as D.A.A.G. to Kitchener, 1898; in S. Africa (A.A.G. in Natal and S. African Hqrs., 1899-'00; commanded Mobile Column, 1901-2). At commencement of present war, Gen. Rawlinson, in command of a Cavalry Division, rendered great assistance to the Belgian Troops. He commanded an Army at Neuve Chapelle, Festubert, Loos, and on the Somme.

W. D. & H. O. WILLS
BRISTOL & LONDON
ISSUED BY THE IMPERIAL TOBACCO CO
(OF GREAT BRITAIN & IRELAND) LTD

318

WILLS'S
W.D. & H.O. WILLS
TRADE MARK
Bristol & London
Cigarettes

319

TO THE CIGARETTE CONNOISSEUR
THE NAME
"*Muratti*"
IS A
GUARANTEE OF PURITY & EXCELLENCE.

320

BRITAIN'S DEFENDERS

NUMBER 3
3-in. Mortar Unit

During the Great War of 1914-18, the trenches of the two opposing armies were often so close together that recourse to weapons other than artillery for bombardment purposes became necessary. Of these, the trench mortar was one of the most effective, for it could throw missiles over the parapet into the opposing trench. The mortars used varied from those which only threw small hand-grenades to the huge German "minethrower." The 3-in. mortar illustrated is a modern version of the trench mortar.

A SERIES OF 50

ARDATH TOBACCO CO LTD
Manufacturers of
STATE EXPRESS
and ARDATH CIGARETTES

321

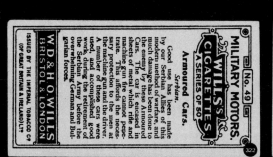

ISSUED BY
W. D. & H. O. WILLS
BRISTOL & LONDON
THE IMPERIAL TOBACCO CO
(OF GREAT BRITAIN & IRELAND) LTD

Good use has been made by our Serbian Allies of this modern method of warfare, and much damage has been done to the enemy by these Armoured Cars. The car is encased in sheets of metal which rifle and machine-gun fire cannot penetrate, and affords the necessary protection to those working the cannon, the machine-gun and the driver. A notable instance is where good work, and accomplished good work, during the retirement of the Serbian Army before the overwhelming German and Bulgarian forces.

Armoured Cars.
Serbian.

MILITARY MOTORS
WILLS'S CIGARETTES
A SERIES OF 50

No. 49

322

ISSUED BY
JOHN PLAYER & SONS
BRANCH OF THE IMPERIAL TOBACCO CO
(OF GREAT BRITAIN & IRELAND) LTD

West Kent Yeomanry,
(QUEEN'S OWN).
*New 27th (Kent Yeo.) Bde.,
R.F.A. (2 Batts.).*

This regiment, first originated in 1794 from independent troops raised in the larger towns but after 1800 were either disbanded or absorbed under the title of "The Kent Corps of Gentlemen and Yeomanry." The corps, together with others, was disbanded in the great peace, but re-raised in 1830 with the title "The West Kent Yeomanry Cavalry." They received the title "Queen's Own," in 1864. The badge is the White Horse of Kent, and the motto "Invicta."

DRUM BANNERS & CAP BADGES
A SERIES OF 50.

No. 4

323

HONOURS & RIBBONS Nº 5.

Order of Merit, India, 1st Class.

LAMBERT & BUTLER'S CIGARETTES.

THE MASCOT OF THE ROYAL WARWICKSHIRE REGIMENT

V.C. HEROES—BOER WAR.
Nº 51.

Capt. H. L. Reed, R.A. V.C.
Awarded the Victoria Cross for gallant
bravery during the attempt to save
the guns at Colenso, 15 Dec. 1899.

Pte. H. H. ROBSON, V.C.

PLAYER'S CIGARETTES.

SHUMRAN 1917 DIYALAH

3RD (INDIAN) CORPS.

43

DRIVER HENRY GLASSOCK V.C.
ROYAL HORSE ARTILLERY

LE CATEAU
MARNE, 1914, '18 MESSINES, 1914, '17, '18
YPRES, 1914, '15, '17, '18 SOMME, 1916, '18
CAMBRAI, 1917, '18 HAVRINCOURT
SAMBRE ITALY, 1917-'18
MACEDONIA, 1915-'17
THE KING'S OWN YORKSHIRE
LIGHT INFANTRY

3-INCH MORTAR UNIT.

JAPAN

PIONEER
MARCHING ORDER

FRANCE.

Gunner of the Artillery.

WILLS'S CIGARETTES.

GEN. SIR H. S. RAWLINSON.

PLAYER'S CIGARETTES.

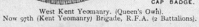

CAP BADGE.

West Kent Yeomanry. (Queen's Own).
Now 97th (Kent Yeomanry) Brigade, R.F.A. (2 Battalions).

WILLS'S CIGARETTES.

ARMOURED CARS

PASSED FOR PUBLICATION BY THE PRESS BUREAU. 21-9-16.

CREST

H.M.S. ALBATROSS

Admiral 1805

DEPTH CHARGE EXPLODING

EYES OF THE FLEET

PLAYER'S CIGARETTES

H.M.S. "SUNFISH"

FIRST CLASS TORPEDO BOAT.

Player's Cigarettes

The East Indiaman "Warren Hastings"

WILLS'S CIGARETTES.

PETTY OFFICER.

COPE'S

Captain E. H. EDWARDS, R.N., D.S.O.

CIGARETTES

THE BO'SUN'S PIPE

LAMBERT & BUTLER'S CIGARETTES.

COMMODORE W. E. GOODENOUGH.

LIFE IN THE ROYAL NAVY

A SERIES OF 50

26

DEPTH CHARGE EXPLODING

Depth charges are bombs, usually containing 300 lb. of high explosive, designed to detonate under water. They are exploded by means of a special device, actuated by the pressure of the water when a certain depth below the surface has been reached. The usual method of projecting depth charges from a destroyer or other vessel is by a simple type of howitzer, known as a depth charge thrower (D.C.T.), or by a simple dropping gear at the stern of the ship. In attacking submarines, four depth charges are dropped at a time, dispersed in a diamond pattern. The explosion of a group of depth charges near a submerged submarine is bound to shake up and strain the vessel and dislocate her electrical arrangements, even if it does not inflict fatal damage.

W.D. & H.O. WILLS

MANUFACTURERS OF GOLD FLAKE, CAPSTAN, WOODBINE AND STAR CIGARETTES.
BRANCH OF THE IMPERIAL TOBACCO CO. (OF GREAT BRITAIN & IRELAND) LTD.

324

No 40

OLD ENGLAND'S DEFENDERS

A SERIES OF 50

AUTHENTIC AND COPYRIGHT DESIGNS

of our Soldiers and Sailors from the time of Charles I. to the Battle of Waterloo.
1 issued with every pkt. of their Cigarettes by

JOHN PLAYER & SONS
LTD
NOTTINGHAM.

325

No 10

H.M.S. Albatross.

TORPEDO-BOAT DESTROYER.

Launched 1898
360 tons
Speed, 32 knots
Complement, 68 men
7,900 horse-power
Length, 227½ feet
Beam, 21½ feet

This interesting & unique series of pictures is issued only with

HILL'S
IMPERIAL CIGARETTES

PURITY GUARANTEED.

326

History of NAVAL UNIFORMS

No. 20

Admiral (1782).

This picture shows an Admiral's uniform towards the end of the 18th century, and the fashion of cutting away the corners of the waistcoat, which influenced to-day's clothes, can be noted. The white facings on the revers and cuffs beneath the gold lace denoting rank, and the waistcoat and three-cornered blue hat were finished with similar gold material. A stock and wig formed part of the attire, and breeches at this time were narrower, showing the tendency towards the tight-fitting garments which were a terwards fashionable with Hessians.

CARRERAS LTD
(ESTD. 1788)
ARCADIA WORKS, LONDON, ENGLAND
KEEP THIS ATTRACTIVE SERIES IN THE CARRERAS "SLIP IN" ALBUM, ON SALE AT ALL TOBACCONISTS (PRICE ONE PENNY).

327

BRITISH NAVAL CRAFT

A SERIES OF TWENTY-FIVE
FROM PAINTINGS BY FRANK H. MASON, R.I.

19

H.M.S. "SUNFISH"
Submarine, "Shark" Class

The Shark class of sea-going submarines is of improved Swordfish design. It numbers eight ships and consists of a useful though relatively small type of vessel. The Sunfish is one of the latest additions, having been completed in 1937. Her armament consists of one 3-inch gun and six tubes for 21-inch torpedoes. She can dive with great rapidity, and when patrolling in coastal waters. Her tonnage is 670 on the surface and 960 when submerged, with respective speeds of 15 and 10 knots, corresponding with horse powers of 1,900 and 1,300. She has a complement of 40, and is capable of carrying 40 tons of fuel. The cost of these vessels varies between £230,000 and £245,000. The Sunfish was built at Chatham Dockyard.

JOHN PLAYER & SONS
BRANCH OF THE IMPERIAL TOBACCO CO. (OF GREAT BRITAIN & IRELAND) LTD.

328

THE NAVY

SERIES OF 48

No. 31

Eyes of the Fleet.

This picture shows the look-out signalman on the quarter-deck of the aircraft carrier Courageous watching for passing shipping, while the aircraft seen above has just taken off—an incident during the annual Spring Cruise exercises. The aircraft is a Blackburn Dart torpedo bomber—a type which is now being superseded by the Shark and Swordfish types. The White Ensign seen here is the official flag of the Royal Navy and is flown in H.M. ships from "Colours" in the morning until sunset.

SENIOR SERVICE
cigarettes

329

OLD NAVAL PRINTS

A SERIES OF 25
FROM THE NATIONAL MARITIME MUSEUM

No. 13

THE EAST INDIAMAN "WARREN HASTINGS."

The Honourable East India Company's fleet of well-found merchant ships enjoyed the monopoly of British trade with the East from 1599 to 1832. Specially built to be "taken up" by the Company, they represented some of the finest ships of the mercantile marine. Outwardly they differed little from the frigates of the Royal Navy and, indeed, were sufficiently well manned and armed to beat off most privateers. They were usually provided with "letters of marque" so as to regularize their Eastern possessions. On a famous occasion in 1804 the homeward-bound H.E.I.C. fleet under Commodore Nathaniel Dance encountered a French squadron and so deceived them by flying naval pendants, and forming a line of battle, that the French retired before an apparently superior force. There was a Warren Hastings in the India fleet on this occasion.

JOHN PLAYER & SONS
BRANCH OF THE IMPERIAL TOBACCO CO. (OF GREAT BRITAIN & IRELAND) LTD.

330

WILLS'S
"THREE CASTLES" Cigarettes.

"There's no sweeter Tobacco comes from Virginia and no better brand than the 'THREE CASTLES'."—THACKERAY.
—"The Virginians."

MANUFACTURED ONLY BY

W.D. & H.O. WILLS, Limited.

331

NAVAL PORTRAITS

A SERIES OF 50

No. 22

Commodore W. E. Goodenough,
R.N., M.V.O.

Born 1867; became Commander of the Royal Naval College, Dartmouth, 1905; and has commanded H.M. Ships Albemarle, Duncan, Cochrane, and Colossus. Appointed to the command of the 1st Light Cruiser Squadron, 1913. (Flag-Ship, H.M.S. Southampton.) This Squadron, together with a strong force of Destroyers, intercepted the German light craft in the successful Naval action off Heligoland, Aug. 28 1914.

ISSUED BY

LAMBERT & BUTLER
BRANCH OF THE IMPERIAL TOBACCO CO. (OF GREAT BRITAIN & IRELAND) LTD.

332

THE NAVY

SERIES OF 48. No 9

THE BO'SUN'S PIPE

This picture shows the bo'sun's mate in H.M.S. Rodney piping orders to the crew. It is possible to give various calls, embodying different notes, with the "pipe" or "whistle," just as it is with a bugle. The expression "to pipe" really refers to the act of calling out the order required in conjunction with the use of the call, but nowadays the entire procedure is generally known as "piping." With the adoption in some ships of the loud speaker, the bo'sun's mate no longer has to tour the ship as he pipes.

ISSUED BY

GALLAHER LTD
VIRGINIA HOUSE, LONDON & BELFAST

333

VC & DSO
NAVAL & FLYING HEROES

Capt. E. H. EDWARDS,
R.N., D.S.O.

Capt. Edwards was in command of H.M.S. "Theseus" when attacked by submarines in the North Sea on 15th October, 1914 Owing to the way in which the "Theseus" was handled the torpedo missed. For this and subsequent services while on patrol work in North Sea, Capt. Edwards was awarded the D.S.O., 7th August, 1915.

COPE BROS & CO LTD
LIVERPOOL & LONDON

334

No 36

WILLS'S
Cigarettes

NAVAL DRESS & BADGES

PETTY OFFICER.

This is a petty officer in the seaman class, but a P.O. may also be a specialist in the Gunnery, Torpedo, Signal, Stoker, or other branch. His pay for the rating (special qualifications being additional) rises from 2s. 8d. to 3s. a day, and he may pass through the grades of Chief P.O. and Bo'sn to commissioned rank. The chevrons are good conduct badges, each of which carries 1d. a day.

W.D. & H.O. WILLS
BRISTOL & LONDON.
ISSUED BY THE IMPERIAL TOBACCO CO. (OF GREAT BRITAIN & IRELAND) LTD.

335

336 (blank card)

337

NAUTICAL SONGS

SERIES OF 30
No. 21.

NELSON
BRAHAM

'Twas in Trafalgar's bay
We saw the Frenchmen lay,
Each heart was bounding then,
We scorn'd the foreign yoke,
For our Ships were British Oak,
And hearts of oak our men!
Our Nelson mark'd them on the
wave,
Three cheers our gallant Seamen
gave,
Nor thought of home or beauty,
Nor thought of home or beauty,
Along the line this signal ran,
England expects that ev'ry man
This day will do his duty.

(By Permission of F. PITMAN HART & Co. Ltd.)

ISSUED BY

The Spinet House

R & J. HILL LTD & HY. ARCHER & Cº
ESTᴰ 1775 LONDON.

338

FAMOUS NAVAL MEN
A SERIES OF 24 REAL PHOTOS.

No. 24

Sir Thomas Masterman Hardy.

Born 1769. Was present at the capture of the "Sabina" in 1796, and in defending the prize, was taken prisoner. Was exchanged in time to take part in the Battle of St. Vincent 1797. Took part in the Battle of the Nile 1798. Became Nelson's Flag-Captain in the various vessels the famous Admiral sailed in between 1799 and 1806. Created Baronet in 1806, First Sea Lord 1830 and Vice-Admiral in 1837. Died 1839.

CARRERAS

HIGH-CLASS CIGARETTES

ARCADIA WORKS, LONDON, ENGLAND.

ENGLAND'S LARGEST INDEPENDENT MANUFACTURERS OF
FINE QUALITY CIGARETTES
ESTABLISHED 1788.

339

BRITISH NAVAL SERIES
50 IN SET No. 17

ADMIRAL
Sir A. D. FANSHAWE,

G.C.B., G.C.V.O. Admiral of the Fleet. Born, 1847. During 1895-7 was A.D.C. to Queen Victoria. Commanded the Australian Station, 1902-5 and Portsmouth, 1908-10. He was President of the Royal Naval College, Greenwich, 1906-8.

Photo by Russell.

ISSUED BY

GALLAHER LTD.

BELFAST & LONDON.

340

THESE PICTURES OF

ENGLAND'S
Naval Heroes

REAR ADMIRAL LORD
CHARLES BERESFORD,
K.C.B.

Born Ireland Feb. 10th 1846. Educated Bayford School. Entered as Cadet "Britannia" 1859. Commanded "Condor" at Alexandria 1882 (medal with clasp) specially mentioned in despatches. Served on Lord Wolseley's staff, Nile Expedition 1884-85. Commanded Naval Brigade at Abu Klea, Abu Kru and Metemmeh, mentioned for gallantry. Commanded Expedition that rescued Sir Charles Wilson's party in "Safia" Lord Commissioner of the Admiralty 1886.

ARE ISSUED SOLELY BY

JOHN PLAYER & SONS,
LIMITED.

And can only be obtained in the PACKETS AND TINS CONTAINING

PLAYER'S NAVY CUT CIGARETTES

341

SECOND SERIES, Nos. 26 to 50

BRITISH WARSHIPS

35

H.M.S. LION

A fine battle-cruiser, and a rare fighter. She was in the Heligoland raid on Aug. 28th, 1914, and helped to sink the "Blucher" on January 24th, 1915. Of 26,350 tons, she steams at 31 knots, having engines of 70,000 h.p. Her chief armament is eight 13.5-in. and sixteen 4-in. guns. Completed, 1911.

Photo. Cribb.

ISSUED BY
STEPHEN MITCHELL & SON
BRANCH OF THE IMPERIAL TOBACCO CO.
(OF GREAT BRITAIN & IRELAND) Lᵀᴰ

342

REAL PHOTOGRAPHIC SERIES

OF

BRITISH WARSHIPS

PACKED EXCLUSIVELY BY

Godfrey Phillips,
LTD

N1

B.D.V. MEDIUM CIGARETTES

343

WILLS's
Cigarettes

NELSON SERIES, No 46

THE VICTORY, 1805.

This noble old three-decker, which earned undying fame at Trafalgar as Nelson's flagship, still exists at Portsmouth. At that momentous battle, the *Victory* carried thirty 32 and 42-pounders, thirty 24-pounders, forty 12-pounders, and two 68-pounder carronades. The *Victory* fought at such close quarters at Trafalgar that Nelson was distinguished by a sharp-shooter on the *Redoubtable* and mortally wounded.

W. D. & H. O WILLS.
BRISTOL & LONDON.

ISSUED BY THE IMPERIAL TOBACCO CO.
(OF GREAT BRITAIN & IRELAND), LTD.

(vertical text left side) ALBUMS FOR THESE PICTURE CARDS CAN BE OBTAINED

(vertical text right side) AT 1/- EACH FROM ALL TOBACCONISTS.

344

INTERNATIONAL
CODE
OF SIGNALS

SERIES OF 50. No 2

NELSON'S
FAMOUS SIGNAL

Flags meaning "England"

Signal flags were first used as a means of communication between ships in the reign of Edward III. These early signals were of the simplest character, and consisted of little more than flying a "Flag of Council" calling together the captains to conference. There was no official Admiralty code, and every admiral drew up the flag signals for use between the ships under his command.

(Continued on Card No. 3.)

INTERNATIONAL
TOBACCO CO. LTD
LONDON

345

FAMOUS SHIPS

No 44

THE ILLUSTRIOUS

The British aircraft carrier *Illustrious* is one of the newest additions to the Fleet Air Arm, and includes many recent improvements. Laid down at Barrow Furness, on April 3rd, 1939. She is planned to augment the striking power of the Navy, and to assist in protecting the world wide interests of the British race. Her length of 740-feet, and her beam close on 96-feet. Launching weight was given as 16,000 tons, and her speed estimated to exceed 30 knots. She was built at Vickers-Armstrong, and named by Lady Henderson.

The *Courageous*, a forerunner of this type of boat was torpedoed by the Germans on September 18, 1939, with a loss of nearly 600 lives.

ISSUED BY
R. & J. HILL LTD.
Proprietors of
HY. ARCHER & CO.
LONDON BIRMINGHAM

346

OUR NAVY
A SERIES OF 50
No 47
Described by 'JACKSTAFF'

H.M.S. WOOLWICH

Destroyer depot ship in the Mediterranean Fleet. Displacement (weight) 8,750 tons, engines 6,500 h.p. speed 14 knots (about). She is a mobile base for destroyers and provides for the immediate needs of both the boats and their crews. In destroyers there is no spare room. For the medical treatment of their crews and for other services in which a large ship is a self-contained unit they depend upon their 'mother' vessel. She is specially equipped for giving all the help required for boats and crews.

CARRERAS LTD
(ESTD. 1788.)
ARCADIA WORKS, LONDON ENGLAND.

KEEP THIS ATTRACTIVE SERIES OF
PICTURE CARDS ON SALE AT THE CARRERAS
ALL TOBACCONISTS (PRICE ONE PENNY)

347

MODERN NAVAL CRAFT

A SERIES OF 50

30

"GIUSEPPE GARIBALDI"
Italian Light Cruiser

Launched in 1936, the general appearance of this class is very pleasing, the beautifully framed stem and compact arrangement of the superstructure being in accordance with the most modern practice. This vessel is of 7,874 tons displacement, and her engines of 100,000 h.p. give her a speed of 35 knots. The armament consists of ten 6-inch guns, disposed in triple and twin turrets, eight 3.9-inch guns and sixteen smaller anti-aircraft guns. There are six 21-inch torpedo tubes, four aircraft and two catapults. The vessel is also equipped for minelaying.

JOHN PLAYER & SONS
BRANCH OF THE IMPERIAL TOBACCO CO.
(OF GREAT BRITAIN & IRELAND) LTD.

(vertical text left side) THIS SURFACE IS ADHESIVE. ASK YOUR TOBACCONIST FOR THE "PLAYER'S" ALBUM (PRICE ONE PENNY) SPECIALLY PREPARED TO HOLD THE COMPLETE SERIES

348

SILHOUETTES
OF WARSHIPS
A SERIES OF 50

FROM
"FIGHTING SHIPS"
FRED T. JANE. Copyright.

No. 38.

German Dreadnoughts.

Helgoland Class—4 ships.
THURINGEN, HELGOLAND,
OSTFRIESLAND, and OLDEN-
BURG. Completed 1911-12.
Displacement, 21,000 tons.
Complement, 1,108. *Length,*
546 ft. *Guns,* 12—12 in. 14—
6 in. and 14—24 pdr. *Torpedo
tubes,* 6—20 in. *Speed,* about
22 knots.

ISSUED BY
W. A. & A. C. CHURCHMAN
BRANCH OF THE IMPERIAL TOBACCO CO
(OF GREAT BRITAIN & IRELAND) LTD

SIR THOMAS MASTERMAN HARDY

NELSON (Portrait.)

"CROSSING THE BAR"

UNION JACK CIGARETTES.
W. & F. Faulkner L™ London, s.e.

H.M.S. LION (Battle-Cruiser).

Lord Charles Beresford

Admiral Sir A. D. FANSHAWE

SUBMARINE E7

ILLUSTRIOUS

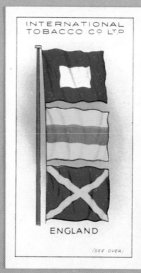

INTERNATIONAL TOBACCO C° L™

ENGLAND

(SEE OVER)

WILLS'S CIGARETTES.

THE VICTORY IN 1805.

H.M.S. WOOLWICH

CHURCHMAN'S CIGARETTES.

GERMAN DREADNOUGHT.   HELGOLAND CLASS.

PLAYER'S CIGARETTES

"GIUSEPPE GARIBALDI" (ITALY)

CIERVA AUTOGIRO C. 30.P

D.H. 86B

LAMBERT & BUTLER'S CIGARETTES.

RADLEY-ENGLAND HYDRO-BIPLANE.

THE SAVOIA-MARCHETTI S. 55

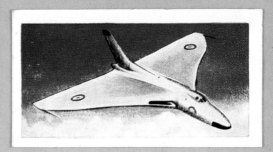

PLAYER'S CIGARETTES

FAIREY "BATTLE" BOMBER

PLAYER'S CIGARETTES

AIR FRANCE: LIORE-ET-OLIVIER H. 24-2

LINCOLN ELLSWORTH   NORTHROP

LAMBERT & BUTLER'S CIGARETTES

SANTOS-DUMONT'S "LA DEMOISELLE." 1908

Sopwith Biplane.

LAMBERT & BUTLER'S CIGARETTES

HANNIBAL   AT   MALAKAL.   ANGLO-EGYPTIAN SUDAN

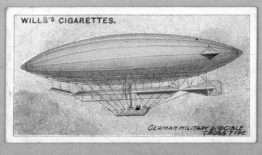

WILL'S'S CIGARETTES.

GERMAN MILITARY DIRIGIBLE
CROSS TYPE.

LAMBERT & BUTLER'S
CIGARETTES

RUDDER DEVICE

ARGENTINE REPUBLIC-NAVAL

AEROPLANES (CIVIL)

A SERIES OF 50
SELECTED FOR THE ATTRACTIVE ALBUM (PRICE ONE PENNY) SPECIALLY PREPARED TO HOLD THE COMPLETE SERIES

7

CIERVA AUTOGIRO
(Great Britain)
C.30 P

Unlike the normal aeroplane, which obtains its lift by forward speed and the resistance of the air to a fixed wing, the Autogiro has three rotating blades which, when turning, obtain sufficient lift to support the aircraft without forward movement. The Autogiro can thus ascend and descend almost vertically, and in the air it can remain practically stationary. A single engine gives the initial start to the rotor blades and maintains the forward motion. The cruising speed is about 95 m.p.h. The Autogiro has proved very successful and may lead to interesting developments in aviation.

JOHN PLAYER & SONS

349

TYPES OF AEROPLANES

A SERIES OF 25

No 13
BRISTOL "BULLDOG"

The Bristol "Bulldog" is one of the latest types of day and night single-seater fighters. Designed especially for service at high altitudes, it is fitted with a Bristol "Jupiter" radial air-cooled engine, and is capable of speeds in the neighbourhood of 170 m.p.h. at an altitude of 12,000 to 15,000 feet.

Constructed completely of steel, this machine is exceptionally manœuvrable and its fighting equipment of machine guns and its remarkable performance, it is undoubtedly among the most advanced types of this class of aircraft which have yet been constructed.

MURRAY SONS & CO LTD
WHITEHALL TOBACCO WORKS
BELFAST IRELAND

350

AVIATION

A SERIES OF 25

No. 8
Radley-England Hydro-Biplane.

This machine was built at Huntingdon by Messrs. Radley and England, in the Circuit of Britain race of 1913. Originally fitted with three 50-h.p. Gnome engines, it was at the last moment fitted with an English Sunbeam engine. Owing to the alteration taking place practically on the eve of the race, the machine was not possible to compete. The machine, however, flew well on its trials at Shoreham, and should have given a very good account of itself in the race.

ISSUED BY
LAMBERT & BUTLER
BRANCH OF THE IMPERIAL TOBACCO CO (OF GREAT BRITAIN & IRELAND) LTD

351

AEROPLANES

SERIES OF 48. No 38

D.H. 86B

The De Havilland 86B is one of the most successful air liners ever built and has an excellent record of service both within this country and on Empire air routes. Ten to sixteen passengers are accommodated, according to the route operated and four Gipsy Six engines of 200 h.p. give the machine a cruising speed of over 140 m.p.h. Large windows, a cabin heater and separate ventilators to each seat make for a high standard of passenger comfort.

ISSUED BY
GALLAHER LTD
VIRGINIA HOUSE, LONDON & BELFAST

352

FILTERTIPS "MILLS"

Aircraft of the World

No. 1
VULCAN A. V. ROE

This is the second of the V-bombers to go into service with the R.A.F. Later types have a modified leading edge to the delta wing introducing a "droop." Latest types to improve engine, increasing area and improving air intake, either Conways or the new Olympus.

Span ... 99 ft.
length 97 ft. 1 in. 16 ft.

353

AIRCRAFT

SERIES No 1. 54 CARDS

No. 52
The
SAVOIA-MARCHETTI S. 55
Twin-engined Reconnaissance Flying-boat.

Built by —
Societá Idrovolanti Alta Italia "Savoia," Sesto Calende, Italy.
Used by —The Italian Air Force.
The Brazilian Naval Air Service.

Span ... 78 ft. 8 in.
Weight loaded ... 14,520 lbs.
Maximum speed ... 174 m.p.h.
Cruising speed ... 146 m.p.h.
Maximum range: 1,350 miles.

Two 800 h.p. Isotta-Fraschini "Asso" engines.

ABOVE IS A WORM'S EYE VIEW

ISSUED BY
GODFREY PHILLIPS
AND ASSOCIATED COMPANIES

354

INTERNATIONAL AIR LINERS

A SERIES OF 50

13

AIR FRANCE: LIORÉ-ET-OLIVIER H. 24-2
(France)

The Lioré-et-Olivier H.24-2 is a four-engined flying-boat used by Air France on its trans-Mediterranean services from Marseilles to Algiers and Tunis. It has a metal hull and wooden wings, with the four 350 h.p. Gnôme-Rhône K.7d engines mounted in two tandem pairs above the wings, where the airscrews are well clear of spray. There is accommodation for a crew of three and ten passengers, and all of the main cabin is the large baggage-hold. The H.24-2 weighs 18,522 lbs. fully loaded, and has a top speed of 137·7 m.p.h.

JOHN PLAYER & SONS
BRANCH OF THE IMPERIAL TOBACCO CO (OF GREAT BRITAIN & IRELAND), LTD.

355

AIRCRAFT OF THE ROYAL AIR FORCE

A SERIES OF 50

11

FAIREY "BATTLE" BOMBER

This aircraft, produced by the Fairey Aviation Co., Ltd., is a low-wing monoplane bomber with monocoque fuselage and metal-skinned wing and tail surfaces. A feature of the fuselage is the continuous transparent fairing over the cockpits which accommodate the crew of 2. A fixed machine-gun is mounted in the starboard wing and a free gun in the rear cockpit. The power unit is a Rolls-Royce "Merlin" supercharged engine. The "Battle" has a top speed of about 257 m.p.h. and a normal range of approximately 1,000 miles. The wing span is 54 feet and the length 42 feet 4½ inches.

JOHN PLAYER & SONS
BRANCH OF THE IMPERIAL TOBACCO CO (OF GREAT BRITAIN & IRELAND) LTD.

356

A HISTORY OF AVIATION

A SERIES OF 25

12

Santos-Dumont's "La Demoiselle," 1908.

The earlier flights of the Brazilian Alberto Santos-Dumont are described on Card No. 11 of this series. He subsequently constructed and flew the light monoplane illustrated, continuing his experiments on the snow-covered plain at Issy, France, in the winter of 1908-9. "La Demoiselle," the smallest and lightest practical machine of its time, rose from the ground in 6·2 sec. (then a record), and attained a speed of 60 m.p.h. Built mainly of bamboo, and used for the main framework, the machine being extremely light and simple in structure; a model may be seen in the Science Museum at S. Kensington. "La Demoiselle" was said to be difficult to fly because of the pendulum effect of the pilot's plane.

ISSUED BY
LAMBERT & BUTLER
BRANCH OF THE IMPERIAL TOBACCO CO (OF GREAT BRITAIN & IRELAND), LTD.

357

FAMOUS AIRMEN & AIRWOMEN

358

No. 19

LINCOLN ELLSWORTH

In 1925 he took part in the Amundsen-Ellsworth expedition to the Arctic, and made a Trans-Polar Flight with Amundsen and Nobile. He also took part in a Trans-Arctic Expedition with Sir Hubert Wilkins, and represented the American Geological Society on the Graf Zeppelin Arctic Flight in 1931.

Is a Fellow of many Aeronautical Societies, has received numerous decorations for his work. Born 1880.

CARRERAS LTD
(ESTD. 1788)
ARCADIA WORKS, LONDON, ENGLAND

KEEP THIS ATTRACTIVE SERIES OF PICTURE CARDS IN THE CARRERAS SLIP-CARDS (OBTAINABLE FROM ALL TOBACCONISTS (PRICE ONE PENNY)

EMPIRE AIR ROUTES

A SERIES OF 50

18

The "Hannibal" at Malakal, Anglo-Egyptian Sudan

South of Khartoum the transition from desert to tropical vegetation begins. We fly over bush country to Koeti, seeing the White Nile below. At Malakal village we may see Shilluk natives, who are of a particularly fine physique, many being over 6 ft. in height. Our illustration shows some of these natives in front of the *Hannibal*, in which we have flown from Alexandria. On their heads and around their necks are gold beads, and across their foreheads may be seen bead-like electrices. At Malakal begin the area of the Sudd swamps.

ISSUED BY THE IMPERIAL TOBACCO CO. (OF GREAT BRITAIN & IRELAND), LTD.
LAMBERT & BUTLER

359

---

(26)
"WORLD'S AIRCRAFT."
A SERIES OF 30.

"Sopwith" Biplane.

This is an old type, but flies very well, when fitted with a 70 H.P. Gnome engine, is approximately 64 M.P. H. The planes are staggered which tends to make the machine more stable. It carries a pilot and one passenger. British Design & Make.

FINLAY'S GOLD FLAKE CIGARETTES.

Finlay & Co., Ltd.,
Newcastle & London.

360

AEROPLANE MARKINGS

A SERIES OF 50

2

ARGENTINE REPUBLIC
Naval Air Service

Aircraft of the Argentine Naval Air Service bear similar rudder markings to those of the Army Air Service (see Card No. 1), but the rings on the wings are replaced by large red naval anchors. Naval aircraft do not carry fuselage markings. The Naval Air Service is under the jurisdiction of the Ministry of Marine and operate from shore bases, landing-planes and flying-boats are used. Naval aircraft are mainly of British and U.S. types, but certain aeroplanes of domestic design and construction emanating from the Military Aircraft Factory at Cordoba are also used.

ISSUED BY THE IMPERIAL TOBACCO CO. (OF GREAT BRITAIN & IRELAND), LTD.
LAMBERT & BUTLER

361

WILLS'S CIGARETTES

AVIATION

A SERIES OF 50 (18)

German Military Dirigibles Gross Type

ALBUMS FOR THESE PICTURE CARDS CAN BE OBTAINED

ISSUED BY THE IMPERIAL TOBACCO CO. (OF GREAT BRITAIN & IRELAND) LTD.
W.D. & H.O. WILLS
BRISTOL & LONDON.

Nos. 1-25, AIRSHIPS.
Nos. 26-50, AEROPLANES.

AT 1/- EACH FROM ALL TOBACCONISTS.

362

TADDY & Co.
LONDON & GRIMSBY

A SERIES OF 25

ISSUED SOLELY BY TADDY & CO.

363

MOTOR CARS

A SERIES OF 50

41

SINGER 11 SALOON

This model is one of the most advanced of British "smallfours." It has independent suspension of the front wheels, and a unique combination of four-speed synchromesh gear-box and a fluid flywheel (allowing the engine to be kept running in gear with the car stationary), which simplifies driving to a marked degree. It has a maximum speed of 65 m.p.h. and a cruising speed of 45-50 m.p.h. The four-cylinder engine is of 66·5 mm. bore, 105 mm. stroke and 1,459 c.c. capacity; the R.A.C. rating is 10·95 h.p. and the annual tax £8 8s. The wheel-base has an 8 ft. 5 in. wheelbase and a 4 ft. 2 in. track. The car is priced at £245.

JOHN PLAYER & SONS

BRANCH OF THE IMPERIAL TOBACCO CO. (OF GREAT BRITAIN & IRELAND), LTD.

364

MOTOR INDEX MARKS

A SERIES OF 50

22

D N
YORK.

York is a picturesque old city of 84,500 inhabitants (1921). The visitor should make a point of seeing York Minster; St. Mary's Abbey; Clifford's Tower; the old city walls and gates or Bars (Micklegate, Bootham Bar, etc.); many old churches of great architectural interest; the quaint Shambles and other old thoroughfares; St. Anthony's Hall, Peaseholme Green, now the Blue Coat School; the Museum and Museum Gardens, etc. King's Square is said to mark the site of the Palace of the Roman Emperors.

LAMBERT & BUTLER

ISSUED BY THE IMPERIAL TOBACCO Cº (OF GREAT BRITAIN & IRELAND) Lᵀᴰ

365

MOTOR CAR RADIATORS

A SERIES OF 25
16

RENAULT.

The sealed dust-proof bonnet of the RENAULT allows a clean engine to be maintained, perfect cooling being obtained under all conditions. The smell of oil and the engine fumes are drawn away by the flywheel gear and cannot reach the body of the car. The radiator (always an expensive component to repair) is screened behind the engine, and the advantage of this feature becomes especially obvious if any accident should occur.

ISSUED BY LAMBERT & BUTLER

BRANCH OF THE IMPERIAL TOBACCO CO. (OF GREAT BRITAIN & IRELAND), LTD

366

MOTOR CARS

SECOND SERIES OF 50

18

FIAT "500"
CONVERTIBLE SALOON

The smallest, fully-fledged motor car in regular production, the Fiat "500" is also entirely unconventional in many features. The small, compact engine is mounted in front of the front axle line; the radiator is behind the engine and the front wheels are independently sprung. Wheels and body are in keeping, but there is good room for two adults. The car does 50 m.p.h. and over 50 m.p.g. The four-cylinder engine is of 52 mm. bore, 67 mm. stroke and 570 c.c. capacity; the R.A.C. rating is 6·7 h.p. and the annual tax £5 5s.; there is a four-speed synchromesh gear-box. The chassis has a 6 ft. 6¼ in. wheelbase and a 3 ft. 7¼ in. track. The car is priced at £120.

JOHN PLAYER & SONS

BRANCH OF THE IMPERIAL TOBACCO CO. (OF GREAT BRITAIN & IRELAND), LTD.

367

MOTOR CARS

A SERIES OF 24   NO. 13

**12.8 h.p. SUNBEAM
"DAWN"**

SPECIFICATION

Number of cylinders, 4; bore, 72 mm.; stroke, 100 mm.; capacity, 1,627 c.c.; R.A.C. rating, 12.8 h.p.; overall length, 13-ft. 6-in.; width, 5-ft. 6-in.; wheelbase, 9-ft. 2-in.; track, 4-ft. 4-in.; maximum height from ground, 5-ft. 6-in.; gear ratios, 5.77, 8.6, 13.85 and 21.4 to 1. Flexibly mounted engine, synchromesh gearbox. Tax, £13.

Gallaher's CIGARETTES

VIRGINIA HOUSE, LONDON & BELFAST

368

MOTOR CARS

3ᴿᴰ SERIES 50

32

MORGAN.

The "Morgan Runabout" has been before the public for sixteen years, having been exhibited at Olympia in 1910, and has proved its efficiency and reliability in all the most important public trials. It has also been very successful on the racing track, covering 97·4 miles in one hour, and looking nearly all the 1,100 c.c. world's records, including the kilometer at 104·6 m.p.h. and the 100 mile at 91·5 m.p.h.

ISSUED BY LAMBERT & BUTLER

BRANCH OF THE IMPERIAL TOBACCO CO (OF GREAT BRITAIN & IRELAND) LTD

369

HINTS & TIPS FOR MOTORISTS

A SERIES OF 25

5

Reversing through Gateway,

Before reversing through a gateway in order to enter a garage, great care should be taken to ensure that the doors of both the garage and the gate are firmly wedged, or otherwise fixed open. When the car is actually moving through a narrow gateway the driver should look on one side only. This will enable him to get in close to that side, and, providing the necessary straightening up is done, the other side may be left to look after itself. This method is both easier and safer than looking from side to side.

ISSUED BY LAMBERT & BUTLER

BRANCH OF THE IMPERIAL TOBACCO CO. (OF GREAT BRITAIN & IRELAND), LTD.

370

THE HOUSE OF CRAVEN

Proprietors: Carreras Ltd, Christopher Martin Road, Basildon, Essex. Registered in England (No 384318).

Vintage cars, series of 50

Craven Black Cat

1921 BENZ
(Germany)

Many German cars of the early 1920s looked more powerful than they actually were, thanks to the aggressive vee-radiators fashionable since 1913. An impoverished home market and a boycott imposed by the victorious Allies on many factories were advanced, since its 16-litre over-head camshaft 4-cylinder engine gave a useful 45bhp and around 60mph. There were four forward speeds, detachable wire wheels were unusual on a small German car of 1921.

371

MOTORS

A SERIES OF 25

23

32 h.p. Motor Omnibus.

This is one of the London Motor Omnibuses constructed by the firm of Sidney Straker & Squire, Ltd., of London. It is fitted with a 4 cylinder petrol motor of 32 h.p., and is capable of maintaining a speed of 12 miles per hour. There is seating accommodation for 34 passengers, viz., 16 inside and 18 outside.

ISSUED BY LAMBERT & BUTLER

BRANCH OF THE IMPERIAL TOBACCO CO. (OF GREAT BRITAIN & IRELAND), LTD.

372

MOTOR CARS

A SERIES OF 25

15

MORRIS MINOR.

"Built like a big car" has always been the slogan of the "Morris" range of cars, and each year it seems to acquire more big car attributes. Thus it now boasts a synchromesh four-speed gear-box, hydraulic brakes and shock absorbers, direction indicators, dip-and-switch headlamps and a battery master switch. Specification:—Engine: four cylinders, bore 57 mm., stroke 83 mm., capacity 847 c.c., R.A.C. rating 8 h.p., annual tax £6 6s.; three valves. Chassis: wheelbase, short 6ft. 6in., long 7ft. 7in., track 3ft. 6in.; 6-volt battery and coil, five-gallon petrol tank at rear. The four-door saloon illustrated is on the long wheelbase and is quite a roomy body for four.

ISSUED BY LAMBERT & BUTLER

BRANCH OF THE IMPERIAL TOBACCO CO (OF GREAT BRITAIN & IRELAND), LTD

373

HOW MOTOR CARS WORK

A SERIES OF 25

23

The Dynamo and Battery.

Electricity is generated in the wire-wound core (a) of the dynamo, and is picked up by brushes (b) from a commutator (c), whence it flows through wiring to the switchboard, thence to the battery which serves as a reservoir of electricity and is charged by the dynamo. It consists of cells (six in the 12 volt type illustrated) connected in series, each containing plates (d) immersed in diluted sulphuric acid. To prevent the battery discharging itself back through the dynamo as a motor when the engine is stopped, or running slowly, an automatic cut-out is used. Thus the cells are connected to the dynamo only when it is running fast enough to charge the battery.

ISSUED BY LAMBERT & BUTLER

BRANCH OF THE IMPERIAL TOBACCO CO. (OF GREAT BRITAIN & IRELAND), LTD.

374

MODERN MOTOR CARS

A SERIES OF 50 REAL PHOTOGRAPHS

No. 42.

THE £100 FORD SALOON.

Although manufacturers had dreamed for years of a £100 Saloon car, this sensational achievement was first announced in Oct. 1935. Not a new introduction, but was an existing model reduced in price as a result of large scale demand. Manufactured in Gt. Britain. Developing 22 h.p.

W.H. & J. WOODS Lᵀᴰ
PRESTON

375

ILLINGWORTH'S CIGARETTES

A SERIES OF 25

No. 16

The Humber.

The chief attributes of the Humber are: low running costs, engine silence, great varnish adorn the coachwork surface of every Humber model. Made in three powers, 8 h.p., 12 h.p. and 15 h.p.

JAMES ILLINGWORTH LTD.,
KENDAL, ENGLAND.
ESTABLISHED 1867

376

LAMBERT & BUTLER'S CIGARETTES.

RENAULT.

DN LAMBERT & BUTLER'S CIGARETTES.

YORK. THE SHAMBLES

TADDY & Cº CIGARETTES

AUSTIN SIXTEEN YORK SALOON   Nº 6

PLAYER'S CIGARETTES

SINGER II SALOON

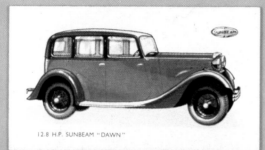

12.8 H.P. SUNBEAM "DAWN"

PLAYER'S CIGARETTES

FIAT "500" CONVERTIBLE SALOON

LAMBERT & BUTLER'S CIGARETTES.

REVERSING THROUGH GATEWAY.

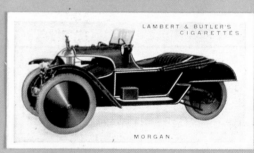

LAMBERT & BUTLER'S CIGARETTES.

MORGAN.

LAMBERT & BUTLER'S CIGARETTES.

UNION JACK

32 H.P. MOTOR OMNIBUS

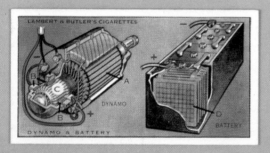

LAMBERT & BUTLER'S CIGARETTES.

DYNAMO

DYNAMO & BATTERY   BATTERY

LAMBERT & BUTLER'S CIGARETTES

MORRIS MINOR SALOON

Humber

Ford

LAMBERT & BUTLER'S CIGARETTES.

L'OLONNOIS.

OGDEN'S CIGARETTES

THE MUTINY OF THE "BOUNTY"

CHURCHMAN'S CIGARETTES

THE "QUEEN MARY"

Mauretania

CHURCHMAN'S CIGARETTES

SHIP'S SHOP, R.M.S.P. LINER.

HIGNETT'S CIGARETTES.

H.M.'S COASTGUARD SERVICE.

Ogden's Cigarettes

WILSON LINE, HULL.

House Flag & Funnel

"BREMEN"

MITCHELL'S CIGARETTES.

P.S. "QUEEN-EMPRESS."

"CARONIA"

COPYRIGHT

CHURCHMAN'S CIGARETTES

A VIKING SHIP

ADELAIDE (1852)

OGDEN'S CIGARETTES

THE RUM-RUNNER

THE MUTINY OF THE "BOUNTY"

When H.M. store ship *Bounty* was sent to the South Seas in 1787 the Admiralty made the mistake of putting her under the command of William Bligh, a fine seaman but a born bully. He goaded his crew—none too good to begin with—into mutiny, but when they turned him adrift in the cutter he got his loyal followers 3,618 miles to safety at the most wonderful boat voyage in history. Many of the mutineers died violent deaths, but some reached Pitcairn Island, repented, and founded a model colony there.

ISSUED BY OGDEN'S — 377

L'Ollonois.

The Capture of the Governor's Ship, Cuba.

In his youth this man, whose real name was Nau, was transported to the W. Indies for his crimes. He rose to high command among the buccaneers winning an unenviable reputation for his atrocious cruelties. On one occasion the Spanish Governor of Havana sent a man-of-war to take him, with a negro executioner on board. L'Ollonois and his French buccaneers captured the ship and executed the hangman. He ravaged the Spanish settlements in Central America, acquiring great wealth. In 1667 he sacked Maracaibo and Gibraltar (Venezuela), securing enormous booty : 260,000 pieces of eight, besides plate, silk and jewels.

ISSUED BY LAMBERT & BUTLER — 378

"MAURETANIA"

The "Mauretania" was built on the Tyne and was launched on November 16th, 1907. She was 787 feet long, 88 feet beam and 36 feet 3 inches draught, with gross tonnage, 30,703. In September, 1910, she won the Atlantic "Blue Riband," when she crossed from Queenstown to New York in four days ten hours and forty-one minutes, or at 26.06 knots. The "Mauretania" again reduced her own unbeaten record in August, 1929, by crossing from New York to Plymouth in four days seventeen hours and forty-nine minutes, or at 27.22 knots. She made her last of 350 Atlantic voyages on September 26th, 1934, and on April 2nd, 1935, was sold for breaking up.

ISSUED BY RICHARD LLOYD & SONS BRANCH OF COPE BROS. & Cº LTD LONDON & LIVERPOOL — 379

Ship's Shop.

R.M.S.P. "A" Class Liner.

In the old days the ship's barber had the privilege of stocking a little shop to suit the best of his ability, and selling all sorts of goods to the passengers. His limited capital frequently made these efforts unsatisfactory, and most companies now pay their barbers generously to stick to their own work, and themselves stock and maintain a much more elaborate shop for the benefit of their passengers. Cigarettes, which have been forgotten, toys of all sorts, souvenirs of the voyage, reading matter and prizes for evening competitions and deck games are on sale in the ship's shop.

ISSUED BY W.A.&A.C.CHURCHMAN — 380

THE "QUEEN MARY"

The latest link in the Cunard White Star express service between Southampton-Cherbourg and New York, the *Queen Mary* is the culmination of nearly a century's experience of the needs of the North Atlantic Service. Britain's masterpiece assumes vast proportions, not for mere effect, but in order satisfactorily to fulfil the conditions of the service for which she is designed. She is a magnificent ship, stately and seaworthy, sturdily constructed to withstand greater stresses than she is likely to encounter, and equipped with modern appliances for safe navigation. She is not only the greatest achievement in the history of British shipbuilding, but marks a new era in ocean travel. Her Majesty Queen Mary launched the giant liner on Sept. 26th, 1934, in the presence of His late Majesty King George V, His Majesty King Edward VIII (then Prince of Wales), and over a quarter of a million spectators.

ISSUED BY W.A.&A.C. CHURCHMAN — 381

"BREMEN" (Germany.)

THIS SURFACE IS ADHESIVE

Spurred on by the feats of the veteran *Mauretania*, the North German Lloyd Line decided to make a bid for the Blue Riband of the Atlantic. Into the *Bremen* went the brains and skill of Germany's foremost naval architects and builders, and the least amazing of the innovations being her bulbous bow which appears so very odd in comparison with the usual sharp stem. The *Bremen* succeeded in regaining the record with an average speed of 28.14 knots.

ISSUED BY STATE EXPRESS CIGARETTES — 382

P.S. "Queen-Empress."

The paddle steamer "Queen-Empress" was built in 1912 by Messrs. Murdoch and Murray, Port Glasgow, for Messrs. John Williamson and Co., of Glasgow, and is a most commodious steamer. She is handsomely-equipped and magnificently appointed. Her machinery is by the Rankine and Blackmore, Eagle Foundry, Greenock, and maintains a good steady speed of 16 knots. During the season she is engaged upon a variety of excursions in the beautiful Firth of Clyde.

ISSUED BY THE STEPHEN MITCHELL & SON — 383

WILSON LINE, Hull.

The Wilson Line, the largest private shipowning firm in the world, was founded by the late Mr. Thomas Wilson in 1835, subsequently conducted by Messrs. Charles and Arthur Wilson under the style of Thos. Wilson, Sons & Co., and which became a private company in 1891. The fleet consists of 98 steamers, with a gross tonnage of 200,800 tons.

ISSUED BY OGDEN'S LIVERPOOL BRANCH OF THE IMPERIAL TOBACCO COMPANY (OF GREAT BRITAIN & IRELAND), LIMITED. — 384

H.M.'s Coastguard Service.

On April 1st, 1923, the control of the Coastguard Service passed from the Admiralty to the Board of Trade, and the Union Jack replaced the White Ensign at all stations. The number of Coastguards under the present scheme is about 900 officers and men, their principal duties being to keep a constant watch both by day and night, to save life and to receive wreck ; all wreck of the sea being the property of the Crown. Coastguards also have charge of the rocket apparatus. The Service is in charge of District Inspectors, who are controlled by a Chief Inspector and his Deputy.

ISSUED BY HIGNETT BROS & Cº (OF GREAT BRITAIN & IRELAND) Lᵀᴰ — 385

A VIKING SHIP

In their warlike raids on the British coasts, the Vikings used large double-ended open boats, from 70 to 80 feet long. We illustrate one of the type of the 9th century A.D. Both ends of the vessel were very high, with projecting stem and stern-posts elaborately carved in runic style. The steering-paddle (or "steer-board") was placed on the starboard quarter, and has given its name, for all time, to that side of a ship. When the wind was fair each vessel set one large square sail, but otherwise the ship was propelled by oars. The rowers worked standing, and in the largest ships there were as many as three men to each oar.

ISSUED BY W.A.&A.C. CHURCHMAN — 386

"CARONIA" — Cunard Line, 20,000 tons.

The "Caronia," one of the latest of the Cunard Fleet, was the first liner to be fitted with the Stone-Lloyd Hydraulic System for closing the water-tight doors, which makes it possible to close the whole of the water-tight doors within a few seconds. This arrangement makes the ship practically unsinkable, as it prevents the water spreading from one compartment to another in the event of a collision or other accident. — 387

THE RUM-RUNNER.

All sorts of ships and craft are used to transport the liquor from "wet" territory to the United States, near to whose coast as is safe. The most popular type is the Schooner, which is fast and seaworthy, and can keep the seas for long periods. She is the type to which the Smugglers are most accustomed in their more lawful work, and her ordinary jobs are fishing among the Grand Banks, or trading among the West Indian Islands, permit her to slip in and out of port, or stay away for a spell, without exciting undue suspicion.

ISSUED BY OGDEN'S BRANCH OF THE IMPERIAL TOBACCO CO (OF GREAT BRITAIN & IRELAND) LTD. — 388

"ADELAIDE."

The "Adelaide" was a sailing ship later taken over by William Scott Russell, and was specially designed for the Australian emigrant and wool trades. She was taken over during the Crimean War as a transport.

ISSUED BY DOMINION TOBACCO CO (1929) LIMITED LONDON-E.13 — 389

Card 390

ALBUMS FOR THESE PICTURE CARDS CAN BE OBTAINED

CELEBRATED SHIPS

No. 40

R.M.S. "Mauretania."

The Cunard express steamer "Mauretania," built on the Tyne, by Swan, Hunter & Richardson, was launched 1907. She was then the largest and most perfect type of ocean liner afloat, although her glories will be eclipsed by the White Star liners "Olympic" and "Titanic." Now running trip (?) her length, of 45,000 tons displacement, has a speed of 25 knots.

WILLS'S CIGARETTES

W.D. & H.O. WILLS, BRISTOL & LONDON.

AT 1/- EACH FROM ALL TOBACCONISTS.

Card 391

BOATS OF THE WORLD.

No. 12—Florentine Fishing Boat.

There is very little water in the Arno during the summer months, but as soon as the Autumn rains swell the mountain streams, the fishermen are busy in their dilapidated boats, which tarred to velvety blackness, gives them the appearance of antiquated gondolas dotting into the murky water. A huge square net attached to a couple of tall poles crossed at the top is the apparatus of the Florentine fisherman.

Cope Bros. & Co., Ltd. LIVERPOOL & LONDON.

Card 392

SERIES OF 50.

BRITISH SEA DOGS

No 18

Admiral.
Time of Henry VIII.

Sea officers had now become diplomatists, explorers, students of nautical astronomy and surveyors of the sea and coasts, as well as being professional fighting men, several of them having written technical manuals for the instruction of their comrades and successors. The gay liveries of this reign were only intended for war in special occasions, but engagements being considered under this head, these doughty warriors always put on their smartest attire to fight in.

ISSUED BY
JOHN SINCLAIR LD.
BARNEY'S TOBACCO WORKS
NEWCASTLE-ON-TYNE.

Card 393

HISTORY OF NAVAL DRESS
A SERIES OF 50

29

SHIP'S COOK, 1790.

Ships' Cooks were originally appointed by the Admirals in command of the fleets, often with unsatisfactory results. In the reign of Queen Anne, however, an order was sent to the Navy Board by the Lord High Admiral, directing them to engage cooks for Her Majesty's ships, and *to give preference to such cripples and maimed persons as are pensioners to the chest at Chatham.* This preference to maimed pensioners apparently continued, as the artist who made the drawing of a Ship's Cook, about 1790 (from which our illustration is taken), has given him a wooden leg.

ISSUED BY
JOHN PLAYER & SONS
BRANCH OF THE IMPERIAL TOBACCO Co.
(OF GREAT BRITAIN & IRELAND), LTD.

Card 394

ISSUED BY
JOHN PLAYER & SONS
NOTTINGHAM
BRANCH OF THE IMPERIAL TOBACCO CO. (OF GREAT BRITAIN & IRELAND), LTD.

SHIPS' FIGUREHEADS.
A SERIES OF 25

26

H.M.S. "Eurydice."

The unfortunate *Eurydice* was built at Portsmouth in 1843, and was a 26-gun frigate of 921 tons. Commissioned in 1877 as a training-ship for boys and seamen, she was returning to Spithead after cruising in the West Indies, when she capsized in a squall off the Isle of Wight. She foundered, and all on board lost their lives. She was afterwards raised, towed into Portsmouth, and broken up. The telescope was found lying across the figure-head as shown in our picture.

Card 395

ALBUMS FOR THESE PICTURE CARDS CAN BE OBTAINED

ISSUED BY THE IMPERIAL TOBACCO CO. (OF GREAT BRITAIN & IRELAND) LTD.

THE WORLD'S DREADNOUGHTS

17

United States Battleship "SOUTH CAROLINA."

16,000 tons. Commenced July, 1906.
Guns: 8—12 in. 22—3 in. 14 pdr, 16 small guns. 2 torpedo tubes.
Armour: Belt, 12in.—8in. On big guns, 12in.—8in.
Speed: 18½ knots, with 16,500 h.p.

Sister ship, *Michigan*. South Carolina, in conception considerably anti-dates the first "all-big-gun" ship, was designed, in fact, before the *Dreadnought*, but considerable delay in her completion delayed her, and she was not launched until 1908.

WILLS'S CIGARETTES
W.D. & H.O. WILLS, BRISTOL & LONDON.

AT 1/- EACH FROM ALL TOBACCONISTS.

Card 396

SHIPS OF ALL AGES
A Series of 50   No. 28

THE CLIPPER

The old sailing Clipper was one of the most handsome craft ever built, carrying a large quantity of canvas and making very long voyages. This sharp-bowed vessel originated in the United States, and at one time threatened British supremacy in the merchant service, but our builders responded gallantly to the challenge, and the Aberdeen Clipper became very famous. The illustration is of the "Thermopylae," built in 1869; she was of 948 tons and the fastest of her class.

Issued by
NICOLAS SARONY
84 PICCADILLY
LONDON, W.

Card 397

WILLS'S CIGARETTES

MERCHANT SHIPS OF THE WORLD.
A SERIES OF 50.

48

The White Star Liner "Olympic" is the largest triple-screw steamer in the world. She is four-funnelled, and has a registered tonnage of 46,439. She is one of the White Star "Big Three" sailing from Southampton and Cherbourg for New York. Spaciousness and luxury are the dominant good taste in all the public rooms on board this upper de luxe. She is 852 feet in length, and if placed beside the Woolworth Building, New York, would tower more than too feet above it. Her breadth is 92 feet, depth 59 feet, and her speed 23 knots.

W.D. & H.O. WILLS, BRISTOL & LONDON.

ISSUED BY THE IMPERIAL TOBACCO Co. (OF GREAT BRITAIN & IRELAND) LTD.

Card 398

OCEAN GREYHOUNDS
A Series of 50

12

S.S. "EMPRESS OF BRITAIN": OLYMPIAN POOL.

When swimming in the magnificent Olympian Pool of the *Empress of Britain*, passengers find it difficult to realize that they are on board an ocean liner. Designed by P. A. Staynes and A. V. H. Jones, the bath is constructed of translucent terrazzo glass and teak, the general effect being enhanced by a series of beautiful pillars. Other facilities for recreation are provided on the Sports Deck, which includes a full-sized tennis court, with spectators' galleries. The ship has also squash racket courts, a gymnasium and Turkish baths.

ISSUED BY
OGDEN'S.
BRANCH OF THE IMPERIAL TOBACCO CO. (OF GREAT BRITAIN & IRELAND), LTD.

Card 399

WILLS'S CIGARETTES
23

SHIPS' BADGES
A SERIES OF 50.

SPENSER.

FLOTILLA LEADER, 1,750 TONS.

Guns: 5—4·7 inch, 1—3 inch A.A.

Badge: Part of the Arms of the family of Spencer.

Translation: (Spenser's *Faerie Queene*, III, xi, 54).

22nd Sept. 1917 Present ship launched (first ship of the name).
1918-19 10th Flotilla, Harwich Force.
27th Feb. 1918 In action Schronwen Bank.
23rd April 1918 Part of covering force during the raid on Zeebrugge.

W.D. & H.O. WILLS BRISTOL & LONDON.

ISSUED BY THE IMPERIAL TOBACCO CO. (OF GREAT BRITAIN & IRELAND) LTD.

Card 400

NOTABLE SHIPS
PAST & PRESENT
A SERIES OF 25 REAL PHOTOGRAPHS

No. 21

The Rotor Ship.

The Rotor ship "Buchau," recently invented by Herr Flettner, is propelled by means of rotating cylinders which create, in conjunction with the wind, varying air pressures which thrust the ship forward. The rotors, if spun in reverse directions, quickly turn the ship. They can be controlled by one man, and can also be used in almost any weather, whilst the sailing ship must reef its sails in a storm. Originally a 660 ton schooner, the "Buchau's" old rigging weighed 35 tons; her rotors total only 7 tons and a speed of 8 knots is obtained with them.

CARRERAS
HIGH-CLASS CIGARETTES
ARCADIA WORKS, LONDON, ENGLAND.
ENGLAND'S LARGEST INDEPENDENT MANUFACTURERS OF FINE QUALITY CIGARETTES

Card 401

Wills for Quality

STRANGE CRAFT
A SERIES OF 50

19

A Great Lakes Freighter.

The steamers specially built for service on the Great Lakes of America and Canada are, at first glance, not unlike the Oil Tanker. The Lakes Freighter, however, has her bridge right forward on the bows, and the great length of her hull between this and the funnel makes her appear enormously long. Some of these vessels are 600 feet from stem to stern, though they look odd. They will carry up to 20,000 tons of cargo. The carrying of grain and ore in bulk are the chief occupations of these big Traders of the Lakes.

W.D. & H.O. WILLS
ISSUED BY THE IMPERIAL TOBACCO CO. (OF GREAT BRITAIN & IRELAND), LTD.

Card 402

EVOLUTION OF THE STEAMSHIP

S.S. "KAISER WILHELM DER GROSSE."

Built in 1897. Length 648 feet 7 inches, beam 66 feet, depth 43 feet. Gross tonnage 14,349. Horse-power 28,000.

DUNCAN'S CIGARETTES

DUNCAN & CO. GLASGOW.

PLAYER'S CIGARETTES.

SHIP'S COOK. 1790.

ADMIRAL. TIME OF HENRY VIII.

WILL'S CIGARETTES.

R.M.S. "MAURETANIA"

COPE'S CIGARETTES.

12—Florentine Fishing Boat.

Clipper

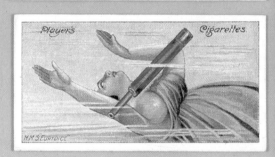

Player's Cigarettes.

H.M.S. EURYDICE

WILLS'S CIGARETTES.

SOUTH CAROLINA

ROTOR SHIP "BUCHAU"

WILLS'S CIGARETTES.

SPENSER

BADGE.

EVERYWHERE BE BOLDE.

MOTTO.

WILLS'S CIGARETTES.

T.S.S. OLYMPIC.

OGDEN'S CIGARETTES

S.S. "EMPRESS OF BRITAIN"—OLYMPIAN POOL

DUNCAN'S CIGARETTES.

WILLS'S CIGARETTES.

A GREAT LAKES FREIGHTER.

CHURCHMAN'S CIGARETTES

PIPES AND FITTINGS

CHURCHMAN'S CIGARETTES

CROSSING QUEBEC BRIDGE, C.N.R.

CHURCHMAN'S CIGARETTES

THE UNION LIMITED

OGDEN'S CIGARETTES

COVENTRY PNEUMATIC RAILCAR

THE "GOLDEN ARROW"

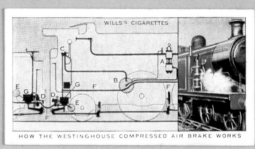

WILL'S CIGARETTES

HOW THE WESTINGHOUSE COMPRESSED AIR BRAKE WORKS

WILL'S CIGARETTES

L.M. & S.R.
HIGH PRESSURE LOCOMOTIVE

Taddy & Co   Railway Locomotives
Cigarettes

SCHOOLS CLASS LEATHERHEAD, SOUTHERN RAILWAY Nº 23

WILL'S CIGARETTES

EXPRESS LOCOMOTIVE, GREAT SOUTHERN RAILWAYS, IRELAND

THE BRIGHTON BELLE
S R

LAMBERT & BUTLER'S CIGARETTES

CALEDONIAN RAILWAY, LOCOMOTIVE 903.

WILL'S CIGARETTES.

STEPHENSON'S LONG BOILER ENGINE 1845.

WILL'S CIGARETTES.

METROPOLITAN RAILWAY

BEAUTIES OF THE CINEMA
A SERIES OF 40 CARDS

LILIAN HARVEY.

Born at Muswell Hill in 1907, but most of her life has been spent in Germany, where she studied dancing, and appeared in revue. Later turned to the screen, her most successful films being "Congress Dances," "Happy Ever After," "My Lips Betray" and "I am Suzanne."

ISSUED BY ROTHMANS LTD.

AND

ASSOCIATED COMPANIES

416

TATLEY'S
VIRGINIA CIGARETTES
MADE IN ENGLAND

FILM STARS
A Series of 32

TATLEY'S renowned Virginia Cigarettes are all made in England. They are the product of a firm that has specialized in Tobacco for over two hundred years. They are specially made for those who really appreciate and require the very best.

TATLEY'S FOR QUALITY

417

WILLS'S CIGARETTES
13
CINEMA STARS
1ST SERIES OF 25

John Gilbert.

Coming of theatrical stock, John Gilbert had a long stage experience before turning to the screen, where he began work as an extra, and since jobs were then few and far between, worked on the technical side of the business as well. Fame was a long time coming, and he played leading rôles without any special distinction until chosen by Elinor Glyn to play in the film version of "His Hour," in which his acting won him immediate fame. Among his later films are "He Who Gets Slapped," "La Bohème," "The Big Parade" and "Twelve Miles Out." Dark haired and brown eyed, he was born in Logan, Utah, U.S.A., on July 10th, 1895, and is 5 ft. 10 ins. high.

W.D. & H.O. WILLS

ISSUED BY THE IMPERIAL TOBACCO CO.
(OF GREAT BRITAIN & IRELAND), LTD.

418

WILLS'S CIGARETTES
7
CINEMA STARS
2ND SERIES OF 25

Priscilla Dean.

The daughter of a professional actress, Priscilla Dean by the time she was four years old, was acting on the stage with her mother. While dancing in the Folies Bergeres in New York, she attracted D. W. Griffith's attention, and played in a series of pictures for him. Then, still in her early teens, she became leading lady in the comedies of Eddie Lyons and Lee Moran. Later, when drama attracted her, she won stardom, and her films include the film version of Ouida's famous novel "Under Two Flags," "Jewels of Desire" and "Birds of Prey." Born in New York in 1896, she has brown hair and eyes, and is 5 ft. 5 ins. tall.

W.D. & H.O. WILLS

ISSUED BY THE IMPERIAL TOBACCO CO.
(OF GREAT BRITAIN & IRELAND), LTD.

419

FILM STARS
A SERIES OF REAL PHOTOS
No. 102

Bing Crosby (PARAMOUNT).

Bing Crosby was born on May 2nd, 1904, in Tacoma, Washington. Real name is Harry Lillis Crosby. He first entered the theatrical profession with two others as "The Three Rhythm Boys." He appeared in the film "The King of Jazz" and then remained in Hollywood, singing in the Cocoanut Grove. Some time later he got his first big part in "The Big Broadcast," and his crooning brought him fame. Has speedily risen to leading roles and some of his best known films are :— "We're Not Dressing," "Mississippi," "Two for To-night" and "Anything Goes."

ISSUED BY

JOHN SINCLAIR LTD
NEWCASTLE - ON - TYNE

420

SHOTS FROM THE FILMS
A SERIES OF 50 CARICATURES
46

"TARZAN ESCAPES" (M.G.M.)

Johnny Weissmuller and Maureen O'Sullivan

Once again that famous character originally created by Edgar Rice Burroughs comes to the screen. In this film we see Tarzan (Johnny Weissmuller), the Olympic swimming champion) and his mate (Maureen O'Sullivan) living happily in the jungle, until a band of traders arrive, who try to take her away from him. However, Tarzan calls the denizens of the jungle to his aid, and triumphs over the intruders. It is interesting to note that Johnny Weissmuller, who is regarded as being as near physical perfection as possible, was so weakly as a child, that he was advised to take up swimming to help him develop his physique.

ISSUED BY

OGDEN'S
BRANCH OF THE IMPERIAL TOBACCO CO.
(OF GREAT BRITAIN & IRELAND), LTD.

421

CINEMA STUDIES
SERIES OF 25

No. 8.
TED WELLS
A Universal Star appearing in "The Riding Demon."

Issued by

NICOLAS SARONY & CO
of 84, PICCADILLY,
LONDON, W.

422

BEAUTIES of TO-DAY

No. 38

JESSIE MATTHEWS

PICTURE BY COURTESY OF GAUMONT BRITISH

A Series of 44 now being issued with these Cigarettes

GODFREY PHILLIPS LTD
AND
ASSOCIATED COMPANIES

423

CINEMA STARS
A SERIES OF 32
No. 1

Marlene Dietrich.

Daughter of a German Cavalry Officer, Marlene Dietrich began as a stage actress. She appeared with great success in several German films, notably "The Blue Angel." Among her other pictures are "Dishonoured," "Morocco," "Shanghai Express," and "The Blonde Venus." Born on December 27th, 1902, in Berlin. Has red hair and blue eyes. Height 5 ft. 5 ins.

ISSUED BY

UNITED KINGDOM TOBACCO Co. Ltd.
LONDON, ENGLAND

424

MURRAY'S CIGARETTES
BATHING BELLES
SERIES OF 40

No. 31
MARY HOWARD.
A Metro-Goldwyn-Mayer player enjoying the breeze and sun shine on the Pacific coast.

ISSUED BY

MURRAY SONS & CO LTD
TOBACCO & CIGARETTE MANUFACTURERS
LONDON & BELFAST

425

STARS OF SCREEN & HISTORY
A SERIES OF 25
20

ANNA NEAGLE AS "NELL GWYN"
(B. & D.)

"Pretty, witty Nell," as Samuel Pepys described her in his famous Diary, began her career as an orange-girl at the Theatre Royal, Drury Lane. But, at the age of sixteen, she was already famous on the stage of that theatre by her creation of leading comedy parts, and she soon gained a wider fame as favourite of King Charles II. In *Nell Gwyn*, her vivacious disposition was delightfully depicted on the screen by Anna Neagle, a versatile actress who has since enhanced her great popularity by her portrayal of Queen Victoria in *Victoria the Great* and *Sixty Glorious Years*. She has recently been in Hollywood, starring in a film based on the heroic story of Nurse Edith Cavell.

STEPHEN MITCHELL & SON
BRANCH OF THE IMPERIAL TOBACCO CO.
(OF GREAT BRITAIN & IRELAND), LTD.

426

FAMOUS FILM STARS
A SERIES OF 54 REAL PHOTOS
No 39

ROBERT MONTGOMERY

Robert Montgomery was born in Beacon, New York, on May 21st, 1904, and educated at the Pawling School in New York. Started as an assistant in theatres and was delighted when given the opportunity to play in small roles. Worked with Stock Companies for eighteen months before appearing on Broadway. First talkie appearance was in "So This is College" and more recent films include: "The First Hundred Years," "Yellow Jack" and "Three Loves Has Nancy."

TOURNAMENT Cigarettes
CHAIRMAN Cigarettes
CHAIRMAN Junior Cigarettes
Manufactured by the Successors to
R. J. LEA LTD. Manchester

427

FILM STARS
SECOND SERIES
29

MARGARET LINDSAY
(Warner-First National)

Born in 1908, in Dubuque, Iowa, Margaret Lindsay is one of a family of five—she has three sisters and one brother. After completing her education, she attended the American Academy of Dramatic Art, and later came to England, where she played in five shows before returning. She then took film tests, and made her début in *The Fourth Horseman*. *Cavalcade* brought her into prominence, for she appeared as the young bride who was drowned on her honeymoon trip in the *Titanic*. Her latest films include *The House on 56th Street*, *Lady Killer*, *Merry Wives of Reno* and *The Dragon Murder Case*.

JOHN PLAYER & SONS
BRANCH OF THE IMPERIAL TOBACCO CO.
(OF GREAT BRITAIN & IRELAND), LTD.

428

CINEMA STARS
A SERIES OF 27
No. 30

Maurice Chevalier.

Born in Menilmontant, Paris, on September 12th, 1893, Maurice Chevalier had a hard life when a child, becoming in turn carpenter's apprentice, printer and doll painter. At the age of eighteen, he was chosen as Mistinguette's dancing partner. His first talkie was "Innocents of Paris." Other talkies, "The Big Pond," "The Smiling Lieutenant," "One hour with You," and "Love Me Tonight."

RICHARD LLOYD & SONS
BRANCH OF
COPE BROS & CO LTD
LIVERPOOL & LONDON.

429

One of this attractive series of 48 Modern Movie Stars and Cinema Celebrities

430

FILM STARS
THIRD SERIES
48

SPENCER TRACY
(Metro-Goldwyn-Mayer)

Born on April 5th, 1900, in Milwaukee, Wisconsin, Spencer Tracy is Irish-American. On leaving college he joined the American Academy of Dramatic Art, and got his first job as a "super" at £5 a week in "R.U.R." After further work he won fame as Killer Mears in "The Last Mile" and then went to Hollywood. He made his film début in 1930 and has since appeared in nearly forty films, winning the annual Academy Award in 1937 for his acting in "Captains Courageous." His latest films are "Test Pilot" and "Boys' Town." His chief interest, apart from films, is polo, and he has his own string of ponies at his San Fernando Valley ranch.

JOHN PLAYER & SONS
BRANCH OF THE IMPERIAL TOBACCO CO.
(OF GREAT BRITAIN & IRELAND), LTD.

431

WILLS'S CIGARETTES.

PRISCILLA DEAN.

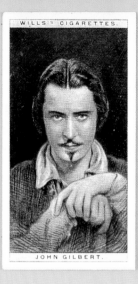

WILLS'S CIGARETTES.

JOHN GILBERT.

JAMES CAGNEY
Warner Bros. & Vitaphone Pictures.

LILIAN HARVEY

JESSIE MATTHEWS

TED WELLS

OGDEN'S CIGARETTES

"TARZAN ESCAPES" M.G.M.

Bing Crosby

Robert Montgomery

MITCHELL'S CIGARETTES

ANNA NEAGLE. B. & D.

Mary Howard

MARLENE DIETRICH

PLAYER'S CIGARETTES

Spencer Tracy

SPENCER TRACY

JULIE SUEDO.

CINEMA STARS

No. 30. MAURICE CHEVALIER.

LLOYD'S CIGARETTES

Player's Cigarettes

Margaret
Lindsay   WARNER - F.N.

Lionel Barrymore

JANE WOODWARD.

DOROTHY LAMOUR.

James Cagney

Lili Damita

PARAMOUNT   Cleopatra

ESTHER RALSTON

CARL BRISSON and ANNY ONDRA in "The Manxman."
British International Pictures.

OLIVIA DE HAVILLAND

"THE MERRY WIDOW"

VIVIENNE OSBORNE.

LEVASSEUR THREATENS M. D'OGERON.

GARY COOPER
PARAMOUNT

MADELEINE CARROLL

Card 432

FILM STARS
A SERIES OF 50
Described by FLORENCE DESMOND
No. 39

JAMES CAGNEY
(Warner Bros. and Vitaphone Pictures)

A torrential downpour was responsible for my first meeting with James Cagney. Unable to get a taxi, and drenched to the skin, I was on my way to the Broadcasting Studio, when, from a passing car, a voice hailed me and offered me a lift. It was James Cagney on his way to broadcast in the same programme. I found him friendly and easy to talk to. He started his stage career in a musical comedy chorus, and after touring for some years started in pictures. James spends his spare time at the Prize Fights; boxing being his favourite sport

CARRERAS LTD
(ESTD. 1788)
ARCADIA WORKS, LONDON. ENGLAND

KEEP THIS ATTRACTIVE SERIES OF ART PICTURES IN THE CARRERAS SLIP-IN ALBUM OBTAINABLE FROM ALL TOBACCONISTS (Price One Penn)

Card 433

FILM STARS
SECOND SERIES OF 54
No. 33.

DOROTHY LAMOUR.
(M.G.M.)

A SERIES OF REAL PHOTOGRAPHS NOW BEING ISSUED WITH THESE CIGARETTES

CARRERAS LTD
ESTD 1788
ARCADIA WORKS, LONDON. ENGLAND

KEEP THIS ATTRACTIVE SERIES OF REAL PHOTOS IN THE CARRERAS SLIP-IN ALBUM OBTAINABLE FROM ALL TOBACCONISTS (Price One Penny)

Card 434

GLAMOUR GIRLS
OF STAGE AND FILMS
A SERIES OF 54
No. 39.

JANE WOODWARD

A SERIES OF REAL PHOTOGRAPHS NOW BEING ISSUED WITH THESE CIGARETTES.

CARRERAS LTD
(ESTD. 1788)
ARCADIA WORKS, LONDON. ENGLAND

KEEP THIS ATTRACTIVE SERIES OF REAL PHOTOS IN THE CARRERAS SLIP-IN ALBUM OBTAINABLE FROM ALL TOBACCONISTS (Price One Penny)

Card 435

SCREEN STARS
SERIES OF 48
NO. 45

LIONEL BARRYMORE
Metro-Goldwyn-Mayer

Barrymore needs no introduction! His latest films are "Ah, Wilderness","The Voice of Bugle Ann". Is soon to be seen in "The Devil Doll", in which he impersonates an old lady), and "The Gorgeous Hussy", (with Crawford). Also scheduled for Silas Marner, which sounds ideal for him.

THIS BACK IS ADHESIVE

GODFREY PHILLIPS LTD.
AND ASSOCIATED COMPANIES

Card 436

CINEMA STARS
A SERIES OF 30
HAND COLOURED PICTURES
No. 29

Esther Ralston

Born at Bar Harbour, Maine, Sept. 17th, 1892, of theatrical parents. She established herself as a "Star" by her portrayal of Mrs. Darling in "Peter Pan," although this was not her first big picture. Miss Ralston is one of the most popular and attractive blondes on the screen to-day, and among her more recent pictures are "The American Venus," "Figures Don't Lie," "Love and Learn," and "Sons of the Sea." Height 5ft. 5ins., with fair hair and blue eyes.

ISSUED WITH
Army Club
CIGARETTES
CAVANDERS LTD
Established, 1775.

Card 437

FAMOUS FILMS
A SERIES OF
27 PHOTOGRAPHS. Nº 26

CLEOPATRA.
PARAMOUNT.

The photograph shows Claudette Colbert in the title rôle and Henry Wilcoxon as Marc Antony in Paramount's "Cleopatra." The film is based on the life and death of Egypt's Queen of Destiny and set against a background of great splendour, the well-known love story of the Queen of Egypt and the Roman soldier is unfolded. This film is one of the most magnificent spectacles ever filmed.

PETER JACKSON
Cigarettes
217, PICCADILLY, W.

Card 438

FILM FAVOURITES
SERIES OF 50

No. 2
LILI DAMITA

Lili Damita, whose home is in Paris, first made her debut in Grand Opera and Ballet. Whilst she was acting in Vienna her talents came to the notice of the Sascha Film Co., who gave her a test, and were so impressed by the result of this that they presented her with a long term contract, her first film being "Red Heels" from the story by Marjory Lawrence. She spent two years making films in Germany, and then proceeded to America, where her English education stood her in good stead in making films for United Artists, her first American film being "The Rescue." Has acted opposite Ronald Colman, Gary Cooper Warren William. In the near future, Lili Damita is to make a film with Jack Buchanan called "Sons of Guns." Hair golden, eyes brown.

ISSUED BY
GODFREY PHILLIPS LTD
AND
ASSOCIATED COMPANIES

Card 439

STARS OF THE SCREEN
A SERIES OF 48
COLOURED PHOTOGRAPHS

No. 4
William Powell
(METRO - GOLDWYN - MAYER.)

Born July 29th, 1892; educated in Pittsburgh. Studied at American Academy of Dramatic Arts. Started on stage at 19, leaving it later for films, playing for Metro-Goldwyn in "Romola," "Moriarty," etc. First appeared in villainous parts, later in suavely humorous roles. Scored great hits in "The Thin Man," "Evelyn Prentice," and "Manhattan Melodrama" with Myrna Loy. Latest pictures : "Escapade" and "Rendezvous." Future films include "After the Thin Man" and "The Great Ziegfeld."

ISSUED BY
GODFREY PHILLIPS LTD
AND ASSOCIATED COMPANIES.

Card 440

SHOTS FROM FAMOUS FILMS
SERIES OF 48. Nº 45

"THE MERRY WIDOW"
A Metro-Goldwyn-Mayer Picture

Maurice Chevalier with Jeannette Macdonald in the film version of Lehar's famous operetta, "The Merry Widow," in which the story has been largely re-written, but the majority of the score retained. The ballroom scene, with hundreds of couples dancing the famous waltz, is a remarkable achievement of direction, and Jeannette Macdonald's fine voice is excellently recorded.

ISSUED BY
GALLAHER LTD
VIRGINIA HOUSE, LONDON & BELFAST

Card 441

MY FAVOURITE PART
SERIES OF 48. No 26

OLIVIA de HAVILLAND
WARNER FIRST NAT. STAR

The picture which I enjoyed making the most was "Four's a Crowd," because it brought me the friendship of Rosalind Russell. In this picture I have an ultra modern rôle, very different from that of Maid Marion in "The Adventures of Robin Hood," and instead of being the sole heroine in the picture, Rosalind Russell and I both engage in difficulties with our respective swains.

Olivia de Havilland

Born Tokyo, Japan. Films include : Call it a Day, Gold is Where You Find It, It's Love I'm After, The Great Garrick, The Adventures of Robin Hood, Four's a Crowd.

ISSUED BY
GALLAHER LTD
VIRGINIA HOUSE, LONDON & BELFAST

Card 442

LOVE SCENES from FAMOUS FILMS
First Series of 25
No. 16
CARL BRISSON AND ANNY ONDRA in "THE MANXMAN"

A masterly film based upon Sir Hall Caine's beautiful and simple story. Carl Brisson plays the part of the lovable, but almost too simple fisherman; Anny Ondra the young wife.

Carl Brisson is Swedish; this is his second film of note, his first being "The Ring."

Anny Ondra is a Czecho-Slovakian and has won for herself a great reputation on the Continent: she will shortly be seen in "Blackmail."
Film Weekly.

Issued with
KENSITAS
CIGARETTES

Manufactured by
J. WIX & SONS, LTD.
174, 5 & 6 Piccadilly - London, W.1

Card 443

A SERIES OF
Prominent Screen Favourites

REPRODUCED FROM ACTUAL PHOTOGRAPHS

Rothmans
LIMITED
5, PALL MALL
LONDON
S.W.1.

Card 444

PORTRAITS OF FAMOUS STARS
SERIES OF 48. Nº 34

MADELEINE CARROLL
(GAUMONT-BRITISH)

Madeleine Carroll is of Franco-British parentage, and was born at West Bromwich, Staffs., in 1906. A graduate of Birmingham University, where she obtained her B.A., she was initially a school teacher at Hove. before making her stage debut in "The Lash." Very soon she was given the principal rôle in the film "Guns of Loos," and her subsequent pictures include "I Was a Spy," "The World Moves On" and "The Thirty-Nine Steps." Here she is depicted as the unhappy queen in the Toeplitz production, "The Dictator"

ISSUED BY
GALLAHER LTD
VIRGINIA HOUSE, LONDON & BELFAST

Card 445

STARS OF SCREEN & STAGE
A SERIES OF 48. Nº 24

GARY COOPER

Gary Cooper was born in America, educated in England, and employed as a newspaper cartoonist in the States before going to Hollywood to begin his film career in 1924 His versatile abilities are shown by his successes in "A Farewell to Arms," "Alice in Wonderland" and "Design for Living." His two latest hits are "Spy 13," with Marion Davies, a story of the early American Wars, and "Now and Forever" with Carole Lombard. He is now in his 34th year.

PARK DRIVE
CIGARETTES
Gallaher Ltd.
VIRGINIA HOUSE, LONDON & BELFAST

Card 446

A SERIES OF 25 Nº 15
CAPTAIN BLOOD
By
RAFAEL SABATINI
Issued with
Morris's
HIGH GRADE CIGARETTES

LEVASSEUR THREATENS M. D'OGERON

The villainous pirate, Levasseur is in love with Mlle. d'Ogeron, daughter of the Governor of Tortuga, whom he kidnaps, together with her brother, and holds for ransom. M. d'Ogeron naturally refuses to leave his sister in the pirate's power, and is threatened with torture by a length of knotted rope wound around his head and tightened. He is saved the terrible pain of this ordeal by the sudden appearance of Captain Blood, who had become suspicious of his partner's movements.

By permission of the Author and with acknowledgments to First National Film Distributors Ltd.

B. MORRIS & SONS LTD.
LONDON, E.1

FILM & STAGE BEAUTIES

REAL PHOTOGRAPHS

A SERIES OF 54

No. 48

ALMA BRAY

A SERIES OF REAL PHOTOGRAPHS NOW BEING ISSUED WITH THESE CIGARETTES

CARRERAS LTD

(ESTD. 1788)

ARCADIA WORKS, LONDON, ENGLAND

KEEP THIS ATTRACTIVE SERIES OF REAL PHOTOS IN THE CARRERAS SLIP-IN ALBUM OBTAINABLE FROM ALL TOBACCONISTS (Price One Penny)

447

FIRST NATIONAL ROSS

No 38

A Series of 50

Famous Film Stars

ARDATH

THE SUPERIOR CORK TIPPED CIGARETTE

State Express 333

LUXURY CIGARETTES

ARDATH TOBACCO CO LTD LONDON

448

CARRERAS

FINE QUALITY CIGARETTES

FILM STARS

Copyright Reserved

MAUREEN O'SULLIVAN

The daughter of an army officer, Maureen moved in Dublin society before she was discovered by Frank Borzage and taken to Hollywood to play in John McCormack's picture "Song O' My Heart." She made her biggest hit in "Tarzan" with Johnny Weissmuller. She has Titian hair and confesses to being a film fan.

M.G.M.

A Series of 72.
Photograph No.º 64

ARCADIA WORKS,
LONDON, ENGLAND.

THIS BACK HAS A GUMMED SURFACE

449

CINEMA CELEBRITIES

SERIES OF 35

No 26

Jean Harlow

Jean Harlow, the original platinum blonde, was born in Kansas City. Her first film for Metro-Goldwyn-Mayer was "The Secret Six." She then appeared in "Beast of the City," "Red Dust," "Hold Your Man," "Blonde Bombshell" and "Dinner at Eight."

THESE CIGARETTES ARE GUARANTEED BEST BRITISH MANUFACTURE

450

451

Film FAVOURITES

No. 10. A Series of 50.

GRACIE FIELDS.

(By courtesy of Bert Aza Ltd.)

You know who this is—Gracie Fields—Britain's Queen of Hearts and a C.B.E. in the 1938 Honours List. Gracie stands for our own particular brand of humour in films, and no woman can play more tricks with her voice; in a flash fine serious singing changes into wildly absurd burlesque. It would hardly be possible for films to have greater success than those in which Gracie Fields appears, and a few for special mention are "Sally in Our Alley", "The Show Goes On" and "He Was Her Man".

CARRERAS LTD

(ESTD. 1788)

ARCADIA WORKS, LONDON, ENGLAND

KEEP THIS ATTRACTIVE SERIES IN THE CARRERAS "SLIP IN" ALBUM, ON SALE AT ALL TOBACCONISTS (Price One Penny)

SCREEN STARS

No. 36

VIVIEN LEIGH

WITH ACKNOWLEDGEMENTS TO LONDON FILMS

A Series of 40 now being issued with these Cigarettes

ABDULLA & Co. Ltd.

173, NEW BOND STREET LONDON. ENGLAND

452

FILM, STAGE AND RADIO STARS

NUMBER 23

WILL HAY

If Will Hay had not been a famous entertainer he might have been one of the country's leading astronomers. Study of the stars is something more than a hobby with him; he is recognized as an authority on the subject, and at his home in South-West London he has his own little observatory. His radio sketches burlesquing school life at St. Michael's are always popular. He is also a great favourite on the "halls" and, being a fully qualified air-pilot, he not infrequently flies to those towns in which he is appearing.

A SERIES OF 50

ARDATH TOBACCO CO. LTD.

Manufacturers of STATE EXPRESS and ARDATH CIGARETTES

453

ACTORS

NATURAL & CHARACTER STUDIES

A SERIES OF 50

30

MATHESON LANG

as Matathias in "The Wandering Jew"

Matheson Lang is one of our most handsome actors, and for that reason has not much inducement to go in for heavy disguise—though his famous Chinese make-up in Mr. Wu showed that he delights in it on occasion. Here, in his Wandering Jew make-up, we have an admirable example of his skill. Notice how clearly the face of Matathias is made to suggest the wisdom, the refinement and the deep weariness of spirit that would come to a man doomed to drag on his existence through centuries of time.

HIGNETT BROS. & Cº

ISSUED BY THE IMPERIAL TOBACCO CO (OF GREAT BRITAIN & IRELAND) LTD.

454

CHAMPIONS OF SCREEN & STAGE

SERIES OF 48. No 40

CAROLE LOMBARD

Carole Lombard first acted when she was twelve, in a silent film, "The Perfect Crime." Later she went on the stage, but returned to the screen to play in "From Hell to Heaven." Her powerful personality has made successes of all her subsequent talkies, which include "The Eagle and the Hawk," "Supernatural" and "White Woman" in which she co-stars with Charles Laughton. This famous actor's portrait is No. 42 in this series. Carole Lombard was born at Fort Wayne, Indiana, in 1909.

PARK DRIVE CIGARETTES

Gallaher Ltd.

VIRGINIA HOUSE, LONDON & BELFAST

455

FILM EPISODES

SERIES OF 48   No 15

"BLACK FURY"

(WARNER)

Paul Muni and Karen Morley in a scene from "Black Fury," a sensational drama in the setting of a coal mine. Paul Muni features as a burly miner, whose sweetheart, Anna, played by Karen Morley, runs away just before their wedding. In his disappointment he gets drunk and instigates a lightning strike. His subsequent adventures in bringing the mine operators to terms make a very exciting story, which is completed with his reconciliation with Anna.

ISSUED BY

GALLAHER LTD

VIRGINIA HOUSE, LONDON & BELFAST

456

SCENES from the FILMS

A SERIES OF 40

No. 13.

Irene Ware and Vic Oliver as they appear in the new British Lion musical "Around the Town." Irene Ware leaped to fame when she won the title "Miss United States." She was at that time a shorthand typist in New York, but her success in the contest quickly brought her offers for stage and film work. (By courtesy of British Lion Film Corp. Ltd.)

ISSUED BY

R. & J. HILL, LTD.

PROPRIETORS OF Hy. Archer & Co. LONDON & BIRMINGHAM

457

FAMOUS FILM STARS

ISSUED BY CARRERAS LIMITED

ARCADIA WORKS LONDON ENGLAND

A SERIES OF 96

LUPE VELEZ

The "Hollywood Fire-brand," was born in Mexico, July 8th, 1910, daughter of an opera singer and an Army officer. Her real name is Guadaloupe Villalobos. She is 5 ft. 5 ins. tall, and has black hair and brown eyes. Films include: "The Broken Wing," "Kongo," "Hot Pepper," "Hot Flame" and "Phantom of the Hollywood Stars, "Hot Heels," rug-making and motoring. Has an adopted daughter.

G.B.

458

FILM PARTNERS

SERIES OF 48. No 30

GERTRUDE LAWRENCE and DOUGLAS FAIRBANKS, Jnr. in "MIMI"

(B.I.P.)

This is the story of the love of a struggling young writer, Rodolph, played by Douglas Fairbanks, Jnr., for Mimi, characterised by Gertrude Lawrence, who becomes the inspiration of his opera. When the opera proves a success, Rodolph is vamped away by an actress until he realises that Mimi is dying from consumption. A very poignant scene takes place when she dies with Rodolph at her bedside. Throughout the film Puccini's original music from La Boheme provides a beautiful background.

ISSUED BY

GALLAHER LTD

VIRGINIA HOUSE, LONDON & BELFAST

459

FAMOUS FILM SCENES

SERIES OF 48. No 10

"THE BAND PLAYS ON"

A METRO-GOLDWYN-MAYER PICTURE

Robert Young and Betty Furness are shown in a scene from "The Band Plays On," a well-depicted romance of American college life. The plot, which develops in an atmosphere of carefree good humour, and also includes some particularly good scenes on the playing fields, describes how four friends all fall in love with the same girl.

ISSUED BY

GALLAHER LTD

VIRGINIA HOUSE, LONDON & BELFAST

460

BRITISH FILM STARS

A SERIES OF 25

4

MADELEINE CARROLL.

Madeleine Carroll is a B.A. of Birmingham University, and began her career as a school teacher at Hove. She went to London to try her luck on the stage, and subsequently toured in The Guns of Loos, a silent film, and since then has become one of the most popular British stars. French-Irish by descent, Madeleine Carroll is of French-Irish birth, with golden hair and blue eyes, and was born in West Bromwich, Feb. 26th, 1906. She made her first appearance on the screen in The Guns of Loos, a silent film, and since then has become one of the most popular British stars. She is married to Capt. Philip Astley, and is the only actress to have been presented at Court while actually appearing on the stage.

W. & A. C. CHURCHMAN

ISSUED BY THE IMPERIAL TOBACCO CO. (OF GREAT BRITAIN & IRELAND) LTD.

461

JEAN HARLOW

Maureen O'Sullivan

LORETTA YOUNG

ALMA BRAY.

HIGNETT'S CIGARETTES

MATHESON LANG

WILL HAY

VIVIEN LEIGH

GRACIE FIELDS

"BLACK FURY"

CAROLE LOMBARD
(M-G-M)

"THE BAND PLAYS ON"

GERTRUDE LAWRENCE
DOUGLAS FAIRBANKS, JNR

Lupe Velez

MADELEINE CARROLL (GAUM. BRIT.)

Player's Cigarettes.

Gallery of Beauty No 45

MISS LETTICE FAIRFAX.

Smoke CHURCHMAN'S Cigarettes.

KINNEAR'S GOLDEN Straight Cut Cigarettes

May Palfrey

LETTICE FAIRFAX.

W. A. & A.C. Churchman

6 Wills's Cigarettes

Mdle Douste.

WILLS's Cigarettes

Miss Shakespere.

Gleo de Berthys

HIGH-CLASS CIGARETTES

PHILLIPS CIGARETTES

Ogden's Cigarettes

MISS SEDOHR RHODES.

OGDEN'S Cigarettes.

462

MURATTI'S

ZINNIA

CIGARETTES

Very Fine

❧ Virginia ❧

463

No 25

Sweet,
Cool,
Fragrant.

"Myrtle Grove"

Tobacco

PACKED IN
1oz. & 2 oz. packets.
¼ lb. ½ lb. & 1lb.
air tight tins.

TADDY & Co LONDON

464

NOTTINGHAM CASTLE
REGISTERED TRADE MARK
GALLERY OF BEAUTY SERIES
A PICTURE from this
Series is included in
each Packet of
Player's Cigarettes.

JOHN PLAYER & SONS, LTD.
CASTLE
TOBACCO FACTORY
NOTTINGHAM.

Series of fifty Pictures

465

KINNEAR'S
KINNEAR LTD.
SEVEN
TRADE SPEARS MARK
LIVERPOOL
CIGARETTES

466

WILLS'S
W.D & H.O WILLS LD
TRADE MARK
Bristol & London
TOBACCO
AND
CIGARETTES

467

BRITISH.
BEAUTIES

REGISTERED

TRADE AK MARK

A. KUIT,
CIGARETTE SPECIALIST
MANCHESTER
LIVERPOOL
SOUTHPORT

468

Salmon & Gluckstein's
RASPBERRY BUDS
CIGARETTES.

BONUS SCHEME.
Return to us, with your
name, and address, post paid
to 41, CLERKENWELL ROAD,
LONDON, E.C.,

100 OF THESE CARDS
and we will send you either
a Saddler's Leather
Cigarette Case, Ladies'
or Gentlemen's Purse,
Sovereign Case, or
Meerschaum and Amber
Cigarette Tube in Case.
STATE WHICH YOU PREFER.

SALMON & GLUCKSTEIN, LTD,
Pioneers of the Smoking
World.

BRANCHES EVERYWHERE
469

WILLS'S
W.D & H.O WILLS LD
TRADE MARK
Bristol & London
Cigarettes

470

Yellow Dwarf
Cigarettes
Sole Makers
LIVERPOOL & LONDON
Am CLARKE & SON
Best 3D Packet
IN THE MARKET

471

WILLS'S
W.D & H.O WILLS LD
TRADE MARK
Bristol & London
Cigarettes

472

FOR THE
PIPE
Churchman's
TORTOISE
SHELL
SMOKING
MIXTURE.

K.832.

473

474

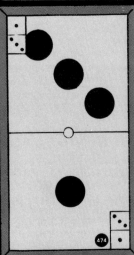

OGDEN'S
WORLD FAMED
TRADE MARK
CIGARETTES
LIVERPOOL
ENGLAND

475

B. 823.

GODFREY
PHILLIPS
& SONS

CIGARETTE
& TOBACCO
MANUFACTURERS

LONDON ENGLAND

476

Smoke
BRISTOL
Navy Cut
CIGARETTES
with
Mouthpieces
10 for 3d
RENOWNED
W·G· AMBER
TIPPED
ROUND or PRESSED
10 FOR 2D

GLASS & Co
BRISTOL.

477

SMOKE
Charlesworth
AND
Austin's
Old Chums
Planters' Pride
SMOKING MIXTURE.

This delightful Mixture has a character entirely its own.

Send P.O **1/6** *for Sample ½ lb. Tin. (Post Free).*

CHARLESWORTH & AUSTIN, LTD.,
319 & 321, Boro', London, S.E.

478

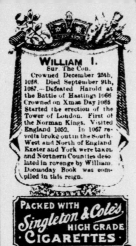

WILLIAM I.
Sur. The Con.

Crowned December 25th, 1066. Died September 9th, 1087.—Defeated Harold at the Battle of Hastings 1066 Crowned on Xmas Day 1066 Started the erection of the Tower of London. First of the Norman Kings. Visited England 1052. In 1067 revolts broke out in the South-West and North of England Exeter and York were taken, and Northern Counties desolated in revenge by William. Doomsday Book was compiled in this reign.

PACKED WITH
Singleton & Cole's
HIGH GRADE
CIGARETTES

479

KINGS & QUEENS OF ENGLAND
A SERIES OF 50. No. 38.

WILLIAM III (1689–1702), King of England and Prince of Orange, was the grandson of Charles I. He married Mary, eldest daughter of James II. In 1688, he was invited by influential Englishmen to bring over an army from Holland to restore the liberties of England. He landed at Torbay, and was joined by many noblemen, and the army of James II melted away. He was proclaimed joint sovereign together with Mary his wife. James II raised an army in Ireland, but was defeated at the battle of the Boyne.

CARRERAS
Virginia

CARRERAS LTD. (ESTD. 1788)

This Back has a Gummed Surface.

480

No. 3
SILVER JUBILEE
1910   SERIES OF 50   1935

H.M. KING EDWARD VII.
At the Coronation, 1902

Born at Buckingham Palace, November 9th, 1841. His Royal Highness succeeded at his birth to the Dukedom of Cornwall His Royal Highness was created Prince of Wales and Earl of Chester, December 8th, 1841, and ascended the throne at the decease of H.M. Queen Victoria, January 22nd, 1901. The solemn and elaborate ceremony of the Coronation took place in Westminster Abbey on August 9th, 1902.

ARDATH POCKET ALBUMS ON SALE AT TOBACCONISTS 1d.

ISSUED BY
ARDATH
THE
Definitely Superior
CORK TIPPED CIGARETTE

481

No 18
WILLS'S Cigarettes

H.R.H.
Princess Henry of Battenberg.

H.R.H. Princess Beatrice Mary Victoria Feodore, youngest daughter of Queen Victoria and the Prince Consort, was born 14th April, 1857. She married 23rd July, 1885, Prince Henry Maurice of Battenberg, who died 20th Jan., 1896. Her only daughter is now Queen of Spain.

W. D. & H. O. WILLS
BRISTOL & LONDON.

ISSUED BY THE IMPERIAL TOBACCO Co
(OF GREAT BRITAIN & IRELAND) Ltd.

482

KINGS & QUEENS OF ENGLAND
A SERIES OF 37
No 15
GODFREY PHILLIPS CIGARETTES

483 **HENRY II.**
succeeded to the English Crown at the age of 21. Energetic, and strong-willed, he was well fitted for the task of bringing England into order.

In 1162 he procured the election of Thomas Beckett to the Archbishopric of Canterbury, but soon quarrelled with him and was the cause of his being slain.

Henry's life was clouded by quarrels with his sons.

GODFREY PHILLIPS, LTD.
LONDON.

THIS SURFACE IS ADHESIVE. ASK YOUR TOBACCONIST FOR THE ATTRACTIVE ALBUM (PRICE ONE PENNY) SPECIALLY PREPARED TO HOLD THE COMPLETE SERIES

KINGS & QUEENS OF ENGLAND
A SERIES OF 50
42
GEORGE IV
(Reigned 1820–30)
(From the painting after Sir T. Lawrence at H.M. Office of Works)
George IV, the son of George III, acted as Regent from 1811–20. A harsh upbringing resulted in dissoluteness and extravagance which lasted all his life. He married in 1785 Mrs. Fitzherbert (whom he was compelled to repudiate) and in 1795 Caroline of Brunswick. Actuated largely by opposition to his father, he was a hindrance rather than a help in public affairs, and was dangerously unpopular, derided by the press and embarrassing to his ministers. But he was brilliantly gifted, cultivated, gracious, a noble patron of art and letters, and in person was the most distinguished monarch since Charles I.

JOHN PLAYER & SONS
BRANCH OF THE IMPERIAL TOBACCO CO
(OF GREAT BRITAIN & IRELAND), Ltd. **484**

CORONATION SERIES
of 50
Elizabeth to Elizabeth
50
H.M. QUEEN ELIZABETH II
H.R.H. Princess Elizabeth Alexandra Mary ascended the throne upon the death of her father, H.M. King George VI, on February 6, 1952. Born April 21, 1926. Married H.R.H. Duke of Edinburgh, Earl of Merioneth and the Baron of Greenwich, on November 20, 1947.

iss..d by
PHILLIP ALLMAN & CO., LTD.
London, W.1
Makers of Fine Cigarettes

485

THIS SURFACE IS ADHESIVE. ASK YOUR TOBACCONIST FOR THE ATTRACTIVE ALBUM (PRICE ONE PENNY) SPECIALLY PREPARED TO HOLD THE COMPLETE SERIES

OUR KING AND QUEEN
A SERIES OF 50
39
AT THE BRUSSELS EXHIBITION, 1935
In July, 1935, the King and Queen (then the Duke and Duchess of York) flew from Hendon to Brussels in an Imperial Airways liner, escorted by the No. 41 (Fighter) Squadron, R.A.F., for the "British Week" of the International Exhibition. This was the first flight made by the Queen. The picture shows Their Majesties walking through Old Brussels at the Exhibition. At a ball held in the British Pavilion, an event which formed the climax of the British Week, the Queen danced with the King of the Belgians, while the King partnered the late Queen Astrid.

W. D. & H. O. WILLS
ISSUED BY THE IMPERIAL TOBACCO CO
(OF GREAT BRITAIN & IRELAND) Ltd. **486**

487
Mills Cigarettes
SERIES OF 25
Kings of England
No. 5

HENRY I (Norman)

Was born in 1068 and came to the Throne in 1100, succeeding his brother, William II. His reign was a period of comparative peace for England. He did much to develop and strengthen the administration, instituting a system of justice throughout the Country and organising the Court of Exchequer. He lost his only son William who was wrecked in the "White Ship" whilst crossing from Normandy to England. He endeavoured to ensure the succession for his daughter Matilda, but on his death in 1135, civil war broke out and the Throne passed to his nephew Stephen.

Issued by
AMALGAMATED TOBACCO CORPORATION Ltd
LUTON, ENGLAND

THIS SURFACE IS ADHESIVE. ASK YOUR TOBACCONIST FOR THE ATTRACTIVE ALBUM (PRICE ONE PENNY) SPECIALLY PREPARED TO HOLD THE COMPLETE SERIES

THE REIGN OF H.M. KING GEORGE V
1910—1935
A SERIES OF 50
50
HER MAJESTY THE QUEEN
The Queen, of whom we give a recent portrait, has shared to the utmost throughout her married life, in those "long and often anxious labours" of which His Majesty spoke last Christmas in the Empire broadcast. There have been few public occasions when the Queen has not been at the King's side ; and beyond this, she has made innumerable charitable causes her own, and lent gracious and unfailing support to the work of women's organisations. Yet while industriously giving herself to the service of the people, Her Majesty has found time also to manage her private household and bring up a family in a way that has won the nation's deep respect as well as its affection.

W. D. & H. O. WILLS
ISSUED BY THE IMPERIAL TOBACCO CO
(OF GREAT BRITAIN & IRELAND) Ltd. **488**

GALLAHER'S

PRINCE ALBERT JOHN OF SCHLESWIG-HOLSTEIN.

Prince Albert John is the eldest surviving son of T.R.H. Prince Frederick Christian Charles of Schleswig-Holstein and Princess Helena, third daughter of Queen Victoria. He was born February 26th, 1869, and was educated at Charterhouse. He is an officer in the 1st Hessian Dragoon Guards.

CIGARETTES

489

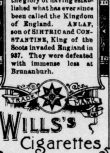

ATHELSTAN.

To ATHELSTAN belongs the glory of having established what has ever since been called the Kingdom of England. ANLAF, son of SIHTRIC and CONSTANTINE, King of the Scots invaded England in 937. They were defeated with immense loss at Brunanburh.

WILLS'S Cigarettes

490

ℰℐℛ
THE NEW ELIZABETHAN AGE

No. 24. HER MAJESTY AND PRINCE CHARLES

A delightfully informal glimpse of the Queen and her son and heir, the young Duke of Cornwall—still better known as Prince Charles, and little known yet as the Duke of Rothesay, his title in the peerage of Scotland. It was in Scotland that this photograph was taken. Her Majesty and the small Duke are looking out of one of the open windows of Balmoral Castle, which is not a State Palace but the Royal Family's private house which the Prince Consort and Queen Victoria built in the "Scottish baronial style", a summer holiday home amid the deer forests of Deeside.

Issued by
MOORGATE TOBACCO CO., LTD. LONDON.

491

Salmon & Gluckstein's
CIGARETTES,
THE BEST IN THE WORLD.

THE holder of six of these pictures can exchange them at any of our branches for a complete and elegant panel of SIX CHROMO LIKENESSES OF
H.M. THE QUEEN,
at various stages in her life, from infancy to the present day.

Salmon & Gluckstein,
LIMITED,
THE PIONEERS OF THE SMOKING WORLD.

BRANCHES EVERYWHERE.

492

Smoke
Taddy's
PREMIER
NAVY CUT.

MILD, MEDIUM & FULL STRENGTHS

PACKED IN 1oz & 2oz Enamelled Tins AND 1oz, 2oz. 4oz. & ½ lb. AIR-TIGHT TINS.

493

H.M. KING EDWARD VII
At His Coronation, 1902

William III

KING
WILLIAM I
ACCESS
1066
DIED
1087

QUEEN VICTORIA
ON HER CORONATION. AGE. 19

PLAYER'S CIGARETTES

GEORGE IV

HENRY II.
BORN: 1133. CROWNED: DEC. 19. 1154.
DIED: JULY 6. 1189. AGE 56.

WILLS'S CIGARETTES.

H.R.H. PSS. HENRY OF BATTENBERG.

ROYALTY SERIES No 25.

Prince Albert John
OF SCHLESWIG HOLSTEIN.

WILLS'S CIGARETTES

HER MAJESTY THE QUEEN

HENRY I

WILLS'S CIGARETTES

AT THE BRUSSELS EXHIBITION

"Royalty" Series No 2

Her Majesty The Queen

Her Most Gracious Majesty
QUEEN VICTORIA. Feb 10. 1840.
BRIDAL.

Copyrighted by
SALMON & GLUCKSTEIN LTD

ATHELSTAN. 925-940.

Player's Cigarettes

The Queen of Sheba

Nº 13.

WARREN HASTINGS, 1733-1818.

CHURCHMAN'S CIGARETTES

G. F. ROBEY

M. CURIE.

EXTRACTING RADIUM FROM PITCHBLEND.

SIR THOMAS LIPTON

CAPTAIN FITZROY.

MITCHELL'S CIGARETTES

EARL JELLICOE

MITCHELL'S CIGARETTES

THE MARQUIS OF MONTROSE

Owen Glendower

PLAYER'S CIGARETTES

THE PERSIAN AMBASSADOR, 1819

PLAYER'S CIGARETTES.

ALICK P. F. RITCHIE

Rt. Hon. J. RAMSAY MACDONALD.

Mr. H. G. WELLS.

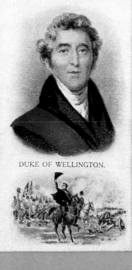

DUKE OF WELLINGTON.

LAMBERT & BUTLER'S CIGARETTES

JOE LOSS

ALBUMS FOR CHURCHMAN'S PICTURE CARDS CAN BE OBTAINED FROM TOBACCONISTS AT ONE PENNY EACH

"IN TOWN TO-NIGHT"
A SERIES OF 50

36

G. F. ROBEY
Old Time Butler

Descended from one of the oldest families of gentlemen's gentlemen, Mr. G. F. Robey is seen here decanting some wine. His grandfather was butler to the Duke of Wellington, and his great-grandfather and great-great-grandfather were also butlers. In 1877, when only twelve years of age, he became a page to Lord John Russell at Pembroke Lodge, Richmond Park, and waited on many celebrities, including Gladstone and Disraeli. In those days the butler was indeed master of the household, control of house and servants being entirely in his hands. Mr. Robey has served three peers, three knights, and a Grandee of Spain

W.A. & A.C. CHURCHMAN
ISSUED BY THE IMPERIAL TOBACCO CO. OF GREAT BRITAIN & IRELAND, LTD. **494**

BUILDERS OF THE EMPIRE
A SERIES OF 50 AUTHENTIC PORTRAITS

495

WARREN HASTINGS.
1733—1818.

1750, went to India and attracted the attention of Clive at Plassey, by whom he was employed in Diplomatic Missions. 1773, at a very critical period made first Governor-General of India, and succeeded beyond all expectations in saving British India from Hyder Ali and the French. He organised native states and subdued the hostile ones; building the foundation of our vast Empire in the East, and saving all that Clive had so gallantly won. He lived to see his plans for the security of India publicly applauded.

WILLS'S CIGARETTES.

A SERIES OF TWENTY-FIVE
FAMOUS BEAUTIES
FROM DRAWINGS BY A.K. MACDONALD
2
THE QUEEN OF SHEBA

Of surpassing beauty, Balkis, as the Queen of Sheba was known to the Arabs, ruled a powerful and wealthy people whose commercial importance attracted many Jewish traders. From these the Queen heard many tales of the greatness and wisdom of Solomon—"And she came to Jerusalem with a very great train, with camels that bore spices, and very much gold, and precious stones." She was greatly impressed by the magnificence of Solomon's court, and by the wisdom of the king himself, who solved all her problems. According to Arabic legends, Balkis bore Solomon a son named Menelek or David, who became King of Abyssinia. It is from this offspring of Solomon that the Abyssinians claim descent.

JOHN PLAYER & SONS
BRANCH OF THE IMPERIAL TOBACCO CO. (OF GREAT BRITAIN & IRELAND). LTD. **496**

A GALLERY OF 1935
A SERIES OF 50

10
EARL JELLICOE

John Rushworth Jellicoe, who was born in 1859, was the son of Capt. J. H. Jellicoe and entered the Navy in 1872. He was Commander in H.M.S. *Victoria* when she was rammed and sunk with appalling loss of life during manoeuvres in 1893. At the attempted relief of the Peking Legations in 1900 he commanded the naval brigade and was severely wounded. Commander-in-Chief of the Grand Fleet, 1914-16, he fought the Battle of Jutland, and at the close of hostilities in 1918 he was raised to the Peerage; he also received a grant of £50,000 and the thanks of the nation. On his return from New Zealand, where he was Governor-General, 1920-24, he was created an Earl. He died in November, 1935, and lies buried in St. Paul's Cathedral, near the tomb of Nelson.

STEPHEN MITCHELL & SON
ISSUED BY THE IMPERIAL TOBACCO CO. OF GREAT BRITAIN & IRELAND, LTD **497**

No. 23
NOTABLE M.P.s
A SERIES OF 50.

CAPTAIN FITZROY.

As Speaker of the House of Commons he presides over its sittings, represents it, controls its procedure and stands by its privileges. The first Commoner in the land. A tall, imposing figure who has royal Stuart blood in his veins. A former Guardsman who fought in France. For many years Deputy Chairman of Ways and Means. An M.P. since 1900 who now represents Daventry.

CARRERAS
HIGH-CLASS CIGARETTES
ARCADIA WORKS, LONDON, ENGLAND.
ENGLAND'S LARGEST INDEPENDENT MANUFACTURERS OF FINE QUALITY CIGARETTES
ESTABLISHED 1788
498

A Series of over 500 SUBJECTS being issued

SWEET CROP SMOKING MIXTURE

a most DELICIOUS SMOKE always reliable · in packets.

COHEN, WEENEN & Co
LONDON **499**

INVENTORS
AND THEIR INVENTIONS SERIES.

NO. 15

M. CURIE.

One of the most interesting discoveries of recent years is that of Radium, which, after long and costly experiments, M. PIERRE CURIE, of Paris, in conjunction with his wife and M. BEMONT, succeeded in separating from pitchblend in 1902. This substance is self-luminous, and constantly emits heat and energy with many remarkable effects.
The Nobel Prize was awarded to M. & Madame CURIE in 1903.
M. CURIE was killed by an accident in Paris, 1906.

Issued by
R. & J. HILL, Ltd.
Pipe Mixture Specialists
LONDON. **500**

DANDIES
FROM PAINTINGS BY CHRISTOPHER CLARK R.I.
A SERIES OF 50

501

39
THE SENSATION OF 1819.

His Excellency the Persian Ambassador with his gorgeously-coloured national costume of silks, satins and furs, made quite a stir when he rode in Hyde Park on his white Arabian. He was quite the lion of the season in spite of his quarrel with the Prince Regent. He demanded precedence over all other Ambassadors, and when this was not allowed, refused to appear at court. When apologising to the Regent for this disrespect, the Ambassador explained that he had been instructed by his sovereign to go first, but when in London he found himself placed last. Pointing to his head, he said *Now this very bad for me when I go back to Persia.*

ISSUED BY
JOHN PLAYER & SONS
BRANCH OF THE IMPERIAL TOBACCO CO. (OF GREAT BRITAIN & IRELAND). LTD.

This Back has a Gummed Surface.

502

CELEBRITIES OF BRITISH HISTORY
A SERIES OF 50 No. 4
OWEN GLENDOWER
(circa 1354—1416)
(Based on the engraving of his Seal in Archæologia).

Descended from Llewellyn, last Welsh Prince of Wales, Glendower was the soul of Welsh nationalism in the fourteenth century. A quarrel with Lord Grey made him renounce his allegiance to Henry IV, and much skirmishing followed. Grey and Sir Edmund Mortimer were captured, and induced by the fierce Celt to marry two of his daughters. Mortimer's kinsman Percy (Hotspur) joined the coalition against Henry IV, who crushed the rebellion at the battle of Shrewsbury. Legend ascribes magical powers to Glendower, who died unsubdued, defying England to the last.

CARRERAS LTD
(ESTD. 1788)
ARCADIA WORKS, LONDON, ENGLAND.
KEEP THIS HISTORICAL SERIES OF 50 PORTRAITS IN THE ATTRACTIVE ALBUM OBTAINABLE FROM ALL TOBACCONISTS (PRICE ONE PENNY)

FAMOUS SCOTS
A SERIES OF 50

12
James Graham, 1st Marquis of Montrose (1612-1650).

Returning from abroad in 1637, Montrose was coldly received by Charles I. In opposition to Argyll he went over to the Royalist side, and with the aid of some of the Highland clans gained brilliant victories for the King, including Inverlochy, Alford and Kilsyth. After his defeat at Philiphaugh in 1645, Montrose retired to the Continent, but in 1650 he returned to Scotland and was defeated at Carbisdale. The picture shows him endeavouring to reach Caithness in disguise, but he was betrayed by Macleod of Assynt, conveyed to Edinburgh and hanged there. His remains received a state funeral of great splendour.

ISSUED BY
STEPHEN MITCHELL & SON
BRANCH OF THE IMPERIAL TOBACCO CO. OF GREAT BRITAIN & IRELAND, LTD. **503**

DANCE BAND LEADERS
A SERIES OF 25

16
JOE LOSS

Joshua Alexander Loss, who was born in London in 1909, commenced studying the violin at seven. He wanted to be a serious musician, but was quick to see the possibilities of a dance band combination, and directed his ambition in this direction. His first engagement was at the Tower, Blackpool; he is now at the Astoria Dance Salon, London. Seven years ago he formed his own combination, which broadcasts at regular intervals. Two of his band's most popular recent numbers are *The Wheel of the Wagon* and *Dinner for One, please James*, while he considers the fox-trot the most popular dance. Joe Loss believes in physical fitness—the twelve members of his orchestra spend as much time as possible in the gymnasium.

LAMBERT & BUTLER
ISSUED BY THE IMPERIAL TOBACCO CO. OF GREAT BRITAIN & IRELAND, LTD **504**

Builders of the British Empire
No. 25

505

Arthur Wellesley, Duke of Wellington, 1769-1852.

Wellington, born in Ireland in the same year as his great adversary, Napoleon, owes his fame as a military commander to the brilliant campaign in the Peninsula. He finally broke Napoleon's power in 1815 at the glorious Battle of Waterloo, where British bravery and a general's judgment laid low the flower of France. As a statesman Wellington's honesty and resolution won him respect and trust, and for twenty-five years England looked to him for guidance.

SMOKE
TRAWLER, CRITIC, CLUB MEMBER
CASKET CIGARETTES

J. A. PATTREIOUEX MANCHESTER

ESTD. 1788
CARRERAS
HIGH-CLASS CIGARETTES

A SERIES OF 25
FAMOUS MEN.

No. 16

H. G. Wells.

This thought-stimulating and prolific writer was born in 1866, and spent his youth under varying conditions, many of his experiences being embodied in his books. He is a B.Sc. of London University, and published his first books in 1895. The future has always had a great fascination for him, and several of his earlier books deal with possible development of a scientific nature. He has poured out an unceasing stream of works, and has found time to produce his "Outline of History," a fascinating sketch of Universal History which won general praise. His great three-volume novel, "The world of William Clissold" was published in 1926.

CITY ROAD
LONDON E.C.I. **506**

507

STRAIGHT LINE CARICATURES
A SERIES OF 50.

40
Rt. Hon. J. Ramsay MacDonald, M.P.

There is an impressive dignity about the fine-shaped head, with its wavy greyish hair, set squarely on broad shoulders. Of late years the worries of office have aged him. He is a thinker and something of a dreamer, a visionary with a statesman's mind. An idealist who does not believe in forcing events, he has often been in conflict with the more impatient rank and file of his party. Although he is confident in debate and eloquent in speech, the listener is impressed more by his warmth of feeling and sincerity than by his brilliance or wit.

ISSUED BY
JOHN PLAYER & SONS
BRANCH OF THE IMPERIAL TOBACCO CO. (OF GREAT BRITAIN & IRELAND) LTD.

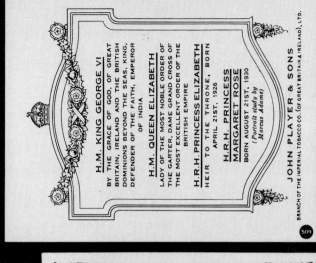

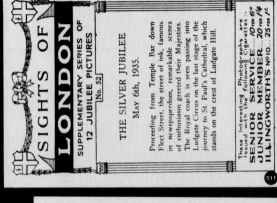

514

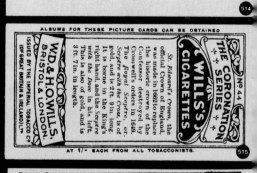

THE ROYAL FAMILY

THE SILVER JUBILEE. MAY 6th, 1935.

THE BRACELETS

MITCHELL'S CIGARETTES

THE UNITED KINGDOM GOVERNMENT PAVILION

SALMON & GLUCKSTEIN'S CIGARETTES

THE SWORD OF STATE

CORONATION 1911.

WILLS'S Cigarettes.

PRINCE CHARLES OF DENMARK.

CORONATION SER. N° 25.

WILLS'S CIGARETTES.

CORONATION REGALIA, 3.

CHURCHMAN'S CIGARETTES

A RAILODOK CAR

38 HONG KONG

PLAYER'S CIGARETTES

HER MAJESTY QUEEN ELIZABETH

THE BRITISH TEXTILES BUILDING

Mr Micawber.   David Copperfield.

Diana Vernon.

10.

34: That's an ill phrase, a vile phrase; 'beautified' is a vile phrase.

Players Cigarettes

BYRON.

WILLS'S CIGARETTES

ROSSINI

PLAYER'S CIGARETTES.

OF THE DOG AND THE ASS.

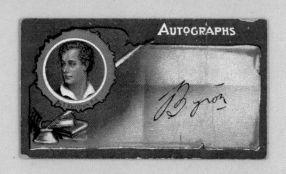

AUTOGRAPHS

Byron

PLAYER'S CIGARETTES.

LADY SANGAZURE

THE SORCERER.

FAUST

S.C.W.S. LTD CIGARETTES

THE TWA BRIGS AYR

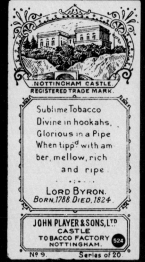

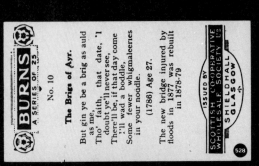
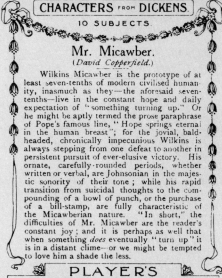
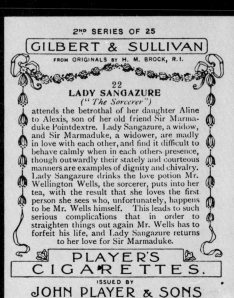

537

Wills's Cigarettes

A. J. Cronin

Player's Cigarettes.

David Copperfield.

CARRERAS CIGARETTES

Pied Piper.

PLAYER'S CIGARETTES

TRILBY.
"TRILBY."

15

Nº 45. THE CROWN.

CONAN DOYLE CHARACTERS

DAME ERMYNTRUDE LORING

COPE'S CIGARETTES

MR. SETH PECKSNIFF

(Kipling Series.)
"EACH OF 'EM DOING HIS
COUNTRY'S WORK."

GRENADIER CIGARETTES.
W. & F. Faulkner Ltd London. S.E.

Player's Cigarettes.

Dobbin
Vanity Fair.

PLAYER'S CIGARETTES

THE BIRTHPLACE. A CORNER OF THE MUSEUM.

The Taming of the shrew. Act. IV.
Scene III.
PETRUCHIO. Why, what, I'devil's name,
tailor, call'st thou this?

15. Hullo, my covey! What's
the row? I suppose you don't
know what a beak is, my flash
com-pan-ion.

Wills's Cigarettes.

"Boy and Rabbit." Sir Henry Raeburn, R.A.

Collins. Rustic Civility.

Landseer. A Highland Scene.

Velasquez. Surrender of Breda.

Morland. First September.

The Last Match.

Offices of the
Port of London
Authority

WILL'S CIGARETTES.
GLAMIS CASTLE.

Dunvegan Castle
FAIRWEATHER'S CIGARETTES

CHURCHMAN'S CIGARETTES.
West Gate, Canterbury.

COLLINS' CIGARETTES.
Homes of England Series—No. 4.

TOWER OF LONDON

CHURCHMAN'S CIGARETTES
WELLS CATHEDRAL.

CHURCHMAN'S CIGARETTES.
A NATIVE HUT, CENTRAL AFRICA.

TAJ MAHAL, AGRA.

WILL'S CIGARETTES.
MOSCOW.

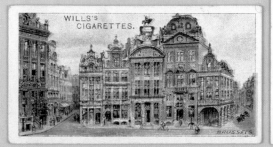
WILL'S
CIGARETTES.
BRUSSELS.

Wills's Cigarettes
The Admiralty Arch, Charing Cross

PLAYER'S CIGARETTES.

DOORWAY. CLONFERT CATHEDRAL.

Wills's Cigarettes

The Talbot, Chaddesley Corbett, Worcestershire

WILLS'S CIGARETTES.

CHEQUERS.

PLAYER'S CIGARETTES.

BOOTHAM BAR, YORK.

WILLIAM'S Cigarettes

Post Office Rangoon

THE GEORGE SALISBURY.

Albert Memorial.

Ogden's Cigarettes

Lichfield Cathedral

MITCHELL'S CIGARETTES.

JOHN HOWARD.

MIDDLE TEMPLE HALL AND GARDENS

WILLS'S CIGARETTES.

RHEIMS.

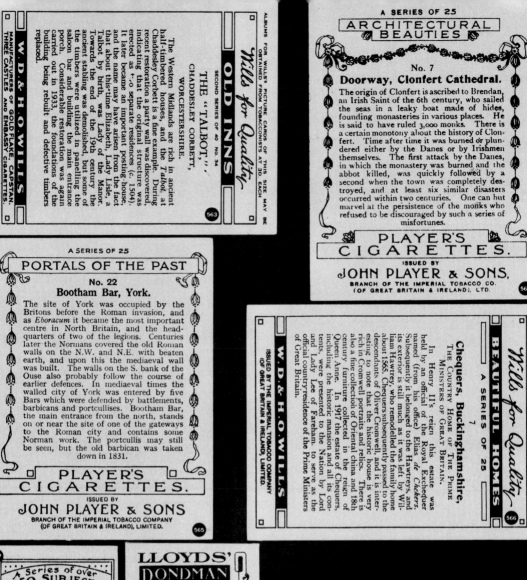

575

VIEWS OF INTEREST

FIFTH SERIES

REAL PHOTOGRAPHS.

No. 214

FORTH BRIDGE, SCOTLAND.

Here is a glimpse of one of the greatest engineering wonders of the world, and perhaps the size of the structure will be better realised when it is remembered that the height of each cantilever is about four feet less than St. Paul's Cathedral, London. The Forth Bridge was begun in 1882 and seven years elapsed before traffic used it. Two railway tracks are carried, and it is slightly over 1½ miles in length. The anchorage of St. Margaret's Hope, with the naval base of Rosyth, lies off the shore of Fife immediately to the west of the Forth Bridge.

(Photograph: Photochrom copyright.)

ISSUED WITH

SUNRIPE & SPINET OVAL CIGARETTES.

R. & J. HILL, Ltd.

SHOREDITCH, LONDON, E.1 & BIRMINGHAM

THE THAMES
FROM LECHLADE TO LONDON
A SERIES OF 50
40

WINDSOR CASTLE.

Undoubtedly the finest situated Royal residence in the world. There is no better view than that from the river. Windsor is associated with the record of all the reigns since the Norman Conquest. The terminus of branch lines of the G.W.R. and L. & S.W.R.; and also well served by the Oxford and Kingston steamers—two leaving in the morning, and two in the afternoon.

576

A Series of 12

VIEWS OF CHESTER

W. WILLIAMS & Co.

CHESTER.

ISSUED BY THE IMPERIAL TOBACCO CO. (OF GREAT BRITAIN & IRELAND.)

577

578

HOLIDAYS IN BRITAIN

A SERIES OF 48

34

WHITLEY BAY, NORTHUMBERLAND

One of the most popular holiday resorts between the Tees and the Forth, Whitley Bay revels in a pure North Sea air, miles of gleaming, tide-washed sands, long, sweeping promenades with wide sea-views and grassy links, and parks and gardens where masses of flowers bloom all the year round. Boating, bathing, children's paddling-pool, tennis, bowls, dancing, cinemas and concerts are all available. Whitley Bay, which is only a few miles from Newcastle, is an excellent centre for Alnwick, Bamburgh and Warkworth castles, Lindisfarne, Hexham Abbey and the Roman Wall, in addition to Otterburn, Rothbury, Wooler and all the historic interests and charms of Northumberland.

W. A. & A. C. CHURCHMAN

BRANCH OF THE IMPERIAL TOBACCO CO. (OF GREAT BRITAIN & IRELAND), LTD.

ALBUMS FOR CHURCHMAN'S PICTURE CARDS CAN BE OBTAINED FROM TOBACCONISTS AT ONE PENNY EACH

ISSUED BY THE SUCCESSORS IN THE UNITED KINGDOM TO THE

Westminster Tobacco Co. London

NEW ZEALAND
FIRST SERIES of 36
No. 30.

General Assembly Library, Wellington.

In this library, which adjoins the Parliament buildings, are kept all the latest books and publications of reference that may be required by the members of the Government and officials of the Parliamentary services. The present building is the surviving wing of the old Parliament House which was destroyed by fire.

579

580

WINGS OVER THE EMPIRE

A SERIES OF 48 AERIAL VIEWS

45

SYDNEY HARBOUR BRIDGE, AUSTRALIA

Rising high above Sydney's magnificent harbour, this great steel arch is indeed a triumph of British engineering. It stretches 1,650 ft., from Milsons Point to Dawes Point, linking Sydney proper with the newer residential neighbourhood of North Sydney. The great arch was built out over the water in two portions, the enormous weight of steelwork being taken by wire cables anchored at the rear of the shore pylons. Sydney's increasing prosperity is largely due to its wonderful natural harbour, which ranks with the great ports of the world.

W. A. & A. C. CHURCHMAN

BRANCH OF THE IMPERIAL TOBACCO CO. (OF GREAT BRITAIN & IRELAND), LTD.

ALBUMS FOR CHURCHMAN'S PICTURE CARDS CAN BE OBTAINED FROM TOBACCONISTS AT ONE PENNY EACH

OVERSEAS DOMINIONS (CANADA)

WILLS'S CIGARETTES

ISSUED BY THE IMPERIAL TOBACCO CO. (OF GREAT BRITAIN & IRELAND) LTD.

W.D. & H.O. WILLS

BRISTOL & LONDON.

No. 10

Ottawa.

Few of the capital cities of the world can surpass Ottawa for its commanding situation and the beauty of its surroundings. Our picture shows the imposing Parliament buildings on the left, and on the extreme right the new Central Station of the Grand Trunk Railway. Ottawa is a city of natural beauty, beautiful natural parks and splendid roadways. The "Canadian Government Commission superintends the laying-out of new roads and parks.

581

582

ISSUED BY THE SUCCESSORS IN THE UNITED KINGDOM TO THE

Westminster Tobacco Co. London

AUSTRALIA
FIRST SERIES of 36
No. 33.

Art Gallery, Sydney.

The Art Gallery, Sydney, has a most valuable collection, not only of Australian art, but also excellent examples of the world's most famous artists.

OVERSEAS DOMINIONS (AUSTRALIA)

WILLS'S CIGARETTES

ISSUED BY THE IMPERIAL TOBACCO CO. (OF GREAT BRITAIN & IRELAND) LTD.

W.D. & H.O. WILLS

BRISTOL & LONDON.

No. 29

Perth, West Australia.

Perth, the capital of Western Australia, has a population of 106,792 (1911). It is built on the right bank of the estuary of the beautiful Swan River, and is 12 miles from Fremantle. The surrounding district is remarkable for the profusion of wild flowers growing there. In recent years the development of the West Australian goldfields has caused a rapid increase in the population and prosperity of the capital city.

584

A series of 24

Chinese Scenes

issued with

"MY PRINCESS" CIGARETTES

MADE IN LONDON

BY

United Kingdom Tobacco Co Ltd

585

586

VIEWS OF LONDON

A SERIES OF 27 REAL PHOTOS

No. 21

The Albert Memorial.

This national monument to Prince Albert of Saxe-Coburg-Gotha, the consort of Queen Victoria, is situated in Kensington Gardens opposite the Royal Albert Hall, and near the site occupied by the Great Exhibition of 1851. Designed by Sir G. Gilbert Scott, it was opened in 1872. The statue by Foley was unveiled in 1876, and is seated beneath a Gothic spire 175 feet high.

CARRERAS

HIGH-CLASS CIGARETTES

ARCADIA WORKS, LONDON, ENGLAND.

ENGLAND'S LARGEST INDEPENDENT MANUFACTURERS OF HIGH QUALITY CIGARETTES.

FORTH BRIDGE, SCOTLAND

CHURCHMAN'S CIGARETTES

WHITLEY BAY, NORTHUMBERLAND

CHURCHMAN'S CIGARETTES

SYDNEY HARBOUR BRIDGE, AUSTRALIA

ART GALLERY, SYDNEY

THE ALBERT MEMORIAL

14 CHINA. A STREET SCENE, HONG KONG

Gov.t House, Calcutta.

LAMBERT & BUTLER'S CIGARETTES.

WINDSOR CASTLE.

WILLIAMS' CIGARETTES.

GROSVENOR BRIDGE, CHESTER.

GENERAL ASSEMBLY LIBRARY, WELLINGTON.

WILLS'S CIGARETTES.

OTTAWA.

View of The Alhambra Granada Spain.

ISSUED BY F. & J. SMITH, GLASGOW.   SERIES I. No 7.

WILLS'S CIGARETTES.

PERTH.

Arms of University of London.

BRITISH COLUMBIA

Arms of The British Empire

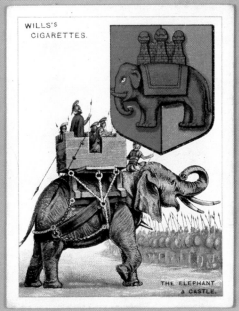

THE ELEPHANT & CASTLE.

King Edward's School, Birmingham

"HERALDRY" SERIES I.　　No. 10. DUKE OF LEINSTER.

CROM A BOO

ARMS OF THE BISHOPRIC, CASHEL.

BERMUDA.

ARMS OF THE BRITISH EMPIRE.

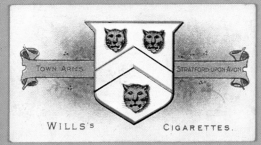

TOWN ARMS　　STRATFORD-UPON-AVON

WILL'S CIGARETTES

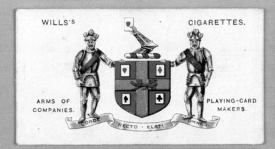

ARMS OF COMPANIES.　　PLAYING-CARD MAKERS.

ARMS OF FOREIGN CITIES.

COPENHAGEN.

HENRY I　　MATILDA OF SCOTLAND

LAMBERT & BUTLER'S CIGARETTES.

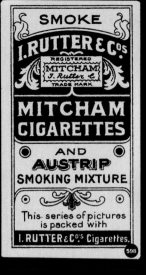

599

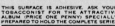

THIS SURFACE IS ADHESIVE. ASK YOUR
TOBACCONIST FOR THE ATTRACTIVE
ALBUM (PRICE ONE PENNY) SPECIALLY
PREPARED TO HOLD THE COMPLETE SERIES

NATIONAL FLAGS
AND ARMS

A SERIES OF 50

22

IRAN

The national flag of Iran—
for many years known also as
Persia—is a tricolour of grass
green, white and red. The emblem is the lion and the sun, the
lion being shown standing up
and holding a sword in his dexter
forepaw. The flag flown on
government buildings and for
government use generally carries
the lion and scimitar in the centre
on the white ground. The Army
flag, however, bears the emblem,
complete with crown and wreath,
in the centre upon the green,
white and red.

JOHN PLAYER & SONS

BRANCH OF THE IMPERIAL TOBACCO CO
(OF GREAT BRITAIN & IRELAND), LTD.

600

WILLS'S CIGARETTES

14

FLAGS OF
THE EMPIRE

A SERIES OF 25.

Flag of the Dominion of
Canada.

The Arms of the Dominion
of Canada, as granted by the
Royal Proclamation of November 21, 1921, are as follows—
the first quarter has the three
lions of England, the second
quarter the red lion of Scotland, the third quarter the harp
of Ireland, and the fourth the
fleurs-de-lis of France. Below
these on a silver field appear
the three maple leaves of
Canada. The fleurs-de-lis are a
reminder of the part played by
French explorers and colonists
in the history of Canada.

Our picture shows signal
flags flying at the yard-arm of
a war-ship.

602

ISSUED BY THE IMPERIAL TOBACCO Co
(OF GREAT BRITAIN & IRELAND) LTD

THE ALLIES FLAGS

SERIES OF 25. No. 20

603 If you cannot obtain Gallaher's
Cigarette Card Albums
from your Tobacconist,

GALLAHER, LTD. BELFAST

will send you one, postage paid,
for 1/- or in exchange for 100
Whole Coupons.

Coupons may be obtained in the
following brands

"Gold Plate" Cigarettes.
"Park Drive" Cigarettes.
"Gold Plate" Navy Cut Tobacco.
"Gallaher's Two Flakes"
Tobacco.
"Gallaher's Rich Dark
Honeydew."

The above Tobaccos are packed in
1, 2, 4 and 8 oz. Tins.

ISSUED BY
GALLAHER LTD
BELFAST & LONDON

HILL'S

NATIONAL FLAG
SERIES
No 17

Issued only
by
R. J. Hill Ltd. Estd 1775
Badminton Tobacco Factories
LONDON.

"OCEANIC"
Tobaccos

NAVY CUT
AND
NAVY MIXTURE
are
a luxury in the Pipe
Give them a Trial.

604

Series of 50

No 21

CAPE COLONY.

This is one of the few
British Colonies which
possess a genuine coat
of arms, these being as-
signed by Royal Warrant
in 1876. The annulet
are taken from the arms
of Van Riebeeck, the
founder of the Colony,
these appearing also in
the Dutch Grant of 1804
to Cape Town. The one
supporter is a gnu, and
the other a gemsbuck or
oryx.

ISSUED BY
John Player & Sons

BRANCH OF THE IMPERIAL
TOBACCO COMPANY (OF GREAT
BRITAIN & IRELAND) LIMITED

NOTTINGHAM.

605

606

607

EDWARDS, RINGER & BIGG
LIMITED

CIGARETTES.
BRISTOL.
FLAGS OF ALL NATIONS.
1st Series. 25 Countries.

TRADE MARK   TRADE MARK

608

PERSIA.
(KINGDOM.)

Capital: Teheran.

Area: 628,000 sq. miles.
Pop.: estimated 10,000,000.

From the Arab conquest right
down to modern times the story
of Persia is an almost unbroken
record of massacres and wars.
Persia was an original member
of the League of Nations.
The present century witnessed
the growth of a strong nation-
alist movement, and increasing
discontent with the corrupt and
incompetent administration of
the government of the ex-Shah.
In 1925 the ruler was deposed,
and the Prime Minister, Riza
Khan Pahlevi, who is one of
the most remarkable characters
of modern times, became Shah.

ISSUED BY
John Player & Sons

FLAGS OF THE
LEAGUE OF NATIONS

A SERIES OF 50.

39

BRANCH OF THE IMPERIAL TOBACCO CO.
OF GREAT BRITAIN & IRELAND), LTD.

UNITED STATES of AMERICA

SCOTLAND.

GALLAHER'S CIGARETTES.

WILLS'S CIGARETTES.

DOMINION OF CANADA

EGYPT

PLAYER'S CIGARETTES

IRAN

Kensitas Cigarettes

ALBANIA

A SERIES OF 60 NATIONAL FLAGS. NO. 47.

PERSIA
IMPERIAL STANDARD

PLAYER'S CIGARETTES.

SPES · BONA

CAPE COLONY.

FLAG.

PLAYER'S CIGARETTES

PERSIA.

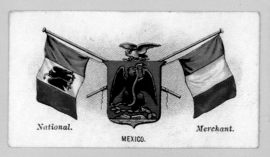

National.

Merchant.

MEXICO.

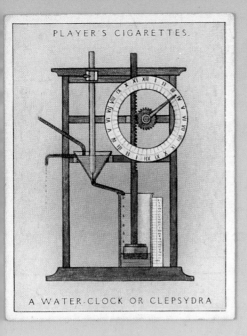

PLAYER'S CIGARETTES.

A WATER-CLOCK OR CLEPSYDRA

WILLS'S CIGARETTES

SÈVRES INKSTAND

OLD POTTERY AND PORCELAIN.
(GERMAN)

Nº 114. DRESDEN.

OLD POTTERY AND PORCELAIN.
(ENGLISH)

FELL. SEWELL & DONKIN.
Sheriff Hill Pottery.

Nº 155. NEWCASTLE.

WILLS'S CIGARETTES.

CANDLESTICK, SNUFFERS, ETC.

OLD POTTERY AND PORCELAIN.
(FRENCH)

Nº 84. MOUSTIERS.

OLD ENGLISH POTTERY AND PORCELAIN.

Nº 26. BRISTOL.

CHURCHMAN'S CIGARETTES

ANTIQUE SILVER TABLE-SERVICE FOUND AT POMPEII

CHURCHMAN'S CIGARETTES.

KNOCKER, CHEPSTOW CASTLE.

OLD POTTERY AND PORCELAIN.

Nº 247. JAPAN NABESHIMA (OKAWAJI).

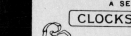

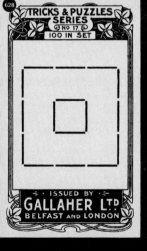

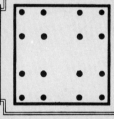

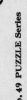

A BLUFF CARD TRICK

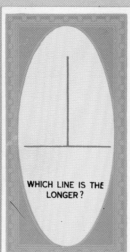

WHICH LINE IS THE LONGER?

CARRERAS CIGARETTES

PICTURE PUZZLE SERIES

SNAKE CHARMER,

FIND SNAKE.

Nº 8

Which of the other two matches will take fire from the flame?

For Answer see Back

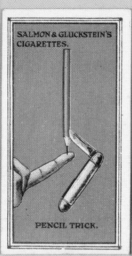

SALMON & GLUCKSTEIN'S CIGARETTES.

PENCIL TRICK.

No. 11

What is the difference between the infant and the soldier?

For Answer see back.

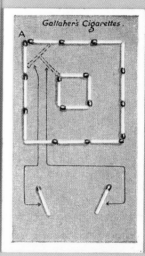

Gallaher's Cigarettes.

Lloyds' TRICKS & PUZZLES

Solution of No. 1 — He cut a square diamond out of the centre, thus—

It is hoped to run several Big-Prize Picture Puzzle Competitions for smokers of "Blue Lagoon" and "Bondman" Cigarettes. Look out for advertisements in the competition journals, or write and register your name to receive particulars from—

Dept. C., Richard Lloyd & Sons, Clerkenwell Road, London, E.C. 1.

Fig 1   Fig 2

What is the difference between

A Honey-comb

and A Honeymoon?

GALLAHER'S CIGARETTES

PORTER'S PUZZLE

Remove eight matches and leave two squares

Nº 17.

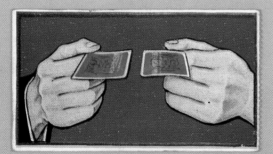

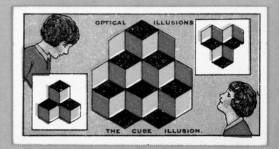

OPTICAL ILLUSIONS

THE CUBE ILLUSION.

WILLS'S CIGARETTES.

GREAT EASTERN EXPRESS ENGINE.

LAMBERT & BUTLER'S CIGARETTES.

NORTH STAFFORDSHIRE RAILWAY. LOCOMOTIVE 87.

WILLS'S CIGARETTES.

GEO. STEPHENSONS ROCKET. 1829.

LAMBERT & BUTLER'S CIGARETTES.

GREAT NORTHERN RAILWAY. LOCOMOTIVE 251.

WILLS'S CIGARETTES.

1ST 2ND & 3RD CLASS CARRIAGES. BODMIN & WADEBRIDGE RLY. 1840.

LAMBERT & BUTLER'S CIGARETTES.

SOUDAN GOVERNMENT RAILWAY. LOCOMOTIVE 110.

WILLS'S CIGARETTES.

1ST LOCOMOTIVE IN THE U.S.A.

LAMBERT & BUTLER'S CIGARETTES.

UNION PACIFIC RAILWAY, LOCOMOTIVE 310.

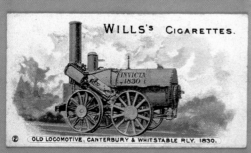

WILLS'S CIGARETTES.

OLD LOCOMOTIVE, CANTERBURY & WHITSTABLE RLY. 1830.

LAMBERT & BUTLER'S CIGARETTES.

ATLANTIC CITY RAILWAY. LOCOMOTIVE 1027.

WILLS'S CIGARETTES.

HEDLEY'S PUFFING BILLY, 1813.

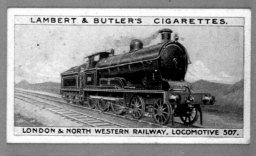

LAMBERT & BUTLER'S CIGARETTES.

LONDON & NORTH WESTERN RAILWAY, LOCOMOTIVE 507.

WILLS'S CIGARETTES.

GREAT WESTERN BROAD GAUGE ENGINE. 1837.

WILLS'S CIGARETTES.

STEPHENSON'S LONG BOILER ENGINE 1845.

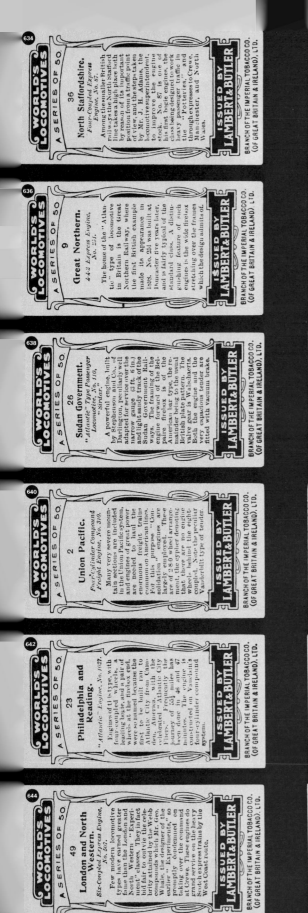

634

WORLD'S LOCOMOTIVES
A SERIES OF 50

36

North Staffordshire.
Four-Coupled Express Engine, No. 87.

Among the smaller British railways the North Stafford line takes a high place both by reason of its important position from a traffic point of view, and the steps taken by Mr. J. H. Adams, the locomotive superintendent, to improve the engine stock. No. 87 is one of his first bogie engines, the class being designed to work heavy passenger traffic in the "Potteries," and throughexpresses to Crewe, Manchester, and North Wales.

ISSUED BY
LAMBERT & BUTLER
BRANCH OF THE IMPERIAL TOBACCO CO.
(OF GREAT BRITAIN & IRELAND), LTD.

636

WORLD'S LOCOMOTIVES
A SERIES OF 50

9

Great Northern.
4-4-2 Express Engine, No. 251.

The home of the "Atlantic" type of locomotive in Britain is the Great Northern Railway, where the first British example made its appearance in 1898. No. 251 was built at Doncaster five years later, and is fairly typical of the standard class. A distinguishing feature of such engines is the wide firebox stretching over the frames which the design admits of.

ISSUED BY
LAMBERT & BUTLER
BRANCH OF THE IMPERIAL TOBACCO CO.
(OF GREAT BRITAIN & IRELAND), LTD.

638

WORLD'S LOCOMOTIVES
A SERIES OF 50

26

Sudan Government.
"Atlantic" Type Passenger Locomotive, No. 110, "Sirdar."

A powerful engine, built by Stephenson and Co., of Darlington, peculiarly well adapted for service over the narrow gauge (3 ft. 6 in.) and light sandy track of the Sudan Government Railways. The framing of the engine forward of the Belpaire firebox is of the American bar type, the remainder being to the usual British plate pattern. The bogie wheels are of all wheels. Both the engine and the very capacious tender are fitted with vacuum brake.

ISSUED BY
LAMBERT & BUTLER
BRANCH OF THE IMPERIAL TOBACCO CO.
(OF GREAT BRITAIN & IRELAND), LTD.

640

WORLD'S LOCOMOTIVES
A SERIES OF 50

2

Union Pacific.
Four-Cylinder Compound Freight Engine, No. 310.

Many very severe mountain sections are included in the Union Pacific system, and engines of great power are needed to haul the enormous freight trains common on American lines. For this purpose "Consolidation" engines are largely employed. These are of 2-8-0 wheel arrangement, the cypher denoting that there are no engine wheels behind the cylinders. Note the peculiar Vanderbilt type of tender.

ISSUED BY
LAMBERT & BUTLER
BRANCH OF THE IMPERIAL TOBACCO CO.
(OF GREAT BRITAIN & IRELAND), LTD.

642

WORLD'S LOCOMOTIVES
A SERIES OF 50

23

Philadelphia and Reading.
"Atlantic" Engine, No. 1027.

Engines of this type, with four-coupled wheels, a leading bogie, and a pair of wheels at the firebox end, were so named because the first to be built ran to Atlantic City, but the run from Philadelphia with the celebrated "Atlantic City Flyer." Frequently the journey of 55½ miles has been done in 46 and 47 minutes. The engine is constructed on Vauclain's four-cylinder compound system.

ISSUED BY
LAMBERT & BUTLER
BRANCH OF THE IMPERIAL TOBACCO CO.
(OF GREAT BRITAIN & IRELAND), LTD.

644

WORLD'S LOCOMOTIVES
A SERIES OF 50

49

London and North Western.
Six-Coupled Express Engine, No. 507.

Few modern locomotive types have excited greater fame than the London and North Western "Experiment" classes. They in fact bid fair to outvie the celebrity attained by the Webb compounds which Mr. Geo. Whale, the designer of the earlier Experiments, so promptly condemned, on taking over the command at Crewe. These engines do grand service on the heavy Scotch express trains by the West Coast route.

ISSUED BY
LAMBERT & BUTLER
BRANCH OF THE IMPERIAL TOBACCO CO.
(OF GREAT BRITAIN & IRELAND), LTD.

635

637

639

641

643

645

646

647

Card 648

MODERN RAILWAYS
A SERIES OF 50
21

COVENTRY PNEUMATIC RAILCAR

London Midland & Scottish Railway

The adaptation of pneumatic tyres to rail travel has been introduced as a standard of comfortable, silent, high speed travel hitherto unknown. The special tyres are fitted with a metal flange to prevent derailing. This type of railcar holds fifty-six passengers and is fitted with luggage and lavatory compartments. Built by Armstrong Siddeley Motors at Coventry, and driven by one of their 12-cylinder "V" petrol engines developing 280 b.h.p., it has a cruising speed of over 70 m.p.h. Weight in running order is 9 tons, fully laden with passengers and luggage, 14 tons. Overall length is 55 ft. The pneumatic railcar is extensively used on the French Railways and one of the cars has been tried on the L.M.S. main line.

HIGNETT BROS. & CO.

Card 649

FAMOUS RAILWAY TRAINS
A SERIES OF 25
3

The Flying Scotsman,

L. & N.E.R.

[text rotated, partially legible]

ISSUED BY THE IMPERIAL TOBACCO CO.
(OF GREAT BRITAIN & IRELAND), LTD.
W. A. & A. C. CHURCHMAN

Card 650

EMPIRE RAILWAYS
A SERIES OF 50
32

Bombay-Poona Special, G.I.P. Railway, India.

The old Great Indian Peninsula Ry., now merged into the Indian State Rys., was one of the first to introduce luxuries: "club" travel on wheels, and they have certainly kept well to the front in this respect; the special trains of this line yield nothing in comfort to the best European or American travel. The most important event in railway electrification in the Empire has been carried out in the Bombay district. The Ghauts, once the terror of the steam locomotive, have been "smoothed out," partly by re-locating certain lines, and partly by the introduction of electric locomotives which easily negotiate the severe gradients.

ISSUED BY THE IMPERIAL TOBACCO CO.
(OF GREAT BRITAIN & IRELAND), LTD.
W. A. & A. C. CHURCHMAN

Card 651

16
RECORDS OF THE WORLD
A SERIES OF 25

The Quickest Train in the World.

The Great Western Railway Co.'s non-stop run from Paddington to Plymouth, a distance of 225 miles, is done in the record time of 247 minutes. This is the quickest railway run of any train in any country. The "North Star" is the name of the powerful engine which takes the train. It consumes 6,600 gallons of water—31 gallons per mile—and burns six tons of coal on each journey.

BRANCH OF THE IMPERIAL TOBACCO CO. (OF GREAT BRITAIN & IRELAND), LTD.
ISSUED BY OGDEN'S

Card 652

EMPIRE RAILWAYS
A SERIES OF 50
25

A Sugar Cane Railway, Jamaica.

Although the railway of our picture is in no sense a public railway, it is one of the important branches of railway work by which our daily necessities are handled. Light railways are laid down on most sugar plantations, and though Jamaica is not by any means the principal sugar producer, many miles of railway, similar to that shown, are in use there. The gauge is usually of 2 ft. 6 in., and the handy little engines burn the waste cane (from which the last vestige of sugar has been extracted), baled into briquettes for their firebox supply.

ISSUED BY THE IMPERIAL TOBACCO CO.
(OF GREAT BRITAIN & IRELAND), LTD.
W. A. & A. C. CHURCHMAN

Card 653

LANDMARKS IN RAILWAY PROGRESS
A SERIES OF 50
34

THE CITY & SOUTH LONDON RY. 1890.

This railway, the first electric railway in Great Britain, was opened to the public on Dec. 18th, 1890. A scheme for electric traction, put forward by Messrs. Mather & Platt of Manchester, was accepted; experimental trains were running in Feb., 1890. The tunnels ran from King William Street in the City to Stockwell (by way of the Elephant & Castle); there were six stations. The trains—and there were three—used hydraulically operated signals as a method of lighting. The fare was twopence for any distance.

ISSUED BY THE IMPERIAL TOBACCO CO.
(OF GREAT BRITAIN & IRELAND), LTD.
W. A. & A. C. CHURCHMAN

Card 654

N° 26
WILLS'S CIGARETTES
2ND SERIES OF 50

DO YOU KNOW

why a Curved Iron hangs over the Rails in many Stations?

In or near most large railway stations one may see hanging from a support, or from the roof, an iron bar bent into the shape of an arch. An important station usually has several of these load-gauges, which show the height of the lowest tunnel or bridge beneath which the railway trucks may have to pass. The load-gauge enables the railway men to know how high the trucks may be loaded in order to pass underneath bridges and tunnels in safety.

W.D. & H.O. WILLS
BRISTOL & LONDON
ISSUED BY THE IMPERIAL TOBACCO Co.
(OF GREAT BRITAIN & IRELAND) LTD

Card 655

THE DONCELLA GOLDEN AGE OF STEAM
Series of 24   No. 10

1919 G.C.R. 4-4-0 No. 506 BUTLER-HENDERSON

J. G. Robinson held office as Chief Mechanical Engineer of the Great Central Railway from 1900 until the Company was absorbed into the London & North Eastern Railway in 1923. During his long years in that same office he produced many fine locomotives. One of the best known is the 'Director' Class 4-4-0's introduced in 1913 and they hauled express trains between London Marylebone, Sheffield and Manchester in L.N.E.R. days 25 more 'Directors' were built for service in Scotland, bringing the total to 46; but No. 506 *Butler Henderson*, the last survivor not being withdrawn until 1960, has now found a new home with the Main Line Steam Trust at Loughborough, Leicestershire.

Cylinders (2) 20" x 26".
Wheel diameter 6' 9".
Boiler pressure 180 lbs.

Collect the series in the special Golden Age of Steam Folder (opens out to a wall chart). Send a 25p postal order plus your name and address to Doncella Album, Dept. 594, The Old Pines, Epsom, Surrey.
Issued by John Player and Sons, Imperial Tobacco Limited, in conjunction with Steam and Sail and Association of Railway Preservation Societies.

Card 656

THE DONCELLA GOLDEN AGE OF STEAM
Series of 24   No. 12

1937 L.N.E.R. 4-6-2 No. 4498 SIR NIGEL GRESLEY

In 1935 the 'Silver Jubilee' high speed train between King's Cross and Newcastle was introduced. Designed the A4 Class 'Pacifics' for this duty were so successful that 35 were built over four years and other high speed trains were introduced. No. 4498 owes its name to having been the 100th 'Pacific' built to the design of Gresley. Although preserved in the North East *Sir Nigel Gresley* has been overshadowed by the more famous No. 4468 *Mallard* which in 1938 attained the world record speed for steam traction of 126 m.p.h. After the A4 'Pacifics' continued their high speed exploits on heavier trains than the pre-war limited load streamliners *Mallard* is preserved in the National Railway Museum at York.

Cylinders (3) 18½" x 26".
Wheel diameter 6' 8".
Boiler pressure 250 lbs.

Collect the series in the special Golden Age of Steam Folder (opens out to a wall chart). Send a 25p postal order plus your name and address to Doncella Album, Dept. 594, The Old Pines, Epsom, Surrey.
Issued by John Player and Sons, Imperial Tobacco Limited, in conjunction with Steam and Sail and Association of Railway Preservation Societies.

Card 657

RAILWAY EQUIPMENT
A SERIES OF 50
19

MODERN SINGLE LINE WORKING METHODS

To prevent two trains running simultaneously on the same section of single track, a driver may not enter a single line section without a token. While the token is out, a similar one cannot be issued for another train on that section from the opposite end. Some tokens are fitted to carriers having rings (as illustrated) to facilitate picking up and setting down the tokens on special lineside posts without stopping the train. With the electrically-controlled token holding instrument (shown inset), a second train token cannot be removed in error, either from that end of the section or from a similar instrument at the other end, until the first token is replaced in either instrument.

W.D. & H.O. WILLS
MANUFACTURERS OF GOLD FLAKE, CAPSTAN, WOODBINE AND STAR CIGARETTES
BRANCH OF THE IMPERIAL TOBACCO CO. (OF GREAT BRITAIN & IRELAND), LTD.

Card 658

THE DONCELLA GOLDEN AGE OF STEAM
Series of 24   No. 9

1892 N.E.R. 0-6-0T No. 8286

No. 8286 was the final L.N.E.R. number of a North Eastern Railway six coupled tank, one of many similar shunting engines built to Worsdell design 1886-95. Normally painted black, works number No. 8286 was given green passenger livery for use as carriage pilot at York station. Another N.E.R. 0-6-0T was similarly treated for use at Newcastle and to the number of 1947 it was finished in a G.E.R. 0-6-0T for Liverpool Street station. London No. 8286 was withdrawn in 1952. A similar but larger engine, No. 69023, built as late as 1951 is preserved at Embsay, near Skipton.

Cylinders (2) 16½" x 22".
Wheel diameter 4' 1¼".
Boiler pressure 140 lbs.

Collect the series in the special Golden Age of Steam Folder (opens out to a wall chart). Send a 25p postal order plus your name and address to Doncella Album, Dept. 594, The Old Pines, Epsom, Surrey.
Issued by John Player and Sons, Imperial Tobacco Limited, in conjunction with Steam and Sail and Association of Railway Preservation Societies.

CHURCHMAN'S CIGARETTES.

"THE FLYING SCOTSMAN."

HIGNETT'S CIGARETTES

COVENTRY PNEUMATIC RAILCAR

OGDEN'S CIGARETTES.

"PLYMOUTH LTD." EXPRESS, G.W.R.

CHURCHMAN'S CIGARETTES

BOMBAY-POONA SPECIAL, G.I.P. RAILWAY, INDIA

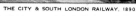

CHURCHMAN'S CIGARETTES

THE CITY & SOUTH LONDON RAILWAY, 1890

CHURCHMAN'S CIGARETTES

A SUGAR CANE RAILWAY, JAMAICA

WILLS'S CIGARETTES.

A LOAD-GAUGE.

WILLS'S CIGARETTES

MODERN SINGLE LINE
WORKING METHODS

LONDON & NORTH WESTERN RAILWAY

CANADIAN PACIFIC RAILWAY

"GOLDEN ARROW"

"DOMINION"

WILLS'S CIGARETTES.

L.N.E.R. "COCK O' THE NORTH."

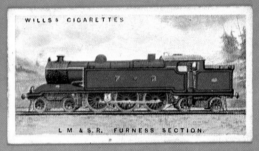

WILLS'S CIGARETTES

L.M. & S.R. FURNESS SECTION.

WILLS'S CIGARETTES.

L.M. & S.R.
HIGH PRESSURE LOCOMOTIVE.

WILLS'S CIGARETTES.

NEW YORK CENTRAL LINES, U.S.A. MICHIGAN CENTRAL R.R.

WILLS'S CIGARETTES.

SOUTHERN RY.
EXPRESS LOCOMOTIVE.

WILLS'S CIGARETTES

S.R. LONDON & SOUTH WESTERN SECTION.

WILLS'S CIGARETTES.

GOLD COAST RYS.
"GOVERNOR" CLASS.

WILLS'S CIGARETTES.

RHÆTIAN RAILWAY.

WILLS'S CIGARETTES.

S. AFRICAN RYS.
"MODIFIED FAIRLIE" LOCOMOTIVE.

WILLS'S CIGARETTES.

RHODESIAN RYS. "MOUNTAIN" TYPE.

673

MODERN RAILWAYS

A SERIES OF 50

29

"SILVER LINK" STREAMLINED LOCO.

London & North Eastern Railway

One of the series of locomotives hauling "The Silver Jubilee," Britain's first streamlined train, between King's Cross, Darlington and Newcastle, the "Silver Link" (No. 2509, 4-6-2 type) is streamlined and painted grey in several tones. The tender has a corridor through it to enable the engine crews to change duty *en route*. The principal dimensions, etc., are: Length over buffers, 70 ft. 3¾ ins.; diameter of driving wheels, 6 ft. 8 ins.; total weight of engine and tender in working order, 165 tons 7 cwt. "The Silver Jubilee" is regularly scheduled to cover the 268·3 miles between King's Cross and Newcastle in exactly 4 hours, an average speed for the whole run of 67·08 miles an hour.

ISSUED BY · OGDEN'S · BRANCH OF THE IMPERIAL TOBACCO CO. (OF GREAT BRITAIN & IRELAND), LTD.

674

LANDMARKS IN RAILWAY PROGRESS

A SERIES OF 50

17

SECOND AND THIRD CLASS TRAVEL, 1840.

We show the type of carriage provided prior to the Regulation of Railways Act of 1844, which made compulsory, by one train a day, enclosed carriages for 3rd class passengers at one penny per mile. The 3rd class vehicle shown was typical, though some lines did not provide seats at all. Its length would be about 15 ft. and width 6 ft., and when benches were provided, 24 passengers were carried. Holes were provided in the floor to carry off the rain-water! The covered coach is for 2nd class passengers and is similar to the vehicles *altogether of handsome appearance* provided by the Eastern Counties Ry. in 1839.

W.A.&A.C.CHURCHMAN

ISSUED BY THE IMPERIAL TOBACCO CO. (OF GREAT BRITAIN & IRELAND), LTD.

675

LANDMARKS IN RAILWAY PROGRESS

A SERIES OF 50

18

THE BEGINNING OF THE G.N.R., 1848.

The charter for this company was granted in 1846, and the first stretch of line, between Louth and New Holland was opened April 1st, 1848. It was not until 1850 that the line was completed to London. We show the first engine to be used on the line, one of a batch of 50 built by Sharp, Roberts & Co., and generally referred to as the *Little Sharps*. The single driving wheels were 5 ft. 6 in. diameter, and the total weight was 18½ tons. They worked the easy traffic for many years, but were unable to cope with the heavy traffic on the main line.

W.A.&A.C.CHURCHMAN

ISSUED BY THE IMPERIAL TOBACCO CO. (OF GREAT BRITAIN & IRELAND), LTD.

676

THIS MECHANIZED AGE

No. 42 of a First Series of 50

THE "FLYING KOLNER"

Hurry and scurry is the fashion, and trains "as slow as a lame snail" aren't popular any more. There is a decided tendency at the present time for electricity and internal combustion engines to threaten steam power, but which will win in the end still remains to be seen. The latest example of "greased lightning" is the express rail coach, "Flying Kölner," which runs daily between Berlin and Cologne, and does the journey in 297 minutes. "Flying Kölner" is diesel engine driven, **her average speed** is 72.67 **miles per hour, and her highest** speed, **maintained** for 159 miles, is 84.35 **miles. This rail coach** has **seating for 81 passengers**, and may only be **used** for journeys over 250 kilometres.

THIS SURFACE IS ADHESIVE

GODFREY PHILLIPS LTD. AND ASSOCIATED COMPANIES

677

Wills for Quality

SPEED

A SERIES OF 50

34

(d) Railways.

"THE CHELTENHAM FLYER."

The 2.30 p.m. from Cheltenham to Paddington on the G.W.R. is booked to cover the 77¼ miles from Swindon to London in 70 mins. At one time the allowance was 75 mins., in itself the highest average in force on any British railway (61·8 m.p.h.). The new timing makes for an average of 66¼ m.p.h., which exceeds anything to be found on any railway in the world. No difficulty is experienced in maintaining this schedule, even with considerable loads, and it is very frequently improved upon.

W.D.& H.O.WILLS

ISSUED BY THE IMPERIAL TOBACCO CO. (OF GREAT BRITAIN & IRELAND), LTD.

678

Wills for Quality

SPEED

A SERIES OF 50

37

(d) Railways.

THE "QUEEN OF SCOTS." (L. & N.E.R.)

Some astonishing runs have been made by this fine all-Pullman train, which runs between King's Cross and Edinburgh on the L. & N.E.R. On one occasion the train left Leeds 27 minutes late and arrived in London on time, averaging 66¼ m.p.h. for the 138½ miles Retford to London, and 69 m.p.h. from Huntingdon. On another occasion 90 m.p.h. was attained north of Hitchin, averaging 87 for 3 miles and 77 for 27 miles! The 76½ miles King's Cross to Peterboro' was covered in 74½ minutes, at an average of 61¼ m.p.h.

W.D.& H.O.WILLS

ISSUED BY THE IMPERIAL TOBACCO CO. (OF GREAT BRITAIN & IRELAND), LTD.

679

Wills for Quality

SPEED

A SERIES OF 50

36

(d) Railways.

THE GLASGOW-LEEDS EXPRESS.

The stretch of line between Darlington and York on the L. & N. E. Railway, has long been recognised as a "galloping ground." The 4.0 p.m. Glasgow-Leeds express is timed to leave Darlington at 9.1 p.m. and arrive at York at 9.44 p.m., thus covering the 44¼ miles in 43 minutes, at an average speed of 61¾ m.p.h. On several occasions the distance has been covered in 38 minutes, which is equivalent to a speed of nearly 70 m.p.h. This is the only train scheduled on the line at a start-to-stop speed of over 60 m.p.h., but many runs are made at higher speeds by trains having time to recover.

W.D.& H.O.WILLS

ISSUED BY THE IMPERIAL TOBACCO CO. (OF GREAT BRITAIN & IRELAND), LTD.

680

MODERN RAILWAYS

A SERIES OF 50

39

TRACK-LAYING TRAIN

London & North Eastern Railway

This recently installed track-laying train is the first of its kind to appear in Britain. It consists of (1) A power van with a 72 B.H.P. petrol driven generating set, providing the electric current for the various motors. (2) A saw trolley with two circular saws so arranged to cut the ends of sleepers to a uniform length of 8 ft. 6 in. (3) The track-layer proper, a 12-wheeled vehicle, upon which is mounted a cantilever crane, and (4) the train trolley which hauls loads the whole length of the train. Rails already fixed to chairs and sleepers are transported to the section to be relayed. The old track is then removed and the new section is lowered in its place.

ISSUED BY · OGDEN'S · BRANCH OF THE IMPERIAL TOBACCO CO. (OF GREAT BRITAIN & IRELAND), LTD.

681

WILLS'S CIGARETTES No 47

ENGINEERING WONDERS

A SERIES OF 50.

(k) Transport by Road, Rail, etc.

Rotary Snow-Plough, Canada.

In countries liable to heavy falls of snow engineers have devised wonderful contrivances in order to keep the railway tracks clear of snow. The wedge-plough is the simplest and oldest form of snow-plough, but is of little use in mountainous districts where slides are frequent. The modern rotary snow-plough has proved itself a much more efficient weapon. It consists of a large scoop wheel, about 11 feet in diameter, comprising a number of cone-shaped scoops set radially. As the wheel revolves, knives cut into the snow, which is caught up and forced out through a shoot in the hood, to fall some 60 feet from the track.

W.D.& H.O.WILLS

ISSUED BY THE IMPERIAL TOBACCO Cº (OF GREAT BRITAIN & IRELAND) LTᴰ

682

Wills for Quality

SPEED

A SERIES OF 50

35

(d) Railways.

"ROYAL SCOT."

On Friday, April 27th, 1928, the *Royal Scot* of the London, Midland and Scottish Railway, ran non-stop from Euston to Glasgow, 401½ miles. Another section of the train made the run to Edinburgh (399¾ miles) on the same day. Both trains ran exactly to schedule times, which do not constitute extraordinary speeds, but wonderful locomotive work was involved. We illustrate the Glasgow *Royal Scot*, which makes a daily non-stop run from Euston to Carlisle, nearly 300 miles. The fine new engines which work these trains are capable of handling 500-ton trains unaided, over the difficult gradients north of Lancaster.

W.D.& H.O.WILLS

ISSUED BY THE IMPERIAL TOBACCO CO. (OF GREAT BRITAIN & IRELAND), LTD.

683

C·W·S SPECIALITY BEATALL RICH DARK FLAKE 8ᴰ PER OZ.

RAILWAY ENGINES (BRITISH). Set of 48.

No. 9.

Locomotive built for N.E.R., 1871.

684

WILLS'S CIGARETTES No. 45

ENGINEERING WONDERS

A SERIES OF 50.

(k) Transport by Road, Rail, etc.

Ice Locomotive, Canada.

In the lumber districts of North America a special type of train has been devised to convey timber over frozen ground. Strictly speaking it is not a "railway," since the train does not travel over rails, but over an ice track. The special locomotive is a combination of traction engine, railway engine and steam-driven automobile, the large fire-box being adapted to burn either wood or coal. The leading bogie has a pair of massive runners, and behind this is a driving or traction device resembling that of the "caterpillar" tractor. The speed ranges from 4 to 5 m.p.h. over a good road, up to 8 m.p.h. over a carefully prepared ice track.

W.D.& H.O.WILLS

ISSUED BY THE IMPERIAL TOBACCO Cº (OF GREAT BRITAIN & IRELAND) LTᴰ

685

C·W·S SPECIALITY BEATALL RICH DARK FLAKE 8ᴰ PER OZ.

RAILWAY ENGINES (FOREIGN). Set of 48.

No. 43.

Powerful American Express Locomotive.

686

THIS MECHANIZED AGE

No. 13 of a First Series of 50

TURBINE LOCOMOTIVE

A steam turbine instead of a steam engine—a move to save coal—and a new move by the L. M. and S. Railway. A turbine built by Metropolitan-Vickers, at Manchester, takes the place of the usual four-cylinder reciprocating type of steam engine. The turbine is 2,000 h.p. non-condensing type, and uses steam at 250 lb. per square inch with a steam temperature of approximately 750° F. Number 6202, as this turbine locomotive is known, works through trains, weighing 500 tons, between London (Euston) and Glasgow; the tender is carried on six wheels and has a capacity for 4,000 gallons of water and 9 tons of coal. The locomotive weighs 109 tons and the tender 54 tons 13 cwts. in working order. It is estimated that the new arrangement will realize a saving of 15 per cent. in coal.

THIS SURFACE IS ADHESIVE

GODFREY PHILLIPS LTD. AND ASSOCIATED COMPANIES

CHURCHMAN'S CIGARETTES

SECOND & THIRD CLASS TRAVEL. 1840

OGDEN'S CIGARETTES

"SILVER LINK" STREAMLINED LOCOMOTIVE

"FLYING KÖLNER"

CHURCHMAN'S CIGARETTES

THE BEGINNING OF THE G.N.R. 1848

WILLS'S CIGARETTES.

"THE QUEEN OF SCOTS"

WILLS'S CIGARETTES

"THE CHELTENHAM FLYER" G.W.R.

OGDEN'S CIGARETTES

TRACK-LAYING TRAIN

WILLS'S CIGARETTES.

THE GLASGOW-LEEDS EXPRESS L.N.E.R.

WILLS'S CIGARETTES

THE ROYAL SCOT. L.M.S.

WILLS'S CIGARETTES.

ROTARY SNOW-PLOUGH.

WILLS'S CIGARETTES.

ICE LOCOMOTIVE.

704

TURBINE LOCOMOTIVE

WILL'S CIGARETTES

BEYER-GARRATT ARTICULATED LOCOMOTIVE

WILL'S CIGARETTES.

N.S.W. GOVT. RYS. FREIGHT LOCOMOTIVE.

MITCHELL'S CIGARETTES

RAILWAY LOCOMOTIVES, 1837 & 1937

LONDON & NORTH WESTERN RAILWAY

WILL'S CIGARETTES

HYDRAULIC BUFFERS

WILL'S CIGARETTES.

CANADIAN NATIONAL RYS. EXPRESS LOCOMOTIVE.

WILL'S CIGARETTES.

DUTCH INDIES RAILWAYS.

WILL'S CIGARETTES.

WESTERN RAILWAY OF FRANCE.

WILL'S CIGARETTES.

G.I.P.R. EXPRESS LOCOMOTIVE.

GREAT WESTERN RAILWAY

WILL'S CIGARETTES.

ASSAM BENGAL RY. FREIGHT LOCOMOTIVE.

"IMPERIAL MAIL"

"UNION LIMITED"

701 — LANDMARKS IN RAILWAY PROGRESS

1ST SERIES OF 12

No. 2

THE OYSTERMOUTH "TRAIN", 1816.

This interesting South Wales railway line is in all probability the oldest existing railway line in the world. Tramways in private ownership had been in existence since Tudor days, but the first application to Parliament for a public railway was that of the Surrey Iron Railway Co. in 1801. As this has now been demolished, the Oystermouth line (now the Swansea and Mumbles Railway) which secured its charter in 1804, claims to be the oldest existing line. The Act authorised mechanical traction, though the only available traction was that illustrated; this "train" was introduced about 1816.

W. A. & A. C. CHURCHMAN

ISSUED BY THE IMPERIAL TOBACCO COMPANY (OF GREAT BRITAIN & IRELAND), LIMITED

702 — RECORDS OF THE WORLD

ISSUED BY OGDEN'S — BRANCH OF THE IMPERIAL TOBACCO CO. (OF GREAT BRITAIN & IRELAND), LTD.

A SERIES OF 25

The Largest Railway Engine in the World.

The three Mallet compound freight locomotives belong to the Erie Railroad Co. of America. These are the largest and most powerful railway engines in the world. The weight of each is 185 tons, exclusive of the tender, which, with 8,500 gallons of water and 16 tons of coal, will weigh another 72 tons, or 255 tons in all. The boilers carry a working pressure of 215 sq. per square inch.

704 — MODERN RAILWAYS

A SERIES OF 50

41

"BRIGHTON BELLE" ALL-PULLMAN ELECTRIC EXPRESS

Southern Railway

The "Brighton Belle" is the present name for the "Southern Belle," which was the first All-Pullman train in Great Britain, and has completed over a quarter-century's service between London and Brighton. The "Southern Belle" first ran as an electric train in 1933 and the change of name took place in 1934. The between-London and Brighton service runs in each direction daily, three in all. Since the inception of the "Southern Belle" in 1908, over 5,000,000 passengers have been carried by the train.

ISSUED BY OGDEN'S

703 — EMPIRE RAILWAYS

A SERIES OF 50

11

Crossing the Sennar Dam, Sudan Govt. Railways.

British administrators and engineers are making a wonderful land out of the desert of the Sudan, and the system of irrigation controlled by the great dams is making a fertile and rich country. In the future the well-ordered system of railways will be extended further, and the line laid along the northern Sennar will link with the already busy Port Sudan, on the Red Sea, by way of Kassala, to Kosti and the market of El Obeid, truly in the heart of the desert. The beginning of the Sudan Railways was purely military, but the future commercial prosperity of the Sudan will depend very largely on railway development.

W. A. & A. C. CHURCHMAN

ISSUED BY THE IMPERIAL TOBACCO CO. (OF GREAT BRITAIN & IRELAND), LTD.

705 — FAMOUS RAILWAY TRAINS

2ND SERIES OF 12

No. 11

"The Golden Arrow" Leaving Calais.

This train, composed entirely of the most luxurious Pullman stock, runs between Paris and Calais—in fact, one may say London, for the connecting train between Dover and Victoria is now called by the same name, being composed of similar stock. The journey is made in five minutes under seven hours, and on the French side some wonderful locomotive work is necessary to make the 185 miles in 3 hrs. 10 mins. The engine shown is one of the Nord "Super-Pacifics," one of the most powerful in Europe.

W. A. & A. C. CHURCHMAN

ISSUED BY THE IMPERIAL TOBACCO COMPANY (OF GREAT BRITAIN & IRELAND), LIMITED.

706 — Wills for Quality — SPEED

A SERIES OF 50

41

(d) Railways.

"THE ATLANTIC CITY FLYER."

The fastest train in the U.S.A. makes the run from Camden, New Jersey, to Atlantic City (55¼ miles) in 55 min. This is equivalent to an average start-to-stop speed of 67·6 m.p.h., and obviously speeds en route exceed this considerably. At one time the schedule was 50 min., and the time actually taken on occasions was even less. Previously the work was done by locomotives of the "Atlantic" type, hence the name given to the 4-4-2 type. Nowadays the load is more than an "Atlantic" can handle, and the "Pacific" is employed to haul the twelve-car train weighing 600 tons.

W.D. & H.O. WILLS

ISSUED BY THE IMPERIAL TOBACCO CO. (OF GREAT BRITAIN & IRELAND), LTD.

707 — Wills for Quality — SPEED

A SERIES OF 50

38

(d) Railways.

THE NORD EXPRESS.

The Northern Railway of France has always maintained a good reputation for really fast expresses, and drivers are encouraged to keep time. Some extraordinary runs are occasionally recorded when attempts are made to recover lost time, and we illustrate one of these. The Paris-Brussels and vice versa, and though the train is not exceptionally heavy, the run from Paris to St. Quentin, 95 miles, with a ruling gradient of 1 in 200, has on several occasions been made in 87 minutes. This speed is equal to 65½ m.p.h. The normal timing for this part of the route is 105 minutes.

W.D. & H.O. WILLS

ISSUED BY THE IMPERIAL TOBACCO CO. (OF GREAT BRITAIN & IRELAND), LTD.

708 — Embassy WORLD OF SPEED

A SERIES OF 36

No 27

APT Class 370

The new Advanced Passenger Train, developed for regular service by British Rail, marks the culmination of 13 years of research and design. Cheaper to run than the HST's currently in use, it has already broken the previous highest speed on B.R. when, in December 1979, it reached 160 m.p.h. during a test run on the Carlisle to Glasgow route. Extensive use of aluminium is made in its construction, and the advanced vehicle suspension maintains passenger comfort at high speeds by allowing the car bodies to tilt through curved sections of track. Electric power of 25,000 volts is taken from a roof mounted pantograph supplying each of the two motor cars which have power units of 5,000 h.p.

Issued by W. D. & H. O. WILLS, IMPERIAL TOBACCO LIMITED

709 — SPEED

A SERIES OF 50

29

"BRISTOLIAN" EXPRESS, G.W.R.

This is the fastest train on the G.W.R. for a start-to-stop distance of over 100 miles. The "Bristolian," which runs approximately 118 miles between Paddington and Bristol, averages 67·6 m.p.h. in the up direction and 67·2 m.p.h. in the down direction. The train, which may weigh in the region of 220 tons, is hauled by a four-cylinder 4-6-0 of the "King" or "Castle" classes (King Richard I is illustrated). Engines of the "Castle" class also haul the "Cheltenham Flyer," which covers the 77·3 miles from Swindon to Paddington in 65 min., an average timing of 71·4 m.p.h. In keeping ordinary time the "Bristolian" may touch speeds of from 83 to 88 m.p.h. in the course of the journey.

W.D. & H.O. WILLS

MANUFACTURERS OF GOLD FLAKE, CAPSTAN, WOODBINE AND STAR CIGARETTES

ALBUM FOR WILLS' PICTURE CARDS CAN BE OBTAINED FROM TOBACCONISTS AT ONE PENNY EACH

710 — LANDMARKS IN RAILWAY PROGRESS

1ST SERIES OF 12

NO. 4

THE "ROCKET", AT RAINHILL, 1829.

George Stephenson built the Rocket to compete for the £500 prize offered by the Liverpool & Manchester Ry. for the most improved locomotive engine, and won the prize in the trials at Rainhill in Oct., 1829. We show this famous engine in its original state and colours. The three other serious competitors all failed at the trials. Rocket hauled her load of 12 tons, 15 cwt. (the load had to be three times her own weight) over the central portion of the track at an average speed of 13·8 m.p.h. Twenty trips had to be made to cover 35 miles. The maximum speed was 24 m.p.h. This engine in its altered state is now preserved at the South Kensington Museum.

W. A. & A. C. CHURCHMAN

ISSUED BY THE IMPERIAL TOBACCO COMPANY (OF GREAT BRITAIN & IRELAND), LIMITED.

711 — FAMOUS RAILWAY TRAINS

2ND SERIES OF 12

No. 2

Electric Kitchen, "The Flying Scotsman."

The kitchen of a travelling restaurant has to be extremely compact and conveniently arranged to come within the limited dimensions available. The one illustrated is probably unique, in that the cooking is done electrically, the necessary current being provided by the dynamo driven from the coach axle. In the restaurant sets, there are three articulated coaches (running on four bogies), which will accommodate 78 passengers at a sitting, and the staff must be prepared for this number, in addition to possible requirements of passengers in other parts of the train.

W. A. & A. C. CHURCHMAN

ISSUED BY THE IMPERIAL TOBACCO COMPANY (OF GREAT BRITAIN & IRELAND), LIMITED.

OGDEN'S CIGARETTES.

LARGEST RAILWAY ENGINE.

OGDEN'S CIGARETTES.

"BRIGHTON BELLE" ELECTRIC EXPRESS

CHURCHMAN'S CIGARETTES

THE OYSTERMOUTH "TRAIN", 1816

CHURCHMAN'S CIGARETTES

CROSSING THE SENNAR DAM, SUDAN GOVT. RAILWAYS

CHURCHMAN'S CIGARETTES.

THE GOLDEN ARROW LEAVING CALAIS.

WILLS'S CIGARETTES.

THE ATLANTIC CITY FLYER.

WILLS'S CIGARETTES.

THE NORD EXPRESS.

APT Class 370

WILLS'S CIGARETTES

"BRISTOLIAN" EXPRESS, G.W.R.

CHURCHMAN'S CIGARETTES.

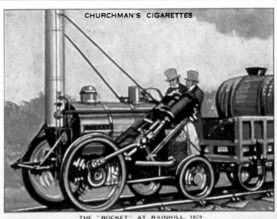

CHURCHMAN'S CIGARETTES

THE "ROCKET" AT RAINHILL, 1829.

AN EARLY RAILWAY COACH

GREAT WESTERN RAILWAY

WILL'S CIGARETTES.

BALTIMORE & OHIO R.R. (U.S.A.) "PRESIDENT" CLASS.

WILL'S CIGARETTES

"CORONATION SCOT" EXPRESS, L.M.S.R.

WILL'S CIGARETTES

"DENVER ZEPHYR" DIESEL FLYER

OGDEN'S CIGARETTES

STREAMLINED RAILCAR

"20TH CENTURY LIMITED"

WILL'S CIGARETTES

STREAMLINED PROPELLER RAILCAR

WILL'S CIGARETTES

"PRINCESS ELIZABETH", L.M.S.R.

"STREAMLINE"

"SIMPLON-ORIENT EXPRESS"

WILL'S CIGARETTES

"CORONATION" EXPRESS, L.N.E.R.

"BLUE TRAIN"

HIGNETT'S CIGARETTES

FREIGHT LOCOMOTIVE NO. 8000

No. 18

SPEED
LAND SEA & AIR
A Series of 50

THIS SURFACE IS ADHESIVE

"COCK O' THE NORTH"
(London & N.E. Rly.)

Although more orthodox in appearance, this fine engine, which was designed to take heavy loads over the hilly and arduous Edinburgh-Aberdeen route, was built in the light of experience gained with her prototype "The 10,000." Huge and powerful, the "Cock o' the North" is the first British engine coupled expressly for making short work of heavy loads by travelling the 131.5 miles in 3 hours 15 minutes.

ISSUED WITH
STATE EXPRESS
CIGARETTES

RAILWAY WORKING
2ND SERIES OF 25

1

Articulated Coaches.

You will notice that the four-wheeled type shown on the reverse of two coaches, and in this way whole trains are made up thus: Two coaches on three bogies, three coaches on four bogies, five on six, and so on. The L. & N.E.R. have many complete units made up in this way—twin sleeping cars on the same bogie, restaurant car and kitchen car between, on four bogies; and five coach sets for suburban traffic. The system is the invention of Mr. Gresley of the L. & N.E.R., but is also in use on the G.W.R.

W.A.&A.C.CHURCHMAN
ISSUED BY THE IMPERIAL TOBACCO CO.
(OF GREAT BRITAIN & IRELAND) LTD.

The Railway Centenary
2ND SERIES 51 TO 75

No. 67.
London & North Western
Railway 1859
(Now LMS).

"Lady of the Lake," built 1862, one of a class of 60 single-wheel express locomotives the first of which was constructed at Crewe to Ramsbottom's designs in 1859. These engines had 16 in. by 24 in. outside cylinders and 7 ft. 6 in. driving-wheels.

SS-60
SUNRIPE
CIGARETTES
50 YEARS
The Spinet House, London REPUTATION

Wills for Quality

SPEED
A Series of 50

39
(d) Railways.

THE SUD EXPRESS.

One of the fastest electric trains is the Sud Express which runs between Paris and Madrid. Portions of the run are made behind huge electric locomotives between Bordeaux and Dax (91½ miles) is made in 89 mins, start-to-stop, an average of 62 m.p.h. As the stretch is a level one, the speed obtained is frequently well up to the limit imposed on the locomotives, 75 m.p.h. The run from Paris to Bordeaux (424 miles) is made at 51 m.p.h. and to Madrid (1,030 miles), in 24¼ hours.

W.D.&H.O.WILLS
ISSUED BY THE IMPERIAL TOBACCO CO.
(OF GREAT BRITAIN & IRELAND) LTD.

RAILWAY WORKING
2ND SERIES OF 25

10

Picking Up and Dropping Mail Bags.

This interesting process generally takes place at night, but in order that some part of the apparatus can be seen. The net hung on the posts catches bags hung from brackets which are swung out from the door of the coach, and the net projected from the coach side catches the standards. These nets are made of stout rope, and that on the coach is collapsible so that it can be pulled back as soon as the bags are in. By these means mail trains can make long non-stop journeys.

W.A.&A.C.CHURCHMAN
ISSUED BY THE IMPERIAL TOBACCO CO.
(OF GREAT BRITAIN & IRELAND) LTD.

RAILWAY WORKING
2ND SERIES OF 25

10

Pantagraph Pick-up Gear.

You may see this apparatus which picks up the current on an electric railway where overhead distribution is used. This one is in use on the North Eastern division of the L. & N.E.R. and a similar one can be seen on the L. & Y. section of the L.M.S.R. Those employed on the Brighton line are of simpler construction. The joints are hinged to allow powerful springs to keep the bows in contact with the wire, also to allow the apparatus to be folded down on to the roof when not in use.

W.A.&A.C.CHURCHMAN
ISSUED BY THE IMPERIAL TOBACCO CO.
(OF GREAT BRITAIN & IRELAND) LTD.

RAILWAY EQUIPMENT
A SERIES OF 50

9

PICKING UP MAILS AT SPEED

Upwards of forty million bags of mail are handled annually by the railways in this country, and seventy travelling Post Offices are in regular use. To enable mails to be set down at points at which the train may not be stopping, nets are provided alongside the track to catch the bags which have been swung out on the side of the coach. Similarly a net swung out from the coach receives the mail which has been hung on special pick-up posts adjacent to the track as illustrated. When not in immediate use, the collecting net is folded flat against the side of the vehicle. *(Photograph Crown Copyright).*

W.D.& H.O. WILLS
MANUFACTURERS OF GOLD FLAKE, CAPSTAN, WOODBINE and STAR CIGARETTES
BRANCH OF THE IMPERIAL TOBACCO CO.
(OF GREAT BRITAIN & IRELAND) LTD.

RAILWAY WORKING
2ND SERIES OF 25

12

How to Describe a Locomotive.

To be up-to-date in describing a locomotive, take the small wheels in front, weight-carriers, two on each side, call it "four"; then the large coupled wheels, drivers as well as weight-carriers, two on each side, again "four"; then the trailing weight-carriers (if any, one on each side, "two"; and we get 4-4-2. Examples shown are: 4-2-2—Singles, not now built. 4-4-0—A very useful class. 4-4-2—"Atlantics." 4-6-2—"Pacifics." 4-6-0—A common class for express work. 4-6-4—"Baltic," tank engines. 0-6-0—Goods engines. 2-8-0—"Consolidation." Other named classes in Britain are 2-6-0 "Mogul," 2-8-2 "Mikado."

W.A.&A.C.CHURCHMAN
ISSUED BY THE IMPERIAL TOBACCO CO.
(OF GREAT BRITAIN & IRELAND) LTD.

THIS SURFACE IS ADHESIVE

WONDERFUL CENTURY
1837—1937
A SERIES OF 50

6

RAILWAY ROLLING STOCK
1st Class, 1837   1st Class Dining Car, 1937

In the early days of railways, the first class compartments, each of which held six passengers, resembled the old stage coaches. They bore such names as the "Marquess of Stafford," the "Traveller" and the "Treasurer"; luggage was carried on the roofs, and frequently guards sat on raised seats at front and rear of the train. People wishing to travel in their private carriage were accommodated as shown in the top picture. Rolling stock rapidly grew in comfort and luxury, and in 1879 the first dining car ran between London and Leeds. The lower picture shows a dining car built for the new London-Portsmouth electric service, inaugurated July, 1937. *(Top picture by courtesy of Science Museum).*

STEPHEN MITCHELL & SON
ISSUED BY THE IMPERIAL TOBACCO CO.
(OF GREAT BRITAIN & IRELAND), LTD.

THIS SURFACE IS ADHESIVE. ASK YOUR TOBACCONIST FOR THE ATTRACTIVE ALBUM (PRICE ONE PENNY) SPECIALLY PREPARED TO HOLD THE COMPLETE SERIES

THE REIGN OF H.M. KING GEORGE V
1910—1935
A SERIES OF 50

24

THE RAILWAY CENTENARY EXHIBITION

Over the route between Stockton and Darlington on which a century before the first passenger train accomplished its fitful run, there passed on July 2nd, 1925, a procession of engines and rolling stock which summarized a hundred years of railway progress. The Duke and Duchess of York were the chief guests at the centenary, and from a point between the two towns watched the earliest locomotives labour slowly past, drawing wagon-loads of passengers wearing the dresses of 1825. These old warriors of the day of Stephenson, Hackworth, Trevithick and Watt had a "guard of honour" of some of the finest modern locomotives on the railroads.

W.D.& H.O. WILLS
ISSUED BY THE IMPERIAL TOBACCO CO.
(OF GREAT BRITAIN & IRELAND) LTD.

LANDMARKS IN RAILWAY PROGRESS
A SERIES OF 50

24

THE FIRST SLEEPING SALOON, 1874.

Sleeping saloons were introduced on the night expresses by the East and West Coast routes to Scotland at about 1874. These trains were only six-wheelers, and the West Coast, saloon (which is illustrated), contained accommodation for twelve passengers. One door was provided on each side in the centre. Bunks were fitted, the lower ones being fixed between the upper one being in the form of a hinged "shelf," similar to the arrangement in use to-day for sleeping berths. They were stowed away during the daytime.

W.A.&A.C.CHURCHMAN
ISSUED BY THE IMPERIAL TOBACCO CO.
(OF GREAT BRITAIN & IRELAND) LTD.

The Railway Centenary
2ND SERIES 51 TO 75

No. 64.
London & North Western
Railway 1846 (Now LMS),

A type of tank engine built to the designs of Francis Trevithick during his regime as locomotive Superintendent at Crewe Works from 1846–1862. Characteristic features of these engines were the two spring balance safety valves, inclined outside cylinders and round section connecting rods.

ISSUED WITH
SUNRIPE
CIGARETTES
The Spinet House, London

RAILWAY WORKING
2ND SERIES OF 25

5

The Train Ferry.

The Train Ferry, the name of which describes its use, now works between Harwich and Zeebrugge, and accounts for the numerous foreign railway trucks to be seen on English railways. It enables manufacturers to ship their goods direct in one truck load to destinations on the Continent or vice versa. These are the same ferries which were built during the Great War for the shipment of guns, tanks, locomotives and other heavy articles from Richborough to French ports.

W.A.&A.C.CHURCHMAN
ISSUED BY THE IMPERIAL TOBACCO CO.
(OF GREAT BRITAIN & IRELAND) LTD.

No. 16

SPEED
LAND SEA & AIR
A Series of 50

THIS SURFACE IS ADHESIVE

"FLYING SCOTSMAN"
(London & N.E. Rly.)

With the smoke pouring from her stack snatched away by the speed of her passage, the miles are reeled off by the wheels of The Flying Scotsman—perhaps the most famous name in British railroad history. It is the oldest established express in the world, having been running since the 1860's. Non-stop from London-Edinburgh in 1931 broke the record for steam locomotives, the run of 108 m.p.h. often hauls the train.

ISSUED WITH
STATE EXPRESS
CIGARETTES

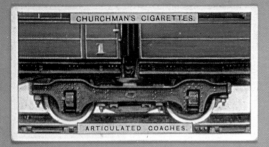

CHURCHMAN'S CIGARETTES.
ARTICULATED COACHES.

"COCK O' THE NORTH"

WILLS'S CIGARETTES.
THE SUD EXPRESS.

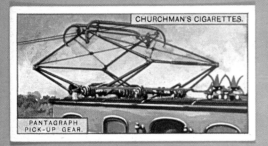

CHURCHMAN'S CIGARETTES.
PANTAGRAPH PICK-UP GEAR.

CHURCHMAN'S CIGARETTES.
PICKING UP AND DROPPING MAIL BAGS.

WILLS'S CIGARETTES
RAILWAY CENTENARY EXHIBITION

MITCHELL'S CIGARETTES
RAILWAY ROLLING STOCK, 1837 & 1937

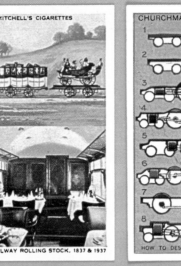

CHURCHMAN'S CIGARETTES.
HOW TO DESCRIBE A LOCOMOTIVE.

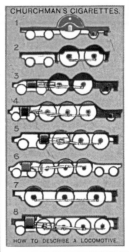

WILLS'S CIGARETTES
PICKING UP MAILS AT SPEED

CHURCHMAN'S CIGARETTES
THE FIRST SLEEPING SALOON, 1874

"FLYING SCOTSMAN"

CHURCHMAN'S CIGARETTES.
THE TRAIN FERRY.

CHURCHMAN'S CIGARETTES

"THE GRANDFATHER OF "THE FLYING SCOTSMAN"", 1852

WILLS'S CIGARETTES

SANTA FE "SUPER CHIEF" DIESEL FLYER

CHURCHMAN'S CIGARETTES

A HUNDRED MILES AN HOUR. G.W.R. 1904

"ROYAL SCOT"

CHURCHMAN'S CIGARETTES

"PUFFING BILLY", 1813

OGDEN'S CIGARETTES

INTERIOR OF ALL-ELECTRIC SIGNAL BOX (S.R.)

WILLS'S CIGARETTES

ITALIAN STATE RYS.
"ANSALDO" EXPRESS LOCOMOTIVE.

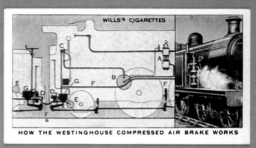

WILLS'S CIGARETTES

HOW THE WESTINGHOUSE COMPRESSED AIR BRAKE WORKS

WILLS'S CIGARETTES.

GT. SOUTHERN RY.
(IRELAND) EXPRESS LOCOMOTIVE.

"FLYING HAMBURGER"

WILLS'S CIGARETTES

NEW ZEALAND GOVT. RYS. PASSENGER LOCOMOTIVE

Card 740
MODERN RAILWAYS — A SERIES OF 50 — 740 — 44

INTERIOR OF ALL-ELECTRIC SIGNAL BOX, BRIGHTON STATION

Southern Railway

This signal box was erected when the line from London to Brighton was electrified in 1933. It controls an intensive area around Brighton Station, all of which is operated by electric signals, the levers which work them being about the size of fountain pens. Every day 226 electric and 74 steam trains use Brighton Station. This signal box operates the 10 platform roads and 77 pairs of points which the station contains. In many cases the signals are operated by the trains themselves, by means of an ingenious system of track circuiting.

ISSUED BY OGDEN'S BRANCH OF THE IMPERIAL TOBACCO CO. (OF GREAT BRITAIN & IRELAND), LTD.

Card 742
Wills for Quality — RAILWAY LOCOMOTIVES — A series of 50 — 742 — 46

Italian State Railways,

"Ansaldo" 2.8.0 Express Locomotive.

These locomotives of the "Consolidation" type have been built by the Ansaldo Co. in Italy, for working express passenger and fast freight trains on the Tyrrhenian and North Tyrrhenian Line, Naples - Reggio, where gradients may run to 1 in 66. With runs of 400 tons, a speed of 45 miles per hour is maintained. As will be seen, the two cylinders are set inside with the valve chests and Walschaerts motion outside, the whole being in one single casing. The cylinders are 23 in. diameter and 28 in. stroke.

W.D. & H.O. WILLS — ISSUED BY THE IMPERIAL TOBACCO CO. (OF GREAT BRITAIN & IRELAND), LTD.

Card 744
ALBUMS FOR WILLS'S PICTURE CARDS CAN BE OBTAINED FROM TOBACCONISTS AT ONE PENNY EACH — RAILWAY EQUIPMENT — A SERIES OF 50 — 744 — 27

HOW THE WESTINGHOUSE COMPRESSED AIR BRAKE WORKS

This brake is used in this country on most electric and some steam trains. While the brake is off, air from the compressor (A) passes from the main reservoir (B) through the driver's brake valve (C) to triple valves (D) and auxiliary reservoirs (E) under each vehicle. The brake is applied by allowing air to escape from the driver's brake valve, guard's emergency valve, or train pipe (F) direct; this moves the triples, so opening direct communication between auxiliary reservoirs and brake pistons in cylinders (G) and applying the brakes. Restoring pressure from the main reservoir to the train pipe, at the driver's brake valve, releases the brakes.

W.D. & H.O. WILLS — MANUFACTURERS OF GOLD FLAKE, CAPSTAN, WOODBINE AND STAR CIGARETTES. BRANCH OF THE IMPERIAL TOBACCO CO. (OF GREAT BRITAIN & IRELAND), LTD.

Card 746
Wills for Quality — RAILWAY LOCOMOTIVES — A series of 50 — 746 — 41

Great Southern Railway (Ireland),

Mixed Traffic Express.

These locomotives were designed by Mr. Bazin, the late chief engineer of the line, and built at Inchicore works, Dublin, primarily for fast goods trains between Dublin and Cork, but they are employed also for fast passenger work. The two cylinders are 19¼ in. bore by 28 in. stroke, boiler steams at 180 lb. per sq. in., and the driving wheels 5 ft. 8 in. diameter. The tender carries 3,870 gallons of water and 8 tons of coal, and the complete locomotive weighs 116¼ tons, with a tractive force of 23,760 lb.

W.D. & H.O. WILLS — ISSUED BY THE IMPERIAL TOBACCO CO. (OF GREAT BRITAIN & IRELAND), LTD.

Card 747
Compound Locomotive for the Paris-Lyons-Mediterranean Railway, 1889.

No. 34. Set of 48.

RAILWAY ENGINES (FOREIGN).

Card 749
SPEED LAND SEA & AIR — A Series of 50 — 749 — No. 30

"FLYING HAMBURGER" (Germany.)

One of the most amazing developments in modern railway design is the adaptation of the diesel engine to railway conditions. One of the first European railcar services was the *Flying Hamburger*, which is already famous. This double-unit car is self-contained, accommodating 102 passengers and containing a buffet. She covers the 178 miles from Berlin to Hamburg at an average speed of 78 m.p.h., and is comfortably capable of 100 m.p.h.

ISSUED WITH STATE EXPRESS CIGARETTES

Card 751
Wills for Quality — RAILWAY LOCOMOTIVES — A SERIES OF 50 — 751 — 42

N. Zealand Government Railways.

4.6.2 Passenger Locomotive.

These useful engines, known as the "Ab." class, are built at Addington works in the Dominion, and are employed on all kinds of work on severely graded lines, where sharp curves abound. They have two cylinders 17 in. diameter and 26 in. stroke, and boiler pressure of 190 lb. per sq. in. In complete working order the locomotive with tender weighs 84 tons 15 cwt. The gauge of the N.Z. lines is 3 ft. 6 in.

W.D. & H.O. WILLS — ISSUED BY THE IMPERIAL TOBACCO CO. (OF GREAT BRITAIN & IRELAND), LTD.

Card 741
LANDMARKS IN RAILWAY PROGRESS — 1ST SERIES OF 12 — 741 — NO. 7

THE "GRANDFATHER OF THE 'FLYING SCOTSMAN.'" 1852.

The first through train from King's Cross to York, en route for Scotland, left that station at 7 a.m. on Oct. 14th, 1852, and can therefore claim to be the *Grandfather of the Flying Scotsman*. It was hauled by the quaint-looking Crampton engine shown. No. 200, which had an intermediate crankshaft coupled to the driving wheels. Though the *Scotsman* which we know to-day did not come into existence till June, 1862, there were, of course, through trains between London and Edinburgh, the time taken being 11½ hours. In 1862 this was reduced to 10½, in 1872 to 9½, and in 1870 to 9 hours.

W. A. & A. C. CHURCHMAN — ISSUED BY THE IMPERIAL TOBACCO COMPANY (OF GREAT BRITAIN & IRELAND) LIMITED

Card 743
ALBUMS FOR WILLS'S PICTURE CARDS CAN BE OBTAINED FROM TOBACCONISTS AT ONE PENNY EACH — SPEED — A SERIES OF 50 — 743 — 33

SANTA FE "SUPER CHIEF" DIESEL FLYER.

The fastest scheduled railway run in the World in the summer of 1966 was 202.4 miles at a start-to-stop speed of 83.7 m.p.h., made by this twin-unit 3,600 h.p. streamlined light-weight Diesel-electric locomotive when running the "Super Chief" cross-continental luxury train of the Atchison, Topeka and Santa Fé Railway. The 2,222-mile journey, between Chicago and Los Angeles, much of which is over single line, is regularly made in a total time of 39¾ hours, including stops. The nine-car stainless steel train has berths for 104 passengers; there are also 26 seats in the dining car and 42 in the lounges, and supper for a crew of...

W.D. & H.O. WILLS — MANUFACTURERS OF GOLD FLAKE, CAPSTAN, WOODBINE AND STAR CIGARETTES. BRANCH OF THE IMPERIAL TOBACCO CO. (OF GREAT BRITAIN & IRELAND), LTD.

Card 745
LANDMARKS IN RAILWAY PROGRESS — 2ND SERIES OF 12 — 745 — NO. 10

A HUNDRED MILES AN HOUR, G.W.R. 1904.

The only authentic record of this speed having been attained on a British railway, was in May, 1904, by the Ocean Mails special from Plymouth to London via Bristol, the *City of Truro* being the engine as far as Bristol. Coming out of Whiteball Tunnel, speed steadily increased till two consecutive quarter miles were covered in 9.2 sec. and 8.8 sec., the latter representing a speed of 102.3 m.p.h., and the half mile speed 100 exactly. This was certified by the late Mr. Charles Rous-Marten, recognised authority on the subject. The load consisted of five 8-wheel postal vans, and the run was down-hill.

W. A. & A. C. CHURCHMAN — ISSUED BY THE IMPERIAL TOBACCO COMPANY (OF GREAT BRITAIN & IRELAND) LIMITED

Card 748
SPEED LAND SEA & AIR — A Series of 50 — 748 — No. 19

"ROYAL SCOT"

(London Mid. & Scottish Rly.)

A far-travelled train is the *Royal Scot*. She had the distinction of representing British railway enterprise by touring all over the U.S.A. and Canada, where she gained enormous appreciation by experts and public alike. The *Royal Scot* covers, during the summer, the 300 miles from Euston to Kingmoor near Carlisle, without a stop, the portion for Glasgow and Edinburgh parting company at Symington in the uplands of Southern Scotland.

ISSUED WITH STATE EXPRESS CIGARETTES

Card 750
LANDMARKS IN RAILWAY PROGRESS — 1ST SERIES OF 12 — 750 — NO. 1

"PUFFING BILLY". 1813.

This famous engine, now at the South Kensington Museum, was built by Hedley in 1813, to work at Wylam Colliery. The notion of the "grasshopper" beam is imparted to the wheels through gearing, and a load of 50 tons was hauled at about 5 m.p.h. The two cylinders were 9 in. bore and 36 in. stroke; steam pressure 50 lb. per sq. in. In 1815 *Puffing Billy* was rebuilt as an eight-wheeler, but on the introduction of better and stronger rails, was reconverted to the original arrangement. The engine remained at work until 1862.

W. A. & A. C. CHURCHMAN — ISSUED BY THE IMPERIAL TOBACCO COMPANY (OF GREAT BRITAIN & IRELAND), LIMITED.

CHURCHMAN'S CIGARETTES.

TAKING IN COAL.

CHURCHMAN'S CIGARETTES

LEVERS IN SIGNAL-BOX.

Mallard

CHURCHMAN'S CIGARETTES.

TRAIN STAFF INSTRUMENT.

OGDEN'S CIGARETTES.

Direction of Train

Centre of Wheel travels
along this line

Rail

PARTS OF A RAILWAY TRAIN
THAT MOVE BACKWARD.

'Bullet' Train

LONDON'S UNDERGROUND

WILLS'S CIGARETTES

WHISTLE

896   100

TRACK SIGNALS

WILLS'S CIGARETTES

LOCOMOTIVE ALONGSIDE
A WATER TANK

THE "ROYAL SCOT"

CHURCHMAN'S CIGARETTES

THREE-POSITION SIGNAL.

OGDEN'S
CIGARETTES

CR34

3-ASPECT ELECTRIC STARTING SIGNAL

CHURCHMAN'S CIGARETTES

THE RACE TO EDINBURGH, 1888

THE ROYAL SCOT
L.M.S

CEYLON GOVERNMENT RAILWAY

THE EARL MARISCHAL
L.N.E.R.

STREAMLINED RAILCAR
G.W.R.

DIESEL ELECTRIC TRAIN
SAN PAULO RAILWAY

ROMNEY, HYTHE & DYMCHURCH RAILWAY

THE CAPITOL LIMITED
BALTIMORE & OHIO RAILROAD

THE TORBAY EXPRESS
G.W.R.

CENTRAL URUGUAY RAILWAY

THE SCARBOROUGH FLIER
L.N.E.R.

THE CHELTENHAM FLYER
G.W.R.

PETROL RAILCAR
SLIGO, LEITRIM & NORTHERN COUNTIES RAILWAY

THE INTERNATIONAL LIMITED
CANADIAN NATIONAL RAILWAYS

THE ROYAL BLUE
BALTIMORE & OHIO RAILROAD

765

TRAINS OF THE WORLD

SERIES OF 48. Nº 10

CEYLON GOVERNMENT RAILWAY

The Ceylon Government Railway maintains excellent services from Colombo, the capital, to various parts of the Island, and the principal trains include comfortable sleeping and dining cars. The first train was run in 1865, and there are now 961 miles of track mainly of 5-ft. 6-in. gauge. There are, however, 117 miles of 2-ft. 6-in. gauge, but despite their toy-like appearance the trains used on these lines are extremely powerful and easily negotiate the steep gradients. In 1936 three diesel-electric trains were built for use on the wider gauge lines.

ISSUED BY

GALLAHER LTD

VIRGINIA HOUSE. LONDON & BELFAST

766

TRAINS OF THE WORLD

SERIES OF 48. Nº 14

THE ROYAL SCOT

LONDON MIDLAND AND SCOTTISH RAILWAY

The Royal Scot runs between London (Euston) and Glasgow and Edinburgh in both directions, accomplishing the 401½ miles from Glasgow to Euston in 7 hours 25 minutes at an average speed of over 54.1 m.p.h. including stops. It holds the world's record for the longest regular non-stop run throughout the year of 299.1 miles between Carlisle and Euston. The train is hauled by giant 159-ton locomotives of the "Princess Royal" class, which take trains of 500 tons without assistance up the severe inclines encountered in Westmoreland and north of the Border.

ISSUED BY

GALLAHER LTD

VIRGINIA HOUSE. LONDON & BELFAST

767

TRAINS OF THE WORLD

SERIES OF 48. Nº 11

STREAMLINED RAILCAR

GREAT WESTERN RAILWAY

In 1934 the G.W.R. introduced its first experimental diesel streamlined railcar and soon followed it with three more of similar design, the equipment including a cafeteria and bar and luggage accommodation. The Company now has seventeen of these cars in service and they are used for taking business people chiefly on cross-country routes between such centres as Birmingham, Oxford and Cardiff. Each car carries sixty-two or sixty-nine passengers, is driven by two 130 h.p. engines and is capable of a speed of over 60 m.p.h.

ISSUED BY

GALLAHER LTD

VIRGINIA HOUSE. LONDON & BELFAST

768

TRAINS OF THE WORLD

SERIES OF 48. Nº 32

THE EARL MARISCHAL

LONDON AND NORTH EASTERN RAILWAY

The Earl Marischal is one of the locomotives of the "Cock o' the North" class—the most powerful passenger engines in Great Britain. It is used to haul the heavy express passenger trains in service over the hilly and tortuous line between Edinburgh (Waverley Station) and Aberdeen. The weight of the engine in working order is 110 tons 5 cwts., while that of the tender is 55 tons 6 cwts. There are three cylinders, size 21-in. diameter × 26-in., and the driving wheels are 6-ft. 2-in. in diameter.

ISSUED BY

GALLAHER LTD

VIRGINIA HOUSE. LONDON & BELFAST

769

TRAINS OF THE WORLD

SERIES OF 48. Nº 5

THE ROMNEY, HYTHE AND DYMCHURCH RAILWAY

This is the world's smallest public railway and is, as far as possible, an exact replica of a full-size system. Opened in 1927, it runs for about fourteen miles on a fifteen-inch gauge and carries yearly a big passenger and goods traffic. The locomotive shown is one of five similar in outline to the L.N.E.R. "Pacifics." Weighing about eight tons, they are designed for the highest speeds that can be got out of such small engines, and can haul a train of 300 passengers at 25 m.p.h. on gradients up to 1 in 100.

ISSUED BY

GALLAHER LTD

VIRGINIA HOUSE. LONDON & BELFAST

770

TRAINS OF THE WORLD

SERIES OF 48. Nº 2

DIESEL-ELECTRIC TRAIN

SAN PAULO RAILWAY (BRAZIL)

This train, which was introduced in 1934 and is driven by a 450 b.h.p. diesel electric engine, consists of a power car and three coaches with accommodation for 168 passengers. In a seven-mile stretch on the route between Santos (on the coast) and San Paulo the line climbs to a height of 2,625-ft., this being achieved by a cable railway. Though there are many cable railways in the world, this one is outstanding on account of the very heavy traffic carried, the annual weight of goods amounting to about 4,000,000 tons.

ISSUED BY

GALLAHER LTD

VIRGINIA HOUSE. LONDON & BELFAST

771

TRAINS OF THE WORLD

SERIES OF 48. Nº 7

THE TORBAY EXPRESS

GREAT WESTERN RAILWAY

The Torbay Express is one of Britain's most popular all-the-year-round holiday trains, and runs between London (Paddington) and Torquay, the centre of the English Riviera, covering the 200 miles in 210 minutes. Both the up and the down services leave at noon, and have been running for over twenty-five years. The locomotives used are of the "King" class. Built for fast running with heavy loads, they are among the most powerful in the country and include the "King George V," which made a great impression at the Baltimore and Ohio Centenary in America in 1927.

ISSUED BY

GALLAHER LTD

VIRGINIA HOUSE. LONDON & BELFAST

772

TRAINS OF THE WORLD

SERIES OF 48. Nº 3

THE CAPITOL LIMITED

BALTIMORE & OHIO RAILROAD (U.S.A.)

The Capitol Limited runs daily between New York (Jersey City Station) and Chicago (Grand Central Station), accomplishing the trip of 991 miles, with stops at twenty-four stations, in just under twenty-two hours. The composition of the train, which is completely air-conditioned, changes during the journey, and at different stages includes Pullman cars, sleepers, diners, sun-room observation lounge car, parlour car and individual seat coach. Among the attendants there are a train-secretary, barber-valet and maid-manicurist.

(From a photo by courtesy of "Modern Transport")

ISSUED BY

GALLAHER LTD

VIRGINIA HOUSE. LONDON & BELFAST

773

TRAINS OF THE WORLD

SERIES OF 48. Nº 4

THE SCARBOROUGH FLIER

LONDON AND NORTH EASTERN RAILWAY

The Scarborough Flier runs every weekday during the summer between London (King's Cross—depart 11.10 a.m.) and Scarborough, the only intermediate stop being at York. Often, when the traffic is very heavy, the train is run in duplicate. It is a restaurant car express and provides the fastest service between London and York—the journey of 188¼ miles being accomplished in three hours at an average speed of 62.75 m.p.h.,—and also between London and Scarborough. On Saturdays in the summer it is one of five restaurant car trains leaving King's Cross within half-an-hour for the Yorkshire coast.

ISSUED BY

GALLAHER LTD

VIRGINIA HOUSE. LONDON & BELFAST

774

TRAINS OF THE WORLD

SERIES OF 48. Nº 31

CENTRAL URUGUAY RAILWAY SOUTH AMERICA

The main line of the Central Uruguay Railway runs north from Montevideo, on the south coast of Uruguay, to Durazno and Rio Negro, a distance of 171 miles: from this point the Northern Extension is continued for 185 miles to a junction near Rivera, on the northern frontier, with the Brazilian railway system. Other extensions and companies under the general control of the Central Company have lines in various parts of Uruguay. All these railways form a combined system of 980 miles of track with a gauge of 4-ft. 8½-in.

ISSUED BY

GALLAHER LTD

VIRGINIA HOUSE. LONDON & BELFAST

775

TRAINS OF THE WORLD

SERIES OF 48. Nº 8

PETROL RAILCAR

SLIGO, LEITRIM AND NORTHERN COUNTIES RAILWAY, IRELAND

This petrol railcar, which is a converted road omnibus and hauls a luggage trailer, was first put into operation in 1935 between Enniskillen and Sligo, two important stations about forty-five miles apart. It has proved very much more economical and provides a quicker and more satisfactory service than the mixed passenger and goods trains which the Company used to run. Its maximum speed is 45 m.p.h. and it can climb the steepest gradients on the journey (1 in 50) in top gear without any undue strain on the engine.

ISSUED BY

GALLAHER LTD

VIRGINIA HOUSE. LONDON & BELFAST

776

TRAINS OF THE WORLD

SERIES OF 48. Nº 6

THE CHELTENHAM FLYER

GREAT WESTERN RAILWAY

The Cheltenham Flyer, Britain's fastest train, was the first in the world scheduled to maintain a regular service at the remarkably high average speed of more than 70 m.p.h., and at one point the train does 92.3 m.p.h. The 77¼ miles between Swindon and London (Paddington) are covered in 65 minutes, but the distance has actually been performed in 54 minutes 47 seconds—an average of 81.6 m.p.h. The locomotive used to haul the express is one of the "Castle" class, first introduced in August, 1923.

ISSUED BY

GALLAHER LTD

VIRGINIA HOUSE. LONDON & BELFAST

777

TRAINS OF THE WORLD

SERIES OF 48. Nº 15

THE ROYAL BLUE

BALTIMORE & OHIO RAILROAD (U.S.A.)

The Royal Blue is shown here hauled by the locomotive "Lady Baltimore," the driving wheels of which measure 7-ft. in diameter. It runs between New York (Jersey City Station) and Washington, and stopping at six stations on the way, it covers the journey of 223.6 miles in four hours. The equipment includes parlour cars, buffet-lounge car, dining car and coaches. The train, which was constructed in 1935 of light-weight metals, has improved springing and automatic coupling arrangements and is fitted with special vestibules, eliminating noise and draught from the passages between cars.

ISSUED BY

GALLAHER LTD.

VIRGINIA HOUSE. LONDON & BELFAST

778

TRAINS OF THE WORLD

SERIES OF 48. Nº 30

THE INTERNATIONAL LIMITED

CANADIAN NATIONAL RAILWAYS

For over a third of a century The International Limited, the crack train of the Canadian National Railways, has been in service between Montreal, Toronto and Chicago, on the only double-track route connecting these cities. The train, which is variously composed of coaches, diners, parlour cars and sleepers, covers the westward journey of 849 miles in 17¼ hours, including stops. Through the tunnel under the St. Clair River joining Lakes Huron and Erie it is hauled by electric locomotives, but on the remainder of the journey steam locomotives are used.

ISSUED BY

GALLAHER LTD

VIRGINIA HOUSE. LONDON & BELFAST

THE BLUE COMET
CENTRAL RAILROAD OF NEW JERSEY

THE BRIGHTON BELLE
S.R.

DIESEL-ELECTRIC TRAIN
BUENOS AYRES GREAT SOUTHERN RAILWAY

STREAMLINED STEAM TRAIN
PARIS, LYONS & MEDITERRANEAN RLY.

THE ZEPHYR
CHICAGO, BURLINGTON & QUINCY RAILROAD

MAIL TRAIN
SUDAN RAILWAYS

STREAMLINED LOCOMOTIVE
PENNSYLVANIA RAILROAD

ELECTRIC TRAIN
RAILWAYS & TRAMWAYS COMPANY OF PIACENZA, ITALY

THE DUBLIN-BELFAST EXPRESS
GREAT NORTHERN RAILWAY, IRELAND

THE MELBOURNE EXPRESS
SOUTH AUSTRALIAN GOVERNMENT RAILWAYS

GREAT INDIAN PENINSULA RAILWAY

THE DOMINION
CANADIAN PACIFIC RLY.

THE CORNISH RIVIERA EXPRESS
G.W.R.

THE SUNNY SOUTH EXPRESS
L.M.S.

SNOW PLOUGH
SWEDISH STATE RAILWAYS

THE NORTH ATLANTIC EXPRESS
LMS. NCC. N. IRELAND

VITZNAU-RIGI RAILWAY

THE FLYING HAMBURGER
GERMAN STATE RAILWAYS

DIESEL TRAIN
NETHERLANDS RAILWAYS

THE LIMITED EXPRESS
NEW ZEALAND GOV. RLYS.

THE IRISH MAIL
L. M. S.

STREAMLINED LOCOMOTIVE
CANADIAN NATIONAL RAILWAYS

MAIL TRAIN
KENYA & UGANDA RAILWAYS.

THE SILVER JUBILEE
L. N. E. R.

DIESEL ELECTRIC RAIL CAR
NORTH WESTERN STATE RAILWAY OF INDIA

DIESEL RAIL MOTOR TRAIN
QUEENSLAND GOV. RAILWAYS

THE EASTERN BELLE
L. N. E. R.

THE ATLANTIC COAST EXPRESS
S. R.

RAILWAY ENGINES — A SERIES OF 50

---

807 — No. 32
ARTICULATED LOCO. "EMIR OF KATSINA," Nigerian Government Railway.

These Beyer-Garratt 4-6-2+2-6-4 articulated locomotives, which bear the name of Nigerian chiefs, have twelve axles because of the very light rails and bridges on certain sections over which they have to run. They are handled entirely by African natives, and during the six months heavy rainy season are used on the Jebba-Minna section. For the rest of the year they are employed on other sections. Passenger trains run from the port of Lagos and Kano, a distance of 700 miles. Each engine was shipped in three parts from the builders in England.

W.D. & H.O. WILLS — ISSUED BY THE IMPERIAL TOBACCO CO. (OF GREAT BRITAIN & IRELAND), LTD.

---

808 — No. 34
EXPRESS LOCOMOTIVE, South African Government Rlys.

These "16 E" class 4-6-2 "Pacific" type locomotives are claimed to be the largest of their wheel arrangement at work on the 3 ft. 6 in. gauge. They have coupled wheels 6 ft. in diameter, and the centre line of the very large boilers 9 ft. 3 in. above the rail-level. In working order, with 12 tons of coal and 6,000 gallons of water, these locomotives weigh 166½ tons. They are built for working express trains, including the "Union Limited," over the 617-mile Beaufort West, Kimberley and Johannesburg section. The "Union Limited" covers the journey of 900 miles between Cape Town and Johannesburg in 28 hours.

W.D. & H.O. WILLS — ISSUED BY THE IMPERIAL TOBACCO CO. (OF GREAT BRITAIN & IRELAND), LTD.

---

809 — No. 33
PASSENGER & FREIGHT LOCOMOTIVE, Kenya & Uganda Railways.

These Darlington-built 2-8-2 engines weigh 90½ tons, with 4 ft. 6 in. coupled wheels; they are among the biggest ordinary-type metre-gauge passenger engines in the world. Their duties include hauling the mail trains running between Nairobi 65,400 ft. above sea level and the coast, a distance of 330 miles. With a break of about 5 hours the return, the round trip of 660 miles occupies 42 hours with trains weighing 400 to 500 tons. On the mail service a relief crew is carried, the driver and fireman being made after each two hours, which constitutes a working day.

W.D. & H.O. WILLS — ISSUED BY THE IMPERIAL TOBACCO CO. (OF GREAT BRITAIN & IRELAND), LTD.

---

810 — No. 31
EXPRESS LOCOMOTIVE "MOHAMED ALI EL KEBIR," Egyptian State Railways.

For some years past the Egyptian State Railway's 4 ft. 8½ in. gauge express services have been scheduled at running speeds of 48 m.p.h., and the principal trains, weighing 400 to 500 tons, have been worked by "Atlantic" type 4-4-2 engines. An acceleration of 56 m.p.h. for these trains has called for improved accelerative power from the locomotives. To meet this demand some of the "Atlantics" have been rebuilt with six coupled wheels as the 4-6-0 type illustrated, and the boiler steam pressure raised. These engines are named after Egyptian Royalty.

W.D. & H.O. WILLS — ISSUED BY THE IMPERIAL TOBACCO CO. (OF GREAT BRITAIN & IRELAND), LTD.

---

811 — No. 18
HEAVY FREIGHT LOCOMOTIVE, P.L.M. Railway, France.

For handling the heaviest freight traffic between Paris and the south by the beautifully-curved Bourbonnais line over the Fontainebleau and Mediterranean Railway has introduced this new design of four-cylinder compound goods engine. An interesting and novel feature of this 2-10-2 locomotive is that the coupling rods between the second and third coupled axles are arranged inside the framing on crank axles, as the high-pressure cylinders. Attached to its tender not shown here and in working order, the locomotive complete weighs just under 182 tons. Two of these engines have mechanical stokers.

W.D. & H.O. WILLS — ISSUED BY THE IMPERIAL TOBACCO CO. (OF GREAT BRITAIN & IRELAND), LTD.

---

812 — No. 19
SUBURBAN TANK LOCOMOTIVE, Eastern Railway, France.

A unique feature of Paris suburban train working is the employment on some sections of powerful steam tank locomotives, which can, immediately pull, their trains of heavy all-steel coaches, weighing over 400 tons. By this method the trains can be reversed at the termini with the minimum of delay. When the engine is pushing, the driver works the controls through special gear from a compartment at what is then the front of the train, the engine being of the 2-8-2 type weighing about 104½ tons, and used by both the Eastern and the French State Railways in the Paris area.

W.D. & H.O. WILLS — ISSUED BY THE IMPERIAL TOBACCO CO. (OF GREAT BRITAIN & IRELAND), LTD.

---

813 — No. 15
EXPRESS LOCOMOTIVE "KESTREL," Great Northern Railway, Ireland.

This 4-4-0 engine is one of a class of five three-cylinder compound express locomotives placed in service in 1932 on the main lines of the Great Northern Railway in 1932, and representing a considerable advance in power compared with earlier engines on this line. The class is employed on the express services between Dublin and Belfast, and at one time was looked on between Dublin and Belfast, and at an average of some 50 m.p.h., and put up some excellent performances with 300-ton trains on this 112½-mile undulating route. The original black livery has recently given place to the more handsome colouring shown here.

W.D. & H.O. WILLS — ISSUED BY THE IMPERIAL TOBACCO CO. (OF GREAT BRITAIN & IRELAND), LTD.

---

814 — No. 27
2 FT. 6 IN. GAUGE LOCOMOTIVE, Lithuanian State Railways.

Despite the total weight (with tender) of 63 tons and an overall length of 51 ft., this 0-10-0 locomotive runs on a gauge measuring only 2 ft. 6 in. It has been designed to haul loads of 300 tons up 1 in 62 grades, with curves at 121 m.p.h., or 200 tons at 25 m.p.h. on straight 1 in 200 grades. The fire-box is designed to burn mixed fuel of wood and coal. The Lithuanian State Railways own about 300 miles of 2 ft. 6 in.- and 2 ft.-gauge lines, in addition to the 4 ft. 8½ in.-gauge railways which replaced the 5 ft.-gauge lines laid down under the previous Russian ownership.

W.D. & H.O. WILLS — ISSUED BY THE IMPERIAL TOBACCO CO. (OF GREAT BRITAIN & IRELAND), LTD.

---

815 — No. 17
EXPRESS LOCOMOTIVE, Paris-Orleans-Midi Railways, France.

A good illustration of the high efficiency of modern steam engines is given by this 4 x 0 French engine, originally built in 1907 as a 4-6-2 type. In 1931 it was considerably modified by the addition of a fourth pair of coupled wheels, a smaller fire-grate, new cylinders and special valves, a double blast-pipe and chimney, a more increased boiler pressure and higher steam temperature, shaking grate, etc. These alterations have produced a machine capable of handling 700-800 tons over the hilly Vierzon-Toulouse line at a high average speed, and with a striking economy in fuel.

W.D. & H.O. WILLS — ISSUED BY THE IMPERIAL TOBACCO CO. (OF GREAT BRITAIN & IRELAND), LTD.

---

816 — No. 16
EXPRESS LOCOMOTIVE "DUKE OF ABERCORN," N.C.C. (L.M.S.R.), Ireland.

The nucleus of the Northern Counties Committee system was the former Belfast & Northern Counties Railway, which was taken by the Midland Railway, England, in 1903. The system thus passed eventually into L.M.S.R. ownership, on the amalgamation of that Railway into that group. Thus the characteristics of L.M.S.R. loco-motive design are to be found on the N.C.C. Our subject, a 2-6-0, is one of a class recently put at the L.M.S.R. works at Derby for express passenger service on the 5 ft. 3 in.-gauge N.C.C. lines. The trains worked include the "North Atlantic Express" and the "Portrush Flyer," between Portrush and Belfast (65½ miles).

W.D. & H.O. WILLS — ISSUED BY THE IMPERIAL TOBACCO CO. (OF GREAT BRITAIN & IRELAND), LTD.

---

817 — No. 9
"KING" CLASS EXPRESS LOCO. "KING GEORGE V.," Great Western Railway.

This four-cylinder 4-6-0 engine belongs to the principal class of G.W.R. express locomotives, and is employed in such services as the "Cornish Riviera Limited" express. No. 6000 was exhibited in America in 1927 at the Balti-more & Ohio Railway's Centen-ary celebrations. Her 6 ft. 6 in. coupled wheels striving on to each of the 4 cylinders driving engine units, between which the boiler is carried. The 40-mile journey, including its steel axles and sharp curves, is completed in a road-time of 60 mins., with trains of steel coaches weighing up to 500 tons. These large engines, running on the 5 ft. 3 in. gauge, are the largest British with equal footing in either direction without being turned.

W.D. & H.O. WILLS — ISSUED BY THE IMPERIAL TOBACCO CO. (OF GREAT BRITAIN & IRELAND), LTD.

---

818 — No. 28
HEAVY FREIGHT LOCO., U.S.S.R. Railway.

Locomotives of the same power and of a similar weight, but designed with fewer axles than this 4-14-4 locomotive, are in use in the U.S.A. But those respon-sible for that so enormous engine found that to get the necessary flexi-bility, and without strengthening the existing road, the weight of the engine would have to be distributed over many more axles than usual, the engine which was built for heavy coal traffic in the Donetz Basin, runs on the 5 ft. gauge, is just under 110 ft. 9 in. long with tender and, in working order, weighs (with ten-der), 327½ tons. It is required to move 2,500-ton loads over heavy grades.

W.D. & H.O. WILLS — ISSUED BY THE IMPERIAL TOBACCO CO. (OF GREAT BRITAIN & IRELAND), LTD.

---

819 — No. 49
ARTICULATED EXPRESS LOCOMOTIVE, San Paulo (Brazilian) Railway.

Employed on the principal expresses between San Paulo and Jundiahy, these 165-ton Beyer-Garratt 4-6-2+2-6-4 engines were the first of their type to be employed for express passenger work. They have coupled wheels 5 ft. 6 in. in diameter, and a total 86½-ton tenders carrying 7,700 gallons of water, and 18 tons of fuel, a total of 205 tons. They run on the 5 ft. 6 in. gauge, hauling freight trains of 1,600 tons over the heavily-graded sec-tion of the B.A.P. main line between La Paz and Jundiahy. At present, in keeping the fire-grade adequately fed with fuel, a pusher device is used on the tender, which moves the coal for-ward to the shovel-plate opening.

W.D. & H.O. WILLS — ISSUED BY THE IMPERIAL TOBACCO CO. (OF GREAT BRITAIN & IRELAND), LTD.

---

820 — No. 50
HEAVY FREIGHT LOCO., Buenos Ayres & Pacific Railway, Argentina.

These powerful 2-8-2 eight-coupled, the "Mikado" locomotives have the distinction of being the biggest ordinary-type locomotives at work in the Argentine. They have coupled wheels 4 ft. 6 in. in diameter, and a 86½-ton tender carrying 7,000 gallons of water and 15 tons of fuel, a total of 205 tons. They run on the 5 ft. 6 in. gauge, hauling freight trains of 1,600 tons over the heavily-graded sec-tion of the railway's main line between La Paz and Villa Mercedes. A pusher device is used on the tender, which moves the coal for-ward to the shovel-plate opening.

W.D. & H.O. WILLS — ISSUED BY THE IMPERIAL TOBACCO CO. (OF GREAT BRITAIN & IRELAND), LTD.

WILL'S CIGARETTES

EXPRESS LOCOMOTIVE, SOUTH AFRICAN GOVERNMENT RAILWAYS

WILL'S CIGARETTES

ARTICULATED LOCOMOTIVE "EMIR OF KATSINA," NIGERIAN GOVT. RLY.

WILL'S CIGARETTES

EXPRESS LOCOMOTIVE "MOHAMED ALI EL KEBIR," EGYPTIAN STATE RLYS.

WILL'S CIGARETTES

PASSENGER & FREIGHT LOCOMOTIVE, KENYA & UGANDA RAILWAYS

WILL'S CIGARETTES

SUBURBAN TANK LOCOMOTIVE, EASTERN RAILWAY, FRANCE

WILL'S CIGARETTES

HEAVY FREIGHT LOCOMOTIVE, P.L.M. RAILWAY, FRANCE

WILL'S CIGARETTES

2 FT. 6 IN. GAUGE LOCOMOTIVE, LITHUANIAN STATE RAILWAYS

WILL'S CIGARETTES

EXPRESS LOCOMOTIVE "KESTREL," GREAT NORTHERN RLY., IRELAND

WILL'S CIGARETTES

EXPRESS LOCOMOTIVE "DUKE OF ABERCORN," N.C.C. (L.M.S.R.), IRELAND

WILL'S CIGARETTES

EXPRESS LOCOMOTIVE, PARIS-ORLEANS-MIDI RAILWAYS, FRANCE

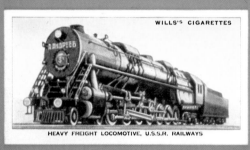

WILL'S CIGARETTES

HEAVY FREIGHT LOCOMOTIVE, U.S.S.R. RAILWAYS

WILL'S CIGARETTES

"KING" CLASS EXPRESS LOCOMOTIVE "KING GEORGE V," G.W.R.

WILL'S CIGARETTES

HEAVY FREIGHT LOCO., BUENOS AYRES & PACIFIC RLY., ARGENTINA

WILL'S CIGARETTES

ARTICULATED EXPRESS LOCOMOTIVE, SAN PAULO (BRAZILIAN) RAILWAY

EXPRESS LOCOMOTIVE "REMEMBRANCE," SOUTHERN RAILWAY

EXPRESS LOCOMOTIVE, BENGAL-NAGPUR RAILWAY, INDIA

"PACIFIC" EXPRESS LOCOMOTIVE "PRINCESS MARGARET ROSE," L.M.S.R.

STREAMLINED EXPRESS LOCOMOTIVE "COCK O'THE NORTH," L.N.E.R.

EXPRESS LOCOMOTIVE "SILVER JUBILEE," L.M.S.R.

EXPRESS LOCOMOTIVE, NEW ZEALAND GOVERNMENT RAILWAYS

EXPRESS LOCOMOTIVE, CANADIAN NATIONAL RAILWAYS

TURBINE-DRIVEN LOCOMOTIVE, L.M.S.R.

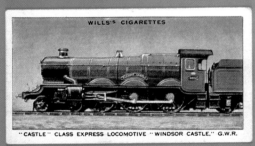

"CASTLE" CLASS EXPRESS LOCOMOTIVE "WINDSOR CASTLE," G.W.R.

DRUMM BATTERY TRAIN, GREAT SOUTHERN RAILWAYS, IRELAND

EXPRESS LOCOMOTIVE, AUSTRIAN FEDERAL RAILWAYS

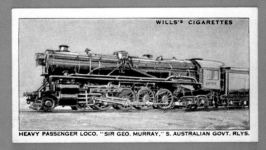

HEAVY PASSENGER LOCO. "SIR GEO. MURRAY," S. AUSTRALIAN GOVT. RLYS.

"PACIFIC" EXPRESS LOCOMOTIVE "PAPYRUS," L.N.E.R.

STREAMLINED EXPRESS LOCOMOTIVE "SILVER LINK," L.N.E.R.

Card 821

RAILWAY ENGINES

A SERIES OF 50 — 37 — **821**

EXPRESS LOCOMOTIVE,
Bengal-Nagpur Railway, India.

Although generally conforming in design to India's largest standard gauge railway's largest standard gauge locomotives of the same gauge and wheel arrangement, these big 5 ft. 6 in.-gauge Bengal-Nagpur Railway locomotives are designed on the De Glehn compound system. They are 4-6-2's employed on the heaviest passenger traffic, including the Calcutta-Bombay Mail, which they work over the section between Calcutta and Nagpur. Steam is first used in a pair of high-pressure cylinders outside the frames, then passes to the two low-pressure cylinders arranged between the frames. In working order, one of these engines weighs 105 tons, and the tender (loaded), 65½ tons.

W. D. & H. O. WILLS
ISSUED BY THE IMPERIAL TOBACCO CO.
(OF GREAT BRITAIN & IRELAND), LTD.

Card 822

RAILWAY ENGINES

A SERIES OF 50 — 12 — **822**

EXPRESS LOCOMOTIVE "REMEMBRANCE,"
Southern Railway.

Between 1914 and 1929 the London, Brighton & South Coast Railway built and placed in service seven express passenger tank locomotives, having six coupled wheels and a four-wheeled bogie at each end. When built, these 2N3-ton engines were the heaviest tank engines in Great Britain, and were amongst the fastest and heaviest in the country. The last of the class to be built was named "Remembrance" in memory of employees of the L.B. & S.C.R. who fell in the Great War. Following the extension of electrification, these engines have been converted into 4-6-0's and supplied with tenders to make them suitable for work over longer distances.

W. D. & H. O. WILLS
ISSUED BY THE IMPERIAL TOBACCO CO.
(OF GREAT BRITAIN & IRELAND), LTD.

Card 823

RAILWAY ENGINES

A SERIES OF 50 — 5 — **823**

STREAMLINED EXPRESS LOCO. "COCK O'THE NORTH."

The first eight-coupled locomotive built for express passenger service in Great Britain, this three-cylinder 2-8-2 engine was also the first ordinary-type engine on a home railway to have a streamlined contour. This class is employed on "The Flying Scotsman" and other expresses between Edinburgh and Aberdeen. In 1934 No. 2001 was tested on the French locomotive testing plant at Vitry, near Paris. Special features include the double blast-pipe and the two chimneys set one behind the other within the same casing, and poppet-valves. In working order this engine weighs 110½ tons, and the tender 55½ tons.

W. D. & H. O. WILLS
ISSUED BY THE IMPERIAL TOBACCO CO.
(OF GREAT BRITAIN & IRELAND), LTD.

Card 824

RAILWAY ENGINES

A SERIES OF 50 — 2 — **824**

"PACIFIC" EXPRESS LOCO "PRINCESS MARGARET ROSE," L.M.S.R.

For hauling the most important Anglo-Scottish expresses over the West Coast route, including the "Royal Scot," "Mid-day Scot," and "Night Scot," the L.M.S.R. employs 4-6-2 locomotives of the "Princess Royal" class, each named after a Royal Family, and weighing with tender, in working order, 158 tons 12 cwt. Like the G.W.R. "King" and "Castle" class engines, these engines have four cylinders and a boiler pressure of 250 lb. per sq. in. On such duties as the Royal Scot express, these engines may work eight through between Euston and Glasgow (401¼ miles) or Euston and Edinburgh (399¼ miles).

W. D. & H. O. WILLS
ISSUED BY THE IMPERIAL TOBACCO CO.
(OF GREAT BRITAIN & IRELAND), LTD.

Card 825

RAILWAY ENGINES

A SERIES OF 50 — 42 — **825**

EXPRESS LOCOMOTIVE,
New Zealand Government Rlys.

Since 1922, provision has been made for the running of a total of thirty of these 3 ft. 6 in. gauge 4-8-2 engines at the New Zealand Government Railways' workshops. One such engine weighs, complete with 51-ton tender, a total of just under 128 tons, and develops about 80 per cent. more power than the previous standard "Pacific" passenger engines, whenever two engines together were previously required, one of these new "K" class locomotives handles the traffic unaided. They have proved themselves very economical and, with their 4 ft. 6 in. coupled wheels, are well suited to the heavily-graded sections of the North Island main trunk route.

W. D. & H. O. WILLS
ISSUED BY THE IMPERIAL TOBACCO CO.
(OF GREAT BRITAIN & IRELAND), LTD.

Card 826

RAILWAY ENGINES

A SERIES OF 50 — 1 — **826**

EXPRESS LOCOMOTIVE "SILVER JUBILEE."
London, Midland & Scottish Rlys.

The interest of this 4-6-0 three-cylinder express passenger engine, completed in May, 1935, centres in the beautiful finish. The shiny black of the boiler, cab and tender sides is contrasted with the chromium plating adopted for wheels and motion work, steam pipe casings, etc. No. 5552 "Silver Jubilee" (built 1911), during Silver Jubilee Week, May, 1935, she worked the honeymoon special conveying the Duke and Duchess of Gloucester from St. Pancras to Kettering.

W. D. & H. O. WILLS
ISSUED BY THE IMPERIAL TOBACCO CO.
(OF GREAT BRITAIN & IRELAND), LTD.

Card 827

RAILWAY ENGINES

A SERIES OF 50 — 3 — **827**

TURBINE-DRIVEN LOCOMOTIVE,
London, Midland & Scottish Rly.

A great deal of interest was aroused in railway circles when it became known that an electric battery had been invented which could be re-charged much more quickly than the usual type. The most familiar exhaust beat of the orthodox steam locomotive is strangely absent when this engine is running, for the drive is by turbine and gearing instead by cylinders and pistons. The smooth turning effort imparted to the driving wheels by a turbine and the very gentle exhaust, thus saving fuel, have long attracted locomotive engineers. This new "W" class, which was introduced in 1935, the first of the type to be built by a railway company in Great Britain. The main turbine, used for forward running, develops 2,000 h.p. and is carried under the casing seen near the front; a smaller turbine for backward running is on the opposite side.

W. D. & H. O. WILLS
ISSUED BY THE IMPERIAL TOBACCO CO.
(OF GREAT BRITAIN & IRELAND), LTD.

Card 828

RAILWAY ENGINES

A SERIES OF 50 — 43 — **828**

EXPRESS LOCOMOTIVE,
Canadian National Railways.

Although not the largest express engines on the Canadian National Railways, this type does a great deal of useful work on both main line four-distance passenger and freight traffic, particularly as the more easily-handled engines of the system. These 4-8-4 engines have done excellent work with the "International Limited" express. This train runs between Montreal, Canada, and Chicago, U.S.A., and except for the short electrically-hauled section under the river between Sarnia and Port Huron, is steam-hauled throughout. These engines are mechanically fitted and, with their tenders, in working order, weigh about 330 tons.

W. D. & H. O. WILLS
ISSUED BY THE IMPERIAL TOBACCO CO.
(OF GREAT BRITAIN & IRELAND), LTD.

Card 829

RAILWAY ENGINES

A SERIES OF 50 — 14 — **829**

DRUMM BATTERY TRAIN,
Great Southern Railways, Ireland.

A great deal of interest was aroused in railway circles when it became known that an electric battery had been invented which could be re-charged much more quickly than the usual type. The Great Southern Railways of Ireland installed these batteries (constructed under patents of the inventor, Dr. J. J. Drumm) in a two-coach electric train, having electric motors on the middle bogie and working on the same principle as an electric train, but without requiring side rail or overhead line current transmission along the track. These trains work between Dublin and Bray, one set performing a total of 1,000 miles a week.

W. D. & H. O. WILLS
ISSUED BY THE IMPERIAL TOBACCO CO.
(OF GREAT BRITAIN & IRELAND), LTD.

Card 830

RAILWAY ENGINES

A SERIES OF 50 — 7 — **830**

"CASTLE" CLASS EXPRESS LOCO. "WINDSOR CASTLE."
Great Western Railway.

During a visit to the G.W.R. Works at Swindon in 1924, His late Majesty King George V personally drove this engine and its train from the Works to Swindon Station. To commemorate the event has since been commemorated on the cab side. It was singularly appropriate that the same engine should be used to draw the Royal Funeral Train bearing the body of the late King from Paddington to Windsor on January 28th, 1936. The "Castle" class of four-cylinder 4-6-0 express engines is world renowned for speed, being used in the form of the famous "Cheltenham Flyer" express.

W. D. & H. O. WILLS
ISSUED BY THE IMPERIAL TOBACCO CO.
(OF GREAT BRITAIN & IRELAND), LTD.

Card 831

RAILWAY ENGINES

A SERIES OF 50 — 41 — **831**

HEAVY PASSENGER LOCO. "SIR GEORGE MURRAY,"
South Australian Govt. Rlys.

An interesting feature of these large English-built, mechanically-fired 4-8-4 locomotives is that although constructed for 5 ft. 3 in.-gauge working, they have been so designed to allow of conversion to 4 ft. 8½ in.-gauge should this be deemed necessary. They had only two small wheels under the cab end, but this has been altered to a four-wheeled truck which a booster or small auxiliary engine has been applied to give greater power for starting and at low speeds. These engines are altered weigh 232 tons, including an 84-ton tender. Their duties include the hauling of the Adelaide-Melbourne expresses.

W. D. & H. O. WILLS
ISSUED BY THE IMPERIAL TOBACCO CO.
(OF GREAT BRITAIN & IRELAND), LTD.

Card 832

RAILWAY ENGINES

A SERIES OF 50 — 26 — **832**

EXPRESS LOCOMOTIVE,
Austrian Federal Railways.

In 1929 the Austrian Federal Railways introduced two experimental Anglo-coupled express locomotives, differing in arrangement, for express passenger traffic. Otherwise generally similar, one engine had three cylinders, the other two. Further engines of the two-cylinder type have since been added, and they are used on the principal international expresses over the heavily-graded 196 miles between Vienna and Salzburg. For an express engine design, these locomotives share a constructional feature with other Central European engines of having two small wheels leading in the form of a truck which are connected to the front pair of coupled wheels.

W. D. & H. O. WILLS
ISSUED BY THE IMPERIAL TOBACCO CO.
(OF GREAT BRITAIN & IRELAND), LTD.

Card 833

RAILWAY ENGINES

A SERIES OF 50 — 4 — **833**

STREAMLINED EXPRESS LOCO. "SILVER LINK,"
London & North Eastern Railway.

Great Britain's first, fully-streamlined locomotive, a 4-6-2, or "Pacific" type three-cylinder engine, "Silver Link" was introduced by the L.N.E.R. in 1935 for working the streamlined London-Newcastle express in honour of His late Majesty King George V's Silver Jubilee. The distance of 268½ miles, with one stop at Darlington, is covered in 4 hours. On an experimental run on September 27th, 1935, she attained a maximum speed of 112½ m.p.h. To minimise wind resistance the sides of the chimney and the front are specially shaped. "Silver Link" is one of four similar engines built for the popular service.

W. D. & H. O. WILLS
ISSUED BY THE IMPERIAL TOBACCO CO.
(OF GREAT BRITAIN & IRELAND), LTD.

Card 834

RAILWAY ENGINES

A SERIES OF 50 — 6 — **834**

"PACIFIC" EXPRESS LOCO. "PAPYRUS,"
London & North Eastern Railway.

For its principal heavy expresses, the L.N.E.R. uses a 4-6-2 or "Pacific" type three-cylinder engine. The latest weigh, with corridor tender, 158 tons 13 cwt., and the majority bear the names of racehorses. No. 2750, "Papyrus," became world-famous since being built by the fact that, after attaining a then world record maximum speed of 108 m.p.h. and covered 12·3 miles at an average of 100·6 m.p.h. with a load of 216½ tons, "Papyrus" ran from King's Cross to Newcastle and back (536·6 miles) in a total running time of 7 hrs. 48 mins. 55 secs. and for 300 miles averaged 80 m.p.h.

W. D. & H. O. WILLS
ISSUED BY THE IMPERIAL TOBACCO CO.
(OF GREAT BRITAIN & IRELAND), LTD.

835 — No. 25 — RAILWAY ENGINES — A SERIES OF 50

ELECTRIC PASSENGER & FREIGHT LOCO.
Swiss Federal Railways.

This 7,500 h.p. single-phase electric locomotive employed on the St. Gotthard line of the Swiss Federal Railways, is the most powerful electric locomotive in Europe. Although running as one unit in service, it really consists of two identical halves, each having its own driving compartment. One of these express passenger trains, is in place of two of the previous type employed. It can haul a 600-ton passenger train at 38 m.p.h. up a 1 in 37 gradient, and a 750-ton goods train at 30 m.p.h., the maximum speed of the locomotive being fixed at 62 m.p.h.

W.D. & H.O. WILLS — ISSUED BY THE IMPERIAL TOBACCO CO. (OF GREAT BRITAIN & IRELAND), LTD.

836 — No. 46 — RAILWAY ENGINES — A SERIES OF 50

EXPRESS PASSENGER LOCOMOTIVE
Northern Pacific Railway, U.S.A.

For working heavy through passenger and special trains over the 906 miles between Jamestown, N.D., and Missoula, Mont.—one of the longest runs in the world on which the same steam locomotive is used throughout, and including some heavy mountain grades—the Northern Pacific Railway employs this 2-10-4 two-cylinder locomotive. Firing is by means of a mechanical stoker capable of feeding approximately 11 tons of coal an hour on to the 115-sq. ft. grate. The main framing of these engines, together with the two cylinders and certain other details, consists of a single casting weighing just over 25 tons.

837 — No. 36 — RAILWAY ENGINES — A SERIES OF 50

EXPRESS LOCOMOTIVE,
North Western Railway, India.

This Lancashire-built 5 ft. 6 in.-gauge 4-6-2 locomotive is one of four four-cylinder non-compound express locomotives. Compared with the very similar two-cylinder engines which form the standard for the fastest and heaviest express passenger duties, such as the Lahore-Karachi Mail on the North Western and on other Indian State-owned railways, these do not mark an advance in power, and vary somewhat in detail design, particularly in the use of poppet-valves. The coal-burning engines of this kind weigh 172½ tons. The coal-burning engines of this and similar types in India are handled by a crew of three.

838 — No. 44 — RAILWAY ENGINES — A SERIES OF 50

HEAVY PASSENGER & FREIGHT LOCOMOTIVE,
Canadian Pacific Railway.

This powerful oil-burning 2-10-4 two-cylinder locomotive is one of a series used for hauling the Canadian Pacific's heavy passenger and freight trains over the mountain sections in Western Canada. With tender complete, in working order, this class weighs 336 tons, and as many as four of these engines may be used at intervals on a 3,500-ton freight train along the 20 miles of 1 in 40 grades up to Glacier Summit. A slightly heavier version of this class, consisting of one locomotive only, No. 5000 is a three-cylinder compound and uses steam at 850 lb. pressure.

839 — No. 35 — RAILWAY ENGINES — A SERIES OF 50

ARTICULATED HEAVY FREIGHT LOCOMOTIVE,
South African Government Rlys.

A product of Manchester, this Beyer-Garratt 4-8-2+2-8-4 locomotive weighs 211 tons, is about 90 ft. in length and is the largest 3 ft. 6 in.-gauge engine in the world. The principal duties are the hauling of heavy freight trains, weighing up to 1,200 tons, over a 38-mile grade of 1 in 66 in Natal, and their use has enabled train loads to be doubled. The great power of these locomotives, which resolve themselves as it were into two engines coupled together, is due to the fact that the separate eight-wheel-coupled units at each end have their own sets of cylinders and motion, power being supplied by the very large boiler arranged between the two engine units.

840 — No. 11 — RAILWAY ENGINES — A SERIES OF 50

"SCHOOLS" CLASS LOCO. "LEATHERHEAD,"
Southern Railway.

For working moderately-heavy trains on which the larger six-coupled express engines are not required, or the use of which is deemed unsuitable by weight or other restrictions, the Southern Railway has a class of three-cylinder, four-coupled bogie engines. The most powerful 4-4-0 type engines in Europe, they are employed on express services on the London-Hastings and London-Portsmouth routes, and elsewhere. They haul loads of ten and eleven coaches, weighing, with passengers, little short of 400 tons in all, at high speeds over hilly roads, and have shown themselves capable of fast work.

841 — No. 39 — RAILWAY ENGINES — A SERIES OF 50

MIXED-TRAFFIC LOCO.,
Canton-Hankow Railway, China.

Though it may be thought that the locomotives used on the railways of far-off China are not representative of British design types, such is far from being the case. The product of a British firm, and designed for the 4 ft. 8½ in. gauge, this thoroughly modern 4-8-4 engine alone weighs just under 116 tons in working order. The tender, weighing 77 tons complete, carries 11½ tons of coal and 6,500 gallons of water. These engines, which are otherwise entirely by Chinese, have been built for working between Canton and Hankow, a distance of approximately 670 miles, and some have been loaned for service on the Nanking-Shanghai Railway.

842 — No. 10 — RAILWAY ENGINES — A SERIES OF 50

"LORD NELSON" CLASS EXPRESS LOCO. "LORD HAWKE,"
Southern Railway.

The Southern Railway routes from London, over which the Dover and Folkestone Continental boat trains, such as the "Golden Arrow" Pullman express, are worked, are by no means easy for the locomotives. There are numerous grades and curves, while near London delays are often met with, especially after sub-urban traffic. The "Lord Nelson" four-cylinder 4-6-0 express locomotives, named after famous seamen, are used on these workings and also on the "Atlantic Coast" and other expresses to and from Waterloo, Western Section. In working order they each weigh 83½ tons, and their eight-wheeled tenders 56 tons 14 cwt.

843 — No. 40 — RAILWAY ENGINES — A SERIES OF 50

EXPRESS LOCOMOTIVE,
Imperial Govt. Rlys. of Japan.

This 4-6-2 locomotive is similar to the principal express type used for hauling the most important trains on the 3 ft. 6 in. gauge of the Tokio-Kobe and other lines of the Imperial Government Railways. The best trains include dining cars by day, and sleeping and observation cars by night. Runs of 115 miles are covered non-stop at an average speed as high as 45 m.p.h. The Japanese like to give their 4-6-2 engine as one of the latest "C 53" class three-cylinder non-compound "Pacifics," with 5 ft. 9 in.-diameter coupled wheels, and weighs (with tender) 128¾ tons. Some of the Japanese expresses bear picturesque names, the English translations being, "The Swallow," "The Cherry Flowers," "The Swallow Limited," etc.

844 — No. 38 — RAILWAY ENGINES — A SERIES OF 50

DIESEL-ELECTRIC PASSENGER LOCOMOTIVE,
Royal Siamese State Railways.

The heavy-oil engine is being increasingly used in rail service, and in addition to many railcars and high-speed light-weight Diesel trains, there are to-day Diesel locomotives of considerable size and power at work. The example illustrated is employed on main-line service in Siam. It weighs 87 tons and replaces a steam locomotive and tender of about the same total weight. Besides doing away with the need for water supplies, it is one of the Siamese section of the Bangkok-Singapore International express, hitherto requiring altogether four locomotives for the various sections, but now worked right through between Bangkok and the border at Padang Besar by the one oil-engined locomotive.

845 — No. 23 — RAILWAY ENGINES — A SERIES OF 50

EXPRESS LOCOMOTIVE,
German State Railways.

This 4-6-2 locomotive is similar to the principal express type used for hauling the most important heavy, long-distance expresses and fast trains on the German State Railways. Alloy steels have been used in the construction of the boilers for this and a sister engine, which work at a steam pressure of 355 lb. per sq. in., as against 227 lb. per sq. in. in numerous other engines which are otherwise generally similar. These new engines have four cylinders working on the compound principle, and an interesting feature incorporated in the design is the provision of electric light at various points to facilitate night overhauling.

846 — No. 48 — RAILWAY ENGINES — A SERIES OF 50

DIESEL-ELECTRIC TRAIN "BURLINGTON ZEPHYR,"
C. B. & Q. Railroad, U.S.A.

In order to recapture long-distance traffic from road and air transport, and to effect more economical operation, the railways of the U.S.A. are adopting streamlined trains. Examples are the stainless steel "Zephyrs" on the Chicago, Burlington and Quincy Railroad, two of which work a double trip per day each between Chicago and St. Paul, a round distance of 862 miles. Other Diesel trains are at work in the U.S.A., Germany, Italy, France, Belgium, Holland, etc. This Diesel train is credited to a Diesel train, and in Germany they regularly run at 100-104 m.p.h.

847 — No. 24 — RAILWAY ENGINES — A SERIES OF 50

HEAVY FREIGHT LOCOMOTIVE,
German State Railways.

These large 2-10-0 freight locomotives, weighing, with their tenders, about 186½ tons in working order, are the heaviest at present employed on the German State Railways. A pressure of 355 lb. per sq. in. is used, and there are four cylinders, two on the compound principle. These engines work in heavily-graded districts. They are capable of a maximum speed of 50 m.p.h. and represent an increase in power of from 10 to 15 per cent. over the standard goods locomotives of the German State Railways. Roller bearings are used extensively in these engines.

848 — No. 47 — RAILWAY ENGINES — A SERIES OF 50

STREAMLINED LOCOMOTIVE "COMMODORE VANDERBILT,"
N.Y.C. Railroad, U.S.A.

One of the well-known "Hudson" or "Baltic" type locomotives of the New York Central Lines has been covered with a streamline cowling, and the streamlining decreases the air resistance by about 30 per cent. In addition, enclosing the cylinders and pipes gives protection from heat losses, an important item. The "Commodore Vanderbilt," as it is named, is employed on the crack "Twentieth Century Limited," an express operating on a 16½-hour schedule between New York and Chicago (960 miles).

WILLS'S CIGARETTES

EXPRESS PASSENGER LOCO., NORTHERN PACIFIC RAILWAY, U.S.A.

WILLS'S CIGARETTES

ELECTRIC PASSENGER AND FREIGHT LOCOMOTIVE, SWISS FEDERAL RLYS.

WILLS'S CIGARETTES

HEAVY PASSENGER AND FREIGHT LOCOMOTIVE, CANADIAN PACIFIC RLY.

WILLS'S CIGARETTES

EXPRESS LOCOMOTIVE, NORTH WESTERN RAILWAY, INDIA

WILLS'S CIGARETTES

"SCHOOLS" CLASS LOCOMOTIVE "LEATHERHEAD," SOUTHERN RAILWAY

WILLS'S CIGARETTES

ARTICULATED HEAVY FREIGHT LOCOMOTIVE, SOUTH AFRICAN GOVT. RLYS

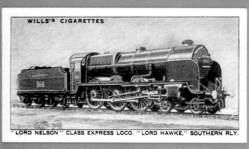

WILLS'S CIGARETTES

"LORD NELSON" CLASS EXPRESS LOCO. "LORD HAWKE." SOUTHERN RLY.

WILLS'S CIGARETTES

MIXED-TRAFFIC LOCOMOTIVE, CANTON-HANKOW RAILWAY, CHINA

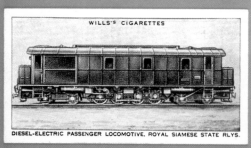

WILLS'S CIGARETTES

DIESEL-ELECTRIC PASSENGER LOCOMOTIVE, ROYAL SIAMESE STATE RLYS.

WILLS'S CIGARETTES

EXPRESS LOCOMOTIVE, IMPERIAL GOVERNMENT RAILWAYS OF JAPAN

WILLS'S CIGARETTES

DIESEL-ELECTRIC TRAIN "BURLINGTON ZEPHYR," C.B. & Q. RAILROAD, U.S.A.

WILLS'S CIGARETTES

EXPRESS LOCOMOTIVE, GERMAN STATE RAILWAYS

WILLS'S CIGARETTES

STREAMLINED LOCO. "COMMODORE VANDERBILT," N.Y.C. RAILROAD, U.S.A.

WILLS'S CIGARETTES

HEAVY FREIGHT LOCOMOTIVE, GERMAN STATE RAILWAYS

PART THREE

HOW TO USE THE CATALOGUE

This catalogue covers the cigarette card issues of British tobacco manufacturers for the home market. Certain export series by these companies are included followed by the word 'export' in brackets.

Manufacturers are featured in alphabetical order, and the issues of each firm are listed alphabetically within suitable sub-divisions such as 'Pre-1919 Issues', 'Post-1920 Issues', 'Post-1940 Issues', 'Silks' and 'Miscellaneous'.

Where a brand name, but no manufacturer's name, is shown on the card, reference should be made to the Index of Brands at the end of the catalogue. Anonymous series are also listed at the end of the catalogue although where there is evidence to link an anonymous issue with a particular company the series is listed as well under that firm in italic.

Information is given in the columns from left to right as follows:

Illustration number: The number corresponds to the numbered illustration in the central section of the book.

Size: The code letter refers to the size of the card as indicated in the chart opposite. A number 1 or 2 after the letter means that the card is slightly larger or smaller than shown.

Printing: The code indicates the printing on the front of the card. BW = black-and-white; C = coloured; CP = colour photograph; P = photograph; U = unicoloured (monochrome).

Number in Set: This figure gives the number of cards in the series. A question mark alongside shows that the exact number is unknown.

Title and Date: The title is as printed on the cards except where there is an asterisk to indicate an 'adopted' title. Where a firm issued several different series with the same title, these are distinguished by the addition of 'Set 1', 'Set 2', etc. and details appear in the appropriate Handbook. 'RB' after the series title refers to the reference book covering a particular manufacturer, and for Wills' issues 'W' after the title refers to the Wills reference book. (For details of these publications please see page 256.) The date of issue where known, is shown in brackets.

Handbook Reference: Un-numbered series, series issued by more than one manufacturer, and different series of the same title issued by a single firm, have been given an 'H' or 'Ha' number cross-referencing to Handbook Parts I and II respectively (please see page 256 for details).

Prices: The last two columns show the London Cigarette Card Company's selling prices for odd cards and complete sets in very good condition. Where no price is shown this does not necessarily mean that the Company are permanently unable to supply and if you require items in this category please request a quotation enclosing a stamped, self-addressed envelope.

CARD SIZES

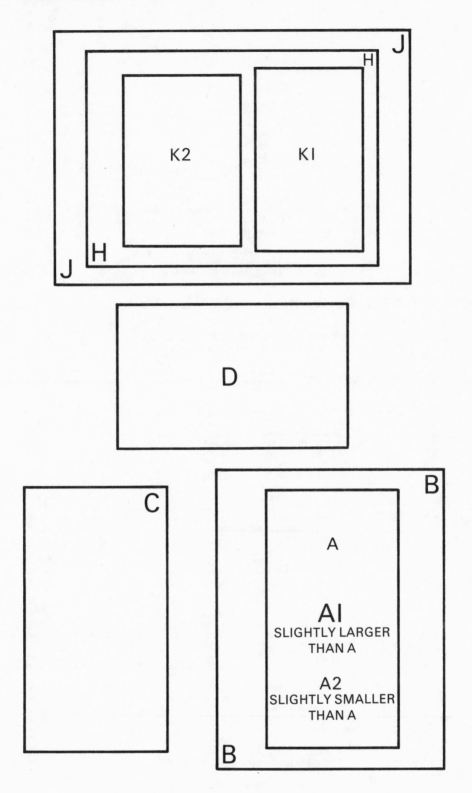

ABDULLA & CO. LTD., London _____

Illus. No.	Size	Print-ing	Number in set		Handbook ref.	Price per card	Complete set
A. Export Issues Post-1920							
	A	BW	50	Beauties of To-Day (1938)..................	Ha.514	£1.50	—
8	A	C	25	British Butterflies (1935)....................	Ha.517–1	30p	£7.50
	A	P	52	Cinema Stars—Set 1	Ha.515–1B	£2.25	—
	A2	U	30	Cinema Stars—Set 2	Ha.515–2	£2.25	—
	A2	U	30	Cinema Stars—Set 3	Ha.515–3	£2.25	—
	A2	U	32	Cinema Stars—Set 4	Ha.515–4	60p	£18.00
	A2	C	32	Cinema Stars—Set 5	Ha.515–5	65p	£21.00
	A2	C	30	Cinema Stars—Set 6	Ha.515–6	£2.25	—
22	D	C	25	Feathered Friends (1935)...................	Ha.516	40p	£10.00
	A2	C	50	Film Favourites (1934)	Ha.517–2	£1.50	—
	A	C	50	Film Stars (1934)........................		£5.00	—
	—	C	24	*Film Stars (128 × 89 mm.)	Ha.517–3		—
59	A	C	25	Old Favourites (1936) (Flowers)	Ha.517–4	13p	£3.25
452	A	C	40	Screen Stars (1939):—			
				A. Normal Abdulla back		14p	£5.75
				B. "Issued by the Successors to ..." back..		50p	£20.00
	A2	C	50	Stage and Cinema Beauties (1935)	Ha.517–5	£1.50	—
	A	U	30	Stars of the Stage and Screen		£2.25	—
B. Miscellaneous							
			? 4	Bridge Rule Cards (various sizes)		£10.00	—
				Great War Gift Packings Cards		£25.00	—
				Message Cards (letters of the alphabet)......		£3.00	—

ADCOCK & SON, Norwich _____

Post-1920 Issue							
	A1	U	12	Ancient Norwich (1928–29).................		—	£30.00
			11/12	Ancient Norwich (No. 6 missing)......		50p	£5.75

ADKIN & SONS, London _____

A. Pre-1919 Issues							
	D	BW	25	*Actresses—French, Nd. 126–150...........	H.1/Ha.1	£20.00	—
	A	C	15	*Beauties—"PAC"........................	H.2/Ha.2	£20.00	—
	A2	C	12	Character Sketches:—	H.3/Ha.3		
				A. Black printing on back (1901).........		£3.50	£42.00
				B. Green printing on back (1902–3)		£3.50	£42.00
	A2	C	12	A Living Picture:—	H.5/Ha.5		
				A. "Adkin & Sons" at top back			
				(i) crimson...........................		£3.50	£42.00
				(ii) scarlet		£3.50	£42.00
				B. "These cards are ..." at top back.......		£3.50	£42.00
	A	BW	25	Notabilities (1915)	H.6	£2.00	£50.00
	A1	C	12	Pretty Girl Series (Actresses)...............	H.7/Ha.7	£13.00	—
	A2	C	12	*Pretty Girl Series—"RASH" (1897):—	H.8/Ha.8		
				I. 1–6 Head and shoulders:			
				A. Calendar back....................		£17.50	—
				B. Advertisements back..............		£8.00	£50.00
				C. Figure and verse back.............		£8.00	£50.00
				II. 7–12 Full length:			
				A. Calendar back....................		£17.50	—
				B. Advertisements back..............		£8.00	£50.00
				C. Figure and verse back.............		£8.00	£50.00
	D	C	12	A Royal Favourite	H.9/Ha.9	£6.00	£75.00
	A	BW		Soldiers of the Queen (1899–1900)—	H.10		
			50	A. Series of 50:—			
				(a) Nos. 1–25 "... and exclusively with"		£7.50	—
				(b) Nos. 1–50 and variety "... and			
				issued with ..."		£2.40	£120.00
			61	B. Series of 60, 59 numbers and varieties ..		£2.00	—
	A	BW	31	*Soldiers of the Queen and Portraits (1901)...	H.11/Ha.11	£3.00	£95.00
258	A	C	30	Sporting Cups & Trophies (1914)		£6.00	—
	A	BW	25	War Trophies (1917)		£2.50	£62.50
B. Post-1920 Issues							
2	A	C	50	Butterflies and Moths (1924)...............	H.80	50p	£25.00
82	A	C	50	Wild Animals of the World (1922–23)	H.77	50p	£25.00
C. Miscellaneous							
			12	Character Sketches (premium issue)........		—	—
		C	? 4	*Games—by Tom Browne, postcard back			
				(135 × 85 mm.)........................	H.4/Ha.4	—	—
			12	A Living Picture (premium issue)		—	—

H. J. AINSWORTH, Harrogate _____

Pre-1919 Issue							
	D	C	30	*Army Pictures, Cartoons, Etc.	H.12	£36.00	

ALBERGE & BROMET, London _____

Pre-1919 Issues						
	A	C	? 25	*Boer War and General Interest:—	H.13/Ha.13	

ALBERGE & BROMET *(continued)*

Illus. No.	Size	Print- ing	Number in set		Handbook ref.	Price per card	Complete set
				A. "Bridal Bouquet" and "El Benecio" wording on green leaf design back......		£22.00	—
				B. "La Optima" and "Federation" wording on green leaf design back...........		£22.00	—
				C. "Bridal Bouquet" and "El Benecio" wording on brown leaf design back.....		£22.00	—
D1		C	40	*Naval and Military Phrases:—	H.14		
				A. "Bridal Bouquet" and "El Benecio"....		£30.00	—
				B. "La Optima" and "Federation"........		£30.00	—
D1		C	30	*Proverbs...................................	H.15	£22.00	—

PHILLIP ALLMAN & CO. LTD., London ————————————

Post-1940 Issues

485	A	C	50	Coronation Series (1953)..................		20p	£10.00
	A1	C		Pin-up Girls (1953):— A. First 12 subjects:—			
			12	Ai unnumbered "For men only".........		20p	£2.50
			12	Aii numbered "Ask for Allman always"..		25p	£3.00
			12	Aiii unnumbered "Ask for Allman always"		50p	£6.00
	A1	C	12	B. Second 12 subjects.....................		70p	£8.50
	A1	C	24	C. Inscribed "1st series of 24".............		—	—
	—	C	24	D. Large size (75 × 68 mm.)..............		70p	£17.50

AMALGAMATED TOBACCO CORPORATION LTD. ("Mills" Cigarettes) ————————————————————

A. Post-1940 Issues

	—	C	25	Famous British Ships "Series No. 1" (75 × 48 mm.) (1952)....................		07p	£0.50
	—	C	25	Famous British Ships "Series No. 2" (75 × 48 mm.) (1952)....................		07p	£0.50
	—	C	50	History of Aviation (75 × 48 mm.) (1952)			
				A. Nos. 1 to 16, 18 to 25 and 27		80p	—
				B. Nos. 17, 26 and 28 to 50		08p	£2.00
487	A	C	25	Kings of England (1954)...................		50p	£12.50
	A	C	25	Propelled Weapons (1953).................		07p	£0.60

B. Export Issues

353	A	C	25	Aircraft of the World (1958)		07p	£0.50
92	A	C	25	Animals of the Countryside (1957)		07p	£0.90
	A	C	25	Aquarium Fish (1961)		07p	£0.80
	A	C	25	Army Badges—Past & Present (1961)		07p	£1.50
	A	C	25	British Coins & Costumes (1958)...........		07p	£0.75
	A	C	25	British Locomotives (1961)................		08p	£2.00
	A	C	25	British Uniforms of the 19th Century (1957).		10p	£2.50
	A	C	25	Butterflies & Moths (1957)................		07p	£0.60
41	A	C	25	Cacti (1961).............................		07p	£0.70
	A	C	25	Castles of Britain (1961)		20p	£5.00
	A	C	25	Coins of the World (1961)		07p	£0.75
	A	C	25	Communications (1961)		20p	£5.00
119	A	C	25	Dogs (1958).............................		07p	£1.00
	A	C	25	Evolution of the Royal Navy (1957).........		07p	£1.25
	A	C	25	Football Clubs and Badges (1961)..........		40p	£10.00
	A	C	25	Freshwater Fish (1958)		07p	£0.50
	A	C	25	Geurriers A Travers Les Ages (French text) (1961)................................		32p	£8.00
	A	C	25	Historical Buildings (1959)		16p	£4.00
	A	C	25	Histoire de L'Aviation, 1st series (French text) (1961).........................		07p	£0.90
	A	C	25	Histoire de L'Aviation, 2nd Series (French text) (1962).........................		07p	£0.60
	A	C	25	Holiday Resorts (1957)....................		07p	£0.50
	A	C	25	Interesting Hobbies (1959).................		10p	£2.50
	A	C	25	Into Space (1958)		07p	£0.70
	A	C	25	Les Autos Moderns (French text) (1961)		08p	£2.00
	A	C	25	Medals of the World (1959)................		07p	£1.50
	A	C	25	Merchant Ships of the World (1961)........		07p	£1.00
	A	C	25	Merveillers Modernes (French text) (1961) ..		24p	£6.00
	A	C	25	Miniature Cars and Scooters (1959)........		40p	£10.00
	A	C	25	Nature (1958)...........................		07p	£0.50
	A	C	25	Naval Battles (1959)......................		07p	£0.90
	A	C	25	Ports of the World (1957).................		07p	£0.50
	A	C	25	Ships of the Royal Navy (1961)		16p	£4.00
	A	C	25	Sports and Games (1958)		20p	£5.00
	A	C	25	Tropical Birds (1959).....................		40p	£10.00
	A	C	25	Weapons of Defence (1961)................		07p	£1.25
96	A	C	25	Wild Animals (1958)		07p	£0.50
	A	C	25	The Wild West (1960)		07p	£1.80
	A	C	25	World Locomotives (1959)		08p	£2.00

THE ANGLO-AMERICAN CIGARETTE MAKING CO., LTD., London ————————————————

Pre-1919 Issue

	A	C	20	Russo-Japanese War Series (1906)	Ha.100	—	—

THE ANGLO CIGARETTE MANUFACTURING CO., London

Illus. No.	Size	Print-ing	Number in set		Handbook ref.	Price per card	Complete set
A. Pre-1919 Issue							
	A	C	36	Tariff Reform Series (1909)	H.16	£10.00	—

E. & W. ANSTIE, Devizes

Pre-1919 Issues							
574	A	C	16	*British Empire Series (1904)	H.17/Ha.17	£7.00	£112.00
		C	8	Puzzles (1902) (26 × 70mm.)	H.18/Ha.18	£30.00	—
		C	5	Royal Mail (1899) (70 × 50mm.)	H.19/Ha.19	£40.00	—
B. Post-1920 Issues							
	A2	C	25	Aesop's Fables (1934)	Ha.518	40p	£10.00
	A	U	50	People of Africa (1926)		£1.40	£70.00
	A	U	50	People of Asia (1926)		£1.40	£70.00
	A	U	50	People of Europe (1925)		£1.40	£70.00
	A2	BW	40	Places of Interest (1939):—			
				A. Varnished front		13p	£4.25
				B. Unvarnished front		50p	£20.00
	A	C	50	*Racing Series (1922):—			
				1–25—Racing Colours		90p	£22.50
				26–50—Horses, Jockeys, Race-courses, etc.		90p	£22.50
	A	C	50	Scout Series (1923)		£1.20	£60.00
	A2	C		Sectional Series:—	Ha.519		
			10	Clifton Suspension Bridge (1938)		20p	£2.00
			10	Stonehenge (1936)		23p	£2.25
			10	The Victory (1936)		33p	£3.25
			20	Wells Cathedral (1935)		30p	£6.00
			20	Wiltshire Downs (1935)		30p	£6.00
			10	Windsor Castle (1937)		25p	£2.50
	A2	BW	40	Wessex (1938)		30p	£12.00
	A	U	50	The World's Wonders (1924)		£1.00	£50.00

C. Silks. Anonymous unbacked woven silks. Width sizes only are quoted as the silks were prepared in ribbon form and length sizes are thus arbitrary.

	—	C	? 9	*Flags, large (width 95 mm.)	Ha.495–1	£1.50	—
	—	C	? 31	*Flags, small (width 42 mm.)	Ha.495–1	70p	—
	—	C	? 80	*Regimental Badges (width 32 mm.)	Ha.495–3	From 50p	—
	—	C		*Royal Standard and Portraits:—	Ha.495–2		
599			1	Royal Standard (width 61 mm.)		—	£0.90
			1	King George V:—			
				(a) Large (width 71 mm.), black frame		—	£40.00
				(b) Large (width 71 mm.), gold frame		—	£30.00
				(c) Small (width 35 mm.)		—	£40.00
			1	Queen Mary:—			
				(a) Large (width 71 mm.)		—	£15.00
				(b) Small (width 35 mm.)		—	£40.00
			1	Lord French (width 71 mm.)		—	£50.00
			1	Lord Kitchener (width 71 mm.)		—	£6.00

H. ARCHER & CO., London

Pre-1919 Issues							
	C	C	? 30	*Actresses—Selection from "FROGA A and B"	H.20/Ha.20		
				A. "Golden Returns" back		£20.00	—
				B. "M.F.H." back		£25.00	—
	C		50	*Beauties—"CHOAB":—	H.21/Ha.21		
		U		A. "Bound to Win" front...............		£8.00	—
		C		B. "Golden Returns" back		£20.00	—
		C		C. "M.F.H." back		£20.00	—
	C	C	20	*Prince of Wales Series	H.22	£13.00	—

ARDATH TOBACCO CO. LTD., London

A. Pre-1919 Issues. All export.							
	—	U	30	Boucher Series (77 × 62 mm.)		£1.20	—
	—	U	30	Gainsborough Series (77 × 62 mm.)		£1.20	—
	A1	U	50	Great War Series..........................		£4.00	—
	A1	U	50	Great War Series "B"		£4.00	—
	A1	U	50	Great War Series "C"		£4.00	—
	A1	U	40	Franz Hals Series, Dutch back		—	—
				Hollandsche Oude Meesters, Dutch back (70 × 60 mm.):—			
	—	U	25	A. First 25 subjects		£4.00	—
	—	U	25	B. Second 25 subjects		£4.00	—
	—	U	30	Raphael Series (77 × 62 mm.)		£1.20	—
	—	U		Rembrandt Series:—			
			30	A. Large size (77 × 62 mm.), English back .		£2.00	—
			40	B. Large size (77 × 62 mm.), Dutch back...		£2.50	—
			30	C. Extra-large size (101 × 62 mm.)........		£2.50	—
	—	U	30	Rubens Series (77 × 61 mm.):—			
				A. English "State Express" back		£1.20	—
				B. English "Winfred" back		—	—
				C. Dutch back		—	—
				D. New Zealand "State Express" back		—	—

Illus. No.	Size	Print-ing	Number in set		Handbook ref.	Price per card	Complete set
—		U	30	Velasquez Series:—			
				A. Large size (77 × 62 mm.)		£1.75	—
				B. Extra-large size (101 × 62 mm.).........		£2.25	—

B. Post-1920 Non-photographic Issues

Illus. No.	Size	Print-ing	Number in set		Handbook ref.	Price per card	Complete set
	A1	C	50	*Animals at the Zoo (export):—	Ha.520		
				A. Back with descriptive text..............		70p	£35.00
				B. Back without description, "Double Ace" issue		£2.75	—
	A	C	96	Ardath Modern School Atlas (export)......		£1.00	—
	A	C	25	Big Game Hunting (export):—			
				A. Back in blue..........................		£1.20	£30.00
				B. Back in black		£2.50	—
321	A	U	50	Britain's Defenders (Dec. 1936) (see RB21/463B)		18p	£9.00
		U	50	British Born Film Stars (export):—			
	A2			A. Small size, back white semi-glossy......		50p	—
	A2			B. Small size, back cream matt...........		50p	—
	—			C. Medium size (67 × 53 mm.)		50p	—
		U		Camera Studies (see RB21/268–2B):—			
	—		36	A. Small size (70 × 44 mm.)		40p	£15.00
	—		45	B. Large size (79 × 57 mm.)		40p	£18.00
	—	C	25	Champion Dogs (95 × 67 mm.) (Nov. 1934) (see RB21/370B).......................		14p	£3.50
147	A	C	50	Cricket, Tennis and Golf Celebrities (Jul. 1935):—			
				A. Home issue, grey back.................		14p	£7.00
				B. Export issue, brownish-grey back, text revised................................		80p	—
	—	U	25	Dog Studies (95 × 68 mm.) (Sep. 1938)......		36p	£9.00
	A	C	25	Eastern Proverbs (export)	Ha.521	70p	£17.50
	A	C	48	Empire Flying-Boat (sectional) (Jan. 1938) ..		15p	£7.50
	A	C	50	Empire Personalities (Apr. 1937)............		40p	£20.00
448	A	C	50	Famous Film Stars (Aug. 1934).............		20p	£10.00
171	A	C	50	Famous Footballers (Oct. 1934)		13p	£6.50
	A	C	25	Famous Scots (Jun. 1935)		24p	£6.00
	—	C	25	Fighting and Civil Aircraft (96 × 68 mm.) (Apr. 1936).............................		90p	£22.50
	A	C	50	Figures of Speech (Feb. 1936)..............		13p	£6.50
453	A	C	50	Film, Stage and Radio Stars (Sep. 1935).....		35p	£17.50
	—	C	25	Film, Stage and Radio Stars (96 × 68 mm.) (Jun. 1935).............................		14p	£3.50
	—	C	50	From Screen and Stage (96 × 68 mm.) (Dec. 1936)..................................		40p	£20.00
283	A	U	50	Life in the Services:—			
				A. Home issue (May 1938), adhesive		13p	£5.50
				B. Export issue, non-adhesive.............		70p	—
	A	C	50	National Fitness:—			
				A. Home issue (Sep. 1938), adhesive.......		16p	£8.00
				B. Export issue, non-adhesive.............		70p	—
	A	U	50	Our Empire (export)	Ha.522	80p	—
	A	C		Proverbs:—			
			25	A. Home issue (Sep. 1936) Nos 1–25		13p	£3.00
			25	B. Export issue Nos 26–50................		70p	—
		U	100	Scenes from Big Films (export):—			
	A			A. Small Size White Back.................		40p	—
	A			B. Small Size Cream Back		40p	—
				C. Medium Size (67 × 52 mm.)		40p	—
481	A	C	50	Silver Jubilee (Mar. 1935).................		15p	£7.50
382, 661 etc.	A	C	50	Speed—Land Sea and Air:—			
				A. Home issue (Jul. 1935), "Issued with State Express"		22p	£11.00
				B. Export issue, Ardath name at base		80p	—
	—	C	25	Speed—Land, Sea and Air (95 × 68 mm.) (Apr. 1938).............................		32p	£8.00
269	A	C	50	Sports Champions (1935):—			
				A. Home issue, with album offer, "State Express" at base		13p	£6.50
				B. Export issue, without album offer, "Ardath" at base......................		80p	—
	A	C	50	Stamps—Rare and Interesting (Jan. 1939)...		55p	£27.50
	A	C	50	Swimming, Diving and Life-Saving (Mar. 1937) (export)	Ha.523	60p	—
	A	C	50	Tennis (Sep. 1937) (export)	Ha.524	60p	—
	A	C	48	Trooping the Colour (sectional) (May 1939) .		60p	£30.00
	A	C	50	Who is This? (May 1936)		13p	£5.00
	—	BW	24	World Views (No. 13 not issued) (95 × 68 mm.) (Oct. 1937).......................		13p	£3.00
	A	C	50	Your Birthday Tells Your Fortune (Jul. 1937)		13p	£5.50

C. Post-1920 Photographic Issues

Illus. No.	Size	Print-ing	Number in set		Handbook ref.	Price per card	Complete set
	A2	P	54	Beautiful English Women (1928) (export) ...		£1.20	—
	A2	P	35	Hand Shadows (export)		—	—
	A2	CP	50	New Zealand Views (1928) (export)		£1.60	—
	H	P		Photocards—Numbered Series (Aug. 1936–Jan. 1937)*—			
			110	"A"—Football Clubs of Lancashire		23p	£25.00
			110	"B"—Football Clubs of North East Counties		32p	£35.00
			110	"C"—Football Clubs of Yorkshire		32p	£35.00
			165	"D"—Football Clubs of Scotland		21p	£35.00
			110	"E"—Football Clubs of Midlands		27p	£30.00

Illus. No.	Size	Printing	Number in set		Handbook ref.	Price per card	Complete set
			110	"F"—Football Clubs of London and Southern Counties....................		20p	£22.50
			99	"Z"—General Interest:—			
				Nos. 111–165.........................		13p	£2.50
				Nos. 166–209.........................		13p	£3.00
			11	"A.s." (1), "C.s." (2–3), "E.s." (4–10), "F.s." (11)—Football Clubs (supplementary)....		70p	£7.50
				*Most cards in these Sets are also found overprinted on back in red-brown "Packed with Ardath Kings 10 for 6d. The Longer Cigarette".			
H		P		Photocards—"A Continuous Series of Topical Interest" (Jul. 1937–May 1938):—	Ha.525		
			22	Group A—Racehorses and Sports..........		14p	£3.00
			22	Group B—Coronation and Sports..........		16p	£3.50
			22	Group C—Lancashire Personalities........		45p	£10.00
			22	Group D—Irish Personalities, etc.		36p	£8.00
			22	Group E—Film Stars and Sports...........		23p	£5.00
			22	Group F—Film Stars and Sportsmen.......		60p	£12.50
			66	"G.S."—Miscellaneous subjects (export).....		75p	—
H		P		Photocards—"A Continuous Series of General Interest", with Album Offer (May–Nov. 1938):—	Ha.526		
			11	Group G—Australian Cricketers..........		£10.00	—
			22	Group H—Film, Radio and Sporting Stars..		45p	£10.00
			22	Group I—Film Stars and Miscellaneous.....		80p	£17.50
		P		Photocards—"A Continuous Series of General Interest", without Album Offer—Uncoloured (Dec. 1938–Oct. 1939):—	Ha.527		
H			22	Group J—Film Stars and General Interest...		16p	£3.50
H			22	Group K—Film, Radio and Sporting Stars:—			
				1. With "Kings" Clause.................		50p	£11.00
				2. Without "Kings" Clause (export)......		60p	—
H			44	Group L—Film Stars and Miscellaneous....		23p	£10.00
			45	Group M—Film Stars and Miscellaneous:—			
C				1. Small size.......................		40p	£18.00
—				2. Large size (80 × 69 mm.), with "Kings" Clause......................		45p	£20.00
				3. Large size (80 × 69 mm.), without "Kings" Clause.....................		45p	£20.00
		P	45	Group N—Film, Stage and Radio Stars:—			
C				1. Small size.....................		45p	£20.00
—				2. Large size (80 × 69 mm.)...............		45p	£20.00
H		CP		Photocards—"A Continuous Series of General Interest", without Album Offer—Hand Coloured (export) (Dec. 1938):—	Ha.528		
			22	Group 1—Views of the World.............		36p	£8.00
			22	Group 2—Views of the World.............		36p	£8.00
			22	Group 3—Views of the World.............		23p	£5.00
				Real Photographs:—			
—		P	45	"A Continuous Series of General Interest"—Films, Stage and Radio Stars (Oct. 1939)..	Ha.529	40p	£18.00
C		P	45	"1st Series of 45"—Film and Stage Stars (Jun. 1939).......................		40p	£18.00
C		P	54	"2nd Series of 54"—Film and Stage Stars (Aug. 1939)........................		40p	£22.00
J2		P	18	"First Series"—Views (Jun. 1937)..........		80p	—
J2		P	18	"Second Series"—Film and Stage Stars (Jun. 1937)...............................		80p	—
J2		P	18	"Third Series"—Views (Nov. 1937).........		80p	—
J2		P	18	"Fourth Series"—Film and Stage Stars (Nov. 1937)...........................		80p	—
J2		P	18	"Fifth Series"—Views (Feb. 1938)...........		80p	—
J2		P	18	"Sixth Series"—Film and Stage Stars (Jan. 1938)...............................		80p	—
H		P	44	"Series One" "G.P.1"—Film Stars (export) (Aug. 1939)........................		34p	£15.00
H		P	44	"Series Two" "G.P.2"—Film Stars (export) (Nov. 1939)........................		13p	£3.00
H		P	44	"Series Three" "G.P.3"—Film Stars (export) (Nov. 1939)........................		£1.20	—
H		CP	44	"Series Three" "C.V.3"—Views (export) (Aug. 1939)........................		34p	£15.00
H		CP	44	"Series Four" "C.V.4"—Views (export) (Nov. 1939)........................		13p	£3.25
J2		P	36	"Series Seven"—Film and Stage Stars (Mar. 1938)...............................		60p	—
J2		P	54	"Series Eight"—Film and Stage Stars (Jul. 1938)...............................		28p	£15.00
		P	54	"Series Nine"—Film and Stage Stars (Oct. 1938):—			
H				A. Medium size........................		28p	£15.00
J2				B. Extra-large size......................		28p	£15.00
		P	54	"Series Ten"—Film and Stage Stars:—			
				A. Large size (80 × 69 mm.) (Feb. 1939)....		28p	£15.00
J2				B. Extra-large size (Jun. 1939)...........		40p	£22.00
—		P	54	"Series Eleven"—Film and Stage Stars 1939.			
—				A. Large size (80 × 69 mm.)...............		28p	£15.00

ARDATH TOBACCO CO. LTD. *(continued)*

Illus. No.	Size	Print-ing	Number in set		Handbook ref.	Price per card	Complete set
	J2			B. Extra-large size		60p	—
—		P	54	"Series Twelve"—Film and Stage Stars (80 × 69 mm.) (Sep. 1939)...............		28p	£15.00
—		P	54	"Series Thirteen"—Film and Stage Stars (80 × 69 mm.) (Dec. 1939)		28p	£15.00
		P	36	"of Famous Landmarks" (Aug. 1939):—			
—				A. Large size (80 × 69 mm.), titled "Real Photographs"........................		£1.20	—
	J2			B. Extra-large size, titled "Real Photographs of Famous Landmarks"........		75p	£27.00
		P	36	"of Modern Aircraft":—			
—				A. Large size (80 × 69 mm.) (Jun. 1939)....		85p	£30.00
	J2			B. Extra-large size (Mar. 1939)...........		75p	£27.00
D. Miscellaneous							
—		C	30	Girls of All Nations (78 × 66 mm.)		£6.00	—
			25	Historic Grand Slams (folders) (101 × 70 mm.).................................		—	—
			48	How to Recognise the Service Ranks (holed for binding)		£1.40	—
			150	Information Slips (holed for binding)		£1.20	—
				Ministry of Information Cards (1941–2):—			
				A. Calendar—"It all depends on me"		50p	—
				B. Greeting Card—"It all depends on me"		—	—
				C. "It all depends on me" (series of 24)		19p	£4.75
				D. Union Jack Folder		—	—
		?	4	Wonderful Handicraft.....................		£6.00	—

THE ASSOCIATED TOBACCO MANUFACTURERS, LTD.

Post-1920 Issues

C2		C	25	Cinema Stars (export):—	Ha.530		
				A. "Issued with Bond Street Turkish Cigarettes"		—	—
				B. "Issued with John Bull Virginia Cigarettes"		—	—
				C. "Issued with Club Virginia Cigarettes".		—	—
				D. "Issued with Heliopolis Turkish Cigarettes"		—	—
				E. "Issued with Sports Turkish Cigarettes"		—	—

A. ATKINSON, London

Pre-1919 Issue

D		C	30	*Army Pictures, Cartoons, etc...............	H.12	—	—

AVISS BROTHERS LTD., London

Pre-1919 Issue

D1		C	40	*Naval and Military Phrases.................	H.14	£35.00	—

J. A. BAILEY, Swansea

Pre-1919 Issue

D1		C	40	*Naval and Military Phrases.................	H.14	—	—

A. BAKER & CO. LTD., London

Pre-1919 Issues

A		BW	20	*Actresses—"BLARM," "A. Baker & Co. Ltd." at foot:—	H.23		
				A. Long design back		£9.00	—
				B. Design altered and shortened		£9.00	—
A		BW	10	*Actresses—"HAGG A"....................	H.24	£9.00	£90.00
		BW		*Actresses "Baker's 3-sizes":—	H.25/Ha.25		
A			25	Small cards............................		£6.00	£150.00
			25	Medium cards (56 × 75 mm.)		£16.00	—
		?	5	Extra Large Cards (67 × 127 mm.)		£36.00	—
C		BW	? 41	*Baker's Tobacconists' Shops:—	H.26/Ha.26		
				A. "Try our 3½d Tobaccos" back..........		£35.00	—
				B. "Cigar, Cigarette, etc. Manufacturers" back..................................		£35.00	—
C		C	25	Beauties of All Nations:—	H.27		
				A. "Albert Baker & Co. (1898) ..." back ..		£6.00	£150.00
				B. "A. Baker & Co...." back..............		£5.00	£125.00
C		BW	16	*British Royal Family	H.28	£18.00	—
A1		BW	20	Cricketers Series	H.29	£30.00	—
A1		C	25	*Star Girls...............................	H.30	£40.00	—

BAYLEY & HOLDSWORTH

Pre-1919 Issue

?		C	26	*International signalling Code...............		£37.50	—

BELFAST SHIPS STORES CO. LTD., Belfast

Illus. No.	Size	Print-ing	Number in set		Handbook ref.	Price per card	Complete set
Pre-1919 Issue							
		C	? 1	*Dickens' Characters (79 × 40 mm.)	H.31	—	—

J. & F. BELL LTD., Glasgow

Pre-1919 Issues						
A	BW	10	*Actresses—"HAGG A" ("Three Bells Cigarettes")	H.24	£12.50	—
C	C	25	*Beauties—Tobacco Leaf Back:—	H.32/Ha.32		
			A. "Bell's Scotia Cigarettes" back		£25.00	—
			B. "Three Bells Cigarettes" back		£25.00	—
A	C	25	Colonial Series		£16.00	£400.00
A	BW	30	*Footballers		£7.50	£225.00
A	C	25	Scottish Clan Series No. 1	H.33	£4.00	£100.00

B. BELLWOOD, BRADFORD

Pre-1919 Issue						
C	C	18	Motor Cycle Series	Ha.469	—	—

RICHARD BENSON, LTD., Bristol

	U	24	Old Bristol Series:—			
—			A. 80 × 70 mm. pre-1940		£1.30	£32.50
—			B. Reprint (88 × 78–83 mm.) (1946)		80p	£20.00

BENSON & HEDGES, London

Post-1940 Issue						
A2	C	1	Advertisement Card The Original Shop (1973)		—	£0.80

FELIX BERLYN, Manchester

Pre-1919 Issue						
	C	25	Golfing Series (Humorous):—			
A1			A. Small size		£38.00	—
—			B. Post Card size (139 × 87 mm.)		—	—

BERRY, London

Pre-1919 Issue						
D	U	? 1	London Views	H.34	—	—

BEWLAY & CO. LTD., London

Pre-1919 Issues						
D1	U	12	Bewlay's War Series (Generals, etc.):—	Ha.477	—	£85.00
			A. "Caps the Lot" Smoking Mixture		£7.00	£85.00
			B. Try Bewlay's "Caps the Lot" Mixture		£7.00	£85.00
			C. Try Bewlay's "Modern Man" Mixture		£7.00	£85.00
D1	U	25	Bewlay's War Series (Photogravure War Pictures)	H.35	—	£90.00
			A. "Modern Man" Mixtures etc.		£3.50	—
			B. "Modern Man" Cigarettes		£3.75	—
			C. "Two Great Favourites"		£3.75	—
A	C	? 5	*Comic Advertisement Cards	H.36	£80.00	—

W. O. BIGG & CO., Bristol

Pre-1919 Issues						
A	C	37	*Flags of All Nations:—	H.37		
			A. "Statue of Liberty" back, 4d oz.		£3.75	—
			B. As A:—(a) altered to 4½d by hand		£3.75	—
			(b) 4½d red seal over 4d		£4.50	—
			C. Panel design "New York" Mixture		£4.00	—
A	C	50	Life on Board a Man of War	H.38	£6.00	£300.00

JAS. BIGGS & SONS, London

Pre-1919 Issues						
C	C	26	*Actresses—"FROGA A"	H.20	£11.00	
C	C	26	*Actresses—"FROGA B"	H.20/Ha.20	£16.00	
A	C	25	*Beauties, with frameline—"CHOAB":—	H.21/Ha.21		
			A. Blue type-set back		£18.00	
			B. Overprinted in black on Bradford cards		£25.00	
C	C		*Beauties, no framelines—selection "BOCCA":—	H.39		

JAS. BIGGS & SONS *(continued)*

Illus. No.	Size	Print-ing	Number in set		Handbook ref.	Price per card	Complete set
			? 4	A. Blue back.............................		£27.50	—
			? 3	B. Black back.............................		£27.50	—
	C	C	30	*Colonial Troops	H.40	£12.50	—
	C	C	30	*Flags and Flags with Soldiers	H.41	£12.50	—
	A1	C	25	*Star Girls.............................	H.30	£60.00	—

R. BINNS, Halifax

Post-1920 Issue

	Size						
	A	U	? 2	*Halifax Footballers	Ha.531	—	—

THE BOCNAL TOBACCO CO., London

Post-1920 Issues

	Size						
	A2	U	25	Luminous Silhouettes of Beauty and Charm (1938)...................................		32p	£8.00
	A2	C	25	Proverbs Up-to-Date (1938)		24p	£6.00

ALEXANDER BOGUSLAVASKY, LTD., London

Post-1920 Issues

Illus. No.	Size						
129	—	C	12	Big Events on the Turf (133 × 70 mm.).......		£2.00	—
533	A2	C	25	Conan Doyle Characters (1923):—			
				A. Back in black, white board............		90p	£22.50
				B. Back in grey, cream board		90p	£22.50
				C. Back in green		90p	£22.50
	A2	C	25	Mythological Gods and Goddesses (1924)...		40p	£10.00
272	A	C	25	*Sports Records, Nd. 1–25 (1925)............		60p	£15.00
	A	C	25	Sports Records, Nd. 26–50 (1925)..........		24p	£6.00
		C	25	Winners on the Turf (1925):—			
	A			A. Small size, captions "sans serif".......		40p	£10.00
	A			B. Small size, captions with "serif"		70p	£17.50
	B			C. Large size...........................		40p	£10.00

R. & E. BOYD, LTD., London

Post-1920 Issues

	Size						
	—	U	25	Places of Interest (72 × 55 mm.)		£25.00	—
	—	U	25	Wild Birds at Home (75 × 57 mm.)	Ha.626	£25.00	—

WM. BRADFORD, Liverpool

Pre-1919 Issues

	Size						
	C	C	50	*Beauties—"CHOAB".......................	H.21	£10.00	—
	D	U	? 5	Beauties—"Jersey Lily Cigarettes"..........	Ha.488	—	—
	D2	BW	20	Boer War Cartoons	H.42	£23.00	—

T. BRANKSTON & CO., London

Pre-1919 Issues

	Size						
	C	C	30	*Colonial Troops:—	H.40		
				A. Golf Club Mixture		£11.00	—
				B. Red Virginia		£11.00	—
				C. Sweet as the Rose		£11.00	—

BRIGHAM & CO., Reading

Pre-1919 Issues

	Size						
	B	U	16	Down the Thames from Henley to Windsor .		—	—
	A	U	16	Reading Football Players..................		£50.00	—
	—	BW	3	Tobacco Growing in Hampshire (89 × 79 mm.) (1915)		£10.00	£30.00

BRITANNIA ANONYMOUS SOCIETY

Pre-1919 Issue

	Size						
	—	C	? 10	*Beauties (60 × 40 mm.)	Ha.532	£75.00	—

BRITISH & COLONIAL TOBACCO CO., London

Pre-1919 Issue

	Size						
	. A1	C	25	*Armies of the World	H.43	£50.00	—

J. M. BROWN, Derby

Pre-1919 Issue

	Size						
	D	C	30	*Army Pictures, Cartoons, Etc.	H.12	£17.00	—

JOHN BRUMFIT, London

Illus. No.	Size	Printing	Number in set		Handbook ref.	Price per card	Complete set
Post-1920 Issue							
	A	C	50	The Public Schools' Ties Series (Old Boys) (1925)		90p	£45.00

G. A. BULLOUGH, Castleford

	Size	Printing	Number in set		Handbook ref.	Price per card	Complete set
Pre-1919 Issue							
	D	C	30	*Army Pictures, Cartoons, Etc.	H.12		—

BURSTEIN, ISAACS & CO., London

(The BI-CO Company, B. I. & Co., Ltd.)

Illus. No.	Size	Printing	Number in set			Price per card	Complete set
Post-1920 Issues							
215	D	BW	25	Famous Prize-Fighters, Nd. 1–25 (1923).....		90p	£22.50
	D	BW	25	Famous Prize-Fighters, Nd. 26–50 (1924) ...		90p	£22.50
	D	P	28	London View Series (1922)		£1.20	—

BYRT WOOD & CO., Bristol

Illus. No.	Size	Printing	Number in set		Handbook ref.	Price per card	Complete set
Pre-1919 Issue							
	A2	U	? 47	*Pretty Girl Series—"BAGG"	H.45/Ha.45	£36.00	—

PERCY E. CADLE & CO. LTD., Cardiff

	Size	Printing	Number in set		Handbook ref.	Price per card	Complete set
Pre-1919 Issues							
	A1	BW	20	*Actresses—"BLARM"....................	H.23	£7.00	£140.00
	C	U	26	*Actresses—"FROGA A"..................	H.20	£20.00	—
	C	C	26	*Actresses—"FROGA B"..................	H.20	£15.00	—
	C	BW	12	*Boer War and Boxer Rebellion Sketches.....	H.46	£18.00	—
	C	BW	? 12	*Boer War Generals—"FLAC".............	H.47/Ha.47	£25.00	—
	A	BW	20	*Footballers	H.48	£7.00	£140.00

CARRERAS LTD., London

Illus. No.	Size	Printing	Number in set		Handbook ref.	Price per card	Complete set
A. Pre-1919 Issues							
—		C	6	*Flags of the Allies (shaped):—	H.49/Ha.49		
				1. Grouped Flags:—			
				A. "All Arms" Cigarettes.............		£11.00	—
				B. "Black Cat" Cigarettes.............		£11.00	—
				2. Allies Flags (5):—			
				A. "Black Cat" Cigarettes.............		£11.00	—
				B. "Life Ray" Cigarettes.............		£22.00	—
301	A	C	140	Raemaeker's War Cartoons (1916):—			
				A. "Black Cat" Cigarettes		60p	£85.00
				B. Carreras Cigarettes....................		£1.50	—
214	A	C	50	The Science of Boxing (1920):—			
				A. "Black Cat" back		75p	£37.50
				B. Carreras Ltd. back		£1.50	—
	A	C	80	Types of London (1919)		65p	£55.00
	A	C	50	Women on War Work		£3.50	£175.00
B. Post-1920 Issues. Mostly home issues, export only issues indicated.							
	A	CP	24	Actresses and Their Pets (Oct. 1926) (export)		£1.60	£40.00
		C	48	Alice in Wonderland (Jun. 1930):—			
534	A			A. Small size, rounded corners............		14p	£7.00
	A			B. Small size, square corners..............		50p	£25.00
	B2			C. Large size.........................		14p	£7.00
			1	Instruction Booklet		—	£5.00
623	A	C	50	Amusing Tricks and How to Do Them (Jan. 1937)..		20p	£10.00
		C		Battle of Waterloo (Jul. 1934):—	Ha.533		
	C		1	1. Paper insert, with instructions.........		—	£4.00
			15	*2. Soldiers and Guns, large size (67 × 70 mm.)		—	—
	A			*3. Soldiers and Guns, small size:—			
			10	Soldiers—Officers' Uniforms		£1.00	£10.00
			12	Soldiers and Guns.....................		£1.00	£12.00
	C1	C	50	Believe it or Not (Oct. 1934)		13p	£5.50
15	A	C	50	Birds of the Countryside (Mar. 1939)........		13p	£5.00
280	A	C	50	Britain's Defences (Sep. 1938)		13p	£6.50
		C	25	British Costumes (Jul. 1927):—			
	C2			A. Small size...........................		50p	£12.50
	B2			B. Large size..........................		60p	£15.00
	A	P	27	British Prime Ministers (Oct. 1928) (export) .		60p	£16.00
502	A	C	50	Celebrities of British History (Sep. 1935):—			

CARRERAS LTD. *(continued)*

Illus. No.	Size	Print-ing	Number in set		Handbook ref.	Price per card	Complete set
				A. Brown on cream back (two shades of ink)...............................		13p	£3.25
				B. Pale brown on bluish black		13p	£3.25
	A	C	25	Christie Comedy Girls (June 1928) (export)..		£1.00	£25.00
151	A	U		Cricketers (May 1934):—			
			30	A. "A Series of Cricketers"		60p	£18.00
			50	B. "A Series of 50 Cricketers":—			
				1. Front in brown and white		50p	£25.00
				2. Front in black and white		£8.00	—
123	A	BW	50	Dogs and Friend (Sep. 1936)...............		13p	£5.00
	A	C	50	Do You Know? (Sep. 1939).................		13p	£3.25
358	A	C	50	Famous Airmen and Airwomen (Jan. 1936) .		45p	£22.50
		C		Famous Escapes (Feb. 1926):—			
	A		25	A. Small size...........................		28p	£7.00
	B2		25	B. Large size...........................		24p	£6.00
	—		10	C. Extra-large size (133 × 70 mm.)........		65p	£6.50
458	A2	C	96	Famous Film Stars (Apr. 1935):—			
				A. Set of 96		28p	£28.00
				B. Alternative pictures for six numbers	Ha.534	£3.00	£18.00
182	A	C		Famous Footballers (Sep. 1935):—			
			48	A. Set of 48		13p	£5.00
			24	B. Nos. 25–48 redrawn		60p	£15.00
506	A	C	25	Famous Men (Dec. 1927) (export)		80p	£20.00
338	B2	P	24	Famous Naval Men (May 1929) (export)		32p	£8.00
	B2	P	12	Famous Soldiers (Mar. 1928) (export).......		£1.75	—
	A	P	27	Famous Women (Apr. 1929) (export)		80p	£20.00
530	A	C	25	Figures of Fiction (Apr. 1924)		60p	£15.00
		P	54	Film and Stage Beauties:—			
447	A2			A. Small size, titled "Film and Stage Beauties" (Jan. 1939)..................		13p	£4.00
	—			B. Medium size (70 × 60 mm.) titled "Film and Stage Beauties" (Mar. 1939):—			
				(a) Without full point after "Carreras Ltd"		13p	£6.50
				(b) With full point after "Carreras Ltd."		16p	£8.00
		P	36	Film and Stage Beauties			
	B1			A. Large size (Feb. 1939)		21p	£7.50
	J2			B. Extra-large size (Nov. 1938)...........		21p	£7.50
451	A	C	50	Film Favourites (Apr. 1938)		22p	£11.00
	A	P	54	Film Stars—"A Series of 54" (Oct. 1937)		13p	£6.50
		P	54	Film Stars:—			
433	A			A. Small size, "Second Series of 54" (Jul. 1938)		13p	£4.00
	—			B. Medium size (68 × 60 mm.) "A Series of 54" (Aug. 1938)		22p	£12.00
	J2	P		Film Stars (export):—			
			36	"A Series of 36".......................		70p	—
			36	"Second Series of 36"		70p	—
			36	"Third Series of 36"....................		70p	—
			36	"Fourth Series of 36"		70p	—
432	A2	C	50	Film Stars, by Florence Desmond (Jan. 1936)		13p	£4.50
449	—		72	Film Stars, oval (70 × 30 mm.) (Jun. 1934):—			
		P		A. Glossy brown photoprints		28p	£20.00
		U		B. Semi-glossy brown half-tones		22p	£16.00
57	A	C	50	Flowers (May 1936).......................		13p	£3.75
175	A2	C	75	*Footballers (Aug. 1934):—			
				A. "Carreras Cigarettes" on front 27 mm. long		13p	£10.00
				B. "Carreras Cigarettes" on front 26 mm. long		13p	£10.00
		C	36	"Fortune Telling" (Jul. 1926):—			
	A			A. Small size—			
				1. Card inset........................		42p	£15.00
				2a. Head inset, black framelines		24p	£8.50
				2b. Head inset, brown framelines		42p	£15.00
	B2			B. Large size—			
				1. Card inset........................		24p	£8.50
				2. Head inset........................		42p	£15.00
			1	Instruction Booklet		—	£2.50
		P		Glamour Girls of Stage and Films (Aug. 1939):—			
434	A2		54	A. Small size...........................		13p	£3.00
	—		54	B. Medium size (70 × 60 mm.)		13p	£3.00
	—		36	C. Large size (76 × 70 mm.)		13p	£3.00
	J2		36	D. Extra-large size		14p	£5.00
		C	50	"Gran-Pop" by Lawson Wood (Dec. 1934):—			
	C1			A. Small size...........................		13p	£3.50
	B			B. Large size...........................		13p	£2.00
		C	52	Greyhound Racing Game (May 1926):—			
	A			A. Small size...........................		13p	£3.25
	B2			B. Large size...........................		13p	£2.25
			1	Instruction Booklet		—	£1.50
		C	48	Happy Family (Jun. 1925):—			
	A1			A. Small size...........................		30p	£15.00
	B2			B. Large size...........................		13p	£6.00
	A	C	25	Highwaymen (Jul. 1924)...................		90p	£22.50
310	A	C	50	History of Army Uniforms (Jun. 1937)		40p	£20.00
327	A	C	50	History of Naval Uniforms (Sep. 1937)......		16p	£8.00

Illus. No.	Size	Print- ing	Number in set		Handbook ref.	Price per card	Complete set
		C		Horses and Hounds (July 1926):—			
	A		25	A. Small size...........................		40p	£10.00
	B2		20	B. Large size...........................		30p	£6.00
	—		10	C. Extra-large size (133 × 70 mm.)........		60p	£6.00
		C	50	Kings and Queens of England (1935):—			
480	A			A. Small size...........................		40p	£20.00
	B2			B. Large size...........................		40p	£20.00
	A	U		A "Kodak" at the Zoo:—			
			50	"Series of Fifty" (Sep. 1924).............		18p	£9.00
			50	"2nd Series of Fifty" (Jan. 1925)..........		18p	£9.00
	A	P	27	Malayan Industries (Oct. 1929) (export).....		13p	£2.25
		P	24	Malayan Scenes:—			
	A			A. Small size (Oct. 1928).................		60p	£15.00
	—			B. Medium size (70 × 60 mm.) (Nov. 1928)		13p	£2.50
	—	C	53	*Miniature Playing Cards (44 × 32 mm.)......		13p	£3.25
		C	50	The "Nose" Game (Jul. 1927):—			
	A			A. Small size...........................		20p	£10.00
	B2			B. Large size...........................		16p	£8.00
			1	Instruction Booklet....................		—	£1.50
		C	50	Notable M.P.s (May 1929):—			
498	A			A. Small size...........................		13p	£5.00
	—			B. Medium size (69 × 60 mm.)............		13p	£2.75
400	A	P	25	Notable Ships—Past and Present (Mar. 1929) (export).............................		60p	£15.00
		C		Old Staffordshire Figures (Sep. 1926):—			
	A		24	A. Small size...........................		32p	£8.00
	—		12	B. Extra-large size (134 × 71 mm.)........		£1.25	£15.00
	B	C	24	Old Staffordshire Figures (different subjects) (Sep. 1926).............................		50p	£12.50
		C	24	Orchids (Oct. 1925):—			
58	A			A. Small size...........................		13p	£2.50
	B			B. Large size...........................		13p	£2.50
43	—			C. Extra-large size (133 × 70 mm.)........		80p	£20.00
346	A	C		Our Navy (Mar. 1937):—	Ha.536		
			20	A. Thick card, selected numbers		30p	£6.00
			50	B. Thin card		30p	£15.00
	C1	C	50	Palmistry (Dec. 1933)		13p	£3.75
	A	P	27	Paramount Stars (June 1929) (export).......		18p	£5.00
621	A	P	25	Picture Puzzle Series (Apr. 1923)..........		50p	£12.50
	—	C	53	Playing Cards (68 × 42 mm.)...............	Ha.535–1A	70p	—
		C		*Playing Cards and Dominoes (May 1929):—	Ha.535–1B		
	C		52	A. Small size—(a) Numbered.............		25p	£12.50
				(b) Unnumbered.............		25p	£12.50
	—		26	B. Large size (77 × 69 mm.)...............			
				(a) Numbered.................		18p	£4.50
				(b) Unnumbered..............		26p	£6.50
180	A	C	48	Popular Footballers (Jan. 1936):—			
				A. White back		13p	£3.50
				B. Cream back..........................		13p	£4.50
	—	C		Popular Personalities, oval (70 × 30 mm.) (Feb. 1935):—	Ha.629		
			72	1. Normal issue.........................		13p	£8.00
			10	2. Replaced subjects (Nos. 1–10) for issue in Eire..............................		—	—
		C		Races—Historic and Modern (Mar. 1927):—			
145	A	C	25	A. Small size...........................		36p	£9.00
	B		25	B. Large size...........................		40p	£10.00
	—		12	C. Extra-large size (133 × 69 mm.)........		£1.00	£12.00
		C		Regalia Series (July 1925):—			
	A		25	A. Small size...........................		13p	£3.00
	B		20	B. Large size...........................		25p	£5.00
	—		10	C. Extra-large size (135 × 71 mm.)........		50p	£5.00
	—	C	50	"Round the World" Scenic Models (folders) (83 × 73 mm.).........................		15p	£7.50
		C		School Emblems (Oct. 1929):—			
	A		50	A. Small size...........................		30p	£15.00
	B		40	B. Large size...........................		20p	£8.00
	—		20	C. Extra-large size (134 × 70 mm.)........		40p	£8.00
	C1	C	48	Tapestry Reproductions of Famous Paint- ings (sectional) (June 1938)...............		25p	£12.50
	A	C	50	Tools—And How to Use Them (Mar. 1935) .		25p	£12.50
586	A	P	27	Views of London (export)		13p	£2.25
	A	P	27	Views of the World (export)		35p	£9.00
45	A	C	25	Wild Flower Art Series (Aug. 1923)		32p	£8.00

C. Post-1940 Turf Slide Issues

	Size	Print- ing	Number in set			Price per card	Complete set
	A	U	50	British Aircraft (1953)....................		30p	£15.00
	A	U	50	British Fish (1954).......................		18p	£9.00
	A	U	50	British Railway Locomotives (1952)........		25p	£12.50
	A	U	50	Celebrities of British History (1951)........		35p	£17.50
	A	U	50	Famous British Fliers (1956)..............		35p	£17.50
	A	U	50	Famous Cricketers (1950).................		40p	
	A	U	50	Famous Dog Breeds (1952)................		16p	£8.00
	A	U	50	Famous Film Stars (1949).................		12p	£6.00
	A	U	50	Famous Footballers (1951)................		25p	£12.50
	A	U	50	Film Favourites (1948)		35p	
	A	U	50	Film Stars (1947)........................		16p	£8.00
	A	U	50	Footballers (1948)........................		25p	—
	A	U	50	Olympics (1948)..........................		35p	£17.50
	A	U	50	Radio Celebrities (1950)..................		15p	£7.50

CARRERAS LTD. (continued)

Illus. No.	Size	Print- ing	Number in set		Handbook ref.	Price per card	Complete set
	A	U	50	Sports Series (1949)		18p	£9.00
	A	U	50	Zoo Animals (1955)		25p	£12.50

(N.B. These prices are for the full slides. If only the cut slides are required these will be half Catalogue price.)

D. Post-1940 Issues

Illus. No.	Size	Print- ing	Number in set		Handbook ref.	Price per card	Complete set
28	A	C	50	British Birds (1976)........................		07p	£1.50
				Album 60p			
51	A	C	50	Flowers all the Year Round (1977)..........		16p	£8.00
				Album 60p			
	A	C	50	Kings & Queens of England (1977)..........		16p	£8.00
				Album 60p			
307	A	C	50	Military Uniforms (1976)...................		07p	£1.50
				Album 60p			
	A	C	50	Palmistry (1980)		—	—
				Album—			
	A	C	50	Sport Fish (1978)		07p	£1.50
				Album 60p			
371	A	C	50	Vintage Cars (1976):—			
				A. With word "Filter" in white oval:—			
				i Thin card, bright red oblong at top ..		15p	£7.50
				ii Thick card, bright red oblong at top .		12p	£6.00
				iii Thin card, dull red oblong at top		15p	£7.50
				B. Without word "Filter" in white oval....		07p	£1.50
				Album 60p			

E. Miscellaneous Pre-1919 Issues

Illus. No.	Size	Print- ing	Number in set		Handbook ref.	Price per card	Complete set
			5	The Black Cat Handy French-English Dictionary (Booklets)....................		£6.00	—
			180	The Black Cat Library (Booklets)..........		£6.00	—
			?	*Lace Motifs*...............................		£5.00	—

F. Miscellaneous Post-1940 Issues

Illus. No.	Size	Print- ing	Number in set		Handbook ref.	Price per card	Complete set
	A	C	60	Flags of All Nations (Prepared but not issued)		—	—
	—	C		Guards Series (68 × 50 mm.):—			
			4	A. Military Mug Series (1971).............		60p	£2.50
			8	B. Order Up the Guards (1970)		60p	—
			16	C. Send for the Guards (1969)		60p	—
	—	C	7	Millionaire Competition Folders (68 × 30 mm.)...................................		50p	£3.50

CARRICK & CO., Hull

Pre-1919 Issue

Illus. No.	Size	Print- ing	Number in set		Handbook ref.	Price per card	Complete set
	D	C	12	*Military Terms (1901)......................	H.50	£17.00	—

P. J. CARROLL & CO. LTD., Dundalk, Glasgow and Liverpool

A. Pre-1919 Issues

Illus. No.	Size	Print- ing	Number in set		Handbook ref.	Price per card	Complete set
	D	C	25	British Naval Series	H.51	£11.00	—
	A	P	20	County Louth G.R.A. Team and Officials (1913)..................................		£5.00	—
	D	BW	25	*Derby Winners (1914–15):—	H.52		
				A. Back in Black		£30.00	—
				B. Back in Green........................		£30.00	—

B. Post-1920 Issues

Illus. No.	Size	Print- ing	Number in set		Handbook ref.	Price per card	Complete set
	D	C	25	Ship Series (1937)		£2.20	£55.00
	D	U		Sweet Afton Jig-Saw Puzzles (1935):—			
			8	1. Inscribed "1" in centre of back.........		£3.50	—
			8	2. Inscribed "2" in centre of back.........		£3.50	—
			8	3. Inscribed "3" in centre of back.........		£3.50	—

C. Miscellaneous

Illus. No.	Size	Print- ing	Number in set		Handbook ref.	Price per card	Complete set
23	D	C	25	Birds (prepared but not issued)	Ha.537	13p	£1.75

THE CASKET TOBACCO & CIGARETTE CO. LTD., Manchester

Pre-1919 Issues

Illus. No.	Size	Print- ing	Number in set		Handbook ref.	Price per card	Complete set
	A2	U	? 2	Cricket Fixture Cards, Coupon Back (1905–06)...............................		—	—
	A2	U	? 2	*Football Fixture Cards, Coupon Back (1905–11)..............................	H.53	£65.00	—
	A2	BW	? 2	Road Maps................................	H.54/Ha.54	—	—

S. CAVANDER & CO., London & Portsea

Pre-1919 Issue

Illus. No.	Size	Print- ing	Number in set		Handbook ref.	Price per card	Complete set
	D	BW	? 1	*Beauties—selection from "Plums"	H.186/Ha.186	—	—

CAVANDERS LTD., London and Glasgow

Post-1920 Issues

Illus. No.	Size	Print- ing	Number in set		Handbook ref.	Price per card	Complete set
	A	C	25	Ancient Chinese (1926)....................		40p	£10.00
	A	C	25	Ancient Egypt (Jul. 1928)..................		50p	£12.50
	B	C	25	Ancient Egypt (different subjects)..........		19p	£4.75
124	A	P	36	Animal Studies		13p	£3.00
		CP	50	Beauty Spots of Great Britain (1927):—			
	A			A. Small size		20p	£1000
	—			B. Medium size (76 × 52 mm.)		20p	£10.00

CAVANDERS LTD. (continued)

Illus. No.	Size	Printing	Number in set		Handbook ref.	Price per card	Complete set
		CP		Camera Studies (1926):—			
	A		54	A. Small size		16p	£8.00
	—		56	B. Medium size (77 × 51 mm.)		16p	£8.00
436	A	C	30	Cinema Stars—Set 6 (1934)	Ha.515–6	13p	£3.50
	—	CP	30	The Colonial Series (77 × 51 mm.) (1925):—			
				A. Small caption, under 1mm. high.......		30p	£9.00
				B. Larger caption, over 1 mm. high		40p	£12.00
	—	C	25†	Coloured Stereoscopic (1931)		18p	£9.00
	D	C	25	Feathered Friends or Foreign Birds (1926):—	Ha.516		
				A. Titled "Feathered Friends"		70p	£17.50
				B. Titled "Foreign Birds"		40p	£10.00
	—	C	25†	Glorious Britain (76 × 51 mm.) (1930)		22p	£11.00
				The Homeland Series (1924–26):—	Ha.539		
	A			Small size—			
		CP	50	A. Back in blue....................		25p	£12.50
		CP	50	B. Back in black, glossy front		25p	£12.50
		CP	54	C. Back in black, matt front		25p	£12.50
	—			Medium size (77 × 51 mm.):—			
		CP	50	D. Back inscribed "Hand Coloured Real Photos"		14p	£7.00
		CP	56	E. As D, with "Reprinted ..." at base		18p	£9.00
		CP	56	F. As D, but words "Hand Coloured" dropped		25p	£12.50
		P	56	G. As D, but words "Hand Coloured" dropped		25p	£12.50
	A	C	25	Little Friends (1924)......................	Ha.540	36p	£9.00
	—	C	25	The Nation's Treasures (77 × 51 mm.) (1925)		24p	£6.00
		P		Peeps into Many Lands—"A Series of ..." (1927):—			
	D		36†	A. Small size		13p	£8.50
			36†	B. Medium size (75 × 50 mm.)		13p	£8.50
	—		36	C. Extra-large size (113 × 68 mm.)........		£1.00	—
		P	36†	Peeps into Many Lands—"Second Series ..." (1928):—			
	D			A. Small size		13p	£8.50
	—			B. Medium size (75 × 50 mm.)		13p	£8.50
		P	24†	Peeps into Many Lands—"Third Series ..." (1929):—			
	D			A. Small size		14p	£7.00
	—			B. Medium size (75 × 50 mm.)		14p	£7.00
				C. As B, but inscribed "Reprinted by Special Request"		25p	£12.50
		P	24†	Peeps into Prehistoric Times—"Fourth Series ..." (1930):—			
	D			A. Small size		20p	£10.00
	—			B. Medium size (75 × 50 mm.)		20p	£10.00
	—	P		*Photographs (54 × 38 mm.) (1924):—	Ha.541		
			30	1. Animal Studies......................		70p	£21.00
			3	2. Royal Family		£2.00	—
	—	C	48	Regimental Standards (76 × 70 mm.)	Ha.502–7	—	—
546	C	C	25	Reproductions of Celebrated Oil Paintings (1925)	Ha.542	44p	£11.00
		CP	108	River Valleys (1926):—			
	A			A. Small size		25p	£27.00
	—			B. Medium size (75 × 50 mm.)		25p	£27.00
	A	C	25	School Badges:—	Ha.543		
				A. Back in dark blue		13p	£2.75
				B. Back in light blue....................		13p	£3.00
	—	CP	30	Wordsworth's Country (76 × 51 mm.) (1926)		34p	£10.00

†Stereoscopic series, consisting of a Right and a Left card for each number, a complete series is thus **double** the number shown.

R. S. CHALLIS & CO. LTD., London

Post-1920 Issues

	D1	C	50	Comic Animals (1936).....................		15p	£7.50
	A	BW	44	Flicketts (Greyhound Racing Flickers)	Ha.589–1	—	—
38	D1	U	36	Wild Birds at Home (1935):—	Ha.626		
				A. Inscribed "Issued with Baldric Cigarettes"		13p	£3.50
				B. Above wording blocked out in black ...		60p	£22.00

H. CHAPMAN & CO.

Pre-1919 Issues

	D	C	30	*Army Pictures, Cartoons, etc...............	H.12	—	—

CHARLESWORTH, & AUSTIN LTD., London

Pre-1919 Issues

	C	U	50	*Beauties—"BOCCA"	H.39	£7.00	£350.00
478	C	BW	16	*British Royal Family	H.28	£12.00	—
	C	C	30	Colonial Troops:—	H.40		
				A. Black back........................		£12.00	—
				B. Brown back........................		£12.00	—
	A1	BW	20	Cricketers Series	H.29	£25.00	—

Illus. No.	Size	Print-ing	Number in set		Handbook ref.	Price per card	Complete set
	C	C	30	*Flags and Flags with Soldiers	H.41	£14.00	—

CHESTERFIELD CIGARETTES

Post-1940 Issue

—		C	6	Cocktails 1980 (76 × 45 mm.)		15p	£0.90

A. CHEW & CO., Bradford

Pre-1919 Issue

	D	C	30	*Army, Pictures, Cartoons, etc.	Ha.12	—	—

W. A. & A. C. CHURCHMAN, Ipswich

A. Pre-1919 Issues

Illus. No.	Size	Print-ing	Number in set		Handbook ref.	Price per card	Complete set
	C	C	26	*Actresses—"FROGA A"....................	H.20	£12.50	—
473	C	C	26	*Actresses—"FROGA B"....................	H.20	£15.00	—
	C	U	? 23	*Actresses, "For the Pipe" back..............	H.55/Ha.55	£19.00	—
	A	C	25	Army Badges of Rank (Mar. 1916).......	H.56	£3.40	£85.00
462	A	C	12	*Beauties—"CERF" (Oct. 1904).............	H.57	£18.00	—
	C	U	25	*Beauties—"FECKSA".................	H.58	£65.00	—
				*Beauties—"CHOAB":—	H.21/Ha.21		
		C	25	I. Circular cards, 55 mm. diameter		£250.00	—
	C	C	25	II. Five different backs		£90.00	—
	C	C	25	*Beauties—"GRACC".....................	H.59	£22.00	—
	A	C	50	Birds & Eggs (May 1906)	H.60	£3.00	£150.00
	D	BW	20	*Boer War Cartoons	H.42	—	—
			20	*Boer War Generals—"CLAM":—	H.61		
	A2	BW		A. Black front		£13.00	—
	A	U		B. Brown front		£13.00	—
	A	C	50	Boy Scouts (Jan. 1916)	H.62	£2.00	£100.00
	A	C	50	Boy Scouts, 2nd Series (Aug. 1916)........	H.62	£2.00	£100.00
	A	C	50	Boy Scouts, 3rd Series (Oct. 1916):—	H.62		
				A. Brown back......................		£2.00	£100.00
				B. Blue back		£3.50	—
	D	P	41	*Celebrities—Boer War Period	H.63		—
				26 Generals, etc.		£7.50	—
				15 Actresses		£7.50	—
	A	C	38	Dogs and Fowls (Apl. 1908)	H.64	£3.50	£135.00
	A		50	East Suffolk Churches:—			
		BW		A. Black front, cream back (1912)........		£1.20	£60.00
		BW		B. Black front, white back (1912)		£1.50	£75.00
		U		C. Sepia front (1917, re-issued 1923)		£1.20	£60.00
	A	C	50	Fish & Bait (May 1914)..................	H.65	£2.00	£100.00
	A	C	50	Fishes of the World (Sep. 1911):—	H.66	—	£165.00
				30 cards as re-issued 1924................		£1.50	£45.00
				20 cards not re-issued		£6.00	—
	A	C	50	Flags & Funnels of Leading Steamship Lines (Feb. 1912)............................	H.67	£3.00	—
	A	C	50	Football Club Colours (Jan. 1909)	H.68	£3.00	£150.00
	A	U	50	*Footballers—Photogravure Portraits		£6.00	—
	A	C	50	Footballers—Action Pictures & Inset (Nov. 1914)...............................		£2.50	£125.00
	C	C	40	*Home and Colonial Regiments:—	H.69		
				20 Caption in Blue		£12.00	—
				20 Caption in Brown		£12.00	—
	A	C	50	Interesting Buildings (Jul. 1905).............	H.70	£2.50	£125.00
	A	C	50	*Medals (Jan. 1910)	H.71	£3.00	£150.00
	A	C	50	*Phil May Sketches (Feb. 1912):—	H.72		
				A. "Churchman's Gold Flake Cigarettes" .		£2.00	£100.00
				B. "Churchman's Cigarettes".............		£3.50	—
	A	C	50	*Regimental Colours and Cap Badges (Aug. 1912)................................	H.73	£2.50	£125.00
	A	C	50	Sectional Cycling Map (Aug. 1913)	H.74	£2.00	£100.00
348	A	C	50	Silhouettes of Warships (Feb. 1915).........		£2.50	£125.00
	A	C	50	A Tour Round the World (Jan. 1911)	H.75	£3.00	£150.00
	A1	C	25	*Types of British and Colonial Troops	H.76	£32.00	—
	A	C	50	Wild Animals of the World (Jun. 1907)......	H.77	£3.00	£150.00

B. Post-1920 Issues

Illus. No.	Size	Print-ing	Number in set		Handbook ref.	Price per card	Complete set
—		C	48	Air-Raid Precautions (68 × 53 mm.) (Aug. 1938)..................................	Ha.544	13p	£5.00
	A	U	50	Association Footballers (Sep. 1938).........		13p	£3.25
170	A	U	50	Association Footballers, 2nd Series (Sep. 1939)................................		13p	£4.50
	A	C	25	Boxing (Dec. 1922)........................	H.311	£1.20	—
220	A	U	50	Boxing Personalities (Dec. 1938)............		13p	£5.50
461	A	U	25	British Film Stars (Feb. 1934)..............		40p	£10.00
198	A	C	55	Can You Beat Bogey at St. Andrews? (Feb. 1934):—			
				A. Set of 55, and three alternatives for No. 55		36p	£20.00
				B. Overprinted in red "Exchangeable ..." .		36p	£20.00
		U		Cathedrals & Churches (Nov. 1924):—	Ha.545		
558	A		25	A. Small size............................		80p	£20.00
	J		12	B. Extra large size......................		£3.00	—
553	A	C	50	Celebrated Gateways (Apr. 1925)		90p	£45.00

Illus. No.	Size	Printing	Number in set		Handbook ref.	Price per card	Complete set
	A	C	25	Civic Insignia and Plate (May 1926).........		70p	£17.50
275	A	C	50	Contract Bridge (June 1935)		13p	£5.50
153	A	C	50	Cricketers (June 1936)......................		60p	£30.00
		C		Curious Dwellings:—			
557	A		25	A. Small size (Jan. 1926).................		70p	£17.50
	B		12	B. Large size (Nov. 1925)................		£1.00	£12.00
	A	C	25	Curious Signs (Sep. 1925)..................		60p	£15.00
		C		Eastern Proverbs:—	Ha.521		
				A. Small size—			
	A		25	1. "A Series of 25" (Aug. 1931)		13p	£3.00
	A		25	2. "2nd Series of 25" (Aug. 1932)......		24p	£6.00
				B. Large size—			
	B		12	1. "A Series of 12" (Jan. 1931)		£1.00	£12.00
	B		12	2. "2nd Series of 12" (1933)...........		50p	£6.00
	B		12	3. "3rd Series of 12" (1933)...........		25p	£3.00
	B		12	4. "4th Series of 12" (1934)..........		17p	£2.00
403, 650 etc.	A	C	50	Empire Railways (Oct. 1931)		90p	£45.00
162	A	C	25	Famous Cricket Colours (May 1928)........		90p	£22.50
		U		Famous Golfers:—			
206	A		50	A. Small size (Oct. 1927).................		50p	£25.00
				B. Large size—			
200	B		12	1. "A Series of 12" (Oct. 1927)		£1.25	£15.00
	B		12	2. "2nd Series of 12" (Mar. 1928)		£1.25	£15.00
		C		Famous Railway Trains (see RB21/ 210/54):—			
406, 649	A		25	A. Small size (Oct. 1929).................		90p	£22.50
				B. Large size—			
	B		12	1. "Series of 12" (Nov. 1928)...........		£1.25	£15.00
705 etc.	B		12	2. "2nd Series of 12" (Jul. 1929).......		£1.25	£15.00
	A	C	52	"Frisky" (May 1925)......................		22p	£11.00
	A	C	50	History and Development of the British Empire (Apr. 1934)......................		40p	£20.00
	—	U	48	Holidays in Britain (Views and Maps) (68 × 53 mm.) (May 1937):—			
				A. White card..........................		13p	£6.00
				B. Cream card		13p	£6.00
578	—	C	48	Holidays in Britain (Views only) (68 × 53 mm.) (June 1938)		18p	£9.00
	A	C	25	The Houses of Parliament and Their Story (Dec. 1931).............................		60p	£15.00
		C		Howlers:—			
	A		40	A. Small size (July 1937).................		13p	£3.75
	B		16	B. Large size (Oct. 1936).................		13p	£1.75
571	A	C	25	The Inns of Court (Feb. 1922)		60p	£15.00
618	A	C	25	Interesting Door-Knockers (Mar. 1928).....		70p	£17.50
	A	C	25	Interesting Experiments (Nov. 1929) (see RB21/210/79)...........................		30p	£7.50
494	A	C	50	"In Town To-night" (May 1938)...........		13p	£3.25
	B	C	12	Italian Art Exhibition, 1930 (Jan. 1931)		90p	£11.00
	B	C	12	Italian Art Exhibition, 1930—"2nd Series" (Aug. 1931).............................		90p	£11.00
		C		The King's Coronation:—			
	A		50	A. Small size (Jan. 1937).................		13p	£3.25
	B		15	B. Large size (May 1937)		23p	£3.50
255	A	U	50	Kings of Speed (May 1939)		13p	£4.00
		C		Landmarks in Railway Progress:—			
653 etc.	A		50	A. Small size (Jan. 1931).................		90p	£45.00
				B. Large size—			
701 etc.	B		12	1. "1st Series of 12" (Jan. 1932)		75p	£9.00
745 etc.	B		12	2. "2nd Series of 12" (Mar. 1932)		£1.00	£12.00
		U		Lawn Tennis:—	Ha.546		
227	A		50	A. Small size (Sep. 1928).................		16p	£8.00
	B		12	B. Large size (Jul. 1928)		70p	£8.50
		C		Legends of Britain (Aug. 1936):—			
	A		50	A. Small size..........................		18p	£9.00
	B		12	B. Large size..........................		40p	£5.00
		C		Life in a Liner:—			
380	A		25	A. Small size (Feb. 1930)		18p	£4.50
	B		12	B. Large size (Apr. 1930)		75p	£9.00
		C		Men of the Moment in Sport:—			
225	A		50	A. Small size (Dec. 1928)		60p	£30.00
				B. Large size—			
	B		12	1. "1st Series of 12" (Mar. 1929)		£1.00	£12.00
	B		12	2. "2nd Series of 12" (May 1929)......		£1.00	£12.00
	—	C	48	Modern Wonders (68 × 53 mm.) (Feb. 1938).		18p	£9.00
	A	C	25	Musical Instruments (Jul. 1924).............	Ha.547	90p	£22.50
		C		Nature's Architects:—			
	A		25	A. Small size (Oct. 1930).................		16p	£4.00
	B		12	B. Large size (May 1930)		75p	£9.00
	—	U	48	The Navy at Work (68 × 53 mm.) (Oct. 1937)		13p	£4.00
	A	C	25	Pipes of the World (Jan. 1927)		£1.20	£30.00
		C		Prominent Golfers:—			
195	A		50	A. Small size (May 1931)		45p	£22.50
	B		12	B. Large size (Aug. 1931)................		£1.25	£15.00
		C		The "Queen Mary":—			
	A		50	A. Small size (Apr. 1936)		35p	£17.50
381	B		16	B. Large size (June 1936)		38p	£6.00
	A	C	50	Racing Greyhounds (Aug. 1934)...........		30p	£15.00

Illus. No.	Size	Print-ing	Number in set		Handbook ref.	Price per card	Complete set
—		C	48	The R.A.F. at Work (68 × 53 mm.) (Dec. 1938)		20p	£10.00
		C		Railway Working:—	Ha.548		
				A. Small size—			
727 etc.	A		25	1. "Series of 25" (Oct. 1926)		£1.00	£25.00
404, 731 etc.	A		25	2. "2nd Series of 25" (July 1927)		80p	£20.00
				B. Large size—			
	B		12	1. "Series of 12" (Sep. 1926)		£2.00	—
	B		13	2. "2nd Series, 13" (Oct. 1927)		£2.00	—
	B		12	3. "3rd Series, 12" (1927)		£2.00	—
	A	BW	50	Rivers and Broads (1922):—			
				A. Titled "Rivers & Broads"		£1.80	—
				B. Titled "Rivers & Broads of Norfolk & Suffolk"		£1.80	—
179	A	C	50	Rugby Internationals (Sep. 1935)		18p	£9.00
207	A	C	50	Sporting Celebrities (Dec. 1931)		30p	£15.00
		C		Sporting Trophies:—			
229	A		25	A. Small size (Apr. 1927)		40p	£10.00
	B		12	B. Large size (May 1927)		£1.25	£15.00
228	A	C	25	Sports & Games in Many Lands (Aug. 1929) (see RB21/210/133)		30p	£7.50
		C		The Story of London (May 1930):—			
	A		50	A. Small size		40p	£20.00
	B		12	B. Large size		80p	£10.00
		C		The Story of Navigation:—			
386	A		50	A. Small size (July 1937)		13p	£3.50
	B		12	B. Large size (1935)		40p	£5.00
199	A	C		3 Jovial Golfers in search of the perfect course (May 1934):—			
			36	A. Home issue		28p	£10.00
			72	B. Irish issue, with green over-printing		80p	—
		C		Treasure Trove:—			
616	A		50	A. Small size (Aug. 1937)		13p	£3.75
	B		12	B. Large size (1935)		20p	£2.50
		C		Warriors of All Nations (see RB21/210/144):—			
	A		25	A. Small size (Dec. 1929)		60p	£15.00
				B. Large Size—			
	B		12	1. "A Series of 12" (Nov. 1929)		60p	£7.50
	B		12	2. "2nd Series of 12" (May 1931)		90p	£11.00
		C		Well-known Ties (1934):—			
	A		50	A. Small size		25p	£12.50
				B. Large size—			
	B		12	1. "A Series of 12"		60p	£7.50
	B		12	2. "2nd Series of 12"		20p	£2.50
	A	C	50	Well-known Ties, "2nd Series" (1935)		13p	£3.50
518	A	U	25	Wembley Exhibition (1924)		90p	£22.50
	A	U	50	West Suffolk Churches (July 1919)		£1.20	£60.00
580	—	C	48	Wings Over the Empire (68 × 53 mm.) (July 1939)		13p	£2.50
		C		Wonderful Railway Travel (Apr. 1937):—			
	A		50	A. Small size		15p	£7.50
	B		12	B. Large size		25p	£3.00
C. Miscellaneous							
—			1	Australian Cricket Fixture Booklet (1899)		—	—
—			1	Christmas Greetings Card (1938)		—	£0.60
—			1	Mystery Wording Revolving Card (1907)		—	—
—		U	55	Olympic Winners Through The Years (Package Designs, 30 small, 25 large)		—	—
—		C	48	Pioneers (68 × 53 mm) (Prepared but not issued)		—	—
—		U	40	The World of Sport (Package Designs, 30 small, 10 large)		—	—
	A	C	50	World Wonders Old and New (prepared but not issued)		40p	£20.00

WM. CLARKE & SON, Dublin

Pre-1919 issues

Illus. No.	Size	Print-ing	Number in set		Handbook ref.	Price per card	Complete set
	A	C	25	Army Life (1915)	H.78	£4.00	£100.00
	A1	BW	? 16	*Boer War Celebrities—"CAG"	H.79	£10.00	—
	A	C	50	Butterflies & Moths (1912)	H.80	£2.50	£125.00
	A	BW	30	Cricketer Series (1901)		£20.00	—
	A1	BW	66	Football Series (1902)	H.81	£3.00	£200.00
	A	C	25	Marine Series (1907)		£5.00	£125.00
	A	C	50	Royal Mail (1914)	H.82	£2.50	£125.00
		C	50	Sporting Terms (38 × 58 mm.):—	H.83/Ha.83		
				14 Cricket Terms		£10.00	—
				12 Cycling Terms		£10.00	—
				12 Football Terms		£10.00	—
				12 Golf Terms		£10.00	—
471	—	C	? 19	*Tobacco Leaf Girls (shaped)	H.84	£225.00	—
—		C	25	Well-known Sayings (71 × 32 mm.)	H.85	£6.00	£150.00

J. H. CLURE, Keighley

Pre-1919 issues

Illus. No.	Size	Print-ing	Number in set		Handbook ref.	Price per card	Complete set
	D	C	30	*Army Pictures, Cartoons, etc.	H.12	—	—
	A	U	50	War Portraits	H.86	—	—

J. LOMAX COCKAYNE, Sheffield

Illus. No.	Size	Print-ing	Number in set		Handbook ref.	Price per card	Complete set
Pre-1919 Issue							
A	U	50	War Portraits..........................		H.86	—	—

COHEN WEENEN & CO. LTD., London

A. Pre-1919 Issues

Illus. No.	Size	Print-ing	Number in set		Handbook ref.	Price per card	Complete set
—		P	? 35	*Actresses, Footballers and Jockeys (26 × 61 mm.)......................................	H.87	£10.00	—
	A1	U	26	*Actresses—"FROGA A".................	H.20	£14.00	—
	A	C	? 21	*Beauties—selection from "BOCCA"........	H.39/Ha.39	£25.00	—
	A1	C	25	*Beauties—"GRACC"..................	H.59	£25.00	—
222	D2	BW	25	*Boxers:—			
				A. Black back..........................		£6.00	£150.00
				B. Green back		£5.00	£125.00
				C. *Without Maker's Name*................		£6.00	—
	A	BW	65	*Celebrities—Black and white:—	H.88		
				A. "Sweet Crop, over 250..." back.....		£2.50	£165.00
				B. "Sweet Crop, over 500..." back.......		£5.00	—
	A	C		*Celebrities—Coloured:—	H.89		
			45	I. 1–45 Boer War Generals etc. "Sweet Crop, over 100..." back:—		—	£90.00
				A. Toned back		£2.00	—
				B. White back		£2.25	—
				C. *Plain Back*.......................		—	—
			121	II. 1–121 Including Royalty, etc. "Sweet Crop, over 250..." back:			
				1–45 as in I...........................		£2.50	—
				46–121 additional subjects..............		£2.25	£170.00
—		C		*Celebrities—"GAINSBOROUGH I":—	H.90/Ha.90		
—			? 2	A. In metal frames (46 × 67 mm.).........		£65.00	—
	D2		39	B. "Sweet Crop, over 250..." back.......		£18.00	—
	D		39	C. "Sweet Crop, over 400..." back.......		£6.00	—
			39	D. *1902 Calendar Back gilt border to front* .		£70.00	—
			39	E. *Plain Back*.......................		£7.00	£280.00
—		P	?157	*Celebrities—"GAINSBOROUGH II":—	H.91/Ha.91		
				In metal frames (46 × 67 mm.)		£9.00	—
				A. *Without frames showing Frame Marks* ..		£3.50	—
				B. *Without Frames no Frame Marks (as issued)*		£8.00	—
156	A2	C	20	*Cricketers, Footballers, Jockeys:— "Sweet Crop, over 250..." back:—	H.92		
				A. Caption in brown		£10.00	£200.00
				B. Caption in grey-black		£10.00	£200.00
	D	C	40	Fiscal Phrases, "Sweet Crop, over 500" back:—	H.93		
				A. "Copyright Regd." on front		£7.00	£280.00
				B. Without "Copyright Regd."		£7.00	£280.00
	A2	C	60	Football Captains, 1907–8—Series No. 5....	H.94	£3.00	£180.00
	A2	BW	? 65	*Heroes of Sport	H.95/Ha.95	£22.00	—
	A	C	40	*Home and Colonial Regiments	H.69		
				A. "Sweet Crop, over 100..." back:—			
				20 Caption in blue....................		£6.00	£120.00
				20 Caption in brown..................		£6.00	£120.00
				B. "Sweet Crop, over 250..." back:—			
				20 Caption in blue....................		£8.00	—
				20 Caption in brown..................		£7.00	—
567	A2	C	20	*Interesting Buildings and Views............	H.96/Ha.96	£6.00	£120.00
	K2	C	52	*Miniature Playing Cards — Bandmaster" Cigarettes		£2.00	—
	D2	C	20	*Nations:—	H.97/Ha.97		
				A. Blue back..........................		£6.00	£120.00
				B. *Plain back—gilt border*		—	—
				C. *1902 Calender back*		—	—
	D	C	40	Naval and Military Phrases:—	H.14		
				A. Red back, "Series No. 1"		£8.00	£320.00
				B. "Sweet Crop, over 250..." back		£14.00	—
	D2	C	50	Owners, Jockeys, Footballers, Cricketers— Series No. 2	H.98	£2.20	£110.00
	D2	C	20	Owners, Jockeys, Footballers, Cricketers— Series No. 3...........................	H.99	£3.75	£75.00
	D	C	30	*Proverbs, "Sweet Crop, over 400..." back ..	H.15	£10.00	—
	A	C	20	Russo-Japanese War Series.................	H.100	£12.00	—
499	A	BW	25	*Silhouettes of Celebrities	H.101	£6.00	£150.00
	D1	C	50	Star Artistes—Series No. 4:—	H.102/Ha.102		
				20 With stage background		£6.00	£120.00
				30 No stage, plain background............		£3.30	£100.00
	D	C	50	V.C. Heroes (of World War I), Nd. 51–100:—			
				51–75—dull greyish card		£5.00	£125.00
				Without Maker's Name on back		£6.00	—
				76–100—glossy white card...............		£5.00	£125.00
	D	U	50	*War Series (World War I):—	H.103		
				1–25 Admirals and Warships:—			
				A. Thick card		£4.00	£100.00
				B. Thin card		£4.00	£100.00

COHEN WEENEN & CO. LTD. (continued)

Illus. No.	Size	Printing	Number in set		Handbook ref.	Price per card	Complete set
				26–50 Leaders of the War:—			
				A. Maker's Name on back................		£4.00	£100.00
				B. *Without Maker's Name on back. See*			
				Anonymous		£7.00	—
	D1	C	30	Wonders of the World—"Series No. 6"	H.104	£4.00	£120.00
B. Post-1920 Issues							
	D2	U	25	*Cricketers (1926)...........................		£1.20	£30.00
	D2	C	20	Nations (1923)............................	H97	£1.00	£20.00
	D1	C	30	Wonders of the World (1923)	H.14	60p	£18.00
C. Silks							
	—	C	? 16	*Victoria Cross Heroes II (72 × 70 mm.)			
				(paper-backed)	Ha.504–2	£12.50	

T. H. COLLINS, Mansfield

Post-1920 Issues							
556	A1	U	25	Homes of England (1924)...................		£1.40	£35.00
231	A	C	25	Sports & Pastimes—Series I	H.225	£1.40	£35.00

F. COLTON Jun., Retford

Pre-1919 Issues							
	D	C	30	*Army Pictures, Cartoons, etc................	H.12	£22.00	—
	A	U	50	War Portraits..............................	H.86	£22.00	—

THE CONTINENTAL CIGARETTE FACTORY, London

Post-1920 Issues							
	A	C	25	Charming Portraits:—	Ha.549		
				A. Back in blue, with firm's name		£2.20	—
				B. Back in blue, inscribed "Club Mixture			
				Tobacco"..............................		£2.20	—
				C. Back in brown, inscribed "Club Mixture			
				Tobacco"..............................		£2.20	—
				D. Plain back		£2.20	—

COOPER & CO's STORES LTD., London

Pre-1919 Issues							
	A	BW	25	*Boer War Celebrities—"STEW":—	H.105		
				A. "Alpha Mixture" back		£65.00	—
				B. "Gladys Cigars" back		£65.00	—

CO-OPERATIVE WHOLESALE SOCIETY LTD., Manchester

A. Pre-1919 Issues							
	A2	C	? 4	*Advertisement Cards.......................	H.106/Ha.106	£200.00	
	A	C	25	Boy Scout Series		£5.00	—
	A	C	50	British Sport Series†.......................	H.112	£10.00	—
	A	C	28	*Co-operative buildings and Works	H.107	£7.00	£200.00
	A	C	25	Parrot Series.............................		£11.00	—
	A	C	18	War Series...............................		£7.00	—

†Note: Cards advertise non-tobacco products, but are believed to have been packed with cigarettes and/or tobacco.

B. Post-1920 Issues							
	A	C	24	African Types (1936)......................		13p	£2.25
	—	U	50	Beauty Spots of Britain (76 × 51 mm.)		13p	£3.75
	A2	C	50	Boy Scout Badges (1939)		20p	£10.00
26	A	C	48	British and Foreign Birds (1938)		13p	£5.50
	D	C	25	*Cooking Recipes (1923)		90p	£22.50
50	A	C	24	English Roses (1924)		£1.60	£40.00
	A	C	50	Famous Bridges (48 + 2 added) (1937).......		22p	£11.00
560	A	C	48	Famous Buildings (1935)		13p	£6.00
	A2	C	25	How to Do It (1924)......................	Ha.550	70p	£17.50
	A	C	48	Musical Instruments (1934).................		90p	£45.00
	A	C	48	Poultry (1927)		90p	£45.00
683 etc.	A	C	48	Railway Engines (1936)		£1.40	£70.00
	A	C	24	Sailing Craft (1935)		50p	£12.50
	A2	C	48	Wayside flowers, brown back (1923)		90p	£45.00
61	A2	C	48	Wayside Flowers, grey back (1928).........		13p	£3.50
69	A2	C	48	Wayside Woodland Trees (1924)...........		90p	£45.00
C. Post-1940 Issue							
	A	C	24	Western Stars (1957)		07p	£0.70

COPE BROS. & CO. LTD., Liverpool

A. Pre-1919 Issues							
		BW	20	*Actresses—"BLARM":—	H.23		
	A1			A. Plain backs, Name panel ¼″ from border		£10.00	—
	A1			B. Black design back, Name ¼″ from			
				border................................		£10.00	—
	D			C. Black design back, Name panel $\frac{1}{16}$″ from			
				border................................		£12.00	—

Illus. No.	Size	Print-ing	Number in set		Handbook ref.	Price per card	Complete set
	A	U	? 6	*Actresses—"COPEIS"	H.108	£45.00	—
	A	U	26	*Actresses—"FROGA A"	H.20	£26.00	—
	D1	P	50	*Actresses and Beauties	H.109	£6.00	—
	K1	P	? 17	*Beauties, Actors and Actresses	H.110	£12.00	—
	A	C	52	*Beauties—P.C. inset	H.111	£15.00	—
	A	C	15	*Beauties—"PAC"	H.2	£22.00	—
391	A1	C	50	Boats of the World		£3.00	£150.00
218	D2	BW	126	Boxers:—			
				1–25 Boxers		£2.00	£50.00
				26–50 Boxers		£2.80	£70.00
				51–75 Boxers		£2.80	£70.00
				76–100 Boxers		£7.00	£175.00
				101–125 Army Boxers		£3.00	£75.00
				126 "New World Champion"		—	£8.00
	A1	C	35	*Boy Scouts and Girl Guides	H.132	£4.00	£140.00
	D	BW	25	British Admirals	H.103	£7.00	£175.00
	A2	C	50	British Warriors:—			
				A. Black on white backs		£2.50	£125.00
				B. Grey on toned backs		£3.00	£150.00
521	A	C	50	Characters from Scott:—			
				A. Wide card		£3.00	£150.00
				B. Narrow card—officially cut		£3.00	—
		U	115	Chinese Series:—	H.113		
	A1			Nos. 1–20		£6.00	—
	A1			21–40		£6.00	—
				41–65:—			
	D			A. Thick brown card		£6.00	—
	A1			B. Re-drawn, smaller format		£10.00	—
	A2			66–115		£7.00	—
	A	C	50	Cope's Golfers:—			
				A. Wide card		£5.00	—
				B. Narrow card—officially cut		£4.00	—
539	A	C	50	Dickens' Gallery		£3.00	£150.00
111	A	C	50	Dogs of the World		£2.00	£100.00
	A	C	25	Eminent British Regiments—Officers' Uniforms:—		—	£175.00
				A. Yellow-brown back		£7.00	—
				B. Claret back		£7.00	—
	A2	C	30	*Flags of Nations:—	H.114		
				A. "Bond of Union" back		£7.00	£210.00
				B. Plain back		£6.00	—
	D	C	24	*Flags, Arms and Types of Nations:—	H.115		
				A. Numbered		£5.00	£125.00
				B. Unnumbered		—	—
		U	20	*Kenilworth Phrases (80 × 70 mm.)	H.116	—	—
	A2	C	50	Music Hall Artistes:—			
				A. Inscribed "Series of 50"		£10.00	—
				B. Without the above		£2.50	£125.00
	A	U	472	Noted Footballers—"Clips Cigarettes":—	Ha.474		
				1. Unnumbered—Wee Jock Simpson		—	£10.00
				120. Series of 120:—			
				A. Greenish-blue frame		£2.00	—
				B. Bright blue frame		£2.00	—
				162. Series of 282:—			
				A. Greenish-blue frame		£2.00	—
				B. Bright blue frame		£2.00	—
				189. Series of 500. Bright blue frame		£2.00	—
	D	P	195	Noted Footballers—"Solace Cigarettes":—		£2.20	—
	A	C	24	*Occupations for Women	H.117	£80.00	—
	A	C	52	*Playing Cards "Rulers" as Court Cards:—	H.118		
				Blue backs:—			
				A. Rounded Corners, Court cards		£16.00	—
				Other than Court cards		£16.00	—
				B. Square Corners, Court cards		£10.00	—
				Other than Court cards		£10.00	—
	—	C	24	Photo Albums for the Million:—	H.119		
				12 Buff cover (25 × 39 mm.)		£10.00	—
				12 Green cover (25 × 39 mm.)		£10.00	—
520	A	C	50	Shakespeare Gallery:—			
				A. Wide card		£3.00	£150.00
				B. Narrow card—officially cut		£3.00	—
	A1	C	25	*Uniforms of Soldiers and Sailors:—	H.120		
				A. Circular Medallion back, wide card		£16.00	—
				B. Circular Medallion back, narrow card, officially cut		—	—
				C. Square Medallion back, wide card		—	—
				D. Square Medallion back, narrow card, officially cut		£13.00	—
334	D	BW		V.C. & D.S.O. Naval & Flying Heroes:—			
			50	Unnumbered (1916)	H.121	£2.80	£140.00
			25	Numbered 51–75 (1917)		£4.00	£100.00
	D	BW	20	*War Pictures	H.122	£7.00	£140.00
	D	BW	50	*War Series (War Leaders and Warships)	H.103	£12.00	—
100	A1	C	25	Wild Animals & Birds		£8.00	—

B. Post-1920 Issues

Illus. No.	Size	Print-ing	Number in set		Handbook ref.	Price per card	Complete set
219	D	BW	25	Boxing Lessons (1935)		26p	£6.50
	—	C	25	Bridge Problems (folders) (85 × 50 mm.)		—	—
555	A1	U	25	Castles† (1939)		13p	£1.75
	A1	U	25	Cathedrals† (May, 1939)		30p	£7.50

COPE BROS. & CO. LTD. *(continued)*

Illus. No.	Size	Print- ing	Number in set		Handbook ref.	Price per card	Complete set
538	—	C	25	Dickens' Character Series (75 × 58 mm.) (1939)		13p	£2.75
270	—	C	25	The Game of Poker† (75 × 58 mm.)		13p	£2.75
	—	C	50	General Knowledge† (70 × 42 mm.)		90p	£45.00
203	—	BW	32	Golf Strokes (70 × 45 mm.) (1923)		£1.25	£40.00
	A1	C	60	"Happy Families" (1937)		40p	£24.00
	—	C	50	Household Hints† (advertisement fronts) (70 × 45 mm.)		60p	£30.00
232	C	BW	30	Lawn Tennis Strokes (1924)		70p	£21.00
	—	U	50	Modern Dancing (folders) (74 × 43 mm.) (1926)		£2.25	—
17	A2	C	25	Pigeons		90p	£22.50
	A2	C	25	Song Birds		£1.00	£25.00
	A1	C	25	Sports & Pastimes (1925)	Ha.551	80p	£20.00
	—	C	25	Toy Models (The Country Fair) (73 × 66 mm.)	Ha.552	13p	£2.25
	A	C	25	The World's Police		£1.20	£30.00

†Joint Cope and Richard Lloyd issues.

E. CORONEL, London ————————————————————————

Pre-1919 Issue

	A	C	25	*Types of British and Colonial Troops	H.76	£30.00	—

DAVID CORRE & CO., London ————————————————

Pre-1919 Issue

	D	C	40	*Naval and Military Phrases (1900)	H.14	£38.00	—

JOHN COTTON LTD., Edinburgh ————————————————

Post-1920 Issues

	—	C	50	*Bridge Hands (folders) (82 × 66 mm.) (1934)		£2.00	—
204	A1	U	50	*Golf Strokes—A/B (1936)		60p	—
	A1	U	50	*Golf Strokes—C/D (1937)		65p	—
	A1	U	50	*Golf Strokes—E/F (1938)		75p	—
	A1	U	50	*Golf Strokes—G/H (1939)		—	—
	A1	U	50	*Golf Strokes—I/J (1939)		—	—

A. & J. COUDENS, LTD., London ————————————————

Post-1920 Issues

	A1	P	60	British Beauty Spots (1923):—	Ha.553		
				A. Printed back, numbered		70p	£42.00
				B. Printed back, unnumbered		70p	£42.00
				*C. Back rubber stamped "Cymox Cigarettes..."		£1.60	—
				*D. *Plain back*		£1.60	—
	A	P	60	Holiday Resorts in East Anglia (1924)		60p	£36.00
224	A2	BW	25	Sports Alphabet (1924)	Ha.551	£1.20	£30.00

W. R. DANIEL & CO., London ————————————————

Pre-1919 Issues

	A2	C	30	*Colonial Troops:—	H.40		
				A. Black back		£24.00	—
				B. Brown back		£15.00	—
	A2	C	25	*National Flags and Flowers—Girls	H.123	—	—

W. T. DAVIES & SONS, Chester ————————————————

A. Pre-1919 Issues

	A	C	? 19	*Actresses—"DIVAN"	H.124/Ha.124	£15.00	—
	A	C	25	Army Life (1915)	H.78	£6.00	—
	A	BW	12	*Beauties (1903)	H.125	£14.00	—
	A	C	50	Flags & Funnels of Leading Steamship Lines (1913)	H.67	£3.00	—
	A	BW	? 9	Newport Football Club	H.126/Ha.126	£30.00	—
	A	BW	5	Royal Welsh Fusiliers	H.127	£60.00	—

B. Post-1920 Issues

	A2	U	42	Aristocrats of the Turf (1924):—	Ha.554		
				1. Nos. 1–30—"A Series of 30"		90p	£27.00
				2. Nos. 31–42—"A Series of 42"		£6.00	—
	A2	U	36	Aristocrats of the Turf, Second Series (1924)		75p	£27.00
	A	C	25	Boxing (1924)	H.311	80p	£20.00

S. H. DAWES, Luton ————————————————————————

Pre-1919 Issue

	D	C	30	*Army Pictures, Cartoons, Etc.	H.12	—	—

J. W. DEWHURST, Morecambe

Illus. No.	Size	Print-ing	Number in set		Handbook ref.	Price per card	Complete set
Pre-1919 Issue							
	D	C	30	*Army Pictures, Cartoons, Etc.	H.12	£30.00	—

R. I. DEXTER & CO., Hucknall

Pre-1919 Issue							
	D2	U	30	*Borough Arms (1900)	H.128	50p	£15.00

A. DIMITRIOU, London

Miscellaneous Post-1920 Issue							
				Advertisement Cards (2 known)		—	—

GEORGE DOBIE & SON LTD., Paisley

A. Post-1920 Issues							
	—	—	? 22	Bridge Problems (folders) (circular 64 mm. diam.)		—	—
	A	C	25	Weapons of All Ages (1924)		£1.60	£40.00
B. Post 1940 Issues							
	—	C	32	Four Square Book (Nd. 1–32)—1963 (75 × 50 mm.)		70p	£22.00
	—	C	32	Four Square Book (Nd. 33–64)—1963 (75 × 50 mm.)		14p	£4.50
	—	C	32	Four Square Book (Nd. 65–96)—1963 (75 × 50 mm.)		13p	£4.00

DOBSON & CO. LTD.

Pre-1919 Issue							
	A	C	8	The European War Series	H.129	£8.00	—

DOBSON MOLLE & CO. LTD.—(See Anonymous)

THE DOMINION TOBACCO CO. (1929) LTD., London

Post-1920 Issues							
	A	U	25	Old Ships (1934)		60p	£15.00
	A	U	25	Old Ships (Second Series) (1935)		13p	£2.25
389	A	U	25	Old Ships (Third Series) (1936)		13p	£2.75
	A	U	25	Old Ships (Fourth Series) (Oct. 1936)		80p	£20.00

JOSEPH W. DOYLE LTD., Manchester

Post-1920 Issues							
	—	P	? 18	*Beauties, Nd.X.1–X.18 (89 × 70 mm.)		£5.00	—
	D	P	? 11	*Beauties, Nd. CC.D.1–CC.D.11		—	—

MAJOR DRAPKIN & CO., London

A. Pre-1919 Issues							
	D	BW	12	*Actresses "FRAN"	H.175	£2.75	—
	—	BW	? 1	*Army Insignia (83 × 46 mm.)	H.130	—	—
	—	—	? 86	"Bandmaster" Conundrums (58 × 29 mm.)	H.131	£2.00	—
	A	BW	? 27	*Boer War Celebrities—"JASAS" ("Sweet Alva" Cigarettes)	H.133	£38.00	—
	A1	P	36	*Celebrities of the Great War (1916)	H.135	55p	£20.00
			34/36	A. Plain back		70p	£24.00
	—	BW	96	Cinematograph Actors (1913) (42 × 70 mm.)	H.134	£2.50	—
	A	C	25	How to Keep Fit—Sandow Exercises:—	H.136		
				A. "Drapkin's Cigarettes"		£3.20	£80.00
				A1. "Drapkin's Cigarettes" short cards, cut officially		£3.20	—
				B. "Crayol Cigarettes"		£3.20	£80.00
	D	U	45	Photogravure Masterpieces (1915)	H.137	£2.50	—
	—	C	25	*Soldiers and Their Uniforms, cutouts:— (1914)	H.138	—	£40.00
				A. "Drapkin's Cigarettes"		From 60p	—
				B. "Crayol Cigarettes"		From 60p	—
	D	BW	12	*Views of the World	H.176	£2.25	£27.00
	D	BW	6	*Warships	H.463	£3.30	£20.00
B. Post-1920 Issues							
	C	C	8	*Advertisement Cards:—	Ha.555		
				1. Packings (4)		£1.25	£5.00
				2. Smokers (4)		£1.25	£5.00
		BW	50	Around Britain (1929) (export):—			
	C			A. Small size		35p	£17.50
	B1			B. Large size		80p	£40.00

MAJOR DRAPKIN & CO. *(continued)*

Illus. No.	Size	Printing	Number in set		Handbook ref.	Price per card	Complete set
		C	50	Around the Mediterranean (1926) (export):—	Ha.610		
	C			A. Small size..........................		60p	£30.00
	B1			B. Large size..........................		90p	£45.00
	A2	P	40	Australian and English Test Cricketers (export)		16p	£6.50
	A1	U	25	British Beauties (1930) (export)		60p	£15.00
		C	15	Dogs and Their Treatment (1924):—			
	A			A. Small size..........................		£1.00	£15.00
	B2			B. Large size..........................		£1.00	£15.00
	A	C	40	The Game of Sporting Snap (Aug. 1928)		30p	£12.00
			1	Instruction Booklet......................		—	£2.50
		C	50	Girls of Many Lands (Aug. 1929):—			
	D			A. Small size..........................		£1.00	—
	—			B. Medium size........................		13p	£2.75
99	A2	BW	54	Life at Whipsnade Zoo (Dec. 1934)	Ha.556	25p	£12.50
	D2	C	50	"Limericks" (June 1929):—	Ha.557		
				A. White card........................		25p	£12.50
				B. Cream card........................		25p	£12.50
	A2	P	36	National Types of Beauty (Apr. 1928).......	Ha.558	35p	£12.50
		C	25	Optical Illusions (June 1926):—			
632	A			A. Small size, Home issue, name panel (23 × 7 mm.)		32p	£8.00
	A			B. Small size, Export issue, name panel (26 × 10 mm.)		80p	—
	B2			C. Large size, Home issue		70p	£17.50
		C	25	Palmistry:—			
	A			A. Small size (Apr. 1927)		48p	£12.00
	B			B. Large size (June 1926) ....:.......		60p	£15.00
		C	25	Puzzle Pictures (July 1926):—			
620	A			A. Small size........................		60p	£15.00
	B			B. Large size........................		70p	£17.50
262	A2	P	36	Sporting Celebrities in Action (1930) (export)		—	£28.00
				35 different (No. 18 withdrawn)............		26p	£9.00

C. Silks

	—	C	40	Regimental Colours & Badges of the Indian Army (70 × 50 mm.) (paper-backed)— "The Buffs"	Ha.502–5	—	£70.00
				38 different		£1.50	£57.00

D. Miscellaneous

	A	C	1	"Greys" Smoking Mixture Advertisement Card (plain back)		—	£4.00

DRAPKIN & MILLHOFF, London ———————————

Pre-1919 Issues

	A	U		*Beauties—"KEWA I":—	Ha.139–1		
			? 1	A. "Eldona Cigars" back		—	—
			? 1	B. "Explorer Cigars" back		—	—
	A	BW	25	*Boer War Celebrities—"PAM" ("Pick-Me-Up" Cigarettes).....................	H.140	£10.00	—
	C	C	30	*Colonial Troops ("Pick-Me-Up" Cigarettes)	H.40	£15.00	—
	—	BW	? 2	*"Pick-me-up" Paper Inserts (112 × 44 mm.)..	H.141	—	—
	—	U	? 1	*Portraits (48 × 36 mm.)....................	H.461	—	—

J. DUNCAN & CO. LTD., Glasgow ———————————

A. Pre-1919 Issues

	D1	C	48	*Flags, Arms and Types of Nations	H.115		
				A. Back in Blue		£11.00	—
				B. Back in Green		—	—
	A	C	20	Inventors and their Inventions		£22.00	—
	A	C	30	Scottish Clans, Arms of Chiefs & Tartans:—	H.142		
				A. Back in black		—	—
				B. Back in green		£8.00	£240.00
	—	C		Scottish Gems: (58 × 84 mm.)	H.143		
	—	C	72	1st Series		£7.50	—
	—	C	50	2nd Series		£6.50	—
	—	C	50	3rd Series		£5.00	—
	D	C	25	*Types of British Soldiers...................	H.144	£30.00	—

B. Post-1920 Issues

402	D1	C	50	"Evolution of the Steamship"..............	Ha.559	—	£27.50
				47/50 ditto...............................		35p	£17.50
	H1	BW	50	Scottish Gems (known as "4th Series")......	Ha.143D	35p	£17.50

G. DUNCOMBE, Buxton ———————————

Pre-1919 Issue

	D	C	30	*Army Pictures, Cartoons, Etc.	H.12	—	—

EDWARDS, RINGER & BIGG, Bristol ———————————

A. Pre-1919 Issues

	A	U	25	Abbeys & Castles — Photogravure series:—			
				A. Type-set back		£6.00	£150.00
				B. "Statue of Liberty" back		£6.00	£150.00
				C. "Stag Design" back		£6.00	£150.00

EDWARDS, RINGER & BIGG *(continued)*

Illus. No.	Size	Print-ing	Number in set		Handbook ref.	Price per card	Complete set
	A	U	25	Alpine Views — Photogravure Series:—			
				A. "Statue of Liberty" back		£6.00	£150.00
				B. "Stag Design" back		£6.00	£150.00
	A	C	12	*Beauties—"CERF" (Jun. 1905)	H.57	£20.00	—
	A	U	25	*Beauties—"FECKSA", 1900 Calendar back	H.58	£15.00	—
	A	C	50	*Birds & Eggs (Jun. 1906)	H.60	£4.00	£200.00
	A	BW	? 1	Boer War and Boxer Rebellion Sketches		—	—
	A	BW	25	*Boer War Celebrities—"STEW", 1901 Calendar back	H.105	£12.00	—
	A	C	1	Calendar for 1899		—	—
	A	C	1	Calendar (1905), Exmore Hunt Stag design back		—	—
	A	C	1	Calendar (1910)		—	—
	A	U	25	Coast & Country—Photogravure Series:— (1911)			
				A. "Statue of Liberty" back		£6.00	£150.00
				B. "Stag Design" back		£6.00	£150.00
102	A	C	23	*Dogs Series (Mar. 1908)	H.64/Ha.64	£1.20	£27.50
	A	C	3	Easter Manoeuvres of Our Volunteers (1897)	H.146	£140.00	—
607	A	C	25	Flags of All Nations, 1st Series (1906)	H.37	£5.00	£125.00
	A	C	12	Flags of All Nations, 2nd Series (1907)	H.37	£10.00	£120.00
	A	C	37	*Flags of All Nations (1907):—	H.37		
				A. Globe & Grouped Flags back		£4.00	—
				B. "Exmoor Hunt" back:—			
				i. 4½d per oz.		£6.00	—
				ii. Altered to 5d by hand		£6.00	—
				iii. 5d label added		£8.00	—
				C. "Stag" design back		£4.00	£150.00
				D. Upright titled back		£6.00	—
	A	C	50	Life on Board a Man of War (Jul. 1905)	H.38	£6.00	—
	—	C	1	"Miners Bound for Klondyke" (1897) (41 × 81 mm.)		—	£140.00
295	A	C	10	Portraits of His Majesty the King in Uniforms of the British & Foreign Nations (1902)	H.147	£16.00	£160.00
	A	C	50	A Tour Round the World (Mar. 1909)	H.75	£4.00	£200.00
	A	C	56	War Map of the Western Front		£3.50	£200.00
	A	U	54	War Map of the Western Front, etc. Series No. 2:—			
				A. "Exmoor Hunt" back		£3.50	£190.00
				B. "New York Mixture" back		£3.50	£190.00

B. Post-1920 Issues

Illus. No.	Size	Print-ing	Number in set		Handbook ref.	Price per card	Complete set
	A	C	25	British Trees & Their Uses (Mar. 1933) (see RB21/209/34)		£1.20	£30.00
	A	C	50	Celebrated Bridges (1924)	H.346	£1.00	£50.00
		U		Cinema Stars (1923):—			
	A2		50	A. Small size		30p	£15.00
	—		25	B. Medium size (67 × 57 mm.)		20p	£5.00
	A	C	25	Garden Life (1934)	H.449	£1.20	£30.00
	A	C	25	How to Tell Fortunes (1929)		£2.00	£50.00
	A	C	50	Mining (1925)	H.450	£1.00	£50.00
	A	C	25	Musical Instruments (Jan. 1924)	Ha.547	80p	£20.00
	A	C	25	Optical Illusions (1936)	Ha.560	90p	£22.50
105	A	C	25	Our Pets (1926)	Ha.561	90p	£22.50
	A	C	25	Our Pets, 2nd Series (1926)	Ha.561	£1.20	£30.00
	A	C	25	Past & Present (1928) (see W/287)		£1.40	£35.00
94	A	C	25	Prehistoric Animals (May 1924)		£1.40	£35.00
	A	C	25	Sports & Games in Many Lands (1935) (see RB21/210/133)		90p	£22.50

E. EISISKI, Rhyl

Pre-1919 Issues

	Size	Print-ing	Number in set		Handbook ref.	Price per card	Complete set
	A	U	? 6	*Actresses—"COPEIS"	H.108	£75.00	—
	A	U	? 18	*Beauties—"FENA"	H.148	£75.00	—
	A	U	? 1	*Beauties—"KEWA I", back inscribed "Eisiski's New Gold Virginia Cigarettes"	Ha.139–1	£75.00	—
	A	U	? 1	*Beauties—"KEWA II", back inscribed "Eisiski's Rhyl Best Bird's Eye Cigarettes"	Ha.139–2	£75.00	—

ELDONS LTD.

Pre-1919 Issue

	Size	Print-ing	Number in set		Handbook ref.	Price per card	Complete set
	A1	C	30	*Colonial Troops—"Leon de Cuba" Cigars	H.40	£60.00	—

EMPIRE TOBACCO CO., London

Pre-1919 Issue

	Size	Print-ing	Number in set		Handbook ref.	Price per card	Complete set
	D	C	? 6	Franco-British Exhibition	Ha.471	—	—

THE EXPRESS TOBACCO CO. LTD., London

Post-1920 Issue

	Size	Print-ing	Number in set		Handbook ref.	Price per card	Complete set
	—	U	50	"How It is Made" (Motor Cars) (1931) (76 × 51 mm.)		£1.10	—

L. & J. FABIAN, London

Illus. No.	Size	Printing	Number in set		Handbook ref.	Price per card	Complete set
Post-1920 Issue							
	D1	P	24	The Elite Series (Beauties) (most numbers preceded by letters "LLF").............		—	—

FAIRWEATHER & SONS, Dundee

	Size	Printing	Number in set			Price per card	
Pre-1919 Issue							
	A	C	50	Historic Buildings of Scotland..............		£32.00	—

W. & F. FAULKNER, London

Illus. No.	Size	Printing	Number in set		Handbook ref.	Price per card	Complete set
A. Pre-1919 Issues							
	C	C	26	*Actresses—"FROGA A"...................	H.20	£24.00	—
	D2	C	12	*'Ation Series (1901)		£9.00	—
	C	C	? 17	*Beauties	H.150	£45.00	—
	A	U	50	*Beauties—"FECKSA"..................	H.58	£7.00	£350.00
	A	BW	16	*British Royal Family (1901)	H.28	£12.00	—
	D2	C	12	*Coster Series (1900)	H.151/Ha.151	£9.00	—
	A	BW	20	Cricketers Series (1901)...................	H.29	£25.00	—
160	D2	C	12	Cricket Terms (1899)...................	H.152/Ha.152	£12.00	—
178	D2	C	12	Football Terms, 1st Series (1900)..........	H.153/Ha.153	£8.00	£95.00
	D2	C	12	Football Terms, 2nd Series (1900)..........	H.154	£8.00	£95.00
	D2	C	12	*Golf Terms (1901)......................	H.155/Ha.155	£11.00	—
	D2	C	12	Grenadier Guards (1899)	H.156/Ha.156	£14.00	£170.00
	A2	C	40	*Kings and Queens (1902)	H.157/Ha.157	£8.00	£320.00
537	D2	C	12	Kipling Series (1900)	H.158/Ha.158	£9.00	£110.00
55	D2	C	12	The Language of Flowers (1900):—	H.159/Ha.159		
				A. "Grenadier" Cigarettes...............		£14.00	—
				B. "Nosegay" Cigarettes		£14.00	—
	D2	C	12	*Military Terms, 1st Series (1899)	H.50	£9.00	£110.00
	D2	C	12	*Military Terms, 2nd Series (1899)...........	H.160/Ha.160	£9.00	£110.00
	D2	C	12	*Nautical Terms, 1st Series (1900)..........	H.161/Ha.161	£7.50	£90.00
336	D2	C	12	*Nautical Terms, 2nd Series (1900):—	H.162		
				A. "Grenadier Cigarettes"...............		£7.50	£90.00
				B. "Union Jack Cigarettes"		£8.00	£100.00
	D2	C		"Our Colonial Troops" (1900):—			
				A. Grenadier Cigarettes:—			
			30	i. With copyright Nos. 1–30...........		£7.00	—
			90	ii. Without copyright Nos. 1–90		£6.00	—
			60	B. Union Jack Cigarettes Nos. 31–90......		£7.00	—
	A	C	20	Our Gallant Grenadiers, 1–20 (1902–3):—	H.163		
				A. Without I.T.C. Clause,			
				i. Thick Card.........................		£7.50	£150.00
				ii. Thin card		£8.00	£160.00
				B. With I.T.C. Clause, thin card		£8.00	£160.00
299	A	C	20	Our Gallant Grenadiers, 21–40		£10.00	£200.00
	D2	C	12	*Policemen of the World (1899)..............	H.164	£24.00	—
	D2	C	12	*Police Terms (1899)	H.165/Ha.165	£9.00	£110.00
	D2	C	12	*Puzzle Series (1897–8):—	H.166		
				A. "Grenadier Cigarettes"................		£45.00	—
				B. "Nosegay Cigarettes"		£30.00	—
	A	BW	25	*South African War Scenes (1901)	H.167	£5.00	£125.00
	D2	C	12	Sporting Terms (1900)......................	H.168/Ha.168	£10.00	—
	D2	C	12	Street Cries (1902)........................	H.169/Ha.169	£10.00	£120.00
B. Post-1920 Issues							
	A	C	25	Angling (Jan. 1929) (see RB21/449)		70p	£17.50
	A	C	50	Celebrated Bridges (Apr. 1925)	H.346	£1.00	£50.00
	A	C	25	Old Sporting Prints (May 1930).............	Ha.563	34p	£8.50
	A	C	25	Optical Illusions (Mar. 1935).............	Ha.560	40p	£10.00
	A	C	25	Our Pets (Feb. 1926).....................	Ha.561	90p	£22.50
112	A	C	25	Our Pets, 2nd Series (July 1926).............	Ha.561	70p	£17.50
132	A	C	25	Prominent Racehorses of the Present Day (1923).................................		80p	£20.00
	A	C	25	Prominent Racehorses of the Present Day, 2nd Series (1924).......................		90p	£22.50
C. Miscellaneous							
				Calendar for 1924..........................		—	—
	A	U	1	Card announcing "Prominent Racehorses of the Present Day"		—	—

FINLAY & CO. LTD., Newcastle-on-Tyne and London

Illus. No.	Size	Printing	Number in set		Handbook ref.	Price per card	Complete set
Pre-1919 Issues							
	D1	BW	? 2	Our Girls..................................	H.170	£45.00	—
360	A	U	30	World's Aircraft		£15.00	—

FRAENKEL BROS., London

Illus. No.	Size	Printing	Number in set		Handbook ref.	Price per card	Complete set
Pre-1919 Issues							
	A	U	? 18	*Beauties—"FENA"........................	H.148/Ha.148	£35.00	—
	A	C	25	*Beauties—"GRACC".....................	H.59	—	—
	A	U	24	*Beauties—"HUMPS".....................	H.222	£75.00	—
	A	U	26	*Music Hall Artistes:—	H.171		

Illus. No.	Size	Print-ing	Number in set	Handbook ref.	Price per card	Complete set
			A. Pink card		£35.00	—
			B. White card		£50.00	—
	A2	C	25 *Types of British and Colonial Troops	H.76	£55.00	—

FRANKLYN, DAVEY & CO., Bristol

A. Pre-1919 Issues

Illus. No.	Size	Print-ing	Number in set	Handbook ref.	Price per card	Complete set
	A	C	12 *Beauties—"CERF" (1905)	H.57	£25.00	—
	D2	C	50 *Birds (? 1895)		£32.00	—
	A2	BW	? 12 *Boer War Generals — "FLAC" (1901)......	H.47	£65.00	—
	A	C	25 Ceremonial and Court Dress (Oct. 1915)	H.145	£4.00	—
	A	C	50 *Football Club Colours (Jan. 1909)	H.68	£3.50	£175.00
	A	C	50 Naval Dress & Badges (Nov. 1916)...........	H.172	£4.00	—
	A	C	25 *Star Girls..............................	Ha.30		—
	A	C	10 Types of Smokers		£32.00	£320.00
91	A	C	50 Wild Animals of the World	H.77	£4.50	£225.00

B. Post-1920 Issues

Illus. No.	Size	Print-ing	Number in set	Handbook ref.	Price per card	Complete set
209	A	C	25 Boxing (1924)...........................	H.311	26p	£6.50
	A	C	50 Children of All Nations (1934) (see RB21/200/168)		15p	£7.50
	A	C	50 Historic Events (1924).....................	H.464	£1.00	£50.00
133	A	U	25 Hunting (1925)...........................		24p	£6.00
	A	U	50 Modern Dance Steps (1929)		£2.00	—
	A	U	50 Modern Dance Steps, 2nd Series (1931)		14p	£7.00
	A	C	50 Overseas Dominions (Australia) (1923)......	H.451	£1.00	£50.00

C. Miscellaneous

Illus. No.	Size	Print-ing	Number in set	Handbook ref.	Price per card	Complete set
—		C	? 1 Comic Dog Folder (opens to 183 × 65 mm.)..	Ha.490	—	—

A. H. FRANKS & SONS, London

Pre-1919 Issues

Illus. No.	Size	Print-ing	Number in set	Handbook ref.	Price per card	Complete set
	D1	BW	56 *Beauties—"Beauties Cigarettes"............	H.173/Ha.173	£16.00	—
	D	C	? 23 *Nautical Expressions	H.174	—	—
	A1	C	25 *Types of British and Colonial Troops	H.76	£38.00	—

J. J. FREEMAN, London

Pre-1919 Issues

Illus. No.	Size	Print-ing	Number in set	Handbook ref.	Price per card	Complete set
	D	BW	12 *Actresses—"FRAN"......................	H.175	£14.00	—
	D	BW	12 *Views of the World........................	H.176	£16.00	—

C. FRYER & SONS, LTD., London

A. Pre-1919 Issues

Illus. No.	Size	Print-ing	Number in set	Handbook ref.	Price per card	Complete set
	A2	C	? 25 *Boer War & General Interest:—	H.13		
			A. Brown leaf design back		—	—
			B. Green leaf design back		—	—
			C. Green daisy design back		—	—
	D	C	40 *Naval and Military Phrases.................	H.14	£13.00	—
	A2	BW	? 8 *"Vita Berlin" Series	H.177/Ha.177	—	—

B. Post-1920 Issue

Illus. No.	Size	Print-ing	Number in set	Handbook ref.	Price per card	Complete set
—		—	48 Clan Sketches (101 × 74 mm.) (paper folders with wording only)—"Pibroch Virginia"..	Ha.628	£2.00	—

FRYER & COULTMAN, London

Pre-1919 Issue

Illus. No.	Size	Print-ing	Number in set	Handbook ref.	Price per card	Complete set
—		C	12 *French Phrases, 1893 Calendar back (96 × 64 mm.)..................................	H.178	—	—

J. GABRIEL, London

Pre-1919 Issues

Illus. No.	Size	Print-ing	Number in set	Handbook ref.	Price per card	Complete set
	A	BW	10 *Actresses—"HAGG A"....................	H.24	£30.00	—
	A2	C	25 *Beauties—"GRACC"....................	H.59	—	—
	A	BW	20 Cricketers Series	H.29	£45.00	—
	A	C	40 *Home and Colonial Regiments:—	H.69		
			20. Caption in blue		£30.00	—
			20. Caption in brown		£30.00	—
	A	U	? 47 *Pretty Girl Series—"BAGG"	H.45/Ha.45	£40.00	—
	A2	C	25 *Types of British and Colonial Troops	H.76	£35.00	—

GALLAHER LTD., Belfast and London

A. Pre-1919 Issues

Illus. No.	Size	Print-ing	Number in set	Handbook ref.	Price per card	Complete set
	D	P	110 *Actors & Actresses	H.179/Ha.179	£2.25	—
603	D	C	25 The Allies Flags:—(1914)		—	£87.50
			A. Toned card		£3.50	—
			B. White card		£3.50	—
194	D	C	100 Association Football Club Colours (1910):—			
			A. Grey border		£2.00	—
			B. Brown border.........................		£2.00	—
			C. A. and B. mixed		—	£200.00
	A	C	52 *Beauties:—	H.180/Ha.180		
			A. Without inset		£10.00	—

Illus. No.	Size	Print-ing	Number in set		Handbook ref.	Price per card	Complete set
				B. With Playing Card inset		£10.00	—
	D	C	50	*Birds & Eggs................................	H.60	£6.00	—
16	D	C	100	Birds Nests & Eggs Series (1919):—			
				A. White card..........................		90p	£90.00
				B. Toned card		£1.10	—
	D	C	100	Boy Scout Series:—			
				A. Grey-green back (1911)			
				(a) "Belfast & London"		£1.25	£125.00
				(b) "London & Belfast"		£1.25	
				B. Ornamental brown back—see Post-1920 issues			
339	D	U	50	British Naval Series (1914).................		£3.00	£150.00
	D	P	100	English & Scotch Views		£2.00	£200.00
	D	C	100	Fables & Their Morals, Series 1 (1912):—			
				A. Numbered in name panel		£1.00	£100.00
				B. & C. Later printings, see Post-1920 issues			
287	D	C	100	The Great War Series (1915)...............		£1.60	£160.00
	D	C	100	The Great War Series—Second Series (1916)		£1.60	£160.00
	D	C		The Great War, Victoria Cross Heroes (1915–16):—			
317			25	1st Series 1–25......................		£1.80	£45.00
			25	2nd Series 26–50.....................		£1.80	£45.00
			25	3rd Series 51–75.....................		£1.80	£45.00
			25	4th Series 76–100		£1.80	£45.00
			25	5th Series 101–125		£1.80	£45.00
			25	6th Series 126–150		£1.80	£45.00
			25	7th Series 151–175		£1.80	£45.00
			25	8th Series 176–200		£1.80	£45.00
	D	C	100	How to do it (1916).................		£1.60	£160.00
	D			Irish View Scenery:—	H.181		
		BW	200	1–200, semi-matt, numbered on back.......		£1.50	—
		BW	200	201–400 matt: A. numbered on back		£1.50	—
				B. unnumbered, plain back		£2.00	—
		P	400	1–400 glossy—see H.181			
				A. Black photo.........................		80p	£320.00
				B. Brown photo.........................		£2.00	—
				C. As A, but series title and No. omitted...		£1.25	—
		P	600	1–600 glossy—see H.181			
				A. Nos 1 to 500		85p	£425.00
				B. Nos 501 to 600		£2.00	—
	D	C	100	"Kute Kiddies" Series (1916)		£1.60	£160.00
	D	P	50	Latest Actresses (1910):—			
				A. Black photo.........................		£6.00	—
				B. Chocolate photo		£9.00	—
	A	C	50	*Regimental Colours and Standards (Nd. 151–200).............................		£2.80	£140.00
489	A	C	50	Royalty Series (? 1902)		£3.00	£150.00
	A	C	111	The South African Series (Nd. 101–211) (1901–2):—		—	£350.00
				A. White back		£3.20	—
				B. Cream back		£3.20	—
250	D	C	100	"Sports" Series (1912).....................		£2.00	£200.00
	D	U	? 75	*Stage and Variety Celebrities (collotype)	H.182/Ha.182		
				A. "Gallager" back		£32.00	—
				B. "Gallaher" back		£32.00	—
				C. as B. but larger lettering, etc............		£32.00	—
628	D	C	100	Tricks & Puzzles Series, green back (1913) ...		£1.60	£160.00
	A	C	50	*Types of the British Army — unnumbered:— A. "Battle Honours" back—	H.183/Ha.183		
				i. white............................		£5.00	£250.00
				ii. lilac tinted..........................		£5.00	£250.00
				B. "The Three Pipes ..." — green back....		£5.00	£250.00
	A	C	50	*Types of the British Army—Nd. 1–50 (1898–1900):—			
				A. "The Three Pipes ..." — brown back...		£5.00	£250.00
				B. "Now in Three ..." — brown back.....		£5.00	£250.00
	A	C	50	*Types of British and Colonial Regiments—Nd. 51–100 (1900):—			
				A. "The Three Pipes ..." — brown back...		£5.00	£250.00
				B. "Now in Three ..." — brown back.....		£5.00	£250.00
	D	C	100	Useful Hints Series (1915)		£1.60	£160.00
	D	U	25	Views in Northern Ireland		£32.00	—
	D	C	50	Votaries of the Weed (1916)		£2.00	£100.00
	D	C	100	"Why is it?" Series (1915):—			
				A. Green back		£1.60	£160.00
				B. Brown back		£1.60	£160.00
75	D	C	100	Woodland Trees Series (1912)		£1.60	£160.00
B. Post-1920 Issues							
352	D	C	48	Aeroplanes (1939)........................		13p	£6.50
	A2	C	25	Aesop's Fables (1931):—	Ha.518		
				A. Inscribed "A Series of 25"		20p	£5.00
				B. Inscribed "A Series of 50"		16p	£4.00
101	D	C	100	Animals & Birds of Commercial Value (Nov. 1921).............................		40p	£40.00
314	D	C	48	Army Badges (Jan. 1939)		30p	£15.00
	—	U	24	Art Treasures of the World (76 × 56 mm.) (1930 and 1937).........................		13p	£2.00
	—	P	48	Beautiful Scotland (77 × 52 mm.) (1939)	Ha.564–1	13p	£6.50

Illus. No.	Size	Print- ing	Number in set		Handbook ref.	Price per card	Complete set
	D	C	100	Boy Scout Series, brown back (1922)		80p	£80.00
19	D	C	48	British Birds (1937)....................		13p	£4.00
	D	C	100	British Birds by Rankin (Dec. 1923):—	Ha.537		
				A. "By Rankin"......................		£3.00	—
				B. "By George Rankin"		40p	£40.00
	D	C	75	British Champions of 1923 (June 1924)......		50p	£37.50
7	D	C	48	Butterflies and Moths (Aug. 1938)		13p	£3.50
	D	C	25	Champion Animals & Birds of 1923 (June 1924).............................		90p	£22.50
	D	C	48	Champions (1934):—			
				A. Front without letterpress		30p	£15.00
				B. Front with captions, subjects re-drawn .		25p	£12.50
238	D	C	48	Champions, 2nd Series (1935).............		13p	£5.00
455	D	C	48	Champions of Screen & Stage (1934):—			
				A. Red back		13p	£5.00
				B. Blue back, "Gallaher's Cigarettes" at base		16p	£8.00
				C. Blue back, "Gallaher Ltd." at base		16p	£8.00
	D	U	100	Cinema Stars (Aug. 1926)................		50p	£50.00
	—	P	48	Coastwise (77 × 52 mm.) (1938)	Ha.564–2	20p	£10.00
		C	24	Dogs (1934):—			
				A. Captions in script letters (white or cream card):—			
	D			1. Small size......................		25p	£6.00
	B			2. Large size......................		25p	£6.00
				B. Captions in block Letters:—			
	D			1. Small size......................		13p	£2.50
104	B			2. Large size......................		13p	£2.50
	D	C	48	Dogs (Sep. 1936)......................		13p	£3.25
122	D	C	48	Dogs, Second Series (Nov. 1938)............		13p	£3.75
	D	C	100	Fables and Their Morals:—			
				A. First printing, pre-1919 issues			
				B. Thin numerals (Mar. 1922)—			
				1. White card.....................		45p	£45.00
				2. Yellow card....................		45p	£45.00
				C. Thick numerals (Nov. 1922)		45p	£45.00
	D	U	100	Famous Cricketers (Mar. 1926).............		80p	£80.00
460	D	C	48	Famous Film Scenes (June 1935)...........		13p	£5.00
	D	U	100	Famous Footballers, green back (1925)......		50p	£50.00
	D	C	50	Famous Footballers, brown back (1926)		70p	£35.00
136	D	C	48	Famous Jockeys (Sep. 1936)		13p	£4.25
456	D	C	48	Film Episodes (Mar. 1936)................		13p	£4.50
459	D	C	48	Film Partners (Dec. 1935)		13p	£4.50
	—	P	48	Flying (77 × 52 mm.) (Feb. 1938)............	Ha.564–3	50p	£24.00
	D	C	100	Footballers, red back (May 1928):—			
				1. Nos. 1–50—Action pictures............		80p	£40.00
				2. Nos. 51–100—Portraits..............		90p	£45.00
168	D	C	50	Footballers in Action (1928)..............		70p	£35.00
49	D	C	48	Garden Flowers (Feb. 1938)		13p	£3.00
	D		100	Interesting Views:—			
		P		A. Uncoloured, glossy (1923)		90p	£90.00
		CP		B. Hand-coloured, matt (1925)		90p	£90.00
	B2	P	48	Island Sporting Celebrities (1938) (Channel Islands).............................		50p	£24.00
274	D	C	50	Lawn Tennis Celebrities (Apr. 1928)		£1.40	£70.00
368	A	C	24	Motor Cars (1934)		£1.40	£35.00
441	D	C	48	My Favourite Part (1939).................		13p	£3.25
333	D	C	48	The Navy (1937):—			
				A. "Park Drive ..." at base of back		13p	£3.75
				B. "Issued by ..." at base of back		13p	£6.50
	—	P	48	Our Countryside (72 × 52 mm.) (1938).......	Ha.564–4	50p	£24.00
63	D	C	100	Plants of Commercial Value (1917 and 1923)		40p	£40.00
444	D	C	48	Portraits of Famous Stars (Sep. 1935)		13p	£3.75
144	D	C	48	Racing Scenes (1938)...................		13p	£3.00
	D	C	100	The Reason Why (1924) (see RB21/345).....		40p	£40.00
	D	C	100	Robinson Crusoe (Oct. 1928)		80p	£80.00
	B2	P	48	Scenes from the Empire (1939) (export)......	Ha.565	13p	£4.00
	—	P	24	Shots from the Films (77 × 52 mm.) (1936)...	Ha.566	£1.00	£24.00
440	D	C	48	Shots from Famous Films (Apr. 1935).......		15p	£7.50
	D	C	48	Signed Portraits of Famous Stars (1935).....		25p	£12.50
235	D	C	48	Sporting Personalities (1936)		13p	£2.50
445	D	C	48	Stars of Screen & Stage (1935):—			
				A. Back in green		13p	£3.50
				B. Back in brown		20p	£10.00
413, 765 etc.	D	C	48	Trains of the World (1937)................		30p	£15.00
624	D	C		Tricks & Puzzles Series, black back (1933):—			
				1–50		13p	£3.75
				51–100		13p	£3.75
95	D	C	48	Wild Animals (1937)		13p	£3.00
62	D	C	48	Wild Flowers (1939).....................		13p	£3.25
	D	C	100	The "Zoo" Aquarium (1924)		60p	£60.00
20	D	C	50	"Zoo" Tropical Birds, 1st Series (1928)......		60p	£30.00
	D	C	50	"Zoo" Tropical Birds, 2nd Series (1929).....		60p	£30.00

C. Silks

		C	24	Flags—Set 1 (68 × 48 mm.) (paper-backed) (1916)	Ha.501–1	£4.00	—
—							

D. Miscellaneous

	D	C	48	Screen Lovers—"Summit" (prepared but not issued)		60p	£30.00

SAMUEL GAWITH, Kendal

Illus. No.	Size	Print-ing	Number in set		Handbook ref.	Price per card	Complete set
Post-1920 Issue							
—		BW	25	The English Lakeland (90 × 70 mm.)		£4.50	—

F. GENNARI LTD., London

Pre-1919 Issue							
	A	U	50	War Portraits	H.86	—	

LOUIS GERARD, LTD., London

Post-1920 Issues							
	D1	U	50	Modern Armaments:—	Ha.567		
				A. Numbered		13p	£3.00
				B. Unnumbered.........................		13p	£4.50
	D1	U	24	Screen Favourites:—	Ha.568		
				A. Inscribed "Louis Gerard & Company".		£1.20	—
				B. Inscribed "Louis Gerard, Limited".....		£1.20	—
	D1	C	48	Screen Favourites & Dancers	Ha.569	30p	£15.00

W. G. GLASS & CO. LTD., Bristol

Pre-1919 Issues							
477	A	BW	20	*Actresses—"BLARM"....................	H.23	£25.00	—
	A2	BW	10	*Actresses—"HAGG A"....................	H.24	£25.00	—
	A	U	25	*Beauties—"FECKSA"....................	H.58	£40.00	—
	D1	BW	20	*Boer War Cartoons ("Roseland Cigarettes")	H.42	£27.00	—
	A	BW	25	*Boer War Celebrities—"STEW"...........	H.105	£27.00	—
	A	BW	16	*British Royal Family (1901)	H.28	£27.00	—
	A2	BW	20	Cricketers Series	H.29	£40.00	—
	D	C	40	*Naval and Military Phrases................	H.14	£40.00	—
	A	BW	19	*Russo-Japanese Series....................	H.184	£20.00	—

R. P. GLOAG & CO., London

(Cards bear advertisements for "Citamora" and/or "The Challenge Flat Brilliantes" without maker's name)

Pre-1919 Issues							
	A2	U	? 5	*Actresses	H.185/Ha.185	—	—
	D			*Beauties — Selection from "Plums":—	H.186/Ha.186		
		BW	? 24	A. "The Challenge Flat" front:			
				(a) i. front in black and white		£35.00	—
				(a) ii. smaller lettering on back........		£40.00	—
		U	? 2	(b) front in brown		£40.00	—
		BW	? 8	B. "Citamora" front in black and white ...		£65.00	—
	A	C	40	*Home and Colonial Regiments:—	H.69		
				20. Caption in blue		£20.00	—
				20. Caption in brown		£20.00	—
	D	C	30	*Proverbs................................	H.15	£40.00	—
	A2	C	25	*Types of British and Colonial Troops	H.76	£30.00	—

GLOBE CIGARETTE CO.

Pre-1919 issue							
	D	BW	? 3	*Actresses—French	H.1	—	—

GOLDS LTD., Birmingham

Pre-1919 Issues							
	A2	BW	1	Advertisement Card (Chantecler)		—	—
	C	C	18	Motor Cycle Series:—	Ha.469		
				A. Back in blue, numbered................		£9.00	—
				B. Back in grey, numbered...............		£9.00	—
				C. Back in grey, unnumbered		£9.00	—
	—	BW	? 14	*Prints from Noted Pictures (68 × 81 mm.)....	Ha.216	—	—

T. P. & R. GOODBODY, Dublin and London

A. Pre-1919 Issues							
	—	U	? 12	*Actresses—"ANGOOD" (36 × 60 mm.).....	H.187	£45.00	
	D	BW		*Boer War Celebrities—"CAG" (1901)	H.79/Ha.79		
			? 24	See H.79—Fig. 79–B		£15.00	—
			? 16	See H.79—Fig. 79–C.....................		£15.00	—
			16	See H.79—Fig. 79–D.....................		£15.00	—
	A2	C	? 39	Colonial Forces:—	H.188/Ha.188		
				A. Brown back.........................		£40.00	—
				B. Black back.........................		£35.00	—
	—	U	40	*Dogs (1910) ... (36 × 60 mm.)............	H.189/Ha.189	£30.00	—
	C	C	26	Eminent Actresses — "FROGA A"..........	H.20	£14.00	£360.00
	C	C	20	Irish Scenery.............................	H.190	£25.00	—
	A2	U	? 47	*Pretty Girl Series—"BAGG":—	H.45/Ha.45		
				A. Red stamped back....................		£36.00	—

T. P. & R. GOODBODY (continued)

Illus. No.	Size	Printing	Number in set		Handbook ref.	Price per card	Complete set
				B. Violet stamped back...................		£36.00	—
	A	C	25	Types of Soldiers.........................	H.144	£15.00	—
	D	U	20	*War Pictures............................	H.122	£8.00	—
	C	C	12	"With the Flag to Pretoria"...............	H.191	£65.00	—
B. Post-1920 Issues							
	D	C	50	Questions & Answers in Natural History (1924)...................................		£1.00	£50.00
	A	C	25	Sports & Pastimes—Series I (1925)..........	H.225	£1.40	£35.00

GORDON'S, Glasgow

Pre-1919 Issue

| | A2 | BW | ? 4 | Billiards—By George D. Gordon........... | | — | — |

GRAVESON, Mexboro'

Pre-1919 Issues

| | A2 | C | 30 | *Army Pictures, Cartoons, Etc.............. | H.12 | — | — |
| | A | U | 50 | War Portraits............................ | H.86 | — | — |

FRED GRAY, Birmingham

Pre-1919 Issue

| | A | C | 25 | *Types of British Soldiers.................... | H.144 | £55.00 | — |

W. J. HARRIS, London

Pre-1919 Issues

	A2	C	26	*Beauties—"HOL"........................	H.192	£11.00	—
	C	C	30	*Colonial Troops.........................	H.40	—	—
	A1	C	25	*Star Girls...............................	H.30	£65.00	—

JAS. H. HARRISON, Birmingham

Pre-1919 Issue

| | C | C | 18 | Motor Cycle Series........................ | Ha.469 | — | — |

HARVEY & DAVEY, Newcastle-on-Tyne

Pre-1919 Issues

	D1	C	50	*Birds & Eggs............................	H.60	£2.50	£125.00
	A1	C	? 10	*Chinese and South African Series...........	H.193/Ha.193	£80.00	—
	C	C	30	*Colonial Troops..........................	H.40	£45.00	—
	A1	C	25	*Types of British and Colonial Troops.......	H.76	£45.00	—

W. & H. HEATON, Birkby

Pre-1919 Issue

| | — | BW | ? 6 | Birkby Views (70 × 39 mm.)................ | H.226 | £50.00 | — |

HENLY & WATKINS LTD., London

Post-1920 Issues

	A1	C	25	Ancient Egyptian Gods—"Matossian's Cigarettes" (1924).......................	Ha.570		
				*A. Plain back..........................		£1.40	£35.00
				B. Back in blue.........................		£1.60	£40.00

HIGNETT BROS. & CO., Liverpool

A. Pre-1919 Issues

Illus. No.	Size	Printing	Number in set		Handbook ref.	Price per card	Complete set
	C	C	26	*Actresses—"FROGA A"..................	H.20	£30.00	—
	A2	U		*Actresses—Photogravure:—	H.194/Ha.194		
			? 23	i. With "Golden Butterfly" on front......		£7.50	—
			? 1	ii. Without "Golden Butterfly" on front..		—	—
	D1	BW	28	*Actresses—"PILPI I"....................	H.195/Ha.195	£20.00	—
	D1	P	50	*Actresses—"PILPI II"..................	H.196	£10.00	—
	A	U	1	Advertisement Card. Smoking mixture......		—	—
80	—	C	60	Animal Pictures...(38 × 70 mm.)...........	H.197/Ha.197	£12.00	—
	D	U	? 46	*Beauties—gravure:—	H.198		
				A. "Cavalier" back....................		£20.00	—
				B. "Golden Butterfly" back..............		£20.00	—
	C	C	50	*Beauties—"CHOAB"....................	H.21	—	—
	A1	C	16	Cabinet, 1900...........................	H.199/Ha.199	£45.00	—
	A	C	25	Cathedrals & Churches (Dec. 1909)........		£2.80	£70.00
	A	C	25	Company Drill (Sep. 1915)................		£2.80	£70.00
	A	C	25	Greetings of the World (Jan. 1907—re-issued 1922)....................................		£1.20	£30.00
	A	C	50	Interesting Buildings (Feb. 1905)...........	H.70	£2.20	£110.00

Illus. No.	Size	Print-ing	Number in set		Handbook ref.	Price per card	Complete set
—		C	40	*Medals (1901–2) (34 × 72 mm.):—	H.200		
				A. "Butterfly Cigarettes"		£8.00	—
				B. Officially cut for use in other brands....		£7.50	—
	A	BW	25	Military Portraits (Dec. 1914)	H.201	£3.00	£75.00
	A	C	25	Modern Statesmen (Nov. 1906):—			
				A. "Butterfly" back		£3.60	£90.00
				B. "Pioneer" back		£3.60	£90.00
	A	C	20	*Music Hall Artistes	H.202	£18.00	—
		C	1	Oracle Butterfly (shaped))		—	£100.00
	A	C	25	Panama Canal (Mar. 1914)		£4.00	£100.00
	A2	C	12	*Pretty Girl Series—"RASH":—	H.8		
				i. 1–6 head and shoulders		£27.00	—
				ii. 7–12 full length		£27.00	—
	—	BW	25	*V.C. Heroes (1901–2) (35 × 72 mm.)	H.203	£25.00	—
	A	C	20	*Yachts (? 1902):—	H.204		
				A. Gold on black back		£40.00	—
				B. Black on white back		£40.00	—

B. Post-1920 Issues

Illus. No.	Size	Print-ing	Number in set		Handbook ref.	Price per card	Complete set
454	A	C	50	Actors—Natural & Character Studies (Feb. 1938)	Ha.571–1	13p	£6.50
191	A	C	50	A.F.C. Nicknames (1933)	Ha.571–2	60p	£30.00
	A	C	50	Air-Raid Precautions (1939)	Ha.544	30p	£15.00
	A	C	50	Arms & Armour (Dec. 1924)	H.273	£1.00	£50.00
	A	C	50	British Birds & Their Eggs (1938)	Ha.571–3	40p	£20.00
	A	U	50	Broadcasting (1935)	Ha.571–4	50p	£25.00
	A	U	50	Celebrated Old Inns (June 1925)		£1.00	£50.00
	A	C	50	Champions of 1936 (June 1937)	Ha.571–5	50p	£25.00
	A	C	25	Common Objects of the Sea-Shore (Jan. 1924)		£1.00	£25.00
	A	C	50	Coronation Procession (sectional) (1937)		£1.00	—
	A	C	50	Dogs (1936)	Ha.571–6	17p	£8.50
165	A	C	50	Football Caricatures (Sep. 1935)	Ha.571–7	35p	£17.50
172	A	C	50	Football Club Captains (1935)	Ha.571–8	35p	£17.50
	A	U	25	Historical London (Aug. 1926)	Ha.571–9	£1.00	£25.00
247	A	C	50	How to Swim (1935)	Ha.571–10	20p	£10.00
226	A	C	25	International Caps and Badges (May 1924)..		£1.00	£25.00
	A	C	25	Life in Pond & Stream (Aug. 1925)		£1.00	£25.00
648 etc.	A	C	50	Modern Railways (Oct. 1936)	Ha.571–11	90p	£45.00
	A	C	50	Ocean Greyhounds (1938)	Ha.571–12	20p	£10.00
	A	U	25	*The Prince of Wales' Empire Tour (1924)....		90p	£22.50
	A	U	50	Prominent Cricketers of 1938 (1938)	Ha.571–13	40p	£20.00
	A	C	50	Prominent Racehorses of 1933 (1934)	Ha.571–14	25p	£12.50
	A	C	50	Sea Adventure (1939)	Ha.571–15	13p	£3.50
	A	C	25	Ships Flags & Cap Badges (Nov. 1926) (see RB21/217/178)		£1.00	£25.00
385	A	C	25	Ships Flags & Cap Badges, 2nd Series (July 1927) (see RB21/217/178)		£1.20	£30.00
	A	C	50	Shots from the Films (1936)	Ha.571–16	50p	£25.00
	A	C	50	Trick Billiards (1934)	Ha.571–17	£1.40	—
	A	U	25	Turnpikes (Apr. 1927)		70p	£17.50
88	A	C	50	Zoo Studies (Aug. 1937)	Ha.571–18	25p	£12.50

R. & J. HILL LTD., London

A. Pre-1919 Issues

Illus. No.	Size	Print-ing	Number in set		Handbook ref.	Price per card	Complete set
	A	C	26	*Actresses—"FROGA A"	H.20	£24.00	—
	D	BW	30	*Actresses, Continental:—	H.205/Ha.205		
				A. "The Seven Wonders" back		£7.00	—
				B. "Black and White Whisky" back		£20.00	—
				C. Plain back		£5.00	—
	D	BW	? 14	*Actresses—"HAGG B":—	H.24/Ha.24		
				A. "Smoke Hill's Stockrider ..."		£17.50	—
				B. "Issued with Hill's High Class"		£15.00	—
	—	BW	25	*Actresses (Belle of New York Series) (1899):—	H.206/Ha.206		
				"The Seven Wonders..." back:			
				A. White back (41 × 75 mm.)		£8.00	£200.00
				B. Toned back, thick card (39 × 74 mm.)..		£10.00	£250.00
	D1	U	20	*Actresses, chocolate tinted (1917):—	H.207/Ha.207		
				A. "Hill's Tobaccos" etc. back		£9.00	—
				B. "Issued with Hill's ..." back		£12.50	—
				C. Plain back		£9.00	—
	C	C	20	*Animal Series (1909):—			
				A. "R. & J. Hill Ltd." back		£12.00	—
				B. "Crowfoot Cigarettes" back		£9.00	—
				C. "The Cigarettes with which ..." back		—	—
				D. Space at back		£9.00	—
				E. Plain Back		—	—
	A	BW	? 13	*Battleships:—	H.208/Ha.208		
				A. "For the Pipe Smoke Oceanic ..." back		—	—
				B. Plain back		—	—
326	A	C	25	*Battleships and Crests (1901–2)		£8.00	£200.00
	D2	C	12	*Boer War Generals ("Campaigners")	H.209/Ha.209	£20.00	£250.00
	A1	C	20	Breeds of Dogs (1914):—	H.211	—	£100.00
				A. "Archer's M.F.H." back		£6.00	—
				B. "Hill's Badminton" back		£5.00	—
				C. "Hill's Verbena Mixture" back		£5.00	—
				D. "Spinet Tobacco" back		£5.00	—

Illus. No.	Size	Print-ing	Number in set		Handbook ref.	Price per card	Complete set
	D1	BW	? 44	*British Navy Series (? 1902–3)...............	H.210/Ha.210	£12.50	—
	C	C		*Colonial Troops:—	H.40		
			30	A. 1–30.			
				i. "Hill's Leading Lines ..." back.....		£12.00	—
				ii. "Perfection vide Dress ..." back....		£10.00	—
			50	B. 1–50. "Sweet American" back.........		£12.00	—
	D1	U	28	Famous Cricketers Series (1912):			
				A. Red back, blue picture................		£16.00	—
				B. Deep blue back, brown picture.........		£16.00	—
				C. Blue back, black picture.............		£18.00	—
	D1	BW	20	Famous Footballers Series (1912–13).......		£8.00	£160.00
547	—	U	25	Famous Pictures:—(41 × 70 mm.)...........	H.468		
				A. "Prize Coupon" back................		£2.50	£62.50
				B. Without "Prize Coupon" back........		£2.50	£62.50
	C	C	30	*Flags and Flags with Soldiers	H.41	£12.00	—
	—	C	24	*Flags, Arms and Types of Nations, "Black & White" Whisky advert back (41 × 68 mm.)	H.115	£5.00	£125.00
	D	BW	20	Football Captain Series, Nd. 41–60 (1906):—			
				A. Small title....................		£8.00	—
				B. Larger title, back re-drawn...........		£9.00	—
	—		10	Fragments from France (1916–17): (38 × 67 mm.):—	H.212/Ha.212		
		C		A. Coloured, caption in script...........		£9.00	£90.00
		U		B. Sepia-brown on buff, caption in block ..		£12.00	£120.00
		U		C. As B, but black and white.............		£18.00	—
	—	C	10	Fragments from France, different subjects, caption in block (38 × 67 mm.)...........	H.212	£9.00	£90.00
	A1	U	25	Hill's War Series	H.35	£5.00	£125.00
500	C2	C	20	Inventors & Their Inventions Series, Nd. 1–20, (1907):—	H.213		
				A. Black back, white card................		£3.50	£70.00
				B. Black back, toned card (shorter)		£4.50	—
	C2	C	20	Inventors & Their Inventions Series, Nd. 21–40, (1907)		£5.00	£100.00
	—		15	*Japanese Series (1904–5) (40 × 66 mm.):—	H.214/Ha.214		
		C		A. "Hills" on red tablet...............		£30.00	—
		BW		B. "Hills" on black tablet................		£25.00	—
	—	C	20	Lighthouse Series—without frame lines to picture (? 1903) (42 × 68 mm.).........		£12.00	£240.00
	—	C	30	Lighthouse Series—with frame line. Nos. 1–20 re-touched and 10 cards added.......		£12.00	£360.00
604	D	C	20	National Flag Series (1914).................	Ha.473	£6.00	£120.00
				Plain back		£6.00	
	—	BW	? 22	*Naval Series (1901–02), Unnumbered (42 × 64 mm.)	H.215/Ha.215	£24.00	—
	D1	BW	? 29	Naval Series (1902–3) Nd. 21–49	H.215/Ha.215	£12.00	—
	C	C	20	Prince of Wales Series (1911)...............	H.22	£6.00	£120.00
				Plain back		—	—
	—	U	? 14	*Prints from Noted Pictures (68 × 81 mm.)....	H.216/Ha.216	£27.00	—
	A	BW	20	Rhymes—black and white sketches	H.217/Ha.217	£15.00	—
	A1		? 28	*Statuary—Set 1:—	Ha.218–1		
		U		A. Brown front		—	—
		BW		B. Black and white front, matt............		—	—
		BW		C. Black and white front, varnished		£5.00	—
	A	BW	30	*Statuary—Set 2:—	Ha.218–2		
				A. Front in black and white..............		£3.00	—
				B. Front greenish-black		£3.00	—
	C1	BW	? 25	*Statuary—Set 3:—	Ha.218–3		
				A. Name panel white lettering on black background......................		£7.00	
				B. Name panel black lettering on grey background................		—	
				C. Name panel black lettering on white background................		—	
	D	C	20	*Types of the British Army (1914):—			
				A. "Badminton" back....................		£16.00	—
				B. "Verbena" back......................		£16.00	—
550	A	U	25	World's Masterpieces—Photogravure, in-scribed "Second Series"		£1.20	£30.00

B. Post-1920 Issues

Illus. No.	Size	Print-ing	Number in set		Handbook ref.	Price per card	Complete set
	C	U	30	The All Blacks (1924)......................		£1.35	£40.00
	A	BW	25	Aviation Series (1934):—			
				A. "Issued by R. & J. Hill ..." at base		32p	£8.00
				B. "Issued with 'Gold Flake Honeydew' ..." at base		40p	£10.00
		U	50	Caricatures of Famous Cricketers (June 1926):—			
	C			A. Small size.....................		45p	£22.50
	B1			B. Large size......................		35p	£17.50
251	D1	C	50	Celebrities of Sport (1939):—			
				A. "Issued by R. & J. Hill ..." at base		30p	£15.00
				B. "Issued with 'Gold Flake Honeydew' ..." at base		40p	£20.00
450	A2	C	35	Cinema Celebrities (1936):—	Ha.572		
				A. Inscribed "These Cigarettes are guaranteed best British Manufacture"..		17p	£6.00
				B. Inscribed "The Spinet House"		23p	£8.00
	D1	BW	40	Crystal Palace Souvenir Cards (inscribed "These Cigarettes are guaranteed best			

Illus. No.	Size	Print- ing	Number in set		Handbook ref.	Price per card	Complete set
				British Manufacture"):—			
				A. Front matt (1936)		30p	£12.00
				B. Front varnished (1937)		25p	£10.00
	D1	C	48	Decorations and Medals (1940):—			
				A. "Issued by R. & J. Hill . . ." at base		80p	£40.00
				B. "Issued with Gold Flake Cigarettes" at base		£1.00	£50.00
		P		Famous Cinema Celebrities (1931)	Ha.573		
			? 48	Set 1:—			
—				A. Medium size (74 × 56 mm.) inscribed "Series A"		—	—
	A			B1. Small size, inscribed "Spinet Cigarettes"		£1.20	—
	A			B2. Small size, without "Spinet Cigarettes"		—	—
			50	Set 2:—			
—				C. Small size (66 × 41 mm.) inscribed "Series C":—			
				1. "Devon Cigarettes" at base of back .		—	—
				2. "Toucan Cigarettes" at base of back		£1.20	—
				3. Space at base of back blank		£1.20	—
				D. Medium size (74 × 56 mm.) inscribed "Series D":—			
				1. "Kadi Cigarettes" at base of back . .		£1.20	—
				2. Space at base of back blank		£1.20	—
	C	U	40	Famous Cricketers (1923)		£1.25	£50.00
		U	50	Famous Cricketers, including the S. Africa Test Team—"Sunripe Cigarettes" (May 1924):—			
150	C			A. Small size		£1.25	£62.50
	B1			B. Large size		£1.25	£62.50
—		C	30	Famous Engravings—Series XI (80 × 61 mm.)		£4.00	—
	A2	BW	40	Famous Film Stars (1938):—			
				A. Text in English		40p	£16.00
				B. *Text in Arabic, caption in English (see also Modern Beauties)*		30p	£12.00
	C	U	50	Famous Footballers (Oct. 1923)		90p	£45.00
176	D	C	50	Famous Footballers (1939):—	Ha.574		
				A. Shoreditch address at base		20p	£10.00
				B. "Proprietors of Hy. Archer . . ." at base.		22p	£11.00
	D	C	25	Famous Footballers, Nd. 51–75 (1939)		26p	£6.50
345	D	C	50	Famous Ships:—			
				A. Front matt (1939)		13p	£3.75
				B. Front varnished (1940)		13p	£3.75
	D	C	48	Film Stars and Celebrity Dancers (1935)		40p	£20.00
		C	50	Historic Places from Dickens' Classics (1926 and 1934):—			
	D			A. Small size		20p	£10.00
	B1			B. Large size:—			
				1. Nos. 1–26, small numerals		30p	—
				2. Nos. 1–50, large numerals		20p	£10.00
		U	50	Holiday Resorts (July 1925):—			
	C			A. Small size:—			
				1. Back in grey		40p	£20.00
				2. Back in brown		80p	—
	B1			B. Large size:—			
				1. Back in grey		40p	£20.00
				2. Back in brown		80p	—
	A		20	*Inventors and Their Inventions (plain back) (1934):—*	H.213		
		BW		A. *Front in black and white*		30p	£6.00
		C		B. *Front in colour*		—	—
				Magical Puzzles—see "Puzzle Series"			
	A2	BW		Modern Beauties (1939):—			
			50	A. Titled "Modern Beauties". Text in English		30p	£15.00
			40	B. *Titled "Famous Film Stars" (selection). Text in Arabic, no captions*		30p	£12.00
		C	30	Music Hall Celebrities—Past & Present (July 1930):—			
	D1			A. Small size		30p	£9.00
	B1			B. Large size		60p	£18.00
	D	C	30	Nature Pictures—"The Spotlight Tobaccos"		33p	£10.00
337	C2	C	30	Nautical Songs (1937)		20p	£6.00
		U	30	"Our Empire" (Nov. 1929):—			
	D1			A. Small size		13p	£3.50
	B1			B. Large size		25p	£7.50
—		BW		Popular Footballers—Season 1934–5 (68 × 49 mm.):—			
			30	"Series A"—Nd. 1–30		80p	£24.00
			20	"Series B"—Nd. 31–50		40p	£8.00
		U		Public Schools and Colleges (Dec. 1923):—	Ha.575		
			50	A. "A Series of 50"—			
	C			1. Small size		35p	£17.50
	B1			2. Large size		40p	£20.00
			75	B. "A Series of 75"—			
	C			1. Small size		40p	£30.00
	B1			2. Large size		40p	£30.00
631	A1	C	50	Puzzle Series:—			

Illus. No.	Size	Print-ing	Number in set		Handbook ref.	Price per card	Complete set
				A. Titled "Puzzle Series" (1937)……….		16p	£8.00
				B. Titled "Magical Puzzles" (1938)…….		30p	£15.00
		U	50	The Railway Centenary—"A Series of 50" (Oct. 1925):—			
	C			A. Small size……………………		30p	£15.00
	B1			B. Large size—			
				1. Back in brown…………………		50p	£25.00
				2. Back in grey …………………		70p	—
		U	25	The Railway Centenary—"2nd Series—51 to 75":—			
728 etc.	C			A. Small size……………………		90p	£22.50
	B1			B. Large size……………………		70p	£17.50
	C2	P	42	Real Photographs—Set 1 (Bathing Beauties):—	Ha.576-1		
				A. "London Idol Cigarettes" at base of back:—			
				1. Front black and white, glossy…….		—	—
				2. Front brown, matt………………		80p	£33.00
				B. Space at base of back blank:—			
				1. Front black and white, glossy…….		80p	—
				2. Front brown, matt………………		80p	£33.00
	C2	P	42	Real Photographs—Set 2 (Beauties)………	Ha.576-2	£1.00	—
				The River Thames—see "Views of the River Thames"			
	D1	P	50	Scenes from the Films (1932):—			
				A. Front black and white……………		70p	—
				B. Front sepia ……………………		70p	—
457	A2	BW	40	Scenes from the Films (1938–9) …………		13p	£4.00
	D1		35	Scientific Inventions and Discoveries (Dec. 1929):—	Ha.213		
		C		A. Small size, "The Spinet House …" back		30p	£10.00
		BW		B. Small size, "The Spotlight Tobaccos …" back …………………		30p	£10.00
	B1	C		C. Large size……………………		30p	£10.00
	D1	P	50	Sports (1934):—			
				A. Titled "Sports", numbered front and back……………………		80p	—
				B. Titled "Sports Series", numbered front only ……………………		90p	—
				*C. Untitled, numbered front only ………		90p	—
	D1	C	100	*Transfers……………………	Ha.596-2	—	—
	B2	CP		Views of Interest:—			
			48	"A First Series …" Nd. 1–48 (1938):—			
				A. "The Spinet House …" back ………		14p	£7.00
				B. "Sunripe & Spinet Ovals …" back ….		13p	£3.00
			48	"Second Series …" Nd. 49–96 (1938) …….		13p	£3.00
			48	"Third Series …" Nd. 97–144 (1939)…….		13p	£2.50
			48	"Fourth Series …" Nd. 145–192 (1939) …..		13p	£6.00
575			48	"Fifth Series …" Nd. 193–240 (1939) …….		14p	£7.00
	B2	CP		Views of Interest—British Empire Series …:—			
			48	"1st Issue—Canada—Nos. 1–48" (1940) ….		18p	£9.00
			48	"2nd Issue—India—Nos. 49–96" (1940)…..		£1.00	£50.00
		U	50	Views of London (1925):—	Ha.577		
	C			A. Small size……………………		40p	£20.00
	B1			B. Large size……………………		45p	£22.50
	D	C	50	Views of the River Thames (1924):—			
				A. Small size—			
				Nos. 1–25 ………………		90p	£22.50
				Nos. 26–50 ………………		30p	£7.50
	B1			B. Large size—			
				1. Back in green (thin card) ………		35p	£17.50
				2. Back in green and black (thick card)		35p	£17.50
		U	50	Who's Who in British Films (Nov. 1927):—			
	A2			A. Small size……………………		22p	£11.00
	B2			B. Large size……………………		30p	£15.00
	C	C	84	Wireless Telephony (1923):—			
				1. Nos. 1–24……………………			
				2. Nos. 25–36—Crystal Series …………		50p	£42.00
				3. Nos. 37–84—Marconiphone Series…..			
	B1	U	20	Wireless Telephony—Broadcasting Series (1923)……………………		£1.00	£20.00
		U	50	Zoological Series (1924):—	Ha.578		
	C			A. Small size—			
				1. Back in light brown…………….		50p	£25.00
				2. Back in grey …………………		70p	£35.00
	B1			B. Large size—			
				1. Back in light brown……………		40p	£20.00
				2. Back in dark brown……………		40p	£20.00

C. Post-1940 Issue

| | A | U | 50 | Famous Dog Breeds 1954 (Admiral Cigarettes Slides) …………………… | | — | — |

D. Canvases. Unbacked canvases. The material is a linen fabric, glazed to give the appearance of canvas. Specimens are found rubber stamped in red on back "The Pipe Tobacco de Luxe Spinet Mixture".

	—	C	30	"Britain's Stately Homes" (78 × 61 mm.) ….		£1.80	£55.00
	—	C	40	*Canvas Masterpieces—Series 1 (73 × 61 mm.):—			
				A. "Badminton Tobacco Factories …" back:—			

R. & J. HILL LTD. *(continued)*

Illus. No.	Size	Printing	Number in set	Handbook ref.	Price per card	Complete set
			1. "H.T. & Co., Ltd., Leeds" at right base		£1.00	—
			2. "Cardigan Press, Leeds" at right base (Nos. 21–40)		£1.00	—
			3. Without printers' credit (Nos. 21–30)		£1.00	—
			4. As 3, but size 73 × 53 mm. (Nos. 23–25)		£1.00	—
			B. "The Spinet House …" back		£1.00	£40.00
—		C	40 *Canvas Masterpieces—Series 2, Nd. 41–80 (73 × 61 mm.)		£1.00	£40.00
—		C	10 *Canvas Masterpieces—Series 2, Nd. 1–10:—			
			Nos. 1 to 5		£1.20	£6.00
			Nos. 6 to 10		£2.40	£12.00
—		C	5 Chinese Pottery & Porcelain—Series 1 (132 × 110 mm.)		—	£10.00
—		C	11 Chinese Pottery & Porcelain—Series 2 (107 × 62 mm.)		£2.25	—
—		C	23 *Great War Leaders—Series 10 (73 × 60 mm.)		£2.00	£46.00

J. W. HOBSON, Huddersfield

Pre-1919 Issue

Illus. No.	Size	Printing	Number in set	Handbook ref.	Price per card	Complete set
C2	C		18 Motor Cycle Series	Ha.469	—	—

J. & T. HODGE, Glasgow

Pre-1919 Issues

Illus. No.	Size	Printing	Number in set	Handbook ref.	Price per card	Complete set
—		C	? 2 *British Naval Crests (70 × 38 mm.)	H.219/Ha.219	—	—
	A	BW	16 British Royal Family		—	—
—		U	*Scottish Views:—	Ha.220		
			? 4 A. Thick card (74 × 39 mm.)		£65.00	—
			? 6 B. Thin card (80 × 45 mm.)		£65.00	—

HUDDEN & CO. LTD., Bristol

A. Pre-1919 Issues

Illus. No.	Size	Printing	Number in set	Handbook ref.	Price per card	Complete set
	C	C	26 *Actresses—"FROGA A"	H.20	£45.00	—
	C	C	25 *Beauties—"CHOAB"	H.21	£15.00	—
	A2	U	? 19 *Beauties—"Crown Seal Cigarettes"	H.221/Ha.221	£85.00	—
	A	U	? 24 *Beauties—"HUMPS":—	H.222		
			A. Blue scroll back		£40.00	—
			B. Orange scroll back		£16.00	—
	D1	C	54 Comic Phrases	H.223	£50.00	—
	A	C	25 *Flags of All Nations	H.37	£6.00	£150.00
—		C	50 *Flowers and Designs (55 × 34 mm.)	H.224	£45.00	—
	A	C	18 *Pretty Girl Series—"RASH"	H.8	£32.00	—
	A	C	25 Soldiers of the Century, Nd. 26–50 (1901)		£28.00	£700.00
	A	C	25 *Star Girls	H.30	£80.00	—
	A	C	25 Types of Smokers		£22.00	£550.00

B. Post-1920 Issues. All export

Illus. No.	Size	Printing	Number in set	Handbook ref.	Price per card	Complete set
	D	U	25 Famous Boxers (1927)	Ha.579	—	—
	C	U	50 Public Schools and Colleges	Ha.575	80p	£40.00
	A	C	25 Sports & Pastimes Series 1	H.225	£30.00	—

HUDSON

Pre-1919 Issue

Illus. No.	Size	Printing	Number in set	Handbook ref.	Price per card	Complete set
	C	C	? 1 *Beauties—selections from "BOCCA"	H.39/Ha.39	£80.00	—

HUNTER, Airdrie

Pre-1919 Issue

Illus. No.	Size	Printing	Number in set	Handbook ref.	Price per card	Complete set
	A	BW	? 11 *Footballers	H.227	—	—

J. T. ILLINGWORTH & SONS, Kendal

A. Pre-1919 Issue

Illus. No.	Size	Printing	Number in set	Handbook ref.	Price per card	Complete set
	A	BW	? 1 Views from the English Lakes	H.228	—	—

B. Post-1920 Issues

Illus. No.	Size	Printing	Number in set	Handbook ref.	Price per card	Complete set
	—	P	48 Beautiful Scotland (77 × 52 mm.) (1939)	Ha.564–1	40p	£20.00
	C1	C	25 *Cavalry (1924)		£2.00	£50.00
	—	P	48 Coastwise (77 × 52 mm.) (1938)	Ha.564–2	25p	£12.50
	A	C	25 "Comicartoons" of Sport (1927)		£1.40	£35.00
	—	P	48 Flying (77 × 52 mm.) (Feb. 1938)	Ha.564–3	25p	£12.50
376	A	C	25 *Motor Car Bonnets (1925)		£2.20	£55.00
	A	C	25 *Old Hostels (1926)		£1.60	£40.00
	—	P	48 Our Countryside (77 × 52 mm.) (1938)	Ha.564–4	20p	£10.00
	—	P	24 Shots from the Films (1937)	Ha.566	80p	£20.00

THE IMPERIAL TOBACCO CO. (of Great Britain & Ireland) Ltd., Bristol

Illus. No.	Size	Print-ing	Number in set		Handbook ref.	Price per card	Complete set
Pre-1919 Issues							
	A	C	50	British Birds	H.229	£3.20	£160.00
	C	C	1	Folder—Coronation of His Majesty King Edward VII (1902)......................		—	£30.00

INTERNATIONAL TOBACCO CO. LTD., London

Illus. No.	Size	Print-ing	Number in set		Handbook ref.	Price per card	Complete set
Post-1920 Issues							
A. Home Issues							
		C	28	Domino Cards (69 × 35 mm.)		20p	£5.50
		U		Famous Buildings and Monuments of Britain (1934) (bronze metal plaques in cellophane envelopes*:—	Ha.580		
			50	"Series A":—			
	A1			1. Nos. 1–30, small size		20p	£6.00
	B2			2. Nos. 31–50, large size..................		40p	£8.00
			50	"Series B":—			
	A1			1. Nos. 51–80, small size		40p	£12.00
	B2			2. Nos. 81–100, large size...............		35p	£7.00
344	A	C	50	International Code of Signals (1934)		13p	£3.25
B. Export Issues. Inscribed "International Tobacco (Overseas), Ltd."							
	A2	C	100	Film Favourites:—	Ha.581		
				A. Back in grey		70p	—
				B. Back in black		70p	—
		C	100	"Gentlemen! The King!" (1937–38)—60 small, 40 large:—	Ha.582		
				A. Back in blue..........................		13p	£7.50
				B. Back in black		13p	£3.75

*The same plaques were also used for an export issue, with envelopes inscribed "International Tobacco (Overseas), Ltd."

J. L. S. TOBACCO CO., London

Illus. No.	Size	Print-ing	Number in set		Handbook ref.	Price per card	Complete set
Pre-1919 Issues							
				("Star of the World" Cigarettes)			
	D	BW	20	*Boer War Cartoons	H.42	£20.00	—
	B2	BW	? 27	*Boer War Celebrities—"JASAS"	H.133	—	—
	A2	C	30	*Colonial Troops	H.40	£32.00	—

PETER JACKSON, London

Illus. No.	Size	Print-ing	Number in set		Handbook ref.	Price per card	Complete set
Post-1920 Issues							
A. Home Issues							
		P		Beautiful Scotland (1939):—	Ha.564–1		
	D		28	A. Small size...........................		30p	£8.50
	—		48	B. Medium size, 77 × 52 mm.		20p	£10.00
		P		Coastwise (1938):—	Ha.564–2		
	D		28	A. Small size...........................		30p	£8.50
	—		48	B. Medium size, 77 × 52 mm.		40p	£20.00
437	D	P	27	Famous Films (1934–35)		80p	£22.00
	D	P	28	Famous Film Stars (1935)		80p	£22.00
	D	P	28	Film Scenes (Sep. 1936)...................		30p	£8.50
	B	P	28	Film Scenes (Sep. 1936)...................		60p	£17.00
		P		Flying (Feb. 1938):—	Ha.564–3		
	D		28	A. Small size...........................		80p	—
	—		48	B. Medium size (77 × 52 mm.)		40p	£20.00
	D	P	28	Life in the Navy (Mar. 1937).............		30p	£8.50
	B	P	28	Life in the Navy (March 1937)		70p	£20.00
		P		Our Countryside (1938):—	Ha.564–4		
	D		28	A. Small size...........................		25p	£7.00
	—		48	B. Medium size (77 × 52 mm.)		40p	£20.00
		P		Shots from the Films (Aug. 1937):—	Ha.566		
	D		28	A. Small size...........................		25p	£7.00
	—		24	B. Medium size (77 × 52 mm.)		30p	£7.50
	D	P	28	Stars in Famous Films.....................		32p	£9.00
B. Export Issues. Inscribed "Peter Jackson (Overseas), Ltd."							
	—	C	100	"Gentlemen! The King!" (1937–38)—60 small, 40 large:—	Ha.582		
				A. Overprinted on International black back..................................		40p	£40.00
				B. Overprinted on International blue back		55p	—
				C. Reprinted with Jackson's name at base:—			
				i. Back in black		50p	—
				ii. Back in blue		50p	—
	—	C	150	The Pageant of Kingship—90 small, 60 large:—			
				A. Inscribed "Issued by Peter Jackson"....		50p	—
				B. Inscribed "Issued by Peter Jackson (Overseas), Ltd.":			
				1. Printed on board..................		50p	—
				2. Printed on paper..................		20p	£30.00
	—	C	250	Speed—Through the Ages (1937–38)—171 small, 79 large	Ha.583	13p	£27.00

JACOBI BROS. & CO. LTD., London

Illus. No.	Size	Print-ing	Number in set	Handbook ref.	Price per card	Complete set
Pre-1919 Issue						
	A	BW	? 27 *Boer War Celebrities—"JASAS"	H.133		
			A. Black and white front..................		—	—
			B. As A, but mauve tinted		£80.00	—

JAMES & CO. (Birmingham) LTD.

Pre-1919 Issue						
	—	C	20 Arms of Countries (70 × 49 mm.)............		£45.00	—

JAMES'S (GOLD LEAF NAVY CUT)

Pre-1919 Issue						
	A	U	? 10 Pretty Girl Series "BAGG"................		—	—

J. B. JOHNSON & CO., London

Pre-1919 Issue						
	A	C	25 *National Flags and Flowers—Girls	H.123	£75.00	—

JONES BROS., Tottenham

Pre-1919 Issues						
186	A	BW	18 *Spurs Footballers:—	H.230		
			A. 12 small titles		From £1.40	—
			10/12 small titles		—	£14.00
			B. 5 large titles		From £1.40	—
			C. 1 Group—Tottenham Hotspur Football Club 1911–12 (group of 34)........		—	—

A. I. JONES & CO. LTD., London

Pre-1919 Issue						
	D	C	12 Nautical Terms	H.231	£15.00	£180.00

A. S. JONES, Grantham

Pre-1919 Issue						
	D	C	30 Army Pictures, Cartoons, etc...............	H.12	—	—

ALEX. JONES & CO., London

Pre-1919 Issues						
	D2	U	? 13 *Actresses—"ANGOOD"...................	Ha.187	—	—
	A	BW	1 Portrait of Queen Victoria 1897............		—	£70.00

T. E. JONES & CO., Aberavon

Pre-1919 Issues						
	D	C	? 4 *Conundrums	H.232/Ha.232	—	—
	—	C	48 *Flags of All Nations (35 × 60 mm.)..........	H.233	£32.00	—
	—	BW	? 4 *Footballers (34 × 63 mm.)	H.234/Ha.234	£32.00	—
	D	C	? 7 Well-known Proverbs	H.235	£32.00	—

C. H. JORDEN LTD., London

Pre-1919 Issue						
	—	P	? 10 *Celebrities of the Great War, 1914–18 (35 × 64 mm.)............................	H.236/Ha.236	£50.00	—

J. & E. KENNEDY, Dublin

Pre-1919 Issue						
	A	U	25 *Beauties—"FECKSA".....................	H.58	£12.00	£300.00

RICHARD KENNEDY, Dundee

Pre-1919 Issue						
	A	U	50 War Portraits...........................	H.86	—	—

KINNEAR LTD., Liverpool

Pre-1919 Issues						
466	A	C	? 13 *Actresses	H.237	£35.00	—
	D1	BW	? 14 *Australian Cricketers (1897)...............	H.238	£60.00	—

KINNEAR LTD. *(continued)*

Illus. No.	Size	Printing	Number in set		Handbook ref.	Price per card	Complete set
	A2	C	25	*Footballers and Club Colours	H.239/Ha.239	£45.00	—
	—	U	1	The Four Generations (Royal Family) (1897) (65 × 70 mm.)		—	£200.00
	—	BW	1	"A Gentleman in Kharki" (1900) (44 × 64 mm.)		—	£18.00
126	A	C	? 33	*Jockeys (1896):—	H.240/Ha.240		
				12—see H.240-A		£17.00	£200.00
				1—see H.240-B		£32.00	—
				1—see H.240-C		£32.00	—
				3—see H.240-D		£32.00	—
				16—see H.240-E		£32.00	—
	A	C	? 2	*Prominent Personages	Ha.479	£23.00	—
	D1	U	13	*Royalty (1897)	H.241		—

B. KRIEGSFELD & CO., Manchester

Pre-1919 Issues

Illus. No.	Size	Printing	Number in set		Handbook ref.	Price per card	Complete set
	A2	U	? 40	*Beauties—"KEWA":—	H.139/Ha.139		
				A. Matt surface		£45.00	—
				B. Glossy surface		—	—
	A	C	? 6	Celebrities	H.242/Ha.242	£80.00	—
	A	C	48	*Flags of All Nations	H.233	£22.00	—
	A	C	50	*Phrases and Advertisements	H.243	£28.00	—

A. KUIT LTD., Manchester

Pre-1919 Issues

Illus. No.	Size	Printing	Number in set		Handbook ref.	Price per card	Complete set
	—	C	? 12	*Arms of Cambridge Colleges (17 × 25 mm.)	H.458	—	—
	—	C	? 12	*Arms of Companies (30 × 33 mm.)	H.459	£20.00	—
468	—	C	30	British Beauties—oval card (36 × 60 mm.)	H.244	£13.00	—
	—	P	? 2	*"Crosmedo" Bijou cards (55 × 37 mm.)	H.245	—	—
	A	U	25	Principal Streets of British Cities & Towns (1916)		£30.00	—
	A	CP	? 4	Types of Beauty	H.246	£65.00	—

LAMBERT & BUTLER, London

A. Pre-1919 Issues

Illus. No.	Size	Printing	Number in set		Handbook ref.	Price per card	Complete set
	A1	BW	20	*Actresses—"BLARM"	H.23	£6.00	£120.00
	—	C	10	*Actresses and Their Autographs:	H.247		
				A. Wide card (70 × 38 mm.):—			
				"Tobacco"		£42.00	—
				"Cigarettes"		—	—
				B. Narrow card (70 × 34 mm.):—			
				"Tobacco"		—	—
				"Cigarettes"		£50.00	—
	A2	BW	50	*Admirals (1900–1 ?):—	H.248		
				A. "Flaked Gold Leaf Honeydew" back		£6.00	—
				B. "May Blossom" back		£6.00	—
				C. "Prize Medal Bird's Eye" back		£6.00	—
				D. "Viking" back		£6.00	—
	C	C	1	*Advertisement Card—Spanish Dancer	H.249	—	£190.00
596	A	C	40	Arms of Kings & Queens of England (1906–8)		£2.50	£100.00
351	A	C	25	Aviation (1915–16)		£1.50	£37.50
	A2	C	26	*Beauties—"HOL":—	H.192		
				A. "Flaked Gold Leaf Honey Dew" back		£9.00	—
				B. "Log Cabin" back		£9.00	—
				C. "May Blossom" back		£9.00	—
				D. "Viking Navy Cut" back		£9.00	—
32	A	C	50	Birds & Eggs (1906 and 1917)	H.60	£1.60	£80.00
	C	BW	? 22	*Boer War and Boxer Rebellion—Sketches (1904)	H.46	£10.00	—
	C	BW	? 12	*Boer War Generals—"FLAC" (1901–2)	H.47	£10.00	—
	C	U	20	*Boer War Generals "CLAM" (1900–1)	H.61		
				I. 10. No frame lines to back:—			
				A. Brown back		£12.00	—
				B. Black back		£12.00	—
				II. 10. With frame lines to back:—			
				A. Brown back		£12.00	—
				B. Black back		£12.00	—
	C	U	1	*Boer War Series—"The King of Scouts" (Col. R. S. S. Baden-Powell)		—	£125.00
629	—	C	50	*Conundrums (1901) (38 × 57 mm.):—	H.250		
				A. Blue back—thick card		£9.00	—
				B. Green back		£6.00	—
	A2	C	12	Coronation Robes (1901–2)	H.251	£7.00	£85.00
	A	C	20	International Yachts (1902)		£25.00	—
	A	C	25	Japanese Series (1904–5):—			
				A. Thick toned card		£3.00	£75.00
				B. Thin white card		£3.60	£90.00
	—	C	4	*Jockeys, no frame lines (35 × 70 mm.)	H.252	£14.00	£56.00
125	—	C	10	*Jockeys, with frames lines (35 × 70 mm.)	H.252	£16.00	£160.00
	A	C	1	*Mayblossom Calendar, 1900		—	—
372	A	C	25	Motors (Nov. 1908):—			
				A. Green back		£7.00	£175.00
				B. Plain back		£8.00	—

LAMBERT & BUTLER (continued)

Illus. No.	Size	Printing	Number in set		Handbook ref.	Price per card	Complete set
	A	BW	25	Naval Portraits (1914)........................	H.253	£2.50	£62.50
332	A	BW	50	Naval Portraits, incl. above 25 (1915)	H.253	£2.00	£100.00
576	A	C	50	The Thames from Lechlade to London:—			
				A. Small numerals (1907).................		£3.00	£150.00
				B. Large numerals (Sep. 1908)		£3.50	£175.00
				C. Plain back		£3.50	—
—		C	4	*Types of the British Army & Navy (? 1897) (35 × 70 mm.):	H.254		
				A. "Specialities" back in brown		£25.00	—
				B. "Specialities" back in black		£25.00	—
				C. "Viking" back in black		£25.00	—
	A	C	25	*Waverley Series (1904)	H.255	£3.40	£85.00
	A	C	25	Winter Sports (1914)		£2.00	£50.00
	A	C	25	Wireless Telegraphy (1909)		£2.00	£50.00
412	A	C	25	World's Locomotives, Nd. 1–25 (1912)......		£2.00	£50.00
634 etc.	A	C	50	World's Locomotives (1913).................		£3.00	£150.00
	A	C	25	World's Locomotives, Nd. 1A–25A, additional series...........................		£3.00	£75.00

B. Post-1920 Issues

Illus. No.	Size	Printing	Number in set		Handbook ref.	Price per card	Complete set
361	A	C	50	Aeroplane Markings (Mar. 1937)		13p	£6.50
74	A	C	25	British Trees & Their Uses (Aug. 1937) (see RB21/209/34)		80p	£20.00
	A	C	25	Common Fallacies (Feb. 1928).............		50p	£12.50
504	A	C	25	Dance Band Leaders (1936)................		50p	£12.50
359	A	C	50	Empire Air Routes (Sep. 1936).............		17p	£8.50
	A	BW	25	Famous British Airmen & Airwomen (1935).		22p	£5.50
89	A	U	25	Fauna of Rhodesia (Mar. 1929).............		50p	£12.50
	A	C	51	Find Your Way (Set of 50 and Joker):—			
				A. Address "Box No. 152, London" (1932)		25p	£12.50
				B. Address "Box No. 152, Drury Lane, London" (1932).......................		25p	£12.50
				C. Overprinted in red (1933)		22p	£11.00
	A	C	50	Footballers 1930–1 (Jan. 1931).............		60p	—
	A	C	25	Garden Life (Apr. 1930)	H.449	28p	£7.00
370	A	C	25	Hints & Tips for Motorists (May 1929) (see RB21/209/50)...........................		80p	£20.00
357	A	U	25	A History of Aviation:—			
				A. Front in green (Apr. 1932)		24p	£6.00
				B. Front in brown (Dec. 1933)		36p	£9.00
143	A	C	50	Horsemanship (June 1938)		30p	£15.00
374	A	C	25	How Motor Cars Work (June 1931).........		28p	£7.00
312	A	C	50	Interesting Customs & Traditions of the Navy, Army & Air Force (Jan. 1939)......		16p	£8.00
	A	C	25	Interesting Musical Instruments (1929)......		60p	£15.00
	A	C	50	Interesting Sidelights on the Work of the G.P.O. (Oct. 1939)......................		30p	£15.00
	A.	C	50	Keep Fit (Nov. 1937) (see RB21/209/63).....		13p	£3.75
	A	C	25	London Characters (1934):—			
				A. With Album Clause		50p	£12.50
				B. Without Album Clause		£4.00	—
366	A	C	25	Motor Car Radiators (Aug. 1928)..........		£1.50	£37.50
	A	C	25	Motor Cars—"A Series of 25", green back (Oct. 1922)		£1.00	£25.00
	A	C	25	Motor Cars—"2nd Series of 25' (June 1923) .		£1.00	£25.00
369	A	C	50	Motor Cars—"3rd Series 50" (Feb. 1926) ...		£1.40	£70.00
373	A	C	25	Motor Cars—"A Series of 25", grey back (Feb. 1934)		44p	£11.00
	A	C	50	Motor Cycles (Nov. 1923)		£1.20	£60.00
365	A	C	50	Motor Index Marks (Dec. 1926)		70p	£35.00
378	A	C	25	Pirates & Highwaymen (Aug. 1926 and Oct. 1932)...................................	Ha.584	18p	£4.50
	A	U	25	Rhodesian Series (Apr. 1928)		40p	£10.00
	A	U	25	Third Rhodesian Series (Aug. 1930)........		20p	£5.00
	A	C	25	Wonders of Nature (Sep. 1924)		40p	£10.00

C. Miscellaneous

Illus. No.	Size	Printing	Number in set		Handbook ref.	Price per card	Complete set
	A	C	50	Travellers Tales (Prepared but not issued) ...		—	—

LAMBKIN BROS., Cork

Post-1920 Issues

Illus. No.	Size	Printing	Number in set		Handbook ref.	Price per card	Complete set
	A	C	36	*Country Scenes—Small size (1924) (6 sets of 6):—			
				Series 1—Yachting..................		£2.00	—
				Series 2—Country		£2.00	—
				Series 3—Far East		£2.00	—
				Series 4—Sailing...................		£2.00	—
				Series 5—Country		£2.00	—
				Series 6—Country		£2.00	—
	C	C	36	*Country Scenes—Large size (1924) (6 sets of 6):—			
				Series 7—Yachting.................		£2.00	—
				Series 8—Country		£2.00	—
				Series 9—Far East		£2.00	—
				Series 10—Sailing.................		£2.00	—
				Series 11—Country		£2.00	—
				Series 12—Windmill Scenes		£2.00	—
—		C	? 9	*Irish Views, anonymous, inscribed "Eagle, Cork" (68 × 67 mm.)	Ha.585	—	—
—		C	? 5	*"Lily of Killarney" Views (73 × 68 mm.).....	Ha.586	—	—

LANCS & YORKS TOBACCO MANUFACTURING CO. LTD., Burnley (L. & Y. Tob. Mfg. Co.)

Illus. No.	Size	Print-ing	Number in set		Handbook ref.	Price per card	Complete set
Pre-1919 Issue							
	C	C	26	*Actresses—"FROGA A"..................	H.20	—	—

C. & J. LAW, Hertford

Illus. No.	Size	Print-ing	Number in set		Handbook ref.	Price per card	Complete set
Pre-1919 Issues							
	A	C	25	*Types of British Soldiers....................	H.144	£8.00	—
	A	U	50	War Portraits	H.86	—	—

R. & J. LEA, LTD., Manchester

Illus. No.	Size	Print-ing	Number in set		Handbook ref.	Price per card	Complete set
A. Pre-1919 Issues							
	A1	C	50	Chairman Miniatures 1–50 (1912):—			
				A. No border		£1.50	£75.00
				B. Gilt border.......................		£1.50	£75.00
	A1	C	50	Chairman & Vice Chair Miniatures, 51–100 (1912).....................		£1.50	£75.00
	A1	BW	25	Chairman War Portraits (marked "War Series" on front) (1915).		£3.60	£90.00
	A	C	70	Cigarette Transfers (Locomotives) (1916) ...		£2.00	
	A	BW	25	Civilians of Countries Fighting with the Allies (1914–15).........................		£5.00	£125.00
60	A1	C	50	Flowers to Grow (The Best Perennials) (1913)		£2.00	£100.00
	A1	C	50	Modern Miniatures (1913).................		—	£275.00
				46 different, less 1, 8, 12, 32..............		70p	£35.00
	A1	C	? 13	More Lea's Smokers (1906–7):	H.256/Ha.256		
				A. Green borders		£40.00	—
				B. Red borders.......................		£40.00	—
614	A1	C	50	Old English Pottery & Porcelain, 1–50 (1912)		£1.40	£70.00
615	A1	C	50	Old Pottery & Porcelain, 51–100 (1912):—			
				A. "Chairman Cigarettes"................		£1.00	£50.00
				B. "Recorder Cigarettes"...............		£3.00	—
612	A1	C	50	Old Pottery & Porcelain, 101–150 (1912–13):—			
				A. "Chairman Cigarettes"................		£1.00	£50.00
				B. "Recorder Cigarettes"...............		£3.00	—
611	A1	C	50	Old Pottery & Porcelain, 151–200 (1913)		£1.00	£50.00
617	A1	C	50	Old Pottery & Porcelain, 201–250		£1.00	£50.00
	A	BW	25	War Pictures (1915–16)...................		£2.00	£50.00
B. Post-1920 Issues							
			48	Coronation Souvenir (1937):—			
	A2	P		A. Small size, glossy—			
				1. Lea's name		14p	£7.00
				2. "Successors to ..."..............		13p	£4.00
	A2	BW		B. Small size, matt—			
				1. Lea's name		30p	£15.00
				2. "Successors to ..."..............		13p	£6.50
	—	P		C. Medium size (77 × 51 mm.)		14p	£7.00
	A2	C	50	Dogs (1923):—			
				1. Nos. 1–25–A. White card		£1.20	£30.00
				B. Cream card..............		£1.20	£30.00
				2. Nos. 26–50.................		£2.00	£50.00
24	A2	C	25	English Birds (1922):—			
				A. Glossy front		£1.20	£30.00
				B. Matt front		£1.80	£45.00
	A2	C	25	The Evolution of the Royal Navy (1925)		50p	£12.50
427	A2	P	54	Famous Film Stars (1939)		14p	£7.00
		CP	48	Famous Racehorses of 1926 (1927):—			
	A2			A. Small size.......................		70p	£35.00
	—			B. Medium size (75 × 50 mm.)		£1.20	£60.00
			48	Famous Views (1936):—			
	A2	P		A. Small size—1. Glossy..............		13p	£5.00
		BW		2. Matt..................		40p	£20.00
	—	P		B. Medium size (76 × 51 mm.)		13p	£4.00
	A2	P	36	Film Stars—"A First Series ..." (1934)......		70p	£25.00
	A2	P	36	Film Stars—"A Second Series ..." (1934) ...		45p	£16.00
	A2	C	25	Fish (1926)		30p	£7.50
	A2		48	Girls from the Shows (1935):—			
		P		A. Glossy front		30p	£15.00
		BW		B. Matt front		40p	£20.00
	A2		54	Radio Stars (1935):—			
		P		A. Glossy front		50p	£25.00
		BW		B. Matt front		50p	£25.00
72	A2	C	50	Roses (1924).......................		35p	£17.50
	A2	C	50	Ships of the World (1925).................		60p	£30.00
			48	Wonders of the World (1938):—			
	A2	P		A. Small size—1. Glossy..............		25p	£12.50
		BW		2. Matt..................		25p	£12.50
		P		B. Medium size (76 × 50 mm.)		13p	£6.00
C. Silks. All paper-backed.							
	—	C		*Butterflies and Moths III:—	Ha.505–7		
9			12	1. Small size (70 × 44 mm.)		30p	£3.50
			12	2. Large size (70 × 88 mm.)		30p	£3.50

R. & J. LEA, LTD. *(continued)*

Illus. No.	Size	Printing	Number in set		Handbook ref.	Price per card	Complete set
1			6	3. Extra-large size (143 × 70 mm.)		40p	£2.50
—		C	54	*Old Pottery—Set 1 (68 × 38 mm.)	Ha.505–14	70p	£37.50
—		C	72	*Old Pottery—Set 2 (61 × 37 mm.)	Ha.505–14	60p	£42.50
—		C	50	Regimental Crests and Badges—Series I (48 mm. sq.)	Ha.502–4	80p	£40.00
—		C	50	Regimental Crests and Badges—Series II (48 mm. sq.)	Ha.502–4	£1.60	£80.00
D. Miscellaneous							
—		C	24	Old English Pottery & Porcelain (Post Card Size) (Inscribed Chairman Cigarette Series or other firms' names)	Ha.257	£5.00	—

J. LEES, Northampton

Pre-1919 Issue

A	C	? 21	Northampton Town Football Club (No. 301–321)		£15.00	

A. LEWIS & CO. (WESTMINSTER) LTD., London

A. Pre-1919 Issue

A	U	50	War Portraits	H.86	£17.50	—

B. Post-1920 Issue

A2	C	52	Horoscopes (1938)	Ha.587	16p	£8.00

H. C. LLOYD & SON, Exeter

Pre-1919 Issues

A	U	28	Academy Gems:—	H.258		
			A. Red-brown tint		£27.00	—
			B. Purple tint		£22.00	—
			C. Green tint		£27.00	—
D	BW	? 25	*Actresses and Boer War Celebrities	H.260/Ha.260	£25.00	—
—	BW		*Devon Footballers and Boer War Celebrities:—	H.259/Ha.259		
		? 25	Set 1—Without framelines (70 × 41 mm.)		£30.00	—
		? 1	Set 2—With framelines (70 × 45 mm.)		—	—
A1	C	25	*Star Girls—"Tipsy Loo Cigarettes"	H.30	£100.00	—
—	BW	36	War Pictures (73 × 69 mm.)		—	—

RICHARD LLOYD & SONS, London

A. Pre-1919 Issues

—		BW	25	*Boer War Celebrities (1899) (35 × 61 mm.)	H.261	£10.00	—
—		U	? 20	*General Interest—Actresses, Celebrities and Yachts (62 × 39 mm.)	H.262/ Ha.262–1	£70.00	—
	A1	C	96	*National Types, Costumes and Flags	H.263	£20.00	—
	A	C	10	*Scenes from San Toy*	H.462	£7.00	£70.00

B. Post-1920 Issues. Most cards inscribed "Branch of Cope Bros. & Co., Ltd.". See also under "Cope Bros.".

379	A	C	25	Atlantic Records (1936)		60p	£15.00
	A2	P	27	Cinema Stars, glossy—"A Series of 27", Nd. 1–27		£1.00	£27.00
429	A2	P	27	Cinema Stars, glossy—"A Series of 27", Nd. 28–54		13p	£3.25
	A2	P	27	Cinema Stars, glossy—"Third Series of 27", Nd. 55–81		£1.00	£27.00
	A2	U	25	Cinema Stars, matt—"A Series of 25"		22p	£5.50
	A	BW	25	*Famous Cricketers (Puzzle Series)) (1930)		£1.50	£37.50
568	D	C		Old Inns:—			
			25	A1. Titled "Old English Inns" (1923)		26p	£6.50
			25	A2. Titled "Old Inns—Series 2" (1924)		90p	£22.50
			50	B. Titled "Old Inns" (1925)		25p	£12.50
630	A	BW	25	Tricks & Puzzles (1935)		13p	£2.00
	A2	U	25	Types of Horses (1926):—			
				A. Back in light brown		80p	£20.00
				B. Back in dark brown		80p	£20.00
98	A2	U	25	"Zoo" Series (1926)	Ha.588	30p	£7.50

LUSBY LTD., London

Pre-1919 Issue

D	C	25	Scenes from Circus Life	H.264	£75.00	—

HUGH McCALL, Edinburgh, Glasgow and Aberdeen

Post-1920 Issue

C	C	? 1	*R.A.F. Advertisement Card	Ha.594	—	—

D. & J. MACDONALD, Glasgow

Illus. No.	Size	Printing	Number in set		Handbook ref.	Price per card	Complete set
Pre-1919 Issues							
	A	C	? 9	*Actresses—"MUTA"	H.265	£60.00	—
	A	BW	25	*Cricketers	H.266	£60.00	—
		BW	? 7	*Cricket & Football Teams	Ha.267	£80.00	—
		C	? 1	County Cricket Team		£350.00	—

MACKENZIE & CO., Glasgow

Illus. No.	Size	Printing	Number in set		Handbook ref.	Price per card	Complete set
Pre-1919 Issues							
—		P	50	*Actors & Actresses (32 × 58 mm.)	H.268	£5.50	—
—		U	50	Victorian Art Pictures—Photogravure (32 × 58 mm.)		£5.50	—
86	A	BW	50	The Zoo		£5.50	—

WM. M'KINNELL, Edinburgh

Illus. No.	Size	Printing	Number in set		Handbook ref.	Price per card	Complete set
Pre-1919 Issue							
	A	C	20	European War Series	H.129	£70.00	—
	A	U	50	War Portraits	H.86	—	—

MACNAUGHTON, JENKINS & CO., LTD., Dublin

Illus. No.	Size	Printing	Number in set		Handbook ref.	Price per card	Complete set
Post-1920 Issues							
—		C	50	Castles of Ireland (1924):—			
				A. Size 76 × 45 mm.		£1.20	£60.00
				B. Size 74 × 44 mm.		£1.40	—
	D	C	50	Various Uses of Rubber (1924)		80p	£40.00

McWATTIE & SONS, Arbroath

Illus. No.	Size	Printing	Number in set		Handbook ref.	Price per card	Complete set
Pre-1919 Issue							
	D	C	30	Army Pictures, Cartoons, etc.	H.12	—	—

THE MANXLAND TOBACCO CO., Isle of Man

Illus. No.	Size	Printing	Number in set		Handbook ref.	Price per card	Complete set
Pre-1919 Issues							
	D	BW	? 1	*Views in the Isle of Man	Ha.491	—	—

MARCOVITCH & CO., London

Illus. No.	Size	Printing	Number in set		Handbook ref.	Price per card	Complete set
A. Post-1920 Issue							
	A2	P	18	*Beauties (anonymous with plain backs, numbered left base of front) (1932)	Ha.627	13p	£1.75
B. Post-1940 Issue							
—		U	7	The Story in Red and White (1955) (75 × 66 mm.)		20p	£1.50

MARCUS & CO., Manchester

Illus. No.	Size	Printing	Number in set		Handbook ref.	Price per card	Complete set
Pre-1919 Issues							
	A	C	? 5	*Cricketers, "Marcus Handicap Cigarettes" (1895)	H.269/Ha.269	£120.00	—
	A	C	25	*Footballers and Club Colours (1896)	H.239/Ha.239	£60.00	—

T. W. MARKHAM, Bridgwater

Illus. No.	Size	Printing	Number in set		Handbook ref.	Price per card	Complete set
Pre-1919 Issue							
—		BW	? 14	Somerset Views and scenes (68 × 42 mm.)		—	—

MARSUMA LTD., Congleton

Illus. No.	Size	Printing	Number in set		Handbook ref.	Price per card	Complete set
Pre-1919 Issue							
205	A	BW	50	*Famous Golfers & Their Strokes		£3.50	£175.00

MARTINS LTD., London

Illus. No.	Size	Printing	Number in set		Handbook ref.	Price per card	Complete set
Pre-1919 Issues							
	A	C	1	"Arf a 'Mo Kaiser!"		—	£17.50
		U	? 4	Carlyle Series—folding card (39 × 84 mm.)	H.270/Ha.270	£75.00	—
	D	U	25	*V.C. Heroes		£7.00	£175.00

R. MASON & CO., London

Illus. No.	Size	Printing	Number in set		Handbook ref.	Price per card	Complete set
Pre-1919 Issues							
	C	C	30	*Colonial Troops	H.40	£32.00	—
	D2	C	40	*Naval and Military Phrases	H.14	£16.00	—

JUSTUS VAN MAURIK

MAY QUEEN CIGARETTES

Post 1940 Issue						
—		C	12	Interesting Pictures (68 × 48 mm.)..........	80p	£10.00

MENTORS LTD., London

Pre-1919 Issue						
—		C	32	Views of Ireland (42 × 67 mm.).............. H.271	£4.00	—

J. MILLHOFF & CO. LTD., London

Illus. No.	Size	Printing	No.	Title	Handbook ref.	Price per card	Complete set
A. Pre-1919 Issue							
—		BW	? 2	*Theatre Advertisement Cards...............	H.272	—	—
B. Post-1920 Issues							
		CP		Antique Pottery (1927):—			
	A2		54	A. Small size....................		50p	£27.00
619	—		56	B. Medium size (74 × 50 mm.)		60p	£34.00
		C		Art Treasures:—			
	D		30	A. Small size (1927)		34p	£10.00
	B		50	B. Large size (1926)		30p	£15.00
542	B	C	25	Art Treasures—"2nd Series of 50", Nd. 51–75 (1928).................		60p	£15.00
	B	C	25	England, historic & picturesque—"Series of 25" (1928).................		40p	£10.00
	B	C	25	England, historic & picturesque—"Second Series..." (1928)...............		26p	£6.50
196	A2	P	27	Famous Golfers (1928)		£1.50	£40.00
		P	27	Famous "Test" Cricketers (1928):—			
	A2			A. Small size....................		£1.50	£40.00
	—			B. Medium size (76 × 51 mm.)		£1.50	£40.00
544	—	C	25	Gallery Pictures (76 × 51 mm.)............		44p	£11.00
	A2	C	50	"Geographia" Map Series (sectional) (1931).		70p	£35.00
		CP		The Homeland Series (Dec. 1933):—	Ha.539		
	A2		54	A. Small size....................		13p	£5.50
	—		56	B. Medium size (76 × 51 mm.)		15p	£7.50
	A2	P	36	In the Public Eye (1930)		25p	£9.00
	D	C	25	Men of Genius (1924)		£1.80	£45.00
	B	C	25	Picturesque Old England (1931)............		30p	£7.50
	A2	P		Real Photographs:—	Ha.538		
			27	"A Series of 27"—A. Matt front		20p	£5.00
				B. Glossy front..........		15p	£4.00
			27	"2nd Series of 27"......................		20p	£5.00
			27	"3rd Series of 27"		20p	£5.00
			27	"4th Series of 27"		20p	£5.00
			27	"5th Series of 27"		20p	£5.00
			27	"6th Series of 27"		30p	£7.50
	C	C	25	Reproductions of Celebrated Oil Paintings (1928).................................	Ha.542	60p	£15.00
52	B	C	25	Roses (1927).............................		60p	£15.00
	A2	C	50	Things to Make—"De Reszke Cigarettes" (1935)...........................		13p	£3.00
	A2	C	50	What the Stars Say—"De Reszke Cigarettes" (1934)...........................		13p	£5.50
87	A2	P	36	Zoological Studies (1929).................		20p	£7.00
C. Miscellaneous							
—		U	74	"RILETTE" Miniature Pictures (60 × 45 mm.).................................	From	80p	—

MIRANDA LTD., London

Post-1920 Issues						
	A	C	20	Dogs....................................... H.211	£1.60	£32.00
	A	C	25	Sports & Pastimes—Series I H.225	£1.40	£35.00

STEPHEN MITCHELL & SON, Glasgow

A. Pre-1919 Issues						
	C	C	50	*Actors and Actresses—Selection from "FROGA B and C".................... H.20	£9.00	—
	C	U	25	*Actors and Actresses—"FROGA C" H.20	£9.00	—
	C	U	50	*Actors and Actresses—"FROGA D" H.20	£9.00	—
	C	U	26	*Actresses—"FROGA B".................... H.20	£9.00	—
	A	U	1	Advertisement Card "Maid of Honour".....		—
	A	C	50	Arms & Armour (Jul. 1916)............... H.273	£2.00	£100.00
	A	C	25	Army Ribbons & Buttons (Oct. 1916 & 1917)	£2.00	£50.00
	C	BW	25	*Boxer Rebellion—Sketches................. H.46	£11.00	—
	D1	BW	25	British Warships, 1—25 (Mar. 1915)	£2.80	£70.00

Illus. No.	Size	Print-ing	Number in set		Handbook ref.	Price per card	Complete set
341	D1	BW	25	British Warships, Second Series 26–50 (Sep. 1915)		£2.80	£70.00
	A	C	50	Interesting Buildings (1905)	H.70	£2.50	£125.00
	A	C	25	Medals (Jan. 1916)	H.71	£3.00	£75.00
	A	C	25	Money (1913)		£2.00	£50.00
	A	C	25	*Regimental Crests, Nicknames and Collar Badges (1900)	H.274	£6.00	£150.00
	A	C	25	Scottish Clan Series No. 1 (1903–4)	H.33	£5.00	£125.00
	A	C	25	Seals (1911)		£2.40	£60.00
261	A	C	25	Sports (1907)	H.275	£3.60	£90.00
572	A	C	25	Statues & Monuments (1914)		£2.40	£60.00

B. Post-1920 Issues

Illus. No.	Size	Print-ing	Number in set		Handbook ref.	Price per card	Complete set
	A	C	50	Air Raid Precautions (1938)	Ha.544	30p	£15.00
	A	C	25	Angling (1928) (see RB21/449)		60p	£15.00
	A	C	50	Clan Tartans—"A Series of 50" (1927)		50p	£25.00
	A	C	25	Clan Tartans—"2nd Series, 25" (1927)		14p	£3.50
514	A	C	25	Empire Exhibition, Scotland, 1938 (1938)		13p	£3.25
	A2	C	25	Famous Crosses (1923)		14p	£3.50
503	A	C	50	Famous Scots (1933)		13p	£5.50
	A	U	50	First Aid (1938)		13p	£6.00
	A	U	50	A Gallery of 1934 (1935)		20p	£10.00
497	A	U	50	A Gallery of 1935 (1936)		13p	£6.00
	A	C	50	Humorous Drawings (1924)	Ha.590	70p	£35.00
	A	C	40	London Ceremonials (1928) (RB21/462)		40p	£15.00
	A	C	30	A Model Army (cut-outs) (1932)		20p	£6.00
259	A	C	25	Old Sporting Prints (1930)	Ha.563	14p	£3.50
	A	U	50	Our Empire (Feb. 1937)	Ha.522	13p	£3.00
383	A	C	70	River & Coastal Steamers (1925)		£1.00	£70.00
	A	C		A Road Map of Scotland (1933):—			
			50	A. Small numerals		80p	£40.00
			50	B. Large numerals in circles		80p	£40.00
			50	C. Overprinted in red		£1.20	£60.00
			1	D. Substitute Card		—	£1.00
	A	C	50	Scotland's Story (1929)		90p	£45.00
190	A	U	50	Scottish Footballers (1934)		20p	£10.00
163	A	U	50	Scottish Football Snaps (1935)		20p	£10.00
426	A	C	25	Stars of Screen & History (1939)		14p	£3.50
	—	C	25	Village Models Series (Apr. 1925):—	Ha.591		
	A			A. Small size		60p	£15.00
	—			B. Medium size (68 × 62 mm.)		90p	£22.50
	—	C	25	Village Models Series—"Second" (May 1925):—			
	A			A. Small size		80p	£20.00
	—			B. Medium size, 68 × 62 mm.		90p	£22.50
690 etc.	A	U	50	Wonderful Century (Oct. 1937)		13p	£3.75
	A	U	50	The World of Tomorrow (Dec. 1936) (see RB21/315)		13p	£6.50

MOORGATE TOBACCO CO., London ─────────────

Post-1940 Issue

Illus. No.	Size	Print-ing	Number in set		Handbook ref.	Price per card	Complete set
491	—	BW	30	The New Elizabethan Age (20 small, 10 large) (1953)			
				A. Matt Front		90p	—
				B. Varnished Front		90p	—

B. MORRIS & SONS LTD., London ─────────────

A. Pre-1919 Issues

Illus. No.	Size	Print-ing	Number in set		Handbook ref.	Price per card	Complete set
	—	BW	30	*Actresses (1898) (41 × 68 mm.)	H.276	90p	£27.00
	C	U	26	*Actresses—"FROGA A"	H.20	£10.00	—
	—	C	? 4	*Actresses—selection from "FROGA B"—"Morris's High Class Cigarettes" on front	H.20	—	—
	A1	P	1	*Advertisement Card (Soldier & Girl) collotype, chocolate brown		—	—
	A	U	21	*Beauties—"MOM"	H.277/Ha.277	£10.00	—
	A	C	50	*Beauties—"CHOAB"	H.21/Ha.21	£12.50	—
	A	U	? 17	*Beauties—Collotype	H.278/Ha.278	£75.00	—
	A	C	20	Boer War, 1900 (V.C. Heroes)	H.279	£14.00	—
	A	BW	25	*Boer War Celebrities—"PAM"	H.140	£15.00	—
	A	C	30	*General Interest—composite series, six cards each entitled:—	H.280		
				i. Agriculture in the Orient		£4.00	£24.00
				ii. Architectural Monuments		£4.00	£24.00
				iii. The Ice Breaker		£4.00	£24.00
				iv. Schools in Foreign Countries		£4.00	£24.00
				v. Strange Vessels		£4.00	£24.00
	D	BW	20	London Views	H.34	£11.00	—
	A	C	25	Marvels of the Universe Series	H.281	£2.00	£50.00
	D	C	50	National & Colonial Arms (1917)		£3.50	£175.00
	C	U	25	War Celebrities (1915)		£3.00	£75.00
	D	C	25	War Pictures	H.51	£3.00	£75.00

B. Post-1920 Issues

Illus. No.	Size	Print-ing	Number in set		Handbook ref.	Price per card	Complete set
83	A1	C	50	Animals at the Zoo (1924):—	Ha.520		
				A. Back in blue		20p	£10.00
				B. Back in grey		13p	£6.50
	A1	C	35	At the London Zoo Aquarium (1928)		13p	£2.75

B. MORRIS & SONS LTD. *(continued)*

Illus. No.	Size	Printing	Number in set		Handbook ref.	Price per card	Complete set
	A1	BW	25	Australian Cricketers (1925)		60p	£15.00
446	A2	C	25	Captain Blood (1937)		15p	£3.75
	D	U	50	Film Star Series (1923)		80p	£40.00
201	D	U	25	Golf Strokes Series (1923) (see RB21/309) ...		40p	£10.00
	A1	—	12	Horoscopes (wording only) (1936):—			
				A. White card		50p	—
				B. Cream card		15p	£1.75
	A2	C	25	How Films are Made (1934):—			
				A. White card		13p	£2.75
				B. Cream Card		13p	£3.00
	A1	BW	50	How to Sketch (1929)		20p	£10.00
	A1	C	25	Measurement of Time (1924)		13p	£3.00
	D	U	25	Motor Series (Motor parts) (Oct. 1922).....		80p	£20.00
	A1	C	25	The Queen's Dolls' House (1925).		60p	£15.00
	D	U	25	Racing Greyhounds—"Issued by Forecasta" (1939)		13p	£1.75
	A1	BW	24	Shadowgraphs (1925)		60p	£15.00
	A1	C	13	Treasure Island (1924)...................		40p	£5.00
	A1	C	50	Victory Signs (1928).....................		13p	£5.00
	A	C	25	Wax Art Series (1931)		13p	£2.75
97	A	C	25	Whipsnade Zoo (1932)		13p	£3.25
	D	C	25	Wireless Series (1923)		90p	£22.50

C. Silks

					Handbook ref.	Price per card	Complete set
	—	C	? 24	Battleship Crests (70 × 50 mm.) (paper-backed)	Ha.504–3	£8.00	—
	—	C		English Flowers (78 × 56 mm.) (paper-backed):—	Ha.505–4		
			25	A. Series of 25...........................		£1.80	£45.00
			50	B. Series of 50...........................		£2.50	—
	—	C	25	English & Foreign Birds (78 × 56 mm.) (paper-backed)	Ha.505–1	£1.40	£35.00
	—	C	25	*Regimental Colours IV (75 × 55 mm.) (un-backed and anonymous)...................	Ha.502–9	£1.20	£30.00

PHILIP MORRIS & CO. LTD., London

Post-1920 Issues

						Price per card	Complete set
	—	U	50	British Views:—			
	C			A. Small size...........................		£1.00	£50.00
	—			B. Large size (79 × 67 mm.)		£1.00	£50.00

P. MOUAT & CO., Newcastle-on-Tyne

Pre-1919 Issue

						Price per card	
	C	C	30	*Colonial Troops	H.40	£38.00	—

MOUSTAFA LTD., London

Post-1920 Issues

					Handbook ref.	Price per card	Complete set
	D2	CP	50	Camera Studies (1923–4):—			
				A. Front with number and caption, back in black		80p	—
				*B. Front without letterpress, plain back		80p	—
	D2	C	25	Cinema Stars—Set 8 (1924)................	Ha.515–8	80p	£20.00
	A2	C	40	Leo Chambers Dogs Heads (1924)		60p	£24.00
	D2	C	25	Pictures of World Interest (1923)		90p	—
	A2	P	25	Real Photos (Views)......................		13p	£2.25

B. MURATTI SONS & CO. LTD., Manchester and London

A. Pre-1919 Issues

					Handbook ref.	Price per card	Complete set
	EL	U	? 9	*Actresses, cabinet size, collotype	H.282/Ha.282	£90.00	—
	C	C	26	*Actresses—"FROGA A".	H.20		
				A. "To the Cigarette Connoisseur" back ..		£8.00	—
				B. "Muratti's Zinnia Cigarettes" back		£15.00	—
	EL	C		*Actresses and Beauties—Green Corinthian column, framework—"Neb-Ka" vertical backs:—			
			? 7	Actresses—selection from "FROGA C".....	H.20	£110.00	—
			? 3	Beauties—selection from "MOM"	H.277	£110.00	—
	EL	C		*Actresses and Beauties—brown and yellow ornamental framework:—			
				I. "Neb-Ka" horizontal backs—			
			? 16	i. Actresses—selection from "FROGA A"......................	H.20	£110.00	—
			? 19	ii. Beauties—selection from "CHOAB"	H.21	£110.00	—
			? 6	II. Rubber stamped back. Beauties—selection from "CHOAB"	H.21	£110.00	—
			? 10	III. Plain back—Beauties—selection from CHAOB".	H.21	£110.00	—
	EL	C		*Advertisement Cards, Globe design back:—	H.283/Ha.283		
			? 5	i. Brown borders to front		£135.00	—
			? 12	ii. White borders to front................		£135.00	—

B. MURATTI SONS & CO. LTD. *(continued)*

Illus. No.	Size	Print-ing	Number in set		Handbook ref.	Price per card	Complete set
463	C	C	50	*Beauties—"CHOAB" (Zinnia back)	H.21		—
				A. Black printing on back		£13.00	
				B. Olive green printing on back		£25.00	
—		C	? 41	*Beautiful Women, Globe design back (54 × 75 mm.)................................	H.284	£18.00	—
—		BW	20	*Boer War Generals "CLAM" (35 × 61 mm.).	H.61	£8.00	—
—		C	15	*Caricatures (42 × 62 mm.):—	H.285	—	£120.00
				A. "Sole Manufacturers of ..." brown back		£8.00	
				B. "Muratti's Zinnia Cigarettes" brown back...........................		£9.00	
				C. "Muratti's Zinnia Cigarettes" black back...........................		£8.00	
				D. "Muratti's Vassos Cigarettes" (not seen)............................		—	
				E. As D, but "Vassos" blocked out, brown back...........................		£20.00	
	—	C	35	Crowned Heads (53 × 83 mm.)..............		£5.00	—
320	C	C	52	*Japanese Series, Playing Card inset (? 1904)..		£5.00	£260.00
				Plain back		£6.00	—
	—	P		Midget Post Card Series:—	H.286/Ha.286		
			? 12	I. Matt front (90 × 70 mm.) — Miscellaneous subjects......................		£8.00	
				II. Glossy front (85 × 65 mm.):—			
			? 53	i. Named—English Views...........		—	
			? 6	ii. Named — Miscellaneous subjects...		£7.00	
			? —	iii. Unnamed — Miscellaneous subjects		£7.00	
—		P	? 36	"Queens" Post Card Series:—(90 × 70 mm.) .	H.287		
				A. Front in black/sepia		£14.00	
				B. Front in reddish-brown..............			
	A1	BW	19	*Russo-Japanese Series (1904)	H.184	£7.00	£135.00
	A1	C	25	*Star Girls.................................	H.30	—	
	A	U	? 47	*Views of Jersey:—	H.288/Ha.288		
				A. Plain back		£8.00	
				B. "Opera House, Jersey" back.........		£14.00	
	A	U	24	*War Series—"MURATTI I", white card (1916)................................	H.289	£5.00	£125.00
	A	U	40	*War Series—"MURATTI II", toned card (1917/18) Nos. 1–25 and alternative cards)	H.290/Ha.290	£7.00	

B. *Post-1920 Issues*

	A2	P	24	Australian Race Horses (export)............		16p	£4.00

C. *Silks.* For summary of paper-backed issues, see Ha.497.

—		C		*Flags—Set 2 (70 × 52 mm.) (unbacked and anonymous):—	Ha.501–2		
			?	A. Numbered...........................		£2.00	—
				B. Unnumbered:—			
			? 23	1. Caption in red.....................		£6.00	—
			? 24	2. Caption in myrtle-green.............		£3.50	—
			? 18	3. Caption in bright green		£3.50	—
			? 17	4. Caption in blue....................		£6.00	—
			? 2	5. Caption in black...................		£7.00	—
—		C		*Flags—Set 3 (70 × 52 mm.) (paper-backed):—	Ha.501–3		
			25	1st Series—Series C, Nd. 20–44		£2.00	—
			25	2nd Series:			
				Series A, Nd. 26–50...................		£2.00	
				Series E, Nd. 48–72, paper backing in grey..................................		£1.75	
				Series E, Nd. 48–72, paper backing in green		£1.75	
—		C		*Flags—Set 8 (paper backed):—	Ha.501–8		
			3	Series A, Nd. 1–3 (89 × 115 mm.)		£6.00	—
			1	Series B, Nd. 19 (70 × 76 mm.)...........		—	—
			18	Series C, Nd. 1–18 (89 × 115 mm.)		£3.00	—
			3	Series D, Nd. 45–47 (89 × 115 mm.)		£4.00	—
			6	Series F, Nd. 73–78 (89 × 115 mm.)		£4.00	—
—		C	18	*Great War Leaders—Series P (89 × 115 mm.) (paper backed)..........................	Ha.504–6	£6.00	—
—		C		*Regimental Badges I (paper backed):—	Ha.502–1		
			25	Series A, Nd. 1–25 (70 × 52 mm.)		£2.25	—
			48	Series B, Nd. 1–48 (76 × 70 mm.).........		£4.00	—
			15	Series B, Nd. 4–18 (76 × 70 mm.).........		£3.25	—
			16	Series G, Nd. 79–94 (76 × 70 mm.)		£5.00	—
—		C	25	*Regimental Colours I—Series CB (76 × 70 mm.) (paper backed)...................	Ha.502–6	£4.00	—
—		C	72	*Regimental Colours V—Series RB (70 × 52 mm.) (paper backed)....................	Ha.502–10	£3.00	—

D. *Canvases.* Unbacked canvases. The material is not strictly canvas, but a linen fabric glazed to give the appearance of canvas.

—		C	40	Canvas Masterpieces—Series M (71 × 60 mm.):—			
				A. Shaded back design, globe 12 mm. diam.		£4.00	
				B. Unshaded back design, globe 6 mm. diam..................................		£1.50	£60.00
—		C	? 16	Canvas Masterpieces—Series P (114 × 90 mm.)...................................		£5.00	—

Illus. No.	Size	Printing	Number in set		Handbook ref.	Price per card	Complete set
A. Pre-1919 Issues							
	A	BW	20	*Actresses—"BLARM":—	H.23		
				A. "Pineapple Cigarettes" back...........		£18.00	—
				B. "Special Crown Cigarettes" back......		£32.00	—
	C	C	? 14	Chess & Draughts Problems—Series F (1912)	H.291	£18.00	—
	A	BW	52	*Cricketers and Footballers—Series H:—	H.292/Ha.292		
				20 Cricketers, A. Thick card................		£13.00	—
				B. Thin card.................		£14.00	—
				C. Brown Printing...........		£15.00	—
				32 Footballers, A. Thick card...............		£11.00	—
				B. Thin card...............		£10.00	—
177	—	C	? 17	Football Flags (Shaped) (60 × 32 mm.)			
				A. Maple Cigarettes.....................		£22.00	—
				B. Murray's Cigarettes..................		£22.00	—
	C	C	25	*Football Rules:—			
				1–12 Rugby Football.....................		£12.00	—
				13–25 Association Football................		£12.00	—
	A	BW	104	*Footballers—Series J........................	H.293	£5.50	—
	C	U	25	*Irish Scenery (1905) Nd. 101–125:—			
				A. "Hall Mark Cigarettes"..............		£10.00	—
				B. "Pine Apple Cigarettes"..............		£10.00	—
				C. "Special Crown Cigarettes"...........		£7.00	—
				D. "Straight Cut Cigarettes"..............		£8.00	—
				E. "Yachtsman Cigarettes"..............		£7.00	—
	C	BW	25	Polo Pictures—E Series (1911).............	H.294	£7.00	£175.00
	—	U		Prominent Politicians—B Series (1909) (41 × 70 mm.):—	H.295/Ha.295		
			? 16	A. Without "... in two strengths" in centre of back.............................		£11.00	—
			50	B. With "... in two strengths" in centre of back:.....................		£1.25	£62.50
	C	U	25	Reproduction of Famous Works of Art—D Series (1910)........................	H.296	£7.00	£175.00
	C	U	25	Reproductions of High Class Works of Art—C Series (1910)........................	H.297	£7.00	£175.00
	A1	C	35	*War Series—Series K........................	H.298/Ha.298	£10.00	—
	C2	U	25	*War Series—Series L, Nd. 100–124:—			
				A. Sepia.............................		£1.80	£45.00
				B. Grey-brown.......................		£2.00	—
				C. Purple-brown......................		£2.20	—
B. Post-1920 Issues							
	D1	P	22	Bathing Beauties (1929)....................		£1.25	—
425	A1	BW	40	Bathing Belles............................	Ha.592	13p	£1.75
	D1	P	22	Cinema Scenes (1929).....................		£1.40	—
	A1	BW	25	Crossword Puzzles........................		—	—
	D1	P	26	Dancers (1929)............................		£1.25	—
	D	P		Dancing Girls (1929):—			
			25	A. "Belfast–Ireland" at base..............		£1.20	£30.00
			25	B. "London & Belfast" at base...........		70p	£17.50
			26	C. Inscribed "Series of 26"...............		£1.20	—
	A	C	20	Holidays by the L.M.S. (1927)..............	Ha.593	£3.00	£60.00
	A1	C	20	Inventors Series (1924).....................	H.213	£1.50	£30.00
633	—	C	50	Puzzle Series (1925):—			
	A1			A. With coupon attached at top..........		£4.00	—
	—			B. Without coupon......................		90p	—
	D2	C	50	Stage and Film Stars—"Erinmore Cigarettes" (see RB21/200/172)..........		70p	£35.00
	A1	BW	25	Steam Ships (1939)........................		18p	£4.50
	A1	C	50	The Story of Ships (1940)..................		13p	£1.75
350	A2	C	25	Types of Aeroplanes (1929)................		15p	£3.75
	C	C	20	Types of Dogs (1924):—	Ha.211		
				A. Normal back......................		90p	£18.00
				B. Normal back, with firm's name rubber stamped in red		90p	£18.00
C. Silks							
	—	C	? 15	*Flags, small (70 × 42 mm.)—"Polo Mild Cigarettes" (plain paper backing).........	Ha.498–1	£7.00	—
	—	C	? 3	*Flags and Arms, large (102 × 71 mm.)—"Polo Mild Cigarettes" (plain paper backing)................................	Ha.498–2	—	—
	—	C	? 31	*Orders of Chivalry II, "Series M" (70 × 42 mm.) (paper-backed). Nd. 35–65..	Ha.504–15	£6.00	—
	—	C	? 22	*Regimental Badges (70 × 42 mm.)—"Polo Mild Cigarettes" (plain paper backing)....	Ha.498–3	£7.00	—

N. J. NATHAN, London

Pre-1919 Issue							
	D	C	40	Comical Military & Naval Pictures..........	H.14	£30.00	—

JAMES NELSON, London

Pre-1919 Issue							
	A	P	? 18	*Beauties—"FENA"........................	H.148/Ha.148	—	—

THE NEW MOSLEM CIGARETTE CO., London

Pre-1919 Issue

	D	C	30	*Proverbs....................................	H.15	£38.00	—

E. J. NEWBEGIN, Sunderland

Pre-1919 Issues

	—	P	? 46	*Actors and Actresses, Etc. (39 × 60 mm.)	H.299/Ha.299	£12.00	—
	A	BW	? 10	*Actresses—"HAGG A"....................	Ha.24	—	—
	D	C	? 4	Advertisement Cards......................		—	—
	A	BW	20	Cricketers Series	H.29	£40.00	—
	A	BW	19	*Russo-Japanese Series....................		—	—
	D	C	? 6	Well-Known Proverbs.....................	H.235	£50.00	—
	D	C	? 18	Well-Known Songs	H.300	£50.00	—

W. H. NEWMAN, Birmingham

Pre-1919 Issues

	C	C	18	Motor Cycle Series.......................	Ha.469	—	—

THOS. NICHOLLS & CO., Chester

Pre-1919 Issue

300	A	C	50	Orders of Chivalry	H.301	£3.50	£175.00

THE NILMA TOBACCO COY., London

Pre-1919 Issues

				(All Cards marked "Series of 70")			
	A	C	40	*Home and Colonial Regiments:—	H.69		—
				20. Caption in blue		£50.00	
				20. Caption in brown		£50.00	—
	D	C	30	*Proverbs.................................	H.15	£50.00	—

M. E. NOTARAS LTD., London

Post-1920 Issues

	A2	P	36	National Types of Beauty	Ha.558	25p	£9.00
	—	U	24	*Views of China (68 × 43 mm.)..............		13p	£1.75

OGDENS LTD., Liverpool

A. Pre-1919 Issues

				Home Issues *(excluding "Guinea Gold" and "Tabs", but including some early issues abroad)*.			
	C	C	? 24	*Actresses—coloured, "Ogden's Cigarettes contain no glycerine" back:—	H.302/Ha.302		
				A. Titled in black........................		£36.00	—
				B. Titled in brown		£36.00	—
	D2	U	? 1	*Actresses—green, green borders	H.303	—	—
	D1	U	50	*Actresses—green photogravure.............	H.304	£4.00	—
	D	P	?533	*Actresses—"Ogden's Cigarettes" at foot	H.305/Ha.305	£2.00	—
	D	P		*Actresses and Beauties—collotype:—	H.306		
			? 75	i. named.			
				A. *Plain back*		—	—
				B. "Midnight Flake" back...............		£14.00	—
			? 19	ii. unnamed.			
				A. *Plain back*		—	—
				B. "Midnight Flake back.................			
				(blue)		£16.00	—
				(red)		—	—
	D	P		*Actresses and Beauties—collotype, "Ogden's Cigarettes" back:—	H.306		
			? 39	i. named............................		£22.00	—
			? 32	ii. unnamed		£22.00	—
	A	P		*Actresses and Beauties—woodbury-type:—	H.307/Ha.307		
			?184	i. named............................		£22.00	—
			? 9	ii. unnamed		£22.00	—
	—	C	192	Army Crests and Mottoes (1902) (39 × 59 mm.)......................................		£1.60	—
475	A	C	? 29	*Beauties—"BOCCA"	H.39/Ha.39	£12.00	—
	—	C	50	*Beauties—"CHOAB":—	H.21		
				1–25 (size 65 × 36 mm.)..................		£15.00	—
				26–50 (size 67 × 37 mm.).................		£15.00	—
	A	C	26	*Beauties—"HOL":—	H.192		
				A. "Guinea Gold" red rubber stamp back .		—	—
				B. Blue Castle design back...............		£7.00	£180.00
	A2	C	52	*Beauties — "Playing Card" series:—	H.308		
				A. 52 with playing card inset		£15.00	—
				B. 26 without playing card inset...........		£17.00	—
290	A2	C	52	*Beauties and Military—P.C. inset		£22.00	—

Illus. No.	Size	Print-ing	Number in set		Handbook ref.	Price per card	Complete set
—		P	50	Beauty Series, numbered, "St. Julien Tobacco" (36 × 54 mm.).		£1.60	£80.00
	D	P	? 21	Beauty Series, unnumbered, issued Australia	H.309/Ha.309	£20.00	—
30	A	C	50	Birds Eggs (Dec. 1904):—		—	£60.00
				A. White back		£1.40	£70.00
				B. Toned back		£1.20	£60.00
	D	P	?111	*Boer War and General Interest—"Ogden's Cigarettes" at foot	H.310/Ha.310	£1.75	—
212	A	C	50	Boxers (Oct. 1915)		£2.80	£140.00
	A	C	25	Boxing (Jul. 1914)	H.311	£1.80	£40.00
—		C	? 4	*Boxing Girls (165 × 94 mm.)		—	—
	A	C	50	Boy Scouts (Jan. 1911):—	H.62		
				A. Blue back		£1.30	£65.00
				B. Green back		£1.60	£80.00
	A	C	50	Boy Scouts, 2nd Series (Feb. 1912):—	H.62		
				A. Blue back		£1.30	£65.00
				B. Green back		£1.60	£80.00
	A	C	50	Boy Scouts, 3rd Series (Oct. 1912):—	H.62		
				A. Blue back		£1.30	£65.00
				B. Green back		£1.60	£80.00
	A	C	50	Boy Scouts, 4th Series, green back (Nov. 1913)		£1.60	£80.00
	A	C	25	Boy Scouts, 5th Series, green back (Sep. 1914)		£1.60	£40.00
33	A	C	50	British Birds:—	H.229		
				A. White back (May 1905)		£1.20	£60.00
				B. Toned back (1906)		£1.00	£50.00
	A	C	50	British Birds, Second Series (Jan. 1908)		£1.20	£60.00
	A	C	50	British Costumes from 100 B.C. to 1904 (Apr. 1905)	H.312	£2.20	£110.00
268	A	C	50	Club Badges (Jul. 1914)		£2.50	£125.00
—		C	? 21	*Comic Pictures (1890–95) (size varies)	H.313	£150.00	—
	A2	C	12	*Cricket and Football Terms—Women, "Ogden's Gold Medal Cigarettes" back	H.314/Ha.314	£110.00	—
	A	U	? 32	*Cricketers and Sportsmen	H.315/Ha.315	£16.00	—
474	A	U	28	*Dominoes—Actresses "FROGA A" back:—	H.20		
				A. Mitred corners (7 backs)		£10.00	—
				B. Unmitred corners (7 backs)		£10.00	—
	A	U	28	*Dominoes—Beauties "MOM" back	H.277	£11.00	—
	A2	BW	55	*Dominoes—black back (Apr. 1909)		£1.00	£55.00
184	A	C	50	Famous Footballers (Jan. 1908)		£1.50	£75.00
384	A	C	50	Flags & Funnels of Leading Steamship Lines (Feb. 1906)	H.67	£1.80	£90.00
—		C	43	*Football Club Badges (shaped for buttonhole)	H.316	£3.00	—
189	A	C	51	Football Club Colours (May 1906):—	H.68		
				Nos. 1–50		£1.50	£75.00
				No. 51		—	£4.00
21	A	C	50	Fowls, Pigeons & Dogs (May 1904)	H.64	£1.20	£60.00
—		C	1	*History of the Union Jack (threefold card) (1901) (51 × 37 mm. closed)		—	£110.00
289	A	BW	50	Infantry Training (Apr. 1915)	H.317	£1.60	£80.00
	A	C	? 1	Lady Cricket and Football Team	H.318	—	—
	K2	C	52	*Miniature Playing Cards — Actresses & Beauties Back:	H.319/Ha.319		
				I. Unnamed, no numeral (76 backs known)		£1.60	—
				II. Unnamed, "numeral 40" (26 backs known)		£1.80	—
				III. Named, "numeral 46" (26 backs known)	H.20	£2.00	—
				IV. Named, no numeral (26 backs known)	H.20	£1.80	—
	K2	C	52	*Miniature Playing Cards, blue Tabs "Shield and Flower" design back (Apr. 1909)		£1.40	£70.00
	K2	C	52	*Miniature Playing Cards, yellow "Coolie Plug" design back:—			
				A. Yellow back (May 1904)		£1.40	£70.00
				B. Yellow back with white border (Nov. 1904)		£1.40	£70.00
	A	BW	50	Modern War Weapons (Nov. 1915):—	H.320		
				A. Original numbering		£1.60	£80.00
				B. Numbering re-arranged		£4.00	—
	A	C	50	Orders of Chivalry (Jan. 1907)		£1.80	£90.00
	A	C	25	Owners, Racing Colours & Jockeys (May 1914)		£1.80	£45.00
128	A	C	50	Owners, Racing Colours & Jockeys (Jan. 1906)		£1.50	£75.00
	A	C	25	Poultry (Aug. 1915):—			
				A. "Ogden's Cigarettes" on front		£1.60	£40.00
				B. Without "Ogden's Cigarettes" on front.		£1.60	£40.00
	A	C	25	Poultry, 2nd Series, as "B" above (Apr. 1916)		£1.60	£40.00
213	A	C	25	Pugilists & Wrestlers, Nd. 1–25 (Oct. 1908)		£2.00	£50.00
	A	C	25	Pugilists & Wrestlers, Nd. 26–50:—			
				A. White back (Aug. 1909)		£2.20	£55.00
				B. Toned back (Oct. 1908)		£2.00	£50.00
	A	C	25	Pugilists & Wrestlers, 2nd Series, Nd. 51–75 (Aug. 1909)		£2.00	£50.00
135	A	C	50	Racehorses (Sep. 1907)		£1.10	£55.00
651 etc.	A	C	25	Records of the World (Jan. 1908)		£1.80	£45.00
	A	C	50	Royal Mail (Sep. 1909)	H.82	£2.00	£100.00
	A	C	50	Sectional Cycling Map (Oct. 1910)	H.74	£2.00	£100.00

OGDENS LTD. *(continued)*

Illus. No.	Size	Print-ing	Number in set		Handbook ref.	Price per card	Complete set
540	A	C	50	*Shakespeare Series:—	H.321		
				A. Unnumbered		£11.00	£550.00
				B. Numbered		£11.00	£550.00
	A	C	50	Soldiers of the King (Oct. 1909):			
				A. Grey printing on front		£3.00	£150.00
				B. Brown printing on front		£3.50	—
	D	C	25	*Swiss Views, Nd. 1–25		£2.00	£50.00
	D	C	25	*Swiss Views, Nd. 26–50		£3.00	£75.00
	D	C	48	Victoria Cross Heroes (1901–02)	H.322/Ha.322	£9.00	£450.00

B. "Guinea Gold" Series (The S and X numbers represent the reference numbers quoted in Cartophilic Society Booklet No. 24).

	Size	Print-ing	Number in set			Price per card	Complete set
	D	P	1148	1–1148 Series:—			
				Nos. 1–200		35p	£70.00
				Nos. 201–500		60p	—
				Nos. 501–900, excl. 523 & 765		60p	—
				Nos. 901–1000, excl. 940, 943, 947 and 1000		75p	—
				Nos. 1001–1148, excl. 1003, 1006–8, 1024, 1030. 1033, 1034, 1037, 1040, 1042, 1048, 1066, 1081, 1082, 1088		£1.00	—
				Scarce Nos:—523, 940, 943, 947, 1000, 1003, 1007, 1008, 1024, 1030, 1033, 1034, 1037, 1040, 1042, 1048, 1066, 1088		£16.00	—
				Very scarce Nos. 765, 1006, 1081, 1082		—	—
	D	CP	?	Selected numbers from 1–1148 series		£1.00	—
	D	P		400 New Series I		70p	£280.00
	D	P		400 New Series B		70p	£280.00
	D	P		300 New Series C		70p	£210.00
	D	P	312	Set 73S Base B Actresses		90p	—
				Set 75S Base D:—			
	D	P	?320	List DA—White Panel Group		50p	—
	D	P	? 57	List DB—The Denumbered Group		80p	—
	D	P	? 62	List DC—The Political Group		60p	—
	D	P	?185	List DD—Boer War Etc.		50p	—
	D	P	? 46	List DE—Pantomime & Theatre Group		£1.00	—
	D	P	?374	List DF—Actors & Actresses		60p	—
	D	P	? 40	Set 76S Base E Actors & Actresses		90p	—
	D	P	? 58	Set 77S Base F Boer War Etc.		60p	—
				Set 78S Base I:—			
				List IA—The small Machette Group:—			
	D	P	83	I. Actors & Actresses		80p	—
	D	P	14	II. London Street Scenes		£1.00	—
	D	P	32	III. Turner Pictures		90p	—
	D	P	11	IV. Cricketers		£5.00	—
202	D	P	18	V. Golf		£4.00	—
	D	P	10	VI. Views & Scenes Abroad		80p	—
	D	P	30	VII. Miscellaneous		80p	—
	D	P	656	List IB—The Large Machette Group		50p	—
	D	P	5	List IC—The White Panel Group		—	—
	D	P	30	Set 79S Base J Actresses		£1.40	—
	D	P	237	Set 80S Base K Actors & Actresses		60p	—
	D	P	215	Set 81S Base L Actors & Actresses		60p	—
				Set 82S Base M:—			
	D	P	3	List Ma Royalty		70p	—
	D	P	77	List Mb Cricketers		£5.50	—
276	D	P	50	List Mc Cyclists		£2.20	—
	D	P	149	List Md Footballers		£2.70	—
	D	P	50	List Me Pantomime & Theatre Group		80p	—
	D	P	33	List Mf Footballers & Cyclists		£2.70	—
	D	P	27	List Mg Boer War & Miscellaneous		50p	—
				List Mh Actors and Actresses:—			
	D	P	60	a. Subjects with white framelines		75p	—
	D	P	33	b. Subjects without names or nicknames		75p	—
	D	P	2846	c. Other subjects		50p	—

Ba. Guinea Gold Series, Large & Medium

	Print-ing	Number in set			Price per card	Complete set
	P	63	Set 73X Actresses Base B		£6.00	—
	P	1	Set 74X Actress Base C		—	£8.00
	P	571	Set 75X Actors, Actresses, Boer War Etc. Base D		80p	—
	P	17	Set 78X Actresses Base I		£20.00	—
	P	403	Set 82X Actors, Actresses, Boer War Etc. Base M		£1.00	—

C. "Tabs" Series

(*Numbers in parentheses following word "item" represent the reference numbers quoted in Cartophilic Society Booklet No. 15. The listing includes both home and overseas "Tabs" issues.*)

	Size	Print-ing	Number in set		Price per card	Complete set
	D	BW	?136	*Actresses (item 7)	£1.20	—
	D	BW	?199	*Actresses and Foreign Views (item 14)	£1.00	—
	D	BW	?330	*Composite Tabs Series, with "Labour Clause" (item 63):—		
				1. General de Wet	—	£0.75
				1. General Interest	—	£2.00
216				17. Heroes of the Ring	£1.60	—
				1. H.M. The Queen	—	£1.00
				2. H.R.H. the Prince of Wales	90p	£1.80
				14. Imperial Interest	60p	£8.50
				105. Imperial and International Interest	50p	—
				3. International Interest	65p	£2.00
				14. International Interest or a Prominent British Officer	60p	£8.50

Illus. No.	Size	Print-ing	Number in set		Handbook ref.	Price per card	Complete set
245				22. Leading Athletes		£1.00	—
				15. Leading Favourites of the Turf.........		£1.00	—
				54. Leading Generals at the War..........		50p	£27.00
				2. Members of Parliament................		80p	£1.60
				11. Notable Coursing Dogs		£1.00	£11.00
				12. Our Leading Cricketers...............		£5.00	—
				17. Our Leading Footballers..............		£1.20	£20.00
				37. Prominent British Officers		40p	£15.00
				1. The Yacht "Columbia"................		—	£1.00
				1. The Yacht "Shamrock"		—	£1.00
	D	BW	? 10	*Composite Tabs Series, without "Labour Clause" (item 64):—			
				8. General Interest........................		£1.30	—
				2. Leading Artistes of the Day............		—	—
	D	BW	? 65	*Composite Tabs Series, Sydney issue (item 65):—			
				15. English Cricketer Series		£14.00	—
				1. Christian de Wet		—	—
				1. Corporal G. E. Nurse, V.C.		—	—
				13. Imperial or International Interest		—	—
				3. International Interest..................		—	—
				1. Lady Sarah Wilson....................		—	—
				25. Leading Generals of the War...........		—	—
				6. Prominent British Officers		—	—
	D	BW	150	General Interest, Series "A"		40p	£60.00
	D	BW	200	General Interest, Series "B"		35p	£70.00
	D	BW	470	General Interest, Series "C":—			
				C.1–200		35p	£70.00
				C.201–300		£1.00	—
				C.301–350		70p	£35.00
				No. Letter, Nd. 1–120		70p	£85.00
	D	BW	200	General Interest, Series "D"		35p	£70.00
	D	BW	120	General Interest, Series "E"		50p	£60.00
	D	BW	420	General Interest, Series "F":—			
				F.1–200		80p	—
				F.201–320		80p	—
				F.321–420		£1.00	—
	D	BW	?500	General Interest, Sydney issue:			
				Nd. 1–100 on front.....................		£1.50	—
				101–400 on back........................		£1.50	—
				Unnumbered, mostly similar numbered cards 101–200 (item 99-a)		£1.50	—
	D	BW	?196	*General Interest, unnumbered, similar style C.201–300 (item 95).....................		60p	—
	D	BW	100	*General Interest, unnumbered, similar style C.301–350 (item 96).....................		60p	£60.00
	D	BW	300	*General Interest, unnumbered, similar style (F.321–420) (item 97):—			
				A. 100 with full stop after caption		60p	—
				B. Without full stop after caption:—			
			79	I Stage Artistes....................		60p	£50.00
			21	II Cricketers		£5.00	—
			25	III Football.......................		£2.20	—
			15	IV Golf...........................		£4.50	—
			10	V Cyclists.........................		£2.20	—
			9	VI Fire Brigades		£2.75	—
			5	VII Aldershot Gymnasium...........		£1.20	£6.00
			36	VIII Miscellaneous		60p	—
	D	BW	? 26	*General Interest, "oblong" back (item 98)...		90p	—
	D	BW	? 75	*Leading Artistes of the Day, numbered 126–200, plain backs (item 109) (see H.1)..		80p	—
	D	BW	? 71	Leading Artistes of the Day with "Labour Clause" (item 110):—			
				A. Type-set back		60p	—
				B. Plain back		80p	—
	D	BW	? 22	Leading Artistes of the Day, without "Labour Clause" (item 111–1):—			
				A. With caption, type-set back............		80p	—
				B. With caption, plain back..............		80p	—
				C. Without caption, type-set back........		80p	—
	D	BW	? 73	Leading Artistes of the Day. without "Labour Clause" (item 111–2):—			
				A. Type-set back		£1.00	—
				B. Plain back		£1.00	—
	D	BW	25	Leading Generals at the War, with descriptive text (item 112):—			
				A. "Ogden's Cigarettes" back.............		80p	—
				B. "Ogden's Tab Cigarettes" back		70p	£17.50
	D	BW	? 47	Leading Generals at the War, without descriptive text (item 113):—			
				A. "Ogden's Tab Cigarettes" back (47 known)		60p	£30.00
				B. "Ogden's Lucky Star" back (25 known)		£2.00	—
	D	BW	50	*Stage Artistes and Celebrities (item 157).....		£1.00	—
D. Post-1920 Issues							
273	A	C	25	ABC of Sport (1927)		80p	£20.00
	A	C	50	Actors—Natural & Character Studies (1938)	Ha.571–1	13p	£3.75
	A	C	50	A.F.C. Nicknames (1933)...................	Ha.571–2	40p	£20.00

Illus. No.	Size	Print-ing	Number in set		Handbook ref.	Price per card	Complete set
	A	C	50	Air-Raid Precautions (1938)	Ha.544	16p	£8.00
	A	C	50	Applied Electricity (1928)		45p	£22.50
	A	U	36	Australian Test Cricketers, 1928–29 (see RB15/21)		£1.10	£40.00
240	A	C	50	Billiards, by Tom Newman (1928) (see RB21/215/33)		50p	£25.00
	A	C	50	Bird's Eggs (cut-outs) (1923)		35p	£17.50
	A	C	50	The Blue Riband of the Atlantic (1929)		90p	£45.00
	A	C	50	Boy Scouts (1929) (see RB21/215/46)		60p	£30.00
	A	C	50	British Birds (cut-outs) (1923) (see RB15/49)		35p	£17.50
14	A	C	50	British Birds & Their Eggs (1939)	Ha.571–3	22p	£11.00
	A	U	50	Broadcasting (1935)	Ha.571–4	20p	£10.00
	A	C	50	By the Roadside (1932)		32p	£16.00
	A	C	44	Captains of Association Football Clubs & Colours (1926)		70p	£30.00
573	A	U	50	Cathedrals & Abbeys (1936):—			
				A. Cream card		32p	£16.00
				B. White card		32p	£16.00
260	A	C	50	Champions of 1936 (1937)	Ha.571–5	13p	£6.00
	A	C	50	Children of All Nations (cut-outs) (see RB21/200/168)		35p	£17.50
	A	C	50	Colour in Nature (1932)		55p	£27.50
	A	C	50	Construction of Railway Trains (1930)		£1.10	£55.00
	A	C	50	Coronation Procession (sectional) (1937)	Ha.571–6	32p	£16.00
	A	U	50	Cricket, 1926		£1.00	£50.00
138	A	C	25	Derby Entrants, 1926 (see RB21/215/71)		70p	£17.50
141	A	C	50	Derby Entrants, 1928		50p	£25.00
142	A	U	50	Derby Entrants, 1929		80p	£40.00
109	A	C	50	Dogs (1936)	Ha.571–7	18p	£9.00
244	A	C	25	Famous Dirt-Track Riders (1929)		80p	£20.00
241	A	U	50	Famous Rugby Players (1926–27)		50p	£25.00
	A	C	50	Football Caricatures (1935)	Ha.571–8	22p	£11.00
	A	C	50	Football Club Captains (1935)	Ha.571–9	25p	£12.50
	A	C	50	Foreign Birds (1924) (see RB21/215/87)		36p	£18.00
	A	U	25	Greyhound Racing—"1st Series ..." (1927–28)		90p	£22.50
	A	U	25	Greyhound Racing—"2nd Series ..." (1928)		90p	£22.50
	A	C	50	How to Swim (1935)	Ha.571–10	13p	£3.50
	A	C	50	Jockeys, and Owners' Colours (1927)		40p	£20.00
	A	C	50	Jockeys, 1930		80p	£40.00
	A	C	50	Leaders of Men (1924–25) (see RB21/215/108)		80p	£40.00
756	A	C	25	Marvels of Motion (1928–29)		80p	£20.00
	A	C	50	Modern British Pottery (1925)		45p	£22.50
405, 680 etc.	A	C	50	Modern Railways (1936)	Ha.571–11	55p	£27.50
	A	C	25	Modes of Conveyance (1927) (see W/264)		80p	£20.00
	A	C	50	Motor Races (1931)		60p	£30.00
398	A	C	50	Ocean Greyhounds (1938)	Ha.571–12	16p	£8.00
	A	C	25	Optical Illusions (1923)	Ha.560	90p	£22.50
	A	C	25	Picturesque People of the Empire (1927) (see RB21/200/288)		40p	£10.00
	A	U	50	Picturesque Villages (1936)		35p	£17.50
	A	C	25	Poultry Alphabet (1924) (see RB15/135)		£1.00	£25.00
	A	C	25	Poultry Rearing & Management—"1st Series ..." (1922)		70p	£17.50
	A	C	25	Poultry Rearing & Management—"2nd Series ..." (1923)		70p	£17.50
152	A	U	50	Prominent Cricketers of 1938 (1938)	Ha.571–13	30p	£15.00
134	A	C	50	Prominent Racehorses of 1933 (1934)	Ha.571–14	22p	£11.00
211	A	U	50	Pugilists in Action (1928) (see RB17/156)		55p	£27.50
	A	C	50	Racing Pigeons (1931)		45p	£22.50
377	A	C	50	Sea Adventure (1939)	Ha.571–15	13p	£2.50
421	A	C	50	Shots from the Films (1936)	Ha.571–16	30p	£15.00
	A	U	25	Sights of London (1923)		80p	£20.00
388	A	C	50	Smugglers and Smuggling (1932–33)		36p	£18.00
	A	U	50	Steeplechase Celebrities (1931)		25p	£12.50
	A	C	50	Steeplechase Trainers, and Owners' Colours (1927)		50p	£25.00
	A	C	50	The Story of Sand (1934) (see RB15/160)		18p	£9.00
	A	C	50	Swimming, Diving and Life-Saving (1931)	Ha.523	25p	£12.50
	A	C	25	Trainers, and Owners' Colours—"1st Series ..." (1925)		60p	£15.00
	A	C	25	Trainers, and Owners' Colours—"2nd Series ..." (1926)		90p	£22.50
256	A	C	50	Trick Billiards (1934)	Ha.571–17	20p	£10.00
	A	C	50	Turf Personalities (1929)		45p	£22.50
	A	C	25	Whaling (1927) (see RB21/215/169)		50p	£12.50
	A	C	50	Yachts & Motor Boats (1930)		60p	£30.00
	A	C	50	Zoo Studies (1937)	Ha.571–18	17p	£8.50

OSBORNE TOBACCO CO. LTD., Portsmouth & London _____

Post-1940 Issues

	Size	Print-ing	Number in set			Price per card	Complete set
	A	U	50	Modern Aircraft (1953):—			
				A. Dark Blue back		07p	£1.25
				B. Light Blue back		07p	£3.00
				C. Brown back		07p	£2.25

W. T. OSBORNE & CO., London

Illus. No.	Size	Print-ing	Number in set		Handbook ref.	Price per card	Complete set
Pre-1919 Issue							
D	C		40	*Naval and Military Phrases	H.14	£12.00	—

J. A. PATTREIOUEX, Manchester

A. 1920's Photographic Series. Listed in order of letters and/or numbers quoted on cards. References after word "back" refer to the nine backs illustrated in Handbook Part II under Ha.595.

	Size	Printing	Number in set	Description	Handbook ref.	Price per card	Complete set
H2	P		50	*Animals and Scenes—Unnumbered ("Junior Member"). Back 4	Ha.595–1	55p	—
H2	P		50	Animals and Scenes, Nd. 1–50. Back 1		55p	—
H2	P		50	*Scenes, Nd. 201–250 ("Junior Member"). Back 4		50p	£25.00
C	P		96	Animals and Scenes, Nd. 250–345:—			
				A. Back in style 2 in (i) grey		60p	—
				(ii) brown		70p	—
				*B. "Junior Member" back 9		60p	—
C	P		96	Animals and Scenes, Nd. 346–441:—			
				A. Back 2		70p	—
				B. Back style 1 and back 3		60p	—
				*C. "Junior Member" back 9		60p	—
H	P		50	*Animal Studies, Nd. A42–A91 ("Junior Member"). Back 4		50p	—
H	P		50	*Animal Studies, Nd. A92–A141 ("Junior Member"). Back 4		70p	—
H	P		50	*Animal Studies, Nd. A151–A200 ("Junior Member"). Back 4		60p	—
C	P			*Natives and Scenes:—			
			36	A. "Series 1/36 B" on front, Nd. 1–36 ("Junior Member"). Back 9		50p	—
			96	B. "Series 1/96 B" on front, Nd. 1–96. Back 6		60p	—
C	P		96	*Foreign Scenes, Nd. 1/96C–96/96C. Back 6		50p	—
C	P		96	Cricketers, Nd. C1–C96, "Casket Cigarettes" on front:—			
				A. Back 5		£3.50	—
				*B. Plain back		£3.50	—
C	P		96	*Animals—"Series Nos. C.A.1 to 96". Back 7		50p	—
C	P		96	*Natives and Scenes:—			
				A. "C.B.1 to 96" on front. Back 7			
				1. Nd. 1–96		50p	—
				2. Nd. C.B.1–C.B.96		60p	—
				B. "J.S.1 to 96" on front. "Junior Member", back 9		60p	—
C	P		96	*Animals and Scenes—"CC1 to 96" on front. Back 7		50p	—
H2	P		50	*British Scenes—"Series C.M.1–50.A" on front. Back style 7		80p	—
H2	P		50	*Foreign Scenes:—			
				A. "Series C.M. 1/50 B" on front. Backstyle 7		80p	—
				B. "J.M. Series 1/50" on front. "Junior Member", back 9		60p	—
H2	P		50	*Foreign Scenes:—			
				A. "Series C.M. 101–150.S" on front. Back style 7		60p	—
				B. Nd. S.101–S.150 on front. Back 4		60p	—
C	P		96	*Foreign Scenes, Nd. 1/96D–96/96D. Back 6		80p	—
H2	P		50	*Foreign Scenes, Nd. 1/50E–50/50E. Back 6		50p	£25.00
H2	P		50	*Foreign Scenes, Nd. 1/50F–50/50F. Back 6		50p	—
C	P		96	Footballers, Nd. F.1–F.96. "Casket" and "Critic" back style 5		£1.25	—
C	P		96	Footballers, Nd. F.97–F.192. "Casket" and Critic" back style 5		£1.25	—
H	P		50	Football Teams, Nd. F.193–F.242. ("Casket" and "Critic")		£1.50	—
C	P		96	*Footballers—"Series F.A. 1/96" on front. Back 8		£1.25	—
C	P		96	*Footballers—"Series F.B. 1–96" on front. Back 8		£1.25	—
C	P		96	*Footballers—"Series F.C. 1/96" on front. Back 8.		£1.25	—
H2	P		50	*Scenes—"G. 1/50" on front. "Junior Member", back 9		80p	—
H2	P		50	*Scenes—"1/50. H" on front. "Junior Member", back 9		70p	—
H2	P		50	*Animals and Scenes, Nd. I.1–I.50. Back style 6		80p	—
H2	P		50	Famous Statues—"J.C.M. 1 to 50 C" on front. Back style 6		55p	—
H2	P		50	*Scenes, Nd. JCM 1/50D–JCM 50/50D—			
				A. Back style 6		50p	—

J. A. PATTRIEOUEX (continued)

Illus. No.	Size	Print-ing	Number in set		Handbook ref.	Price per card	Complete set
				B. Back style 9 ("Junior Member")		60p	—
	B1	P	30	Child Studies, Nd. J.M. No. 1–J.M. No. 30. "Junior Member", back style 9		90p	—
	B1	P	30	*Beauties, Nd. J.M.1–J.M.30. "Junior Member", back style 9		90p	—
	H2	P	50	*Foreign Scenes—"J.M. 1 to 50 A" on front. "Junior Member", back style 9		50p	—
	H2	P	50	British Empire Exhibition "J.M. 1 to 50 B" on front		90p	—
	C	P	96	*Animals and Scenes—"J.S. 1/96 A" on front. "Junior Member", back style 9		60p	—
	H2	P	50	*Scenes, Nd. S.1–S.50. "Junior Member", back 4		90p	—
	H2	P	50	*Scenes, Nd. S.51–S.100. "Junior Member", back 4		70p	—
	B1	P	50	*Cathedrals and Abbeys, Nd. S.J. 1–S.J. 50. Plain back	Ha.595–3	—	—
	B1	P	50	*British Castles, Nd. S.J. 51–S.J. 100. Plain back	Ha.595–3	—	—
	H2	P	? 4	*Scenes, Nd. V.1–V.4. "Junior Member", back 4		—	—

B. Coloured and Letterpress Series

Illus. No.	Size	Print-ing	Number in set		Handbook ref.	Price per card	Complete set
519	A	C	50	British Empire Exhibition Series		90p	£45.00
505	A	C	50	Builders of the British Empire..............		90p	£45.00
210	A	C	50	Celebrities in Sport......................		80p	£40.00
148	A	C	75	Cricketers Series		£1.50	—
264	A	C	50	Dirt Track Riders		£1.00	£50.00
	A	C	30	Drawing Made Easy		£1.00	£30.00
	A	C	52	The English & Welsh Counties..............		90p	£45.00
	A	C		Footballers Series:—			
			50	A. Captions in blue.....................		£1.30	—
			100	B. Captions in brown		£1.30	—
	A	C	25	"King Lud" Problems.....................		£8.00	—
	A	C	26	Maritime Flags		£4.50	—
	A	U	25	Photos of Football Stars..................		—	—
549	D	C	50	Railway Posters by Famous Artists		£2.00	—
234	A	C	50	Sports Trophies.........................		90p	£45.00
	A2	CP	51	*Views...........................	Ha.597	90p	£45.00

C. 1930's Photographic Series

Illus. No.	Size	Print-ing	Number in set		Handbook ref.	Price per card	Complete set
		P		Beautiful Scotland (1939):—	Ha.564–1		
	D		28	A. Small size............................		14p	£4.00
	—		48	B. Medium size (77 × 52 mm.)		13p	£4.50
	—	P	48	The Bridges of Britain (Apr. 1938) (77 × 52 mm.)...............................		13p	£3.75
	—	P	48	Britain from the Air (77 × 52 mm.) (1939)....		13p	£3.25
408, 758 etc.	—	P	48	British Railways (77 × 52 mm.) (Nov. 1938)..		13p	£5.50
		P		Coastwise (Jan. 1939):—	Ha.564–2		
	D		28	A. Small size...........................		20p	£5.50
	—		48	B. Medium size (77 × 52 mm.)		13p	£3.25
	D	P	54	Dirt Track Riders (1930). Front black and white or sepia:—			
				A. Descriptive back		£1.70	—
				*B. Non-descriptive back.................		£1.70	—
	—	P	48	Dogs (1939):—			
				A. Size 76 × 51 mm.		13p	£2.25
				B. Size 74 × 48 mm.		—	—
		P		Flying (1938):—	Ha.564–3		
	D		28	A. Small size............................		80p	£22.50
	—		48	B. Medium size (77 × 52 mm.)		32p	£16.00
	A2	P	78	Footballers in Action (1934)		£1.25	—
	—	P	48	Holiday Haunts by the Sea (77 × 52 mm.) (Aug. 1937)............................		13p	£3.25
329	—	P	48	The Navy (May 1937):—			
				A. Large captions		13p	£3.75
				B. Smaller captions		30p	£15.00
		P		Our Countryside (1938):—	Ha.564–4		
	D		28	A. Small size...........................		28p	£8.00
	—		48	B. Medium size (77 × 52 mm.)		13p	£2.50
	A2	P	54	Real Photographs of London (1936)		70p	£37.50
	D	P	28	Shots from the Films (1938)		50p	£14.00
	—	P	48	Sights of Britain—"Series of 48" (76 × 51 mm.) (1936)		13p	£3.50
	—	P	48	Sights of Britain—"Second Series ..." (76 × 51 mm.) (1936):—			
				A. Large captions		13p	£2.75
				B. Smaller captions		13p	£3.75
	—	P	48	Sights of Britain—"Third Series ...." (76 × 51 mm.) (1937)		13p	£3.25
	—	P	48	Sights of London—"First Series ..." (76 × 51 mm.) (1935)		35p	£17.50
511	—	P	12	Sights of London—"Supplementary Series of 12 Jubilee Pictures" (76 × 51 mm.) (1935)..		50p	£6.00
233	A2	P	54	Sporting Celebrities (1935)		£1.10	£60.00
257	—	P	96	Sporting Events and Stars (76 × 50 mm.) (1935)................................		22p	£22.00
	A2	P	54	Views of Britain (1937)		80p	£42.50
	—	P	48	Winter Scenes (76 × 52 mm.) (1937)		13p	£2.25

J. A. PATTRIEOUEX (continued)

Illus. No.	Size	Print-ing	Number in set		Handbook ref.	Price per card	Complete set
D. Miscellaneous							
—		C	1	Advertisement Card (70 × 40 mm.)		—	—
—		C	24	Cadet's Jackpot Jigsaws (90 × 65 mm.) (1969)		—	—
—		C	24	Treasure Island (65 × 45 mm.) (1968)		—	—

W. PEPPERDY

Pre-1919 Issues

	A	C	30	*Army Pictures, Cartoons, etc...............	H.12	—	—

M. PEZARO & SON, London

Pre-1919 Issues

	D	C	25	*Armies of the World	H.43	£70.00	—
	D	C	? 14	Song Titles Illustrated	H.323	£85.00	—

GODFREY PHILLIPS LTD., London

A. Pre-1919 Issues

Illus. No.	Size	Print-ing	Number in set		Handbook ref.	Price per card	Complete set
	D1	C	25	*Actresses "C" Series, Nd. 101–125:—			
				A. Blue Horseshoe design back		£7.00	—
				B. Green back, "Carriage" Cigarettes.....		£16.00	—
				C. Blue back, "Teapot" Cigarettes		£65.00	—
				D. Blue back, "Volunteer" Cigarettes		£55.00	—
				E. Blue back, "Derby" Cigarettes.........		£65.00	—
				F. Blue back, "Ball of Beauty" Cigarettes .		£65.00	—
	—	C	50	*Actresses—oval card (1916–1917) (38 × 62 mm.):—	H.324/Ha.324		
				A. With name.........................		£4.00	—
				B. *Without Maker's and Actress's Name* ...		£2.00	£100.00
	D	C	40	Animal Series (pre-1908)		£3.50	£140.00
476	D1	C	25	*Beauties, Nd. B.801–825 (pre-1908)	H.325	£6.00	£150.00
	A1	U	? 24	*Beauties, collotype—"HUMPS" (? 1895)....	H.222	£28.00	—
	A	C	30	*Beauties, "Nymphs" (? 1896)	H.326	£30.00	—
	D			*Beauties—"Plums" (1897–8):—	H.186		
		BW	? 9	A. Front in black and white..............		—	—
		C	50	B. Plum-coloured background............		£16.00	—
		C	50	C. Green background		£16.00	—
	A1	C	50	Beautiful Women (? 1908):—	H.284		
				A. Inscribed "W.I. Series"...............		£3.50	—
				B. Inscribed "I.F. Series"...............		£4.00	—
	—	C	50	Beautiful Women, Nd. W.501–550 (55 × 75 mm.)................................	H.284	£4.50	—
	D1	C	25	*Boxer Rebellion—Sketches (1904)	H.46	£10.00	—
	—	C	30	*British Beauties—Oval Card (36 × 60 mm.)			
				Plain back	H.244	£1.70	£50.00
	D	U	50	"British Beauties" (? 1916) photogravure....	H.327	£2.20	£110.00
	—	PC	76	British Beauties (? 1916) (37 × 55 mm.)		£2.00	£150.00
	A	C	54	British Beauties (1914–15), Nd. 1–54	H.328		
				(a) Blue back, grey-black, glossy front		£1.80	£90.00
				(b) *Plain back, grey-black, glossy front*		—	—
				(c) *Plain back, sepia, matt front*		£1.80	—
	A	C	54	British Beauties (1914–15), Nd. 55–108:—	H.328		
				A. Blue back, grey-black, semi-glossy front		£1.80	£90.00
				B. Blue back, grey-black matt front		£1.80	£90.00
				C. *Plain back, grey-black matt front*		£1.80	—
5	D1	C	30	British Butterflies, No. 1 issue (1911)		£2.40	£72.50
	D1	U	25	British Warships, green photo style (1915)...		£3.20	£80.00
	L	U	25	British Warships, green photo style (1915)...		—	—
342	A1	P	80	British Warships, "real photographic"	H.329	£5.00	—
	D1	C	50	*Busts of Famous People (1906–7):—			
				A. Pale green back, caption in black.......		£6.00	—
				B. Brown back, caption in black		£12.00	—
				C. Green back, caption in white, "Patent No. 20736"		£3.00	£150.00
	D1	C	25	*Chinese Series (? 1910):—	H.330		
				A. Back in English		£2.80	£70.00
				B. "Volunteer" Cigarettes back...........		£3.20	£80.00
	A	C	50	*Colonial Troops (1904)	H.40	£12.00	—
36	D1	C	30	Eggs Nests & Birds, No. 1 issue (1912–13):—	H.331		
				A. Unnumbered........................		£2.70	£80.00
				B. Numbered		£2.70	£80.00
	D	C	25	First Aid Series, green back (1914–15).......		£3.00	£75.00
	A	C	13	*General Interest (? 1895)....................	H.332	£20.00	£260.00
	—	BW	100	*Guinea Gold Series, unnumbered (1899–1901) (64 × 38 mm.) Inscribed "Phillips' Guinea Gold", matt	H.333/Ha.333	£1.60	—
	—	BW	90	*Guinea Gold Series, numbered 101–190 (68 × 41 mm.) Inscribed "Smoke Phillips' ..."—			
				A. Glossy.............................		£2.25	—
				B. Matt...............................		£2.25	—
			160	*Guinea Gold Series, unnumbered (63 × 41 mm.).................................	H.333		
			134	Actresses:—			
		BW		A. Black front.........................		£1.80	—

Illus. No.	Size	Print-ing	Number in set		Handbook ref.	Price per card	Complete set
		U		B. Brown front		£4.00	—
		BW	26	Celebrities, Boer War		£3.50	—
	D1	C	25	How to do it Series (1913–14)		£4.00	£100.00
	D	C	25	Indian Series (1908–9)		£5.00	£125.00
	K1	C	52	*Miniature Playing Cards	H.334	—	—
	D1	C	30	Morse and Semaphore Signalling (1916):—	H.335		
				"Morse Signalling" back		£3.00	£90.00
				"Semaphore Signalling" back		£3.00	£90.00
—		P	27	Real Photo Series—Admirals and Generals of the Great War. Cut-outs for buttonhole—20 × 40 mm.		£6.00	—
	A	C	20	Russo-Japanese War Series	H.100	£100.00	—
	D1	C	30	Semaphore Signalling—See "Morse & Semaphore Signalling"			
	D1	C	25	Sporting Series.		£7.00	—
	D1	C	25	*Statues & Monuments (cut-outs) (1907):—			
				A. Provisional Patent No. 20736		£3.20	£80.00
				B. Patent No. 20736.		£3.20	£80.00
	D	C	25	*Territorial Series (Nd. 51–75) (1908)		£11.00	—
	A1	C	25	*Types of British and Colonial Troops (1899–1900)	H.76	£24.00	—
291	D1	C	25	*Types of British Soldiers (Nd. M.651–675) (1900).	H.144	£8.00	£200.00
	A	C	63	*War Photos (1916)	H.336	£3.00	—

B. Post-1920 Issues

Illus. No.	Size	Print-ing	Number in set		Handbook ref.	Price per card	Complete set
	A2	C	1	*Advertisement Card—"Grand Cut" (1934)..		—	£12.00
	A2	C	1	*Advertisement Card—"La Galbana Fours" (1934).		—	£12.00
	A	C	50	Aircraft (1938).	Ha.598	50p	£25.00
354	A2	C	54	Aircraft—Series No. 1 (1938):—			
				A. Millhoff and Phillips names at base of back		£3.00	—
				B. Phillips and Associated Companies at base of back:—			
				1. Front varnished		28p	£15.00
				2. Front matt		28p	£15.00
	A2	U	50	*Animal Studies (Australia)	Ha.538	£2.00	—
85	—	C	30	Animal Studies (61 × 53 mm.) (1936)		13p	£3.00
66	A2	C	50	Annuals (1939):—			
				A. Home issue		13p	£2.25
				B. New Zealand issue (dates for planting 4–6 months later).		20p	£10.00
	D	BW	50	Australian Sporting Celebrities (1932) (Australia)		£1.00	—
	B	C	25	Arms of the English Sees (1924)		£2.00	£50.00
423	A	C	44	Beauties of To-Day, small—"A Series of 44 ..." (1937).		27p	£12.00
	A	C	50	Beauties of To-Day, small—"A Series of 50 ..." (1938).	Ha.514	13p	£4.75
	A2	P	54	Beauties of To-Day, small—"A Series of Real Photographs ..." (1939).		27p	£15.00
	A	C	36	Beauties of To-Day, small—"A Series of 36 ... Second Series" (1940)		13p	£2.50
—		P		Beauties of To-Day, large (83 × 66 mm.) (see RB13/21–22):—			
			36	First arrangement, known as "Series A" ...		£1.30	—
			36	Second arrangement, known as "Series B" .		£1.30	—
	J2	P	36	Beauties of To-Day, extra-large, unnumbered (1937) (see RB13/23)		75p	£27.00
	J2	P	36	Beauties of To-Day, extra large—"Second Series" (1938).		42p	£15.00
	J2	P	36	Beauties of To-Day, extra-large—"Third Series" (1938).		33p	£12.00
	J2	P	36	Beauties of To-Day, extra-large—"Fourth Series" (1938).		50p	£18.00
	J2	P	36	Beauties of To-Day, extra-large—"Fifth Series" (1938).		20p	£7.00
	J2	P	36	Beauties of To-Day, extra-large—"Sixth Series" (1939).		17p	£6.00
	J2	P	36	Beauties of To-Day, extra-large—Unmarked (1939):—			
				A. Back "Godfrey Phillips Ltd. and Associated Companies"		15p	£5.50
				B. Back "Issued with B.D.V. Medium Cigarettes ..."		13p	£2.75
	A2	BW	36	Beauties of the World—Stage, Cinema, Dancing Celebrities (1931)		42p	£15.00
	A2	C	36	Beauties of the World—Series No. 2—Stars of Stage and Screen (1933).		80p	£30.00
—		C	30	Beauty Spots of the Homeland (126 × 89 mm.) (1938)		40p	£12.00
37	A	C	50	Bird Painting (1938).		13p	£6.50
12	A	C	50	British Birds and Their Eggs (1936)		22p	£11.00
	A	C	25	British Butterflies:—	Ha.517–1		
				A. Back in pale blue (1923)		40p	£10.00
				B. Back in dark blue (1927)		18p	£4.50
				C. "Permacal" transfers (1936)		13p	£2.75
	A2	C	25	British Orders of Chivalry & Valour (1939):—	Ha.599		

GODFREY PHILLIPS LTD. *(continued)*

Illus. No.	Size	Print-ing	Number in set		Handbook ref.	Price per card	Complete set
				A. Back "Godfrey Phillips Ltd. and Associated Companies"		£1.00	£25.00
				B. Back "De Reszke Cigarettes" (no maker's name)		90p	£22.50
—		C	36	Characters Come to Life (61 × 53 mm.) (1938)		13p	£2.25
—		P	25	*Cinema Stars—Circular cards (57 mm. diam.) (1924) (see RB13/49)		28p	£7.00
A		P	52	Cinema Stars—Set 1	Ha.515–1A	80p	£40.00
A2		U	30	Cinema Stars—Set 2	Ha.515–2	£1.10	
A2		U	30	Cinema Stars—Set 3 (cream, yellow or orange tint)...........................	Ha.515–3	80p	£24.00
A2		C	32	Cinema Stars—Set 4	Ha.515–4	40p	£12.50
A2		BW	32	Cinema Stars—Set 5	Ha.515–5	50p	£16.00
		C		Come to Life Series—see "Zoo Studies" Coronation of Their Majesties (1937):—			
	A2		50	A. Small size........................		13p	£2.50
510	—		36	B. Medium size (61 × 53 mm.)		13p	£2.25
	—		24	C. Postcard size (127 × 89 mm.)		36p	£9.00
		P		Cricketers (1924):—			
	K2		210	*A. Miniature size, "Pinnace" photos (Nd. 16c–225c)		£1.40	—
	D		192	B. Small size, brown back (selected Nos., see RB13/58).....................		£1.40	—
	B1		?	*C. Large size, "Pinnance" photos (number unknown)		£3.00	—
	B1		25	D. Large size, brown back (selected Nos., see RB13/58).....................		£3.00	—
	—		?	E. *Cabinet size*		£6.00	—
	D	C	25	Derby Winners & Jockeys (1923)...........		90p	£22.50
	D1	C	25	Empire Industries (1927)	Ha.600	40p	£10.00
	A2	C	50	*Evolution of the British Navy* (1930)		—	£45.00
			49/50	Ditto (No. 40 missing).....................		40p	£20.00
	D	C	25	Famous Boys (1924)......................		50p	£12.50
	D	C	32	Famous Cricketers (1926)		90p	£30.00
	A	C	25	Famous Crowns (1938)...................		13p	£3.00
	A2	C	50	*Famous Footballers* (1936) (see RB13/66)		36p	£18.00
	—	C	36	Famous Love Scenes (60 × 53 mm.) (1939)...		13p	£3.25
	A2	C	50	Famous Minors (1936)		13p	£2.50
	—	C	26	Famous Paintings (128 × 89 mm.) (1938)		80p	£20.00
	D	C	25	Feathered Friends (1928)	Ha.516	40p	£10.00
438	A2	C	50	Film Favourites (1934)	Ha.517–2	13p	£4.00
	D	BW	50	Film Stars (Australia) (1934)...............		90p	—
	A2	C	50	Film Stars (1934)........................		22p	£11.00
	—	C	24	*Film Stars—"... No.... of a series of 24 cards ..." (128 × 89 mm.) (1934):—			
				A. Postcard format back..................		28p	£7.00
				B. Back without postcard format		90p	—
	—	C	24	*Film Stars—"... No.... of a series of cards", Nd. 25–48 (128 × 89 mm.) (1935):—			
				A. Postcard format back..................		£1.00	
				B. Back without postcard format		—	—
	—	C	24	*Film Stars—"... No.... of a series of cards", vivid backgrounds (128 × 89 mm.) (1936):—			
				A. Postcard format back..................	Ha.517–3	40p	£10.00
				B. Back without postcard format		90p	—
	D	C	50	First Aid (1923)..........................		40p	£20.00
	D	C	25	*Fish (1924)		60p	£15.00
54		C	30	Flower Studies (1937):—			
				A. Medium size (61 × 53 mm.)		13p	£1.75
				*B. Postcard size (128 × 89 mm.)..........		40p	£12.00
		P		Footballers—"Pinnace" photos (1922–24):—			
	K2			A. Miniature size:—			

(Prices shown apply to numbers 1 to 940, for numbers above 940 prices are doubled)

			112	1a. "Oval" design back, in brown		50p	—
			400	1b. "Oval" design back, in black		50p	—
			517	2. Double-lined oblong back.........		50p	—
			1109	3. Single-lined oblong back, address "Photo"..........................		35p	—
				4. Single-lined oblong back, address "Pinnace" photos:—			
			2463	a. Name at head, team at base......		35p	—
			?1651	b. Name at base, no team shown....		35p	—
			??217	c. Team at head, name at base......		35p	—
	—		?	B. Large size (83 × 59 mm.):—			
				1. "Oval" design back		90p	—
				2. Double-lined oblong back:—			
				a. Address "Photo".................		90p	—
				b. Address "Pinnace" photos.......		90p	—
				3. Single-lined oblong back:—			
				a. Name at head, team at base......		70p	—
				b. Name at base, no team shown....		70p	—
				c. Team and name at base..........		70p	—
				C. Cabinet size.........................		£2.50	—
	—	C	30	Garden Studies (128 × 89 mm.) (1938).......		25p	£7.50
108	A2	C	25	Home Pets (1924)	Ha.540	70p	£17.50
	A2	U	25	How to Build a Two Valve Set (1929)........		40p	£10.00

Illus. No.	Size	Print-ing	Number in set		Handbook ref.	Price per card	Complete set
	D	C	25	How to Make a Valve Amplifier ..., Nd. 26–50 (1924)		90p	£22.50
	A	C	25	How to Make Your Own Wireless Set (1923)		80p	£20.00
	A2	C	54	In the Public Eye (1935)		13p	£3.75
174	A2	C	50	International Caps (1936) (see RB13/66)		20p	£10.00
483	A2	C	37	Kings & Queens of England (1925):—			
				Nos. 1 and 4		£16.00	—
				Other numbers		60p	£21.00
243	A2	U	25	Lawn Tennis (1930)		44p	£11.00
	K2	C	53	*Miniature Playing Cards (1932–34):—			
				A. Back with exchange scheme:—			
				1. Buff. Offer for "pack of playing cards"		30p	—
				2. Buff. Offer for "playing cards, dominoes or chess"		30p	£16.00
				3. Buff. Offer for "playing cards, dominoes or draughts"		30p	£16.00
				4. Lemon		30p	—
				5. White, with red over-printing		30p	—
				B. *Blue scroll back, see Fig. 30, Plate 5, RB13*		30p	£16.00
692	A2	C	25	Model Railways (1927) (see RB13/101)		80p	£20.00
	D	C	50	Motor Cars at a Glance (1924)		£1.00	£50.00
	D	C	20	Novelty Series (1924)		£3.00	—
	A2	C	48	The "Old Country" (1935)		25p	£12.50
	A	C	25	Old Favourites (1924)	Ha.517–4	44p	£11.00
545	—	C	36	Old Masters (60 × 53 mm.) (1939)		25p	£9.00
242	A	U	36	Olympic Champions Amsterdam, 1928		50p	£18.00
622	A	C	25	Optical Illusions (1927)		44p	£11.00
		C		"Our Dogs" (1939):—			
	A2		36	A. Small size (export)		17p	£6.00
	—		30	B. Medium size (60 × 53 mm.)		13p	£3.25
	—		30	*C. Postcard size (128 × 89 mm.)		£1.00	£30.00
118	—	BW	48	"Our Favourites" (60 × 53 mm.) (1935)		13p	£2.25
	—	C	30	Our Glorious Empire (128 × 89 mm.) (1939) .		60p	£18.00
		C	30	"Our Puppies" (1936):—			
110	—			A. Medium size (60 × 53 mm.)		20p	£6.00
	—			*B. Postcard size (128 × 89 mm.)		17p	£5.00
	A2	C	25	Personalities of To-Day (Caricatures) (1932)		30p	£7.50
	A2	C	25	Popular Superstitions (1930)		40p	£10.00
	A	C	25	Prizes for Needlework (1925) (see RB13/116)		60p	£15.00
659 etc.	D	C	25	Railway Engines (1924)		90p	£22.50
	D	C	25	Red Indians (1927)	Ha.601	80p	£20.00
	A	C	25	School Badges (1927)	Ha.543	36p	£9.00
	A	C		Screen Stars (1936–37):—			
			48	First arrangement, known as "Series A" (see RB13/121):—			
				A. Frame embossed		13p	£5.50
				B. Frame not embossed		13p	£5.50
435			48	Second arrangement, known as "Series B" (see RB13/122)		13p	£4.50
	A2	C		A Selection of B.D.V. Wonderful Gifts:—			
			48	"... based on 1930 Budget" (1930) (see RB13/84)		30p	£15.00
			48	"... based on 1931 Budget" (1931) (see RB13/85)		20p	£10.00
			48	"... based on 1932 Budget" (1932) (see RB13/86)		13p	£6.50
	D	C	25	Ships and Their Flags (1924)	Ha.602	£1.50	£37.50
	—	C	36	Ships that have Made History (60 × 53 mm.) (1938)		13p	£2.50
	—	C	48	Shots from the Films (60 × 53 mm.) (1934)		13p	£4.50
	A2	C	50	Soccer Stars (1936) (see RB13/66)		13p	£6.00
285	A2	C	36	Soldiers of the King (1939):—	Ha.603		
				A. Inscribed "This surface is adhesive"		30p	£11.00
				B. Without the above:—			
				1. Thin card		20p	£7.00
				2. Thick card		30p	£11.00
		C		Special Jubilee Year Series (1935):—			
508	—		20	A. Medium size (60 × 53 mm.)		13p	£2.50
	—		12	B. Postcard size (128 × 89 mm.)		90p	£11.00
230	A2	U	30	Speed Champions (1930)		33p	£10.00
246	A2	U	36	Sporting Champions (1929)		30p	£11.00
249	D	C	25	Sports (1923):—			
				A. White card		£1.50	—
				B. Grey card		£1.50	—
252	A2	C	50	*Sportsmen—"Spot the Winner" (1937):—			
				A. Inverted back		13p	£3.00
				B. Normal back		13p	£4.50
	A2	C		Stage and Cinema Beauties (1933–34):—	Ha.572		
			35	First arrangement—known as "Series A" ..		14p	£5.00
			35	Second arrangement—known as "Series B"		26p	£9.00
	A2	C	50	Stage and Cinema Beauties (1935)	Ha.517–5	35p	£17.50
	D	C	50	Stars of British Films (Australia) (1934):—			
				A. Back "B.D.V. Cigarettes ..."		90p	—
				B. Back "Grey's Cigarettes ..".		90p	—
				C. Back "De Reszke Cigarettes ..."		90p	—
				D. Back "Godfrey Phillips (Aust.) ..".		90p	—
	A2	CP	54	Stars of the Screen—"A Series of 54" (1934) .		33p	£18.00

Illus. No.	Size	Print-ing	Number in set		Handbook ref.	Price per card	Complete set
439	A2	C	48	Stars of the Screen—"A Series of 48" (1936):—			
				A. Frame not embossed		13p	£4.50
				B. Frame embossed		13p	£4.50
				C. In strips of three, per strip		28p	£4.50
	D	BW	38	Test Cricketers, 1932–1933 (Australia):—			
				A. "Issued with Grey's Cigarettes ..."		£1.50	—
				B. "Issued with B.D.V. Cigarettes ..."		£1.50	—
				C. Back "Godfrey Phillips (Aust.)"		£1.50	—
	A	U	25	The 1924 Cabinet (1924)...................		60p	£15.00
676 etc	A	C	50	This Mechanized Age—First Series (1936):—			
				A. Inscribed "This surface is adhesive"		13p	£2.25
				B. Without the above		13p	£3.25
	A	C	50	This Mechanized Age—Second Series (1937)		25p	£12.50
	A2	C	100	*Who's Who in Australian Sport (Australia) (1933) (see RB13/147)....................		80p	—
	D2	C		Victorian Footballers (Australia) (1933):—			
			50	1. "Series of 50":—			
				A. "Godfrey Phillips (Aust.) ..."		80p	—
				B. "B.D.V. Cigarettes ..."		80p	—
				C. "Grey's Cigarettes ...".............		80p	—
			75	2. "Series of 75":—			
				D. "B.D.V. Cigarettes ..."		80p	—
	D	BW	50	Victorian League and Association Footballers (Australia) (1934).................		80p	—
	—	C	30	Zoo Studies—Come to Life Series (1939) (101 × 76 mm.)............................		50p	£15.00
				Spectacles for use with the above...........		—	£0.50

C. Silks. Known as "the B.D.V. Silks". All unbacked. Inscribed "B.D.V. Cigarettes" or "G.P." (Godfrey Phillips), or anonymous. Issued about 1910–25.

Illus. No.	Size	Print-ing	Number in set		Handbook ref.	Price per card	Complete set
	—	C	? 61	*Arms of Countries and Territories (73 × 50 mm.)—Anonymous......................	Ha.504–12	£1.25	—
	—	C	32	*Beauties—Modern Paintings (B.D.V.):—	Ha.505–13		
				A. Small size (70 × 46 mm.)		£2.60	—
				B. Extra-large size (143 × 100 mm.)		£11.00	—
	—	C	100	*Birds II (68 × 42 mm.)—B.D.V.	Ha.505–2	£1.00	—
	—	C	12	*Birds of the Tropics III—B.D.V.:—	Ha.505–3		
				A. Small size (71 × 47 mm.)		£3.50	—
				B. Medium size (71 × 63 mm.)		£3.50	—
				C. Extra-large size (150 × 100 mm.)		£6.00	—
	—	U	24	*British Admirals (83 × 76 mm.)—Anonymous.	Ha.504–5	£2.00	£50.00
	—	C		*British Butterflies and Moths II—Anonymous:—	Ha.505–6		
			40	Nos. 1–40. Large size, 76 × 61 mm.		£1.00	—
			10	Nos. 41–50. Medium size, 70 × 51 mm.......		£1.00	—
	—	C	108	*British Naval Crests II:—	Ha.504–4		
				A. B.D.V., size 70 × 47 mm.		60p	—
				B. Anonymous, size 70 × 51 mm...........		80p	—
	—	C	25	*Butterflies I (70 × 48 mm.)—Anonymous	Ha.505–5	£5.00	—
	—	C	47	Ceramic Art—B.D.V.:—	Ha.505–16		
				A. Small size (70 × 43 mm.)		50p	£25.00
				B. Medium size (70 × 61 mm.)		60p	£30.00
	—	C		*Clan Tartans:—	Ha.505–15		
				A. Small size (71 × 48 mm.):—			
			49	1. Anonymous.....................		50p	£25.00
			65	2. B.D.V.............................		50p	£32.50
			65	B. Medium size (70 × 60 mm.—B.D.V.) ...		£2.00	—
			12	C. Extra-large size (150 × 100 mm.)—B.D.V. (selected Nos.)....................		£1.50	£18.00
	—	C	108	*Colonial Army Badges (71 × 50 mm.)—Anonymous...........................	Ha.502–3	£1.25	—
	—	C	17	County Cricket Badges (69 × 48 mm.):—	Ha.505–8		
				A. Anonymous		£6.00	—
				B. B.D.V..............................		£6.00	—
	—	C	108	*Crests and Badges of the British Army II:—	Ha.502–2		
				A1. Small size (70 × 48 mm.)—Anonymous:—			
				(a) Numbered.......................		40p	£42.50
				(b) Unnumbered.....................		40p	£42.50
				A2. Small size (70 × 48 mm.)—B.D.V.		35p	£37.50
				A3. Medium size (70 × 60 mm.):—			
				(a) Anonymous......................		80p	—
				(b) B.D.V............................		70p	—
	—	C		*Flags—Set 4—Anonymous:—	Ha.501–4		
			?143	A. "Long" size (82 × 53) mm...............		£3.00	—
				B. "Short" size, (70 × 48) mm.:—			
			?143	1. First numbering arrangement (as A) .		£1.20	—
			?119	2. Second numbering arrangement		40p	—
			?115	3. Third numbering arrangement.......		50p	—
	—	C		*Flags—Set 5—Anonymous:—	Ha.501–5		
				A. Small size, (70 × 50 mm.):—			
			20	1. With caption....................		70p	—
			6	2. Without caption, flag 40 × 29 mm. ...		60p	—
			? 6	3. Without caption, flag 60 × 41 mm. ...		70p	—
			? 2	B. Extra-large size (155 × 108) mm.........		£6.00	—
	—	C	18	*Flags—Set 6—Anonymous:—	Ha.501–6		
				A. Size (69 × 47) mm.		50p	£9.00
				B. Size (71 × 51) mm.		50p	£9.00

Illus. No.	Size	Print-ing	Number in set		Handbook ref.	Price per card	Complete set
—		C	20	*Flags—Set 7 (70 × 50 mm.)—Anonymous	Ha.501–7	60p	—
—		C	50	*Flags—Set 9 ("5th Series") (70 × 48 mm.)—Anonymous	Ha.501–9	60p	£30.00
—		C		*Flags—Set 10:—	Ha.501–10		
			120	"7th Series" (70 × 48 mm.)—Anonymous ...		30p	—
			120	"10th Series" (70 × 62 mm.)—Anonymous ..		40p	—
			120	"12th Series" (70 × 48 mm.)—Anonymous ..		80p	—
			75	"15th Series" (70 × 62 mm.) (selected Nos.)—B.D.V.		90p	—
			75	"16th Series" (70 × 62 mm.) (selected Nos.)—B.D.V.		90p	—
			132	"20th Series" (70 × 48 mm.)—B.D.V., in brown or red		80p	—
			126	"25th Series" (70 × 48 mm.)—B.D.V., in brown or black		40p	—
			75	"25th Series" (70 × 62 mm.) (selected Nos.), B.D.V.		£2.50	—
			120	"26th Series" (70 × 48 mm.)—B.D.V., in brown or blue		40p	—
			75	"28th Series" (70 × 48 mm.) (selected Nos.), B.D.V.		40p	—
—		C		*Flags—Set 12:—	Ha.501–12		
			1	A. "Let 'em all come" (70 × 46 mm.)—Anonymous		—	£3.00
				B. Allied Flags (grouped):—			
			1	Four Flags—Anonymous:—			
				1. Small size, (70 × 46 mm.)		—	£6.00
				2. Extra-large size, (163 × 120 mm.)....		—	—
			1	Seven Flags (165 × 116 mm.):—			
				1. Anonymous......................		—	£4.00
				2 B.D.V., in brown or orange........		—	£5.00
			1	Eight Flags (165 × 116 mm.)—B.D.V. ...		—	—
—		C		*Flags—Set 13:—	Ha.501–13		
			? 23	A. Size 163 × 114 mm.—Anonymous.......		80p	£18.00
			? 27	B. Size 163 × 114 mm.—B.D.V., in brown, orange, blue, green or black...........		70p	—
			? 23	C. Size 150 × 100 mm.—B.D.V.		70p	£16.00
—		C	? 26	*Flags—Set 14 ("House Flags") (68 × 47 mm.)—Anonymous......................	Ha.501–14	£2.75	—
—		C	25	*Flags—Set 15 (Pilot and Signal Flags) (70 × 50 mm.):—	Ha.501–15		
				A. Numbered 601–625—Anonymous.......		80p	£20.00
				B. Inscribed "Series 11"—B.D.V..........		70p	£17.50
—		C	90	*Football Colours:—	Ha.505–9		
				A. Anonymous, size 68 × 49 mm...........		£1.75	—
				B. B.D.V., size 68 × 49 mm...............		75p	—
				C. B.D.V., size 150 × 100 mm.		70p	—
—		C	126	G.P. Territorial Badges (70 × 48 mm.).......	Ha.502–12	60p	£75.00
—		U	25	*Great War Leaders II (81 × 68 mm.)—Anonymous................................	Ha.504–7	£1.25	£32.50
—		U	? 51	*Great War Leaders III and Warships, sepia, black or blue on white or pink material (70 × 50 mm.)—Anonymous...............	Ha.504–10	£2.50	—
—		C		*Great War Leaders IV and Celebrities:—	Ha.504–11		
			3	A. Small size, (70 × 48 mm.)—Anonymous .		£2.00	—
			4	B. Small size (70 × 48 mm.)—B.D.V.......		£2.00	—
			3	C. Medium size, 70 × 63 mm.—Anonymous.		£2.00	—
			2	D. Medium size (70 × 63 mm.)—B.D.V. ...		£2.50	—
			? 18	E. Extra-large size (150 × 100 mm.)—B.D.V..................................		£1.50	£27.00
			? 4	F. Extra-large size, (150 × 110 mm.)—Anonymous		£2.50	£10.00
			? 1	G. Extra-large size (150 × 110 mm.)—B.D.V..................................		—	£7.00
			? 26	H. Extra-large size (163 × 117 mm.)—Anonymous		£2.00	—
			? 46	I. Extra-large size (163 × 117 mm.)—B.D.V..................................		£1.50	—
—		C		Heraldic Series—B.D.V.:—	Ha.504–17		
			25	A. Small size (68 × 47 mm.)		50p	£12.50
			25	B. Small size (68 × 43 mm.)		50p	£12.50
			25	C. Medium size (68 × 60 mm.)		£1.60	—
			12	D. Extra-large size (150 × 100 mm.) (selected Nos.)............................		£1.50	£18.00
—		C	10	*Irish Patriots—Anonymous:—	Ha.505–11		
				A. Small size (67 × 50 mm.)		£3.25	—
				B. Large size (83 × 76 mm.)		£4.50	—
				C. Extra-large size (152 × 110 mm.)........		£4.50	—
—		C	1	*Irish Republican Stamp (70 × 50 mm.).......	Ha.505–12	—	£1.25
—		C	54	*Naval Badges of Rank and Military Head-dress (70 × 47 mm.)—Anonymous	Ha.504–9	£2.50	—
—		C	? 40	*Old Masters—Set 1 (155 × 115 mm.)—B.D.V.	Ha.503–1	£8.00	—
—		C	20	*Old Masters—Set 2 (150 × 105 mm.):—	Ha.503–2		
				A. Anonymous		£2.00	£40.00
				B. B.D.V. wording above picture		£1.50	£30.00
				C. B.D.V. wording below picture		£2.00	—
—		C		*Old Masters—Set 3A (70 × 50 mm.):—	Ha.503–3A		

Illus. No.	Size	Print- ing	Number in set		Handbook ref.	Price per card	Complete set
			40	A. B.D.V.		£1.00	—
			? 55	B. Anonymous		£1.25	—
—		C	30	*Old Masters—Set 3B (70 × 50 mm.)— Anonymous	Ha.503–3B	£1.00	—
—		C	120	*Old Masters—Set 4 (70 × 50 mm.)— Anonymous:—	Ha.503–4		
				Nos. 1–60		80p	£50.00
				Nos. 61–120		£1.40	—
		C		*Old Masters—Set 5 (70 × 50 mm.):—	Ha.503–5		
			20	A. Unnumbered—Anonymous		£1.50	
			60	B. Nd. 1–60—B.D.V.		40p	£24.00
			20	C. Nd. 101–120—Anonymous:—			
				1. Numerals normal size		80p	
				2. Numerals very small size		60p	£12.00
			20	D. Nd. 101–120—B.D.V.		60p	£12.00
—		C	50	*Old Masters—Set 6 (67 × 42 mm.)—B.D.V.	Ha.503–6	60p	£30.00
—		C	50	*Old Masters—Set 7, Nd. 301–350 (67 × 47 mm.)—Anonymous	Ha.503–7	£1.50	£75.00
—		C	. 50	*Orders of Chivalry I (70 × 48 mm.)— Anonymous	Ha.504–14	£1.00	—
—		C	24	*Orders of Chivalry—Series 10 (70 × 50 mm.):—	Ha.504–16		
				A. Nd. 1–24—B.D.V.		80p	£20.00
				B. Nd. 401–424—G.P.		£1.00	£25.00
—		C	? 67	*Regimental Colours II (76 × 70 mm.)— Anonymous	Ha.502–7	£1.50	—
—		C		*Regimental Colours and Crests III:—	Ha.502–8		
				A. Small size (70 × 51 mm.):—			
			40	1. Colours with faint backgrounds— Anonymous		70p	—
			120	2. Colours without backgrounds— Anonymous		80p	—
			120	3. Colours without backgrounds— B.D.V.		80p	—
			120	B. Extra-large size (165 × 120 mm.):—			
				1. Anonymous—Unnumbered		£4.00	—
				2. B.D.V.—Numbered		£3.00	—
—		C	50	*Regimental Colours—Series 12 (70 × 50 mm.)—B.D.V.	Ha.502–11	70p	£35.00
—		C	10	*Religious Pictures—Anonymous:—	Ha.505–10		
				A. Small size (67 × 50 mm.)		£4.50	—
				B. Large size (83 × 76 mm.)		£5.00	—
				C. Extra-large size (155 × 110 mm.)		£6.00	—
—		C	75	*Town and City Arms—Series 30 (48 un- numbered, 27 numbered 49–75)— B.D.V.:—	Ha.504–13		
				A. Small size (70 × 50 mm.)		40p	—
				B. Medium size (70 × 65 mm.)		70p	—
—		C	25	*Victoria Cross Heroes I (70 × 50 mm.)— Anonymous	Ha.504–1	£3.50	—
—		C	? 24	*Victoria Cross Heroes II (70 × 50 mm.)— Anonymous	Ha.504–2	£5.50	—
—		C	90	*War Pictures (70 × 48 mm.)—Anonymous	Ha.504–8	£2.00	—

D. Miscellaneous

				B.D.V. Sports Cartons (1933–34) (several hundred)		50p	—
	D	BW	1	Cricket Fixture Card (Radio Luxembourg) (1936–37)		—	£3.00
				"Private Seal" Wrestling Holds (export)) (No. 15 highest seen)		£14.00	—
				Rugs (miscellaneous designs)		£5.00	—
				Stamp Cards (four colours, several wordings)		65p	—
				For other miscellaneous items, see RB13/100			

JOHN PLAYER & SONS, Nottingham ────────────

A. Pre-1919 Issues

Illus. No.	Size	Print- ing	Number in set		Handbook ref.	Price per card	Complete set
	A	C	25	*Actors and Actresses (1898)	H.337	£10.00	£250.00
	D	BW	50	*Actresses	H.339	£12.00	—
	A	C	? 7	*Advertisement Cards (1893–94)	H.338	From £110.00	—
	J	C	10	Allied Cavalry or Regimental Uniforms:—	H.340		
				Allied Cavalry (1914)		£4.50	£45.00
				Regimental Uniforms		£4.50	£45.00
304	A	C	50	Arms & Armour (Apr. 1909)	H.273	£1.40	£70.00
302	A	C	25	Army Life (Oct. 1910)	H.78	70p	£17.50
	J	C	12	Artillery in Action (1917)		£2.50	£30.00
	A	C	50	Badges & Flags of British Regiments (Feb. 1904):—	H.341		
				A. Brown back, unnumbered		£1.50	£75.00
				B. Brown back, numbered		£1.50	£75.00
305	A	C	50	Badges & Flags of British Regiments:—			
				A. Green back, thick card		£1.50	£75.00
				B. Green back, thin card		£1.50	£75.00
		P	10	*Bookmarks—Authors (Size 148 × 51 mm.)	H.342	£35.00	—
	A	C	50	British Empire Series (1904):—	H.343		
				A. Grey-white card, matt		60p	£30.00
				B. White card, semi-glossy		70p	£35.00

Illus. No.	Size	Print-ing	Number in set		Handbook ref.	Price per card	Complete set
		C	25	British Livestock:—	H.344		
	A			Small card (June 1915)		44p	£11.00
	J			Extra-large card, brown back (May 1916) ..		£1.80	£45.00
6	A	C	50	Butterflies & Moths (Dec. 1904).............	H.80	90p	£45.00
		C		Bygone Beauties:—			
	A		25	A. Small card (Jul. 1914)................		44p	£11.00
	J		10	B. Extra-large card (May 1916) ....:.....		£1.50	£15.00
—		U		*Cabinet Size Pictures, 1898–1900 (220 × 140 mm.):—	Ha.476		
			10	A. Plain back		—	—
			? 5	B. Printed back		—	—
	A	C	20	Castles, Abbeys etc. (? 1894–5):—	H.345		
				A. Without border		£15.00	£300.00
				B. White border........................		£15.00	£300.00
	A	C	50	Celebrated Bridges (Nov. 1903)	H.346	£1.50	£75.00
	A	C		Celebrated Gateways (Jul. 1909):—	H.347		
			50	A. Thick card		70p	£35.00
			25	B. Thinner card (26–50 only)		£1.00	—
	A	C	25	Ceremonial and Court Dress (May 1911)....	H.145	44p	£11.00
		C		Characters from Dickens:—			
	A		25	Small card, 1st series (Mar. 1912)		44p	£11.00
522	J		10	Extra large card (Oct. 1912)	H.348	£1.40	£14.00
	A	C	25	Characters from Dickens, 2nd Series (Jun. 1914).................................		44p	£11.00
536	A	C	25	Characters from Thackeray (Jul. 1913)		40p	£10.00
	A	C	50	Cities of the World:—		—	£160.00
				A. Grey-mauve on white back		£3.20	—
				B. Grey-mauve on toned back		£3.20	—
				C. Bright mauve on white back		£3.20	—
	A	C	25	Colonial & Indian Army Badges (Jun. 1916).		50p	£12.50
	A	C	25	*Counties and Their Industries:—	H.349		
				A. Unnumbered (? 1910).................		40p	£10.00
				B. Numbered (Jul. 1914)		40p	£10.00
605	A	C	50	*Countries—Arms and Flags:—			
				A. Thick card (Oct. 1905)................		30p	£15.00
				B. Thin card (Jun. 1912)		30p	£15.00
	A	C	50	*Country Seats and Arms (Jun. 1906)		36p	£18.00
	A	C		*Country Seats and Arms, 2nd Series (Jan. 1907):—			
			25	A. Nd. 51–75 First Printing..............		£1.00	—
			50	B. Nd. 51–100 Second printing		36p	£18.00
	A	C	50	*Country Seats and Arms, 3rd Series (Jun. 1907).................................		36p	£18.00
		C		Cries of London:—	H.350		
	A		25	Small cards, 1st Series (Apr. 1913)		90p	£22.50
	J		10	Extra large cards, 1st Series (Oct. 1912).....		£1.40	£14.00
	J		10	Extra large cards, 2nd Series (Apr. 1914) ...		£1.40	£14.00
	A	C	25	Cries of London (2nd Series) (Nov. 1916 and 1922).................................		60p	£15.00
	A	C	25	Egyptian Kings & Queens, and Classical Deities (Jun. 1911)		40p	£10.00
	J	C	10	Egyptian Sketches (Jun. 1915)	H.351	£2.80	£28.00
	A	C	25	*England's Military Heroes (1898–9):—	H.352		
				A. Wide card.........................		£20.00	—
				A1. Wide card plain back.................		£14.00	—
				B. Narrow card		£14.00	—
				B2. Narrow card, plain back...............		£12.00	—
	A	C	25	England's Naval Heroes (1897–8):—	H.353		
				A. Wide card.........................		£20.00	—
				B. Narrow card		£14.00	—
340	A	C	25	England's Naval Heroes (1898–9), descriptions on back:—	H.353		
				A. Wide card		£20.00	—
				A2. Wide card, plain back.................		£14.00	—
				B. Narrow card		£13.00	£325.00
				B2. Narrow card, plain back...............		£11.00	—
	A	C	25	Everyday Phrases by Tom Browne (1901):—	H.354		
				A. Thick card		£8.00	£200.00
				B. Thin card		£8.00	£200.00
524		C	20	Famous Authors and Poets (1902–3):—			
	A			A. Wide card..........................		£12.50	£250.00
				B. Narrow card		£7.50	£150.00
548	J	C	10	Famous Paintings (Jun. 1913, reprint 1914)..	H.355	£2.25	£22.50
	A	C	50	Fishes of the World (Feb. 1903)	H.66	£1.60	£80.00
465	A	C		Gallery of Beauty (? 1896):—	H.356		
				A. Wide card:—			
				I. Set of 50....................		£13.00	£650.00
				II. 5 Alternative Pictures		£40.00	—
				B. Narrow Card:—			
				I. Set of 50....................		£11.00	—
				II. 5 Alternative Pictures		—	—
	A	C	25	Gems of British Scenery (Sep. 1914)........		40p	£10.00
294	A	C	25	Highland Clans (Sep. 1908 reprint 1914).....		£1.50	£37.50
	J	C	10	Historic Ships (Oct. 1910):—			
				A. Thick card		£2.25	£22.50
				B. Thin card		£2.75	£27.50
	A	C	50	Life on Board a Man of War in 1805 and 1905 (Oct. 1905)	H.38	£1.30	£65.00
279	A	C	50	Military Series (1900–01)		£9.00	£450.00

Illus. No.	Size	Print-ing	Number in set		Handbook ref.	Price per card	Complete set
	A	C	25	Miniatures (Dec. 1916, re-issue Jun. 1923) ...		28p	£7.00
	A	C	25	Napoleon (Sep. 1915)	H.364	70p	£17.50
		C		Nature Series:—			
	A		50	Small card (June 1908)		70p	£35.00
	J		10	Extra large card (Birds) (Oct. 1908)		£12.00	—
	J		10	Extra large card (Animals) (Oct. 1913)		£4.00	£40.00
325	A	C	50	Old England's Defenders		£9.00	£450.00
	A	C	25	Players—Past & Present (May 1916, re-issue 1923)................................		36p	£9.00
	A	C	25	Polar Exploration (Jun. 1911)..............		60p	£15.00
	A	C	25	Polar Exploration, 2nd Series (? 1915).......		60p	£15.00
	A	C	25	Products of the World:—			
				A. Thick card (May 1909)		40p	£10.00
				B. Thin card (Feb. 1908)................		40p	£10.00
	A	C	50	*Regimental Colours and Cap Badges (Oct. 1907)...................................		60p	£30.00
	A	C	50	*Regimental Colours and Cap Badges—Territorial Regiments (May 1910):—			
				A. Blue back		60p	£30.00
				B. Brown back		60p	£30.00
	J	C	10	Regimental Uniforms—See "Allied Cavalry".			
306	A	C	50	Regimental Uniforms (1–50):—			
				A. Blue back (Jul. 1912)		80p	£40.00
				B. Brown back (Jul. 1914)		90p	£45.00
	A	C	50	Regimental Uniforms (51–100) (Jul. 1914)...		70p	£35.00
	A	C	50	Riders of the World:—	H.358		
				A. Thick grey card (Jan. 1905)		60p	£30.00
				B. Thinner white card (Jul. 1914).........		70p	£35.00
	—	P	6	The Royal Family (1902) (101 × 154 mm.) ...	H.359	—	£100.00
	—	P.	? 22	Rulers and Viewers (101 × 154 mm.)........	H.363/Ha.363	£35.00	—
541	A	C	25	Shakespearean Series (Jul. 1914, re-issue 1916)................................		40p	£10.00
394	A	C	25	Ships' Figureheads (Oct. 1912):—			
				A. Numerals "sans serif"		70p	£17.50
				B. Numerals with serif		70p	£17.50
	A	BW	? 47	Stereoscopic Series	H.357	£10.00	
	A	C	25	Those Pearls of Heaven (Jul. 1914)		40p	£10.00
	A	BW	66	Transvaal Series (1903–4):—	H.360		
				A. Black front........................		£2.00	—
				B. Violet-black front		£2.00	—
40	A	C	50	Useful Plants & Fruit (Apr. 1904)...........	H.361	£1.50	£75.00
	A	C	25	Victoria Cross (Jun. 1914)		60p	£15.00
	A	C		Wild Animals of the World (Sep. 1902):—	H.77		
			50	A. "John Player & Sons Ltd."		£2.00	£100.00
			50	B. "John Player & Sons, Branch, Nottingham".....................		£2.25	—
			52	C. As B, "Branch" omitted...........		—	—
				C1. As B. "Branch" omitted but showing traces of some or all of the letters ...		£3.00	—
			52	C2. As B. New printing with "Branch" omitted.................		£2.00	£100.00
	A1	C	45	Wild Animals of the World, narrow card:—	H.77		
				A. "John Player & Sons Ltd."		£3.00	£135.00
				B. "John Player & Sons, Branch, Nottingham".....................		£3.00	—
				C. As B, "Branch" omitted...........		—	—
				C1. As B. "Branch" omitted but showing traces of some or all of the letters.....................		£4.00	—
				C2. As B. New printing with "Branch" omitted		£3.00	£135.00
	A	C	50	Wonders of the Deep (Aug. 1904)	H.365	90p	£45.00
	A	C	25	Wonders of the World, blue back (Oct. 1913)	H.362	40p	£10.00
	J	C	10	Wooden Walls (May 1909):—			
				A. Thick card		£3.00	£30.00
				B. Thin card		£3.00	£30.00
208	A	C	25	Wrestling and Ju-Jitsu (blue back) (Jan. 1911)	H.467	40p	£10.00

B. Post-1920 Issues. Series with I.T.C. Clause. For export issues see RB21.

Illus. No.	Size	Print-ing	Number in set		Handbook ref.	Price per card	Complete set
		C	1	*Advertisement Card (Sailor):—			
				A. Small size........................		—	£2.25
				B. Large size........................		—	£16.00
349	A	C	50	Aeroplanes (see RB21/217/6):—			
				A. Home issue (Aug. 1935)—titled "Aeroplanes (Civil)"		15p	£7.50
				B. Irish issue (July 1935)—titled "Aeroplanes"		20p	£10.00
356	A	C	50	Aircraft of the Royal Air Force (Aug. 1938) (see RB17/7).........................		13p	£6.50
84	A	C	50	Animals of the Countryside (Aug. 1934) (see RB17/9):—			
				A. Home issue—adhesive................		13p	£4.00
				B. Irish issue—non-adhesive, green numerals overprinted.................		30p	—
	B	C	25	Aquarium Studies (Sept. 1932).............		60p	£15.00
564	B	C	25	Architectural Beauties (Nov. 1927).........		70p	£17.50
316	A	C	50	Army, Corps & Divisional Signs, 1914–1918 (Mar. 1924)................................		13p	£6.00

Illus. No.	Size	Print-ing	Number in set		Handbook ref.	Price per card	Complete set
	A	C	100	Army, Corps & Divisional Signs, 1914–1918, "2nd Series" (Feb. 1925):—			
				Nos. 51–100		13p	£6.00
				Nos. 101–150		13p	£6.00
167	A	U	50	Association Cup Winners (Jan. 1930)		20p	£10.00
		C		Aviary and Cage Birds:—			
11	A		50	A. Small size (Aug. 1933):—			
				1. Cards..........................		17p	£8.50
				2. Transfers......................		14p	£7.00
13	B		25	B. Large size (Feb. 1935)		44p	£11.00
29	A	C	50	Birds & Their Young (1937) (see RB17/23):—			
				A. Home issue—adhesive...............		13p	£3.25
				B. Irish issue—1. Adhesive...........		60p	—
				2. Non-adhesive..............		60p	—
	A	C	25	Boxing (May 1934).......................		90p	£22.50
	A	C	50	Boy Scout & Girl Guide Patrol Signs & Emblems (Jan. 1933):—			
				A. Cards.............................		13p	£4.25
				B. Transfers		13p	£5.00
3	B	C	25	British Butterflies (Jan. 1934)		50p	£12.50
	J	C	25	British Live Stock (blue back) (1923)	H.344	80p	£20.00
328	B	C	25	British Naval Craft (Feb. 1939)............		20p	£5.00
	J	C	20	British Pedigree Stock (Nov. 1925)..........		70p	£14.00
	B	C	25	British Regalia (Mar. 1937)................		24p	£6.00
10	A	C	50	Butterflies (Mar. 1932):—			
				A. Cards.............................		20p	£10.00
				B. Transfers		13p	£6.50
115	B	C	24	Cats (Mar. 1936)........................		£1.00	£24.00
	B	C	25	Championship Golf Courses (Jan. 1936).....		36p	£9.00
531	A	C	50	Characters from Dickens (Nov. 1923).......	H.348	32p	£16.00
535	B	C	25	Characters from Fiction (Oct. 1933)........		44p	£11.00
610	B	C	20	Clocks—Old & New (Aug. 1928)............		90p	£18.00
517	A	C	50	Coronation Series Ceremonial Dress (Mar. 1937) (see RB17/53)...................		13p	£5.00
253	B	C	25	Country Sports (Sept. 1930)		30p	£7.50
154	A	C	50	Cricketers, 1930 (June 1930)		32p	£16.00
155	A	C	50	Cricketers, 1934 (May 1934)		18p	£9.00
149	A	C	50	Cricketers, 1938 (June 1938) (see RB17/62) ..		13p	£4.00
159	A	C	50	Cricketers, Caricatures by "Rip" (June 1926)		32p	£16.00
27	A	C	50	Curious Beaks (Oct. 1929)		13p	£6.50
236	A	C	50	Cycling (May 1939) (see RB17/67):—			
				A. Home issue—adhesive		13p	£5.00
				B. Irish issue—1. Adhesive		50p	—
				2 Non-adhesive		50p	—
		C		Dandies:—			
501	A		50	A. Small size (July 1932)................		13p	£5.00
	B		25	B. Large size (May 1932)		20p	£5.00
	A	C	50	Derby and Grand National Winners (Apr. 1933):—			
				A. Cards.............................		30p	£15.00
				B. Transfers		25p	£12.50
		C		Dogs (1924–5)—Scenic backgrounds (see RB17/71):—			
116	A		50	A. Small size		13p	£6.00
	J		12	B. Extra-large size		60p	£7.50
		C		Dogs (1926–29)—Heads (see RB17/72):—			
114	A		50	A. Small size—Home issue (Apr. 1929)....		26p	£13.00
	A		25	B. Small size—Irish issue, "A Series of 25" (Apr. 1927)		60p	£15.00
	A		25	C. Small size—Irish issue, "2nd Series of 25" (Dec. 1929)		60p	£15.00
	B		20	D. Large size—Home issue, "A Series of 20" (Dec. 1926)		60p	£12.00
	B		20	E. Large size—Home issue, "2nd Series of 20" (May 1928)		60p	£12.00
		C		Dogs (1931–33)—Full length:—			
121	A		50	A. Small size (Sept. 1931):—			
				1. Cards		13p	£6.50
				2. Transfers......................		14p	£7.00
	B		25	B. Large size (May 1933)		40p	£10.00
	A	C	50	Dogs' Heads (silver-grey backgrounds) (Aug. 1940)................................		50p	—
323	A	C	50	Drum Banners & Cap Badges (Sept. 1924):—			
				A. Base panel joining vertical framelines...		35p	£17.50
				B. Fractional space between the above		30p	£15.00
526	B	BW	25	Fables of Aesop (Mar. 1927)...............		70p	£17.50
496	B	C	25	Famous Beauties (Sept. 1937) (see RB17/86).		13p	£3.25
139	A	C	50	Famous Irish-Bred Horses (Nov. 1936)......		40p	£20.00
103	A	C	50	Famous Irish Greyhounds (Mar. 1935)......		60p	£30.00
	A	C	50	Film Stars—"Series of 50" (Mar. 1934)......		25p	£12.50
428	A	C	50	Film Stars—"Second Series...":—			
				A. Home issue—Album "price one penny" (Dec. 1934)		14p	£7.00
				B. Irish issue—Album offer without price (Nov. 1935)........................		30p	£15.00
431	A	C	50	Film Stars (see RB17/92):—			
				A. Home issue—titled "Film Stars—Third Series..." (Nov. 1938)		13p	£5.50
				B. Irish issue—titled "Screen Celebrities" (Jan. 1939)............................		90p	—

Illus. No.	Size	Print-ing	Number in set		Handbook ref.	Price per card	Complete set
	B	BW	25	Film Stars—Large size (Nov. 1934):—			
				A. Home issue—with album offer		70p	£17.50
				B. Irish issue—without album offer		80p	—
	A	C	50	Fire-Fighting Appliances (Dec. 1930)		30p	£15.00
608	A	C	50	Flags of the League of Nations (Mar. 1928)..		15p	£7.50
166	A	C	50	Football Caricatures by "Mac" (Sep. 1927)..		13p	£6.00
183	A	C	50	Football Caricatures by "Rip" (Aug. 1926)..		13p	£6.00
	A	C	50	Footballers, 1928 (Oct. 1928)		26p	£13.00
164	A	C	25	Footballers, 1928–9—"2nd Series" (Feb. 1929)..		44p	£11.00
	A	C		Fresh-Water Fishes:—			
			50	A. Small size, Home issue—			
				1. Pink card (Nov. 1933)..............		22p	£11.00
				2. White card (Feb. 1934).............		30p	£15.00
	B		25	B. Large size, Home issue—adhesive (June 1935)..		44p	£11.00
	B		25	C. Large size, Irish issue—non-adhesive...		60p	—
	A	C	25	From Plantation to Smoker (Mar. 1926).....		26p	£6.50
		C		Game Birds and Wild Fowl (see RB21/217/105):—			
35	A		50	A. Small size (June 1927)		25p	£12.50
	B		25	B. Large size (Nov. 1928)................		90p	£22.50
		C		Gilbert and Sullivan—"A Series of ...":—			
	A		50	A. Small size (Dec. 1925)		26p	£13.00
	J		25	B. Extra-large size (Apr. 1926)...........		80p	£20.00
		C		Gilbert and Sullivan—"2nd Series of ...":—			
	A		50	A. Small size (Dec. 1927)		17p	£8.50
529	B		25	B. Large size (Jan. 1928)................		80p	£20.00
197	B	C	25	Golf (July 1939) (see RB17/109).............		26p	£6.50
76	A	C	25	Hidden Beauties (July 1929)...............		13p	£3.50
	A	C	50	Hints on Association Football (Sep. 1934) (see RB21/217/112)		22p	£11.00
		C		History of Naval Dress:—			
393	A		50	A. Small size (Sep. 1930)...............		22p	£11.00
	B		25	B. Large size (July 1929)...............		80p	£20.00
355	A	C	50	International Air Lines (see RB17/116):—			
				A. Home issue—Album "price one penny" (Nov. 1936)..........................		13p	£6.50
				B. Irish issue—Album offer without price (July 1937)...........................		20p	£10.00
	A	C	25	Irish Place Names—"A Series of 25" (Aug. 1927).................................		80p	£20.00
	A	C	25	Irish Place Names—"2nd Series of 25" (Apr. 1929).................................		80p	£20.00
		C	50	Kings & Queens of England:—			
484	A			A. Small size (Apr. 1935)		20p	£10.00
	B			B. Large size (Sep. 1935)................		50p	£25.00
	A	C	25	Live Stock (Aug. 1925)		70p	£17.50
282	A	C	50	Military Head-Dress (Mar. 1931)..........		32p	£16.00
278	A	C	50	Military Uniforms of the British Empire Overseas (Feb. 1938) (see RB17/126)......		14p	£7.00
347	A	C	50	Modern Naval Craft (see RB17/129):—			
				A. Home issue—adhesive (Feb. 1939)		13p	£3.25
				B. Irish issue—non-adhesive (Aug. 1939)..		30p	—
364	A	C	50	Motor Cars—"A Series of 50" (see RB17/130):—			
				A. Home issue—Album "price one penny" (Mar. 1936)...........................		32p	£16.00
				B. Irish issue—Album offer without price (July 1936)...........................		70p	£35.00
367	A	C	50	Motor Cars—"Second Series ..." (May 1937) (see RB17/131)...................		22p	£11.00
	B	U	20	Mount Everest (June 1925)		90p	£18.00
600	A	C	50	National Flags and Arms (see RB17/134):—			
				A. Home issue—Album "price one penny" (Sep. 1936)..........................		13p	£5.50
				B. Irish issue—Album offer without price (Mar. 1937)..........................		25p	£12.50
	B	C	25	The Nation's Shrines (Oct. 1929) (see RB17/135)..............................		60p	£15.00
		C		Natural History:—			
93	A		50	A. Small size (June 1924)		15p	£7.50
	J		12	B. Extra-large size—"A Series of 12" (Nov. 1923).................................		80p	£10.00
	J		12	C. Extra-large size—"2nd Series of 12" (Sep. 1924)............................		80p	£10.00
	B	C	24	A Nature Calendar (Apr. 1930)		90p	£22.00
140	B	C	25	"Old Hunting Prints" (Feb. 1938) (see RB17/140)...............................		60p	£15.00
330	B	C	25	Old Naval Prints (Oct. 1936) (see RB17/141).		70p	£17.50
	J	BW	25	Old Sporting Prints (Dec. 1924)............		80p	£20.00
	B	C	25	Picturesque Bridges (Feb. 1929)............		70p	£17.50
	B	C	25	Picturesque Cottages (Dec. 1929)...........		70p	£17.50
552	B	C	25	Picturesque London (Sep. 1931)		70p	£17.50
565	B	C	25	Portals of the Past (Dec. 1930)		50p	£12.50
34	A	C	50	Poultry (Dec. 1931):—			
				A. Cards..................................		22p	£11.00
				B. Transfers		18p	£9.00

Illus. No.	Size	Print-ing	Number in set		Handbook ref.	Price per card	Complete set
	A	C	50	Products of the World—Scenes only (June 1928) (see RB21/200/294)		14p	£7.00
	A	C	25	Racehorses (Dec. 1926)...................		£1.00	£25.00
127	A	U	40	Racing Caricatures (Aug. 1925)		30p	£12.00
	B	C	25	Racing Yachts (July 1938) (see RB17/159)...		26p	£6.50
	A	C	50	R.A.F. Badges (Nov. 1937) (see RB17/160):—			
				A. Without motto		13p	£5.50
				B. With motto		13p	£6.50
	A	C	50	Regimental Standards and Cap Badges (Mar. 1930)..................................		32p	£16.00
509	—	C	1	The Royal Family (Mar. 1937) (85 × 66 mm.)		—	£0.75
				Screen Celebrities—see Film Stars			
	A	C	50	Sea Fishes (see RB17/172):—			
				A. Home issue—Album "price one penny" (Nov. 1935)......................		13p	£5.50
				B. Irish issue—Album offer without price (Dec. 1937)		60p	—
	A	C	50	A Sectional Map of Ireland		£1.00	£50.00
	B	C	20	Ship-Models (Sep. 1926).................		90p	£18.00
	B	C	25	Ships' Figure-Heads (Dec. 1931)		70p	£17.50
271	A	C	50	Speedway Riders (Aug. 1937).............		22p	£11.00
507	A	C	50	Straight Line Caricatures (Dec. 1926)		18p	£9.00
48	A	C	25	Struggle for Existence (Feb. 1923):—			
				A. With comma in I.T.C. Clause, back chocolate-brown		24p	£6.00
				B. Without comma, back reddish-brown ..		24p	£6.00
223	A	C	50	Tennis (July 1936)....................		13p	£5.00
	B	C	25	Treasures of Britain (Apr. 1931)		30p	£7.50
	A	C	25	Treasures of Ireland (May 1930)		90p	£22.50
130	B	C	25	Types of Horses (Feb. 1939) (see RB17/190) .		44p	£11.00
308	A	C	50	Uniforms of the Territorial Army (Oct. 1939)		13p	£6.50
281	A	C	90	War Decorations & Medals (Mar. 1927).....		35p	£32.00
		C		Wild Animals (see RB17/196):—			
90	A		50	A. Small size—"Wild Animals' Heads" (Jan.–June 1931)		14p	£7.00
	A		25	B. Small transfers, number in series not stated (1931)		50p	—
	A		50	C. Small transfers—"A Series of 50" (1931)		16p	£8.00
	B		25	D. Large size—"Wild Animals—A Series of..." (July 1927)		60p	£15.00
	B		25	E. Large size—"Wild Animals—2nd Series ..." (Dec. 1932)		36p	£9.00
		C		Wild Birds:—			
31	A		50	A. Small size (Oct. 1932):—			
				1. Cards		14p	£7.00
				2. Transfers......................		13p	£6.00
	B		25	B. Large size (June 1934)		50p	£12.50
	B	C	25	Wild Fowl (June 1937)		50p	£12.50
	A	C	25	Wonders of the World (grey back) (Aug. 1926)............................	H.362	50p	£12.50
	A	C	25	Wrestling & Ju-Jitsu (grey back) (May 1925).	H.467	60p	£15.00
	A	C	26	Your Initials (transfers) (July-Dec. 1932)		40p	£10.00
78	B	C	25	Zoo Babies (Oct. 1938) (see RB17/205)		20p	£5.00

C. Post-1940 Issues

Illus. No.	Size	Print-ing	Number in set		Handbook ref.	Price per card	Complete set
	—	BW	9	Basket Ball Fixtures (1972) (114 × 71 mm.) ..		55p	—
	—	C	32	British Birds (1980) (89 × 50 mm.)...........		—	—
	—	C	30	British Mammals (90 × 50 mm.) (1982)		—	—
	—	C	32	Country Houses and Castles (90 × 50 mm.) (1981)		—	—
	—	U	116	Corsair Game (63 × 38 mm.) (Player/Wills Joint issue)		32p	
	—	C	28	Famous MG Marques (90 × 50 mm.) (1981) .		—	—
	—	C	24	The Golden Age of Flying (1977) (89 × 50 mm.)................................		07p	£1.80
	—	C	1	The Golden Age of Flying Completion Offer (1977) (89 × 50 mm.)		—	£0.25
	—	C	24	The Golden Age of Motoring (1975) (89 × 50 mm.):—			
				A. With set completion offer		55p	—
				B. Without set completion offer...........		07p	£1.80
	—	C	24	The Golden Age of Sail (1978) (89 × 50 mm.) Album—50p		07p	£1.80
	—	C	1	The Golden Age of Sail Completion Offer (1978) (89 × 50 mm.)....................		—	£0.25
655 etc.	—	C	24	The Golden Age of Steam (1976) (89 × 50 mm.) .... Album—50p		07p	£1.80
	—	C	1	The Golden Age of Steam Completion Offer (1976) (89 × 50 mm.)....................		—	£0.25
	—	U	7	Grandee Limericks (1977) (86 × 50 mm.)		55p	—
	—	C	24	History of the V.C. (1980) (89 × 50 mm.)		—	—
	—	BW	5	Jubilee Issue 1960 (70 × 55 mm.)		50p	£2.50
	—	C	32	Myths and Legends (72 × 57 mm.) (1982)....		—	—
	—	C	24	Napoleonic Uniforms (1979) (89 × 50 mm.)..		08p	£2.00
	—	C	1	Napoleonic Uniforms Completion Offer (1979) (89 × 50 mm.)		—	£0.25
	—	C	8	Panama Puzzles (89 × 50 mm.)		75p	—

JOHN PLAYER & SONS (continued)

Illus. No.	Size	Print-ing	Number in set		Handbook ref.	Price per card	Complete set
—		BW	6	Play Ladbroke Spot-Ball (1975) (90 × 50 mm.)..........................		60p	—
—		U	4	Tom Thumb Record Breakers (82 × 65 mm.) (1976)...........................		60p	—
—		C	25	Top Dogs (1979) (89 × 50 mm.)........		—	—
—		C	6	World of Gardening (1976) (90 × 50 mm.) ...		60p	—
D. Unissued Series							
	A	C	25	Birds & Their Young, 1st series		13p	£2.50
	A	C	25	Birds & Their Young, 2nd series		13p	£2.50
	A	C	50	Civil Aircraft (Prepared but not issued)......		—	—
	A	C	25	Cries of London, "2nd Series ..." (black back)....................................		£3.50	—
	A	C	50	Decorations & Medals		£1.00	£50.00
	A	C	50	Dogs' Heads by Biegel.....................		13p	£6.50
107	B	C	25	Dogs—Pairs and Groups...................		30p	£7.50
	A	C	25	Napoleon (black back)	H.364	—	—
	A	C	50	Products of the World—Scenes only (black back)...................................		—	—
	A	C	50	Shipping.................................		90p	£45.00
	A	C	50	Wonders of the Deep (black back)	H.365	—	—
	A	C	25	Wonders of the World (black back)		—	—
E. Miscellaneous							
	A1	U	1	Advertisement Insert Grosvenor Cigarettes (1970).................................		—	£0.75
	A	C	1	Card Scheme—Joker Card (?1930's)		—	£3.25
	—	C	?	Football Fixture Folders (1946–61)		£3.00	—
	—	C	8	Snap Cards (93 × 65 mm.) (1930's)		£6.50	—

JAS. PLAYFAIR & CO., London

Pre-1919 Issue

	A	C	25	How to Keep Fit—Sandow Exercises	H.136	£12.00	—

THE PREMIER TOBACCO MANUFACTURERS LTD., London

Post-1920 Issues

	D	U	48	Eminent Stage & Screen Personalities (1936).	Ha.569	90p	—
	—	BW		Stage & Screen Personalities (1937) (57 × 35 mm.):—			
			100	A. Back in grey		50p	—
			50	B. Back in brown (Nos. 51–100)		50p	—

PRITCHARD & BURTON LTD., London

Pre-1919 Issues

	A2	C	50	*Actors and Actresses—"FROGA B and C":—	H.20/Ha.20		
				A. Blue back............................		£8.00	—
				B. Grey-black back		£14.00	—
	A	C	15	*Beauties—"PAC"..........................	H.2	£22.00	£330.00
	D	BW	20	*Boer War Cartoons (1900).................	H.42/Ha.42	£38.00	—
601	A1	C		*Flags and Flags with Soldiers:—	H.41		
				A. Flagstaff Draped:			
			30	1st printing		£5.00	150.00
			15	2nd printing.........................		£10.00	£150.00
			15	B. Flagstaff not Draped (Flags only)		£7.00	—
	D	U	25	*Holiday Resorts and Views	H.366	£6.00	—
	A	C	40	*Home and Colonial Regiments:—	H.69		
				20. Caption in blue		£30.00	—
				20. Caption in brown		£30.00	—
	D	U	25	*Royalty Series (1902)......................	H.367	£7.00	—
	A2	C	25	*Star Girls................................	H.30	£75.00	—
	D	U	25	*South African Series (1901)................	H.368	£6.00	—

G. PRUDHOE, Darlington

Pre-1919 Issues

	C	C	30	*Army Pictures, Cartoons, etc................	Ha.12	—	—

JAMES QUINTON LTD., London

Pre-1919 Issue

	A	C	26	*Actresses—"FROGA A"...................	H.20	—	—

RAY & CO. LTD., London

Pre-1919 Issues

	A	BW	25	War Series—1–25—Battleships		£9.00	—
	A	C	75	War Series—26–100—British & Foreign Uniforms................................		£7.50	—
	A	C	25	War Series—101–125—British & Dominion Uniforms...............................		£10.00	—

RAYMOND REVUEBAR, London _____

Illus. No.	Size	Printing	Number in set		Handbook ref.	Price per card	Complete set

Post-1940 Issue

| | | P | 25 | Revuebar Striptease Artists (1960) (72 × 46 mm.)............................... | | £3.00 | — |

RECORD CIGARETTE CO., London _____

Post 1920 Issue

| | | U | ? 25 | The "Talkie" Cigarette Card—Variety Series of 25 (gramophone record on reverse) (70 mm. square)............................. | | £20.00 | — |

J. REDFORD & CO., London _____

Pre-1919 Issues

A	BW	20	*Actresses—"BLARM"....................		H.23	£36.00	—
A2	C	25	*Armies of the World		H.43	£36.00	—
A2	C	25	*Beauties—"GRACC"....................		H.59	£65.00	—
A2	C	30	*Colonial Troops		H.40	£32.00	—
D2	C	40	*Naval and Military Phrases................		H.14	£18.00	—
D	C	? 23	*Nautical Expressions.....................		H.174	£65.00	—
A	C	25	Picture Series		H.369	£14.00	—
A	C	25	Sports & Pastimes Series 1		H.225	—	—
D1	BW	50	Stage Artistes of the Day		H.370	£3.00	£150.00

RELIANCE TOBACCO MFG. CO. LTD. _____

Post-1920 Issues

A2	C	24	British Birds		Ha.604	£1.80	£45.00
A2	C	35	*Famous Stars*		Ha.572	£1.80	£62.50

RICHARDS & WARD _____

Pre-1919 Issue

A1	P	? 2	*Beauties "Topsy Cigarettes"................		H.371	—	—

THE RICHMOND CAVENDISH CO. LTD., London _____

Pre-1919 Issues

A2	C	26	*Actresses—"FROGA A"..................		H.20	£10.00	—
D2	BW	28	*Actresses—"PILPI I"		H.195	£5.00	—
D	P	50	*Actresses—"PILPI II"		H.196	£5.00	—
A	U		*Actresses Photogravure, "Smoke Pioneer Cigarettes" back:—		H.372/Ha.372		
		50	I. Reading bottom to top...........			£4.00	£200.00
		?164	IIA. Reading top to bottom. Different Subjects....................			£4.00	—
		? 13	B. Plain back..................			—	—
A	C	14	*Beauties "AMBS" (1899–1900):		H.373		
			A. Verses "The Absent-minded Beggar" back (4 verses and 4 choruses).........			£20.00	
			B. Verses "Soldiers of the Queen" back (3 verses and 1 chorus)...............			£20.00	—
A	C	52	*Beauties—"ROBRI" playing card inset		H.374	£22.00	—
—	C	40	*Medals (34 × 72 mm.)		H.200	£7.00	£280.00
A2	C	20	Music Hall Artistes		H.202	£12.00	£240.00
A	C	12	*Pretty Girl Series—"RASH":—		H.8		
			i. 1–6 Head and Shoulders..............			£16.00	£95.00
			ii. 7–12 Full length......................			£16.00	£95.00
A	C	20	*Yachts:—		H.204		
			A. Gold on black back			£25.00	—
			B. Black on white back			£25.00	—

R. ROBERTS & SONS, London _____

Pre-1919 Issues

A2	C	26	*Actresses—"FROGA A"..................		H.20	£36.00	—
A	C	25	*Armies of the World:—		H.43		
			A. "Fine Old Virginia" back..............			£22.00	—
			B. Plain back..........................			£16.00	—
A2	C	50	*Beauties—"CHOAB":—		H.21		
			1–25 without borders to back			£50.00	—
			26–50 with borders to back			£70.00	—
A2	C	50	*Colonial Troops:—		H.40		
			1–30 "Fine Old Virginia"			£10.00	—
			31–50 "Bobs Cigarettes"			£20.00	—
A	BW	28	*Dominoes			£75.00	—
K1	C	52	*Miniature Playing Cards		H.334/Ha.334	—	—
D2	C	? 23	*Nautical Expressions:—		H.174		
			A. "Navy Cut Cigarettes" on front........			£40.00	—
			B. Firm's name only on front			£45.00	—
A2	C	70	Stories without words—10 sets of 7 cards:— per card and per set of 7			£17.00	—
A2	C	25	*Types of British and Colonial Troops		H.76/Ha.76	£32.00	—

ROBINSON & BARNSDALE LTD., London

Illus. No.	Size	Printing	Number in set		Handbook ref.	Price per card	Complete set
Pre-1919 Issues							
—		C	1	*Advertisement Card—Soldier, "Colin Campbell Cigars" (29 × 75 mm.)		—	£55.00
—		BW	? 19	*Actresses, "Colin Campbell Cigars":—	H.375		—
				A. Size—43 × 70 mm.		£50.00	
				B. Officially cut narrow—32 × 70 mm.		£35.00	
	A	P	? 14	*Actresses, "Cupola" Cigarettes	H.376	£85.00	—
	A1	P	? 13	*Beauties—collotype:—	H.377		
				A. "Our Golden Beauties" back in black		—	—
				B. "Nana" back in red on white		—	—
				C. "Nana" back in vermillion on cream		—	—
	A	C	? 1	*Beauties—"Blush of Day"	H.378	—	—
	—	C	? 4	*Beauties—"Highest Honors" (44 × 73 plus—i.e. card probably cut), "Virginia Crown" label on back	H.379/Ha.379	—	—

E. ROBINSON & SONS LTD., Stockport

Illus. No.	Size	Printing	Number in set		Handbook ref.	Price per card	Complete set
A. Pre-1919 Issues							
	A1	C	10	*Beauties—"ROBRI"	H.374	£32.00	—
	A	BW	? 4	Derbyshire and the Peak	H.380	—	—
	A2	C	25	Egyptian Studies		£8.00	£200.00
	A	C	? 6	Medals and Decorations of Great Britain	Ha.484	—	—
	A2	C	40	Nature Studies		£6.00	£240.00
	A2	C	25	Regimental Mascots (1916)		£27.00	—
71	A2	C	25	Wild Flowers		£6.00	£150.00
B. Post-1920 Issue							
	A	C	25	King Lud Problems		£11.00	

ROTHMAN'S LTD., London

Illus. No.	Size	Printing	Number in set		Handbook ref.	Price per card	Complete set
A. Post-1920 Issues							
		C		Beauties of the Cinema (1939):—	Ha.605		
416	D1		40	A. Small size		16p	£6.50
	—		24	B. Circular cards, 64 mm. diam.:—			
				1. Varnished		40p	£10.00
				2. Unvarnished		32p	£8.00
	A2	P	24	Cinema Stars—Small size		30p	£7.50
	B	P	25	Cinema Stars—Large size		13p	£2.00
	C	U	36	Landmarks in Empire History		17p	£6.00
	D1	U	50	Modern Inventions (1935)		20p	£10.00
	B2	P	54	New Zealand		50p	£27.00
443	D1	U	24	Prominent Screen Favourites (1934)	Ha.568	13p	£3.25
	A2	BW	50	"Punch Jokes"		13p	£4.25
B. Post-1940 Issues							
	—	C	30	Country Living (Consulate) (112 × 102 mm.) (1973)		—	£10.00
	A1	C	5	Rare Banknotes (1970)		70p	—
C. Miscellaneous							
	—	C	6	Diamond Jubilee Folders (1950) (127 × 95 mm.)		—	—
		?		Metal Charms		75p	—

WM. RUDDELL LTD., Dublin and Liverpool

Illus. No.	Size	Printing	Number in set		Handbook ref.	Price per card	Complete set
Post-1920 Issues							
527	D	C	25	Grand Opera Series (1924)		£1.40	£35.00
	A2	C	25	Rod & Gun (1924)		£1.40	£35.00
	D	C	50	Songs that will Live for Ever		£1.20	£60.00

I. RUTTER & CO., Mitcham

Illus. No.	Size	Printing	Number in set		Handbook ref.	Price per card	Complete set
Pre-1919 Issues							
	D	BW	15	*Actresses—"RUTAN"	H.381	£13.00	—
				A. Rubber-stamped on plain back		£15.00	—
				B. Red printed back		£11.00	—
				C. Plain back		—	—
	A	BW	1	Advertisement Card "Tobacco Bloom"	Ha.485		
	A	BW	? 7	*Boer War Celebrities	H.382/Ha.382	£17.00	—
	D1	C	54	*Comic Phrases	H.223	£6.50	£350.00
	A	BW	20	Cricketers Series	H.29	£30.00	—
	C	C		*Flags and Flags with Soldiers:—	H.41		
			15	A. Flagstaff Draped, 2nd printing		£9.00	—
			15	B. Flagstaff not Draped (Flags only)			
				(a) white back		£9.00	—
				(b) cream back		£9.00	—
598	C	C	24	*Girls, Flags & Arms of Countries:—	H.383		
				A. Blue back		£15.00	—
				B. Plain back		—	—
	A	C	? 20	Proverbs	H.384/Ha.384	£14.00	—
	A	C	25	*Shadowgraphs	H.44	£16.00	—

S.D.V. TOBACCO CO. LTD., Liverpool

Illus. No.	Size	Print-ing	Number in set		Handbook ref.	Price per card	Complete set

Pre-1919 Issues

| | A | BW | 16 | British Royal Family...................... | H.28 | £75.00 | — |

ST. DUNSTAN'S, London

Post-1920 Issue

| | — | C | 6 | Famous Posters (folders) (65 × 41 mm.) ..... | Ha.606 | £9.00 | — |

ST. PETERSBURG CIGARETTE CO. LTD., Portsmouth

Pre-1919 Issues

| | A | BW | ? 4 | Footballers............................. | H.410/Ha.410 | — | — |

SALMON & GLUCKSTEIN LTD., London

A. Pre-1919 Issues

		C	1	*Advertisement Card ("Snake Charmer" Cigarettes) (73 × 107 mm.)...............		—	£135.00
266	C	C	15	*Billiard Terms:—			
				A. Small numerals.....................		£10.00	£150.00
				B. Larger numerals		£10.00	£150.00
	A	C	12	British Queens (? 1897)	Ha.480	£14.00	£170.00
	—	C	30	*Castles, Abbeys & Houses (76 × 73 mm.):—			
				A. Brown back..........................		£12.00	—
				B. Red back		£14.00	—
	C	C	32	*Characters from Dickens	H.385	£10.00	£320.00
513	A	C	25	Coronation Series (1911)		£4.00	£100.00
	—	U	25	*Famous Pictures—Brown photogravure (57 × 76 mm.)......................	H.386	£3.60	£90.00
	—	U	25	*Famous Pictures—Green photogravure (58 × 76 mm.)......................	H.387	£3.60	£90.00
492	A2	C	6	Her Most Gracious Majesty Queen Victoria (1897):—	H.388		
				A. Thin card.........................		£13.00	£80.00
				B. Thick card........................		£12.00	£75.00
516	A	C	50	The Great White City		£3.50	£175.00
309	C	C	40	Heroes of the Transvaal War (1901–2)	H.389	£6.00	£240.00
	C	C	30	*Music Hall Celebrities...................		£7.00	£210.00
	C	C	? 20	*Occupations, narrow cards	H.390/Ha.390	£150.00	—
	C	C	20	"Owners & Jockeys" Series...............	H.392	£11.00	—
	—	C	48	*The Post in Various Countries (41 × 66 mm.)	H.391	£16.00	—
	A2	C	6	*Pretty Girl Series—"RASH" ("Raspberry Buds" Cigarettes)......................	H.8	£27.00	—
	—	C	22	Shakespearian Series:—	H.393		
				A. Large format, frame line back (38 × 69 mm.)		£8.00	£175.00
				B. Re-drawn, small format, no frame line to back (37 × 66 mm.)..................		£9.00	—
469	A	C	25	*Star Girls:—	H.30		
				A. Red back		£65.00	—
				B. Brown back, different setting..........		£65.00	—
	A	C	25	Traditions of the Army & Navy (? 1917):—			
				A. Large numerals......................		£4.00	£100.00
				B. Smaller numerals, back redrawn		£4.00	£100.00

B. Post-1920 Issues

| 626 | D2 | C | 25 | Magical Series (1923)..................... | | £1.20 | £30.00 |
| | A2 | C | 25 | Wireless Explained (1923) .... | | £1.20 | £30.00 |

C. Silks

	—	C	50	*Pottery Types (paper-backed) (83 × 55 mm.) (see RB21/311):—			
				1. Numbered on front and back		£1.80	£90.00
				2. Numbered on back only		£1.80	£90.00

W. SANDORIDES & CO. LTD., London

Post-1920 Issues

		U	25	Aquarium Studies from the London Zoo— "Lucana" (1925):—	Ha.607		
		C2		A. Small size:—			
				1. Small lettering on back............		£1.20	£30.00
				2. Larger lettering on back...........		£1.20	£30.00
		B1		B. Large size........................		£1.20	£30.00
		C	25	Cinema Celebrities (1924):—	Ha.530		
		C2		A. Small size.........................		80p	£20.00
		—		B. Extra-large size, (109 × 67 mm.)........		£1.00	£25.00
		C	25	Cinema Stars (export):—	Ha.530		
		C2		A. Small size, with firm's name at base of back................................		—	—
		C2		B. Small size, "Issued with Lucana Cigarettes ..."		—	—
		C2		C. Small size, "Issued with Big Gun Cigarettes" ..."......................		—	—

W. SANDORIDES & CO. LTD. (continued)

Illus. No.	Size	Printing	Number in set		Handbook ref.	Price per card	Complete set
—				D. Extra-large size, (109 × 67 mm.) "Issued with Big Gun Cigarettes …"		£1.00	—
		U	50	Famous Racecourses (1926) — "Lucana":—	Ha.608		
	C2			A. Small size		80p	£40.00
	B1			B. Large size		80p	£40.00
	C2	U	50	Famous Racehorses (1923):—	Ha.609		
				1A. Back in light brown		80p	£40.00
				1B. Back in dark brown		80p	£40.00
				2. As 1A, with blue label added, inscribed "Issued with Sandorides Big Gun Cigarettes …"		—	—
	A	C	25	Sports & Pastimes—Series I—"Big Gun Cigarettes"	H.225	—	—

NICHOLAS SARONY & CO., London

A. Pre-1919 Issue

Illus. No.	Size	Printing	Number in set		Handbook ref.	Price per card	Complete set
—		U	? 1	Boer War Scenes (67 × 45 mm.)	H.394	—	—

B. Post-1920 Issues

Illus. No.	Size	Printing	Number in set		Handbook ref.	Price per card	Complete set
		C	50	Around the Mediterranean (June 1926):—	Ha.610		
	C2			A. Small size		25p	£12.50
	B1			B. Large size		30p	£15.00
		U	25	Celebrities and Their Autographs, Nd. 1–25 (1923):—			
	C1			A. Small size		26p	£6.50
	B1			B. Large size		26p	£6.50
		U	25	Celebrities and Their Autographs, Nd. 26–50 (1924):—			
	C1			A. Small size:—			
				1. Small numerals		26p	£6.50
				2. Large numerals		26p	£6.50
	B1			B. Large size:—			
				1. Small numerals		26p	£6.50
				2. Large numerals		26p	£6.50
		U	25	Celebrities and Their Autographs, Nd. 51–75 (1924):—			
	C1			A. Small size		26p	£6.50
	B1			B. Large size		26p	£6.50
		U	25	Celebrities and Their Autographs, Nd. 76–100 (1925):—			
	C1			A. Small size		26p	£6.50
	B1			B. Large size		26p	£6.50
	A2	U	50	Cinema Stars—Set 7 (June 1933)	Ha.515–7	18p	£9.00
—		U		Cinema Stars—Postcard size (137 × 85 mm.):—			
			38	"of a Series of 38 Cinema Stars" (June 1929)		£1.75	—
			42	"of a second Series of 42 Cinema Stars"		60p	£25.00
			50	"of a third Series of 50 Cinema Stars"		70p	£35.00
			42	"of a fourth Series of 42 Cinema Stars"		60p	£25.00
			25	"of a fifth Series of 25 Cinema Stars"		60p	£15.00
422	D	U	25	Cinema Studies (Sep. 1929)		13p	£3.50
		C	25	A Day on the Airway (Feb. 1928):—			
	C2			A. Small size		22p	£5.50
	B2			B. Large size		22p	£5.50
	A2	P	54	Life at Whipsnade Zoo (Dec. 1934)	Ha.556	18p	£9.00
		BW	25	Links with the Past—First 25 subjects, Nd. 1–25 (1925):—			
	C1			A. Small size		34p	£8.50
	B			B. Large size		30p	£7.50
		BW	25	Links with the Past—Second 25 subjects (1926):—			
	C			A. Home issue, Nd. 26–50:—			
				1. Small size		26p	£6.50
	B			2. Large size, descriptive back		22p	£5.50
	B			3. Large size, advertisement back		£1.50	—
				B. Sydney issue, Nd. 1–25:—			
	C			1. Small size		22p	£5.50
	B			2. Large size		32p	£8.00
	C			C. Christchurch issue, Nd. 1–25:—			
				1. Small size		28p	£7.00
				2. Large size		16p	£4.00
		BW	25	Museum Series (1927):—			
				A. Home issue:—			
	C2			1 Small size		14p	£3.50
	B			2. Large size, descriptive back		13p	£2.50
	B			3. Large size, advertisement back		20p	£5.00
	B			B. Sydney issue, large size		13p	£3.25
				C. Christchurch issue:—			
	C2			1. Small size		14p	£3.50
	B			2. Large size		13p	£3.25
		P	36	National Types of Beauty (Apr. 1928):—	Ha.558		
	A2			A. Small size		20p	£7.00
	—			B. Medium size (76 × 51 mm.)		17p	£6.00
		C	15	Origin of Games (1923):—			
248	A			A. Small size		£1.10	£16.50
	B2			B. Large size		£1.10	£16.50

NICHOLAS SARONY & CO. *(continued)*

Illus. No.	Size	Printing	Number in set		Handbook ref.	Price per card	Complete set
		C	50	'Saronicks' (June 1929):—	Ha.557		
	D2			A. Small size....................		13p	£3.00
	—			B. Medium size (76 × 51 mm.)		13p	£3.00
		C	50	Ships of All Ages (Dec. 1929):—			
	D			A. Small size....................		13p	£3.00
396	—			B. Medium size (76 × 52 mm.)		13p	£4.00
	D	C	25	Tennis Strokes (1923)		70p	£17.50

SCOTTISH CO-OPERATIVE WHOLESALE SOCIETY LTD., Glasgow ("S.C.W.S.")

Post-1920 Issues

Illus. No.	Size	Printing	Number in set		Handbook ref.	Price per card	Complete set
528	A2	C	25	Burns (1924):—	Ha.611		
				A. Printed back:—			
				1. White card		70p	—
				2. Cream card.....................		15p	£3.75
				*B. Plain back		70p	—
	C	C	20	Dogs (1925)...........................	H.211	£1.60	£32.00
	A2	C	25	Dwellings of All Nations (1924):—	Ha.612		
				A. Printed back:—			
				1. White card		90p	—
				2. Cream card		80p	£20.00
				*B. Plain back		—	—
	B	C	25	Famous Pictures (1924)...................		£1.50	£37.50
	H2	C	25	Famous Pictures—Glasgow Gallery:—			
				A. Non-adhesive back (1927)		80p	£20.00
				B. Adhesive back		60p	£15.00
	H2	C	25	Famous Pictures—London Galleries:—			
				A. Non-adhesive back (1927)		80p	£20.00
				B. Adhesive back		60p	£15.00
18	A2	C	50	Feathered Favourites:—			
				A. Grey borders (1926)		70p	£35.00
				B. White borders:—			
				1. Non adhesive back (1926)		70p	£35.00
				2. Adhesive back		70p	£35.00
	A	C	25	Racial Types (1925)		£1.80	£45.00
	A2	C	50	Triumphs of Engineering (1926):—			
				A. Brown border.....................		£1.00	£50.00
				B. White border......................		£1.25	—
	A2	C	50	Wireless (1924)........................		£1.20	£60.00

SELBY'S TOBACCO STORES, Cirencester

Post-1920 Issue

Illus. No.	Size	Printing	Number in set		Handbook ref.	Price per card	Complete set
—		U	? 12	"Manikin" Cards (79 × 51 mm.)		—	—

SHARPE & SNOWDEN, London

Pre-1919 Issue

Illus. No.	Size	Printing	Number in set		Handbook ref.	Price per card	Complete set
	A	U	? 8	*Views of London.........................	H.395	—	—

W. J. SHEPHERD, London

Pre-1919 Issue

Illus. No.	Size	Printing	Number in set		Handbook ref.	Price per card	Complete set
	A	U	25	*Beauties—"FECKSA".....................	H.58	£45.00	—

SHORT'S, London

Post-1920 Issue

Illus. No.	Size	Printing	Number in set		Handbook ref.	Price per card	Complete set
—		BW		*Short's House Views:—	Ha.562		
			? 13	1. Numbered (75 × 60 mm.)		—	—
			? 5	2. Unnumbered (77 × 69 mm.)...........		—	—

JOHN SINCLAIR LTD., Newcastle-on-Tyne

A. Pre-1919 Issues

Illus. No.	Size	Printing	Number in set		Handbook ref.	Price per card	Complete set
	D2	U	? 57	*Actresses (42 × 63 mm.)...................	H.396	£25.00	—
	D	P	50	Football Favourites, Nd. 51–100 (? 1910)....		£16.00	—
	A	BW	4	*North Country Celebrities.................	H.397	£20.00	£80.00
	D	P	? 80	Northern Gems...........................		£40.00	—
625	A	C	50	Picture Puzzles & Riddles.................		£9.00	£450.00
627	A	C	50	Trick Series............................		£10.00	£500.00
	D2	C	50	World's Coinage.........................	H.398	£6.00	£300.00

B. Post-1920 Issues

Illus. No.	Size	Printing	Number in set		Handbook ref.	Price per card	Complete set
—		P		*Birds (1924):—	Ha.613		
		C	? 13	A. Small size, back "Specimen Cigarette Card"		£1.25	—
		C	48	B. Small size, descriptive back:—			
				1. White front.......................		90p	£45.00
				2. Pinkish front.....................		90p	£45.00
	—		50	C. Large size (78 × 58 mm.)		£1.50	£75.00
392	A	C	50	British Sea Dogs (1926)...................		£1.30	£65.00

JOHN SINCLAIR LTD. *(continued)*

Illus. No.	Size	Printing	Number in set		Handbook ref.	Price per card	Complete set
		P		Champion Dogs—"A Series of . . ." (1938):—			
106	A2		54	A. Small size................................		13p	£2.25
	B2		52	B. Large size................................		13p	£3.75
		P		Champion Dogs—"2nd Series . . ." (1939):—			
	A2		54	A. Small size............................		45p	£24.00
	B2		52	B. Large size............................		45p	£24.00
192	A2	P	50	English & Scottish Football Stars (1935)		13p	£4.50
	A	P	54	Film Stars—"A Series of 54 Real Photos" (1934)............................		22p	£11.00
	A	P	54	Film Stars—"A Series of Real Photos", Nd. 1–54 (1937).............................		20p	£10.00
420	A	P	54	Film Stars—"A Series of Real Photos", Nd. 55–108 (1937).............................		13p	£4.25
		P		*Flowers and Plants (1924):—	Ha.614		
	C		? 11	A. Small size, back "Specimen Cigarette Card"		£1.25	—
	C		96	B. Small size, descriptive back:—			
				1. White front........................		90p	£90.00
				2. Pinkish front		90p	£90.00
	—		? 96	C. Large size, 78 × 58 mm.................		£1.50	—
	A	P	54	Radio Favourites (1935).................		35p	£19.00
	K2	C	53	Rubicon Cards (miniature playing cards)....		£1.25	—
	A	BW	50	Well-Known Footballers—North Eastern Counties (1938).........................		13p	£3.00
193	A	BW	50	Well-Known Footballers—Scottish (1938) ..		13p	£1.75
C. Silks		C		*Flags—Set 11 (unbacked and anonymous):—	Ha.501–11		
			50	"Fourth Series" (49 × 70 mm.).............		£4.00	—
			50	"Fifth Series" (49 × 70 mm.)		£4.00	—
			50	"Sixth Series":			
				1. Nos. 1–25 (49 × 70 mm.).............		—	—
				2. Nos. 26–50 (68 × 80 mm.)		—	—
			? 9	"Seventh Series" (115 × 145 mm.)		—	—
	—	C	? 1	The Allies (140 × 100 mm.) (Numbered 37) ..		—	£4.00
	—	C	50	*Regimental Badges I (includes two Regimental Colours and a Union Jack) (paperbacked) (70 × 52 mm.)....................	Ha.502–1	£1.25	—
	—	C	? 24	*Regimental Colours II (unbacked and anonymous):—	Ha.502–7		
				1. Nos. 38–49 (No. 49 not seen) (76 × 70 mm.)...............................		—	—
				2. Nos. 50–61 (65 × 51 mm.)		—	—

ROBERT SINCLAIR TOBACCO CO. LTD., Newcastle-on-Tyne ——

A. Pre-1919 Issues							
	A2	U	28	Dominoes		—	—
	A	BW	? 3	*Footballers	H.399	£65.00	—
	D	C	12	*Policemen of the World (? 1899)	H.164	£65.00	—
B. Post-1920 Issues							
	C2	C		Billiards by Willie Smith (1928):—			
			10	1. First Set of 10........................		£1.20	£12.00
			15	2. Second Set of 15.....................		£1.20	£18.00
			3	3. Third Set of 25 (Nos. 26–28 only issued)		£3.00	£9.00
		C	12	The "Smiler" Series (1924):—			
	A			A. Small size (inscribed ". . . 24 cards", 12 only issued)		£2.00	£24.00
	H			B. Large size		£2.00	—
C. Silks	*Unbacked silks, inscribed with initials "R.S." in circle.*						
	—	C	4	*Battleships and Crests (73 × 102 mm.).......	Ha.499–1	£16.00	£65.00
	—	C	? 7	*Flags (70 × 51 mm.)	Ha.499–2	—	—
	—	C	? 4	*Great War Area—Cathedrals and Churches (140 × 102 mm.).........................	Ha.499–3	£8.00	—
	—	C	? 9	*Great War Heroes (70 × 51 mm.)...........	Ha.499–4	£8.00	—
	—	C	? 1	*Red Cross Nurse (73 × 102 mm.)...........	Ha.499–5	—	£45.00
	—	C	? 4	*Regimental Badges (70 × 51 mm.)..........	Ha.499–6	—	—

J. SINFIELD, Scarborough ——————————————————

Pre-1919 Issue							
	A	U	? 24	*Beauties—"HUMPS"....................	H.222	£75.00	—

SINGLETON & COLE LTD., Shrewsbury ——————————

A. Pre-1919 Issues							
387	A	C	50	*Atlantic Liners (1910)		£9.00	£450.00
	D1	BW	50	*Celebrities—Boer War Period:—	H.400		
				25. Actresses		£7.00	£175.00
				25. Boer War Celebrities		£7.00	£175.00
	A	BW	35	Famous Officers—Hero Series:—			
				A1. "Famous Officers" on back toned card (1915)		£7.00	£250.00
				A2. "Famous Officers" thin white card.		£22.00	—
				B. "Hero Series" on back		£32.00	—
	D1	BW	50	*Footballers, Nd. on front..................		£19.00	

SINGLETON & COLE LTD. *(continued)*

Illus. No.	Size	Print-ing	Number in set		Handbook ref.	Price per card	Complete set
479	C	C	40	*Kings and Queens (1902)	H.157	£8.00	£320.00
	A	C	25	Maxims of Success:—	H.401		
				A. Orange border		£7.00	—
				B. Lemon yellow border.................		£12.00	—
	A	BW	? 14	Orient Royal Mail Line:—	H.402		
				A. "Orient-Pacific Line," Manager's back .		£15.00	
				B. "Orient Royal Mail Line," Singleton & Cole back.............................		£13.00	
				C. "Orient Line", Manager's back		£18.00	—
	A	C	25	Wallace Jones—Keep Fit System		£6.00	£150.00

B. Post-1920 Issues

Illus. No.	Size	Print-ing	Number in set		Handbook ref.	Price per card	Complete set
	A	C	25	Bonzo Series (1928) (see RB21/217/25)		£1.20	£30.00
221	A2	BW	35	Famous Boxers (1930):—			
				A. Numbered..........................		£1.50	—
				B. Unnumbered.......................		—	—
	A2	BW	25	Famous Film Stars (1930)		£1.25	—
	—	U	? 12	"Manikin" Cards (79 × 51 mm.)		—	—

C. Silks

Illus. No.	Size	Print-ing	Number in set		Handbook ref.	Price per card	Complete set
	—	C	110	Crests & Badges of the British Army (paper-backed) (66 × 40 mm.)..................	Ha.502–2	£4.00	—

F. & J. SMITH, Glasgow

(Refer to F. & J. Smith reference book for further information)

A. Pre-1919 Issues

Illus. No.	Size	Print-ing	Number in set		Handbook ref.	Price per card	Complete set
	A	C	25	*Advertisement Cards.......................	H.403	£80.00	—
	A	C	50	Battlefields of Great Britain (Dec. 1913).....	Ha.475	£4.00	£200.00
	A1	BW	25	*Boer War Series (1900) "Studio" Cigarettes back		£12.00	£300.00
315	A	C	50	*Boer War Series (1900–01).................		£14.00	—
263	D	BW		*Champions of Sport (1902–3):—	H.404/Ha.404		
			50	Red back. Numbered		£13.00	—
			50	Blue back. Unnumbered..................		£16.00	—
161	A	U	50	Cricketers (May 1912).....................		£4.00	£200.00
	A	U	20	Cricketers, 2nd Series, Nd. 51–70 (Aug. 1912)		£10.00	£200.00
146	A	U	50	Derby Winners (Jul. 1913).................		£2.50	£125.00
	A	C	50	Famous Explorers (Oct. 1911).............		£2.80	£140.00
	D	U	120	*Footballers, "Cup Tie Cigarettes," brown back (1902–3).......................		£8.00	—
	A	U	50	*Footballers, "Cup Tie Cigarettes," blue back "10 for 2½d" (1910–11) Nd. 1–52 (Nos. 1 and 13 not issued):—		—	£150.00
				A. Black portrait.......................		£3.00	—
				B. Brown portrait......................		£3.00	—
	A	U	50	*Footballers, "Cup Tie Cigarettes," blue back, "In packets of 10" (1910–11). Nd. 55–104 (Nos. 53 and 54 not issued):—		—	£150.00
				A. Black portrait.......................		£3.00	—
				B. Brown portrait......................		£3.00	—
173	A	U	150	*Footballers, var. advertisements, yellow frame line (Nov. 1914):—		—	£300.00
				A. Pale blue back......................		£2.00	—
				B. Deep blue back		£2.00	—
	A	C	50	Football Club Records, 1913 to 1917 (?1918)		£3.00	£150.00
	A	C	50	Fowls, Pigeons & Dogs (May 1908)	H.64	£2.80	£140.00
296	A	C		*Medals:—	H.71/Ha.71		
			20	A. Unnumbered—thick card (Apr. 1902)..		£4.50	£90.00
			50	B. Numbered. "F. & J. Smith" thick card (1902)		£3.20	£160.00
			50	C. Numbered. "The Imperial Tobacco Co." very thin card (1903)		£10.00	—
			50	D. Numbered. "The Imperial Tobacco Company" thin card (Feb. 1906)		£3.20	£160.00
	A	C	50	Naval Dress & Badges:—	H.172/Ha.172		
				A. Descriptive back (Oct. 1911)		£3.40	£170.00
				B. Non-descriptive back (Nov. 1914).....		£3.40	£170.00
	A	C	50	*Phil May Sketches, blue-grey back (May 1908)................................	H.72/Ha.72	£3.40	£170.00
	A	C	40	Races of Mankind:—	Ha.483		
				A. Series title on front		£27.00	
				*B. Without series title		£30.00	
	A	C	25	Shadowgraphs (Apr. 1915)	H.466/Ha.466	£3.60	£90.00
583	A	C	50	*A Tour Round the World:—			
				A. Script Advertisement back (Jan. 1904)..		£10.00	£500.00
				B. Post-card format back (Sep. 1905)......		£22.00	£1100.00
	A	C	50	A Tour Round the World (titled series, different from previous item) (Jan. 1906) ..	H.75/Ha.75	£3.40	£170.00
	A	BW	25	War Incidents (Nov. 1914):—	H.405		
				A. White back..........................		£3.60	£90.00
				B. Toned back		£3.00	£75.00
	A	BW	25	War Incidents, 2nd Series (Feb. 1915):—	H.405		
				A. White back		£3.60	£90.00
				B. Toned back		£3.00	£75.00

B. Post-1920 Issues

Illus. No.	Size	Print-ing	Number in set		Handbook ref.	Price per card	Complete set
	A	C	25	"Cinema Stars"	Ha.615	£1.60	£40.00
188	A	C	50	Football Club Records, 1921–2 (Oct. 1922)..		£3.00	£150.00
	A	C	25	Holiday Resorts (July 1925)		£1.20	£30.00

F. & J. SMITH (continued)

Illus. No.	Size	Printing	Number in set		Handbook ref.	Price per card	Complete set
	A	C	50	Nations of the World (Oct. 1923)	H.454	£1.20	£60.00
	A	C	50	Phil May Sketches (brown back) (Sep. 1924).	Ha.72	£1.80	£90.00
	A	C	25	Prominent Rugby Players (Nov. 1924)		£1.40	£35.00

SNELL & CO., Plymouth and Devonport

Pre-1919 Issue

	A	BW	25	*Boer War Celebrities—"STEW"............	H.105	£75.00	—

SOCIETE JOB, London (and Paris)

A. Pre-1919 Issues

Illus. No.	Size	Printing	Number in set		Handbook ref.	Price per card	Complete set
120	D	BW	25	*Dogs (? 1911)	H.406	£3.60	£90.00
	D	BW	25	*Liners (1912)	H.407	£12.00	—
	D	BW	25	*Racehorses—1908-9 Winners (1909)........	H.408	£4.00	£100.00

B. Post-1920 Issues

	A	C	25	British Lighthouses		£1.60	£40.00
	—	U	48	*Cinema Stars (58 × 45 mm.)—"Cigarettes Job" on front..........................	Ha.616	—	£20.00
			46/48	Ditto....................................		14p	£7.00
	A2	C	25	Orders of Chivalry (1924).................		£1.20	£30.00
	A2	C	25	Orders of Chivalry (Second Series) (1927) ...		£1.20	£30.00
	A2	C	3	Orders of Chivalry (unnumbered) (1927)		£2.00	£6.00

LEON SOROKO, London

Post-1920 Issue

	—	U	6	Jubilee Series (1935):—			
				A. Small size (75 × 41 mm.)		—	—
				B. Large size (83 × 73 mm.)		—	—

SOUTH WALES TOB. MFG. CO. LTD., Newport and London

Pre-1919 Issues

	A	U	25	*Views of London...........................	H.409	£7.00	£175.00
	A	BW	? 91	Game of Numbers		£38.00	—

SOUTH WALES TOBACCO CO. (1913) LTD., Newport

Pre-1919 Issue

	D	C	30	*Army Pictures, Cartoons, etc................	H.12	£70.00	—

S. E. SOUTHGATE & CO., London

Pre-1919 Issue

	A1	C	25	*Types of British and Colonial Troops	H.76	—	—

G. STANDLEY, Newbury

Post-1920 Issue

	—	U	? 12	"Manikin" Cards (79 × 51 mm.)	Ha.481	—	—

A. & A. E. STAPLETON, Hastings

Post-1920 Issue

	—	U	? 12	*"Manikin" Cards (79 × 51 mm.)	Ha.481	—	—

H. STEVENS & CO., Salisbury

Post-1920 Issues

	A1	C	20	*Dogs (1923).............................	H.211	£1.60	£32.00
	A1	U	25	*Zoo Series (1926).......................	Ha.588	£1.20	£30.00

A. STEVENSON, Middleton

Pre-1919 Issue

	A	U	50	War Portraits	H.86	—	—

ALBERT STOCKWELL, Porthcawl

Pre-1919 Issue

	D	C	30	*Army Pictures, Cartoons, etc................	H.12	—	—

STRATHMORE TOBACCO CO. LTD., London

Post-1920 Issue

	—	U	25	British Aircraft (76 × 50 mm.).............		22p	£5.50

TADDY & CO., London

Illus. No.	Size	Printing	Number in set		Handbook ref.	Price per card	Complete set
Pre-1919 issues							
—		U	? 71	*Actresses—collotype (40 × 70 mm.)	H.411/Ha.411	£35.00	—
464	A	C	25	*Actresses—with flowers		£50.00	—
	A	BW	38	Admirals & Generals—			
				The War A.	H.412	£6.50	—
				Scarce Cards B.		£16.00	—
	A	BW	38	Admirals & Generals—The War (South African printing).................		£12.00	—
	A1	BW	1	*Advertisement Card, "Imperial Tobacco" ...		—	—
525	A	C	25	Autographs.............................	H.413	£6.00	£150.00
	A	C	20	Boer Leaders:—			
				A. White back		£7.50	£150.00
				B. Cream back		£8.00	—
	A	C	50	British Medals & Decorations—Series 2.....		£3.50	£175.00
	A	C	50	British Medals & Ribbons		£3.60	£180.00
	A	C	20	*Clowns and Circus Artistes	H.414	£200.00	—
	C2	C	30	Coronation Series (38 × 66 mm.):—			
				A. Grained card......................		£7.00	£210.00
				B. Smooth card		£7.00	£210.00
	A	BW	238	County Cricketers.......................	H.415	£7.00	—
113	A	C	50	Dogs	Ha.487	£7.00	£350.00
	C	U	5	*English Royalty—collotype	H.416	£135.00	—
	A	C	25	Famous Actors—Famous Actresses.........		£6.00	£150.00
	A	BW	50	Famous Horses & Cattle		£16.00	—
137	A2	C	25	Famous Jockeys:—	H.417		
				A. Without frame line—blue title		£7.00	£175.00
				B. With frame line—brown title..........		£5.00	£125.00
	A	BW	? 32	Footballers (export issue).................	H.418	£20.00	—
593	A	C	25	"Heraldry" Series		£6.00	£150.00
313	A	C	25	Honours & Ribbons......................		£8.00	£200.00
	C	C	10	Klondyke Series		£17.00	£170.00
	C	BW	60	Leading Members of the Legislative Assembly (export issue).....................		—	—
	A	C	25	*Natives of the World	H.419	£28.00	£700.00
	A	C	25	Orders of Chivalry	H.301	£6.00	£150.00
	A	C	25	Orders of Chivalry, Second Series	H.301	£14.00	£350.00
187	A	BW	?996	Prominent Footballers—Grapnel and/or Imperial back:—	H.420		
				A. 595 Without "Myrtle Grove" footnote .		£2.25	—
				B. 401 With 'Myrtle Grove" footnote		£2.25	—
	A	BW	?311	Prominent Footballers—London Mixture back	H.420/Ha.420	£6.00	—
—		C	20	*Royalty, Actresses, Soldiers (39 × 72 mm.)...	H.421	£75.00	—
493	A	C	25	"Royalty" Series......................		£4.00	£100.00
	A	C	25	*Russo-Japanese War (1904) (1–25)..........		£4.00	£100.00
	A	C	25	*Russo-Japanese War (1904) (26–50)........		£8.00	£200.00
	A	BW	16	South African Cricket Team, 1907	H.422	£12.00	—
	A	BW	26	South African Football Team, 1906–7.......	H.423	£8.00	—
	A	C	25	Sports & Pastimes—Series 1	H.225	£4.00	£100.00
	A	C	25	Territorial Regiments—Series I (1908)		£8.00	£200.00
	A	C	25	Thames Series		£10.00	£250.00
	C	C	20	Victoria Cross Heroes (1–20)		£18.00	—
	C	C	20	Victoria Cross Heroes (21–40)		£18.00	—
311	A	C	20	V.C. Heroes—Boer War (41–60):—			
				A. White back		£9.00	—
				B. Toned back		£6.50	£130.00
	A	C	20	V.C. Heroes—Boer War (61–80):—			
				A. White back		£9.00	—
				B. Toned back		£6.50	£130.00
	A	C	20	V.C. Heroes—Boer War (81–100):—			
				A. White back		£9.00	—
				B. Toned back		£7.00	£140.00
	A	C	25	Victoria Cross Heroes (101–125)............		·£45.00	—
	A2	BW	2	*Wrestlers	H.424	£75.00	—

TADDY & CO., London and Grimsby

Post-1940 Issues							
—		C	8	Advertisement Cards, three sizes (1980)		20p	£1.60
363	A	C	26	Motor Cars, including checklist (1980):—			
				A. "Clown Cigarettes" back		13p	£3.25
				B. "Myrtle Grove Cigarettes" back		13p	£3.25
411	A	C	26	Railway Locomotives including checklist (1980):—			
				A. "Clown Cigarettes back		13p	£3.25
				B. "Myrtle Grove Cigarettes" back		13p	£3.25

TAYLOR WOOD, Newcastle

Pre-1919 Issue							
	C	C	18	Motor Cycle Series........................	Ha.469	—	—

W. & M. TAYLOR, Dublin

Illus. No.	Size	Print-ing	Number in set		Handbook ref.	Price per card	Complete set
Pre-1919 Issues							
	A	C	8	European War Series	H.129	—	—
	A	U	25	*War Series—"Muratti II":—	H.209		
				A. "Bendigo Cigarettes" back		—	—
				B. "Tipperary Cigarettes" back		£5.00	£125.00

TEOFANI & CO. LTD., London

A. Post-1920 Home Issues

Illus. No.	Size	Print-ing	Number in set		Handbook ref.	Price per card	Complete set
				Cards inscribed with Teofani's name.			
303	A2	C	24	Past & Present—Series A—The Army (1938)		£1.00	
				A. With Framelines		£1.00	—
				B. Without Framelines		15p	£3.75
284	A2	C	24	Past & Present—Series B—Weapons of War (1939)		13p	£2.75
	A2	C	52	Past & Present—Series C—Transport		£1.75	

B. Post-1920 Export Issues

				Cards mostly without Teofani's name.			
	C2	U	25	Aquarium Studies from the London Zoo ("Lucana" cards with green label added, inscribed "Issued with Teofani Windsor Cigarettes")	Ha.607	—	—
	D1	U	50	Cinema Celebrities:—	Ha.617		
				A. "Presented with Broadway Novelties"..		—	—
				B. "Presented with these well-known choice cigarettes"		£1.20	—
		C	25	Cinema Stars:—	Ha.530		
				1. *Anonymous printings:—*			
	C2			A. *Small size.*		90p	£22.50
				B. *Extra-large size, (109 × 67 mm.)*		£1.20	£30.00
				2. *Teofani printings:—*			
	C2			A. Small size—"Issued with Blue Band Cigarettes"		—	—
	C2			B. Small size—"Three Star Cigarettes"		—	—
	C2			C. Small size—"Three Star Magnums"		90p	—
	—			D. Extra-large size, (109 × 67 mm.)—"Three Star Magnums"		£1.20	—
217	D	U	25	*Famous Boxers—"Issued with The 'Favourite' Magnums..."	Ha.579	£1.50	—
	C2	P	32	Famous British Ships and Officers—"Issued with these High Grade Cigarettes"		£1.00	£32.00
	B1	U	50	Famous Racecourses ("Lucana" cards with mauve label added, inscribed "Issued with The Favourite Cigarettes")	Ha.608	—	—
	A	U	? 24	Famous Racehorses		—	—
	—	BW	12	*Film Actors and Actresses (56 × 31 mm.) (plain back)	Ha.618	34p	£4.00
	C2	C	20	*Great Inventors.*	H.213	£2.00	—
	A	C	20	*Head Dresses of Various Nations (plain back)	Ha.619–1	—	—
	—	BW	12	*London Views (57 × 31 mm.) (plain back)	Ha.620	13p	£1.50
430	D2	U	48	*Modern Movie Stars and Cinema Celebrities .*	Ha.569	13p	£5.00
	A	C	50	*Natives in Costume (plain back)	Ha.619–2	£2.50	—
	C	U	50	Public Schools & Colleges—"Issued with these Fine Cigarettes"	Ha.575	£3.00	—
	D	C	50	Ships and Their Flags—"Issued with these well-known cigarettes"	Ha.602	£1.00	£50.00
	A	C	25	Sports & Pastimes—Series I—"Smoke these cigarettes always"	H.225	—	—
	—	P	22	*Teofani Gems I—Series of 22 (53 × 35 mm.) (plain back)	Ha.621–1	40p	—
	—	P	28	*Teofani Gems II—Series of 28 (53 × 35 mm.) (plain back)	Ha.621–2	40p	—
	—	P	36	*Teofani Gems III—Series of 36 (53 × 35 mm.) (plain back)	Ha.621–3	40p	—
	A2	P	36	Views of the British Empire—"Issued with these Famous Cigarettes":—			
				A. Front in black and white		33p	£12.00
				B. Front in light brown		33p	£12.00
	C	U	50	Views of London—"Issued with these World Famous Cigarettes"	Ha.577	£1.50	—
	C2	U	24	*Well-Known Racehorses*	Ha.609	—	—
	A	C	50	*World's Smokers (plain back)	Ha.619–3	£2.50	—
	C	U	50	Zoological Studies	Ha.578	£3.50	—

TETLEY & SONS LTD., Leeds

Illus. No.	Size	Print-ing	Number in set		Handbook ref.	Price per card	Complete set
Pre-1919 Issues							
	A2	C	1	*"The Allies" (grouped flags)	H.425	—	—
288	A	U	50	War Portraits	H.86	£11.00	—
	D	C	25	World's Coinage	H.398	£17.00	—

THEMANS & CO., Manchester

Illus. No.	Size	Printing	Number in set		Handbook ref.	Price per card	Complete set
A. Pre-1919 Issues							
	A	C	? 1	*Advertisement card with Riddles	H.426	—	—
	A1	C	? 1	Allied Flags ("United Strength" in centre)	Ha.486	—	—
	A	—	55	Dominoes (sunspot broad issue)		—	—
	C	C	18	Motor Cycle Series	Ha.469	£10.00	—
	A	U	50	*War Portraits	H.86	£22.00	—
	—		13	War Posters (63 × 41 mm.)		—	—
B. Silks							
				Anonymous silks with blue border, plain board backing. Reported also to have been issued with firm's name rubber stamped on backing.			
	—	C		*Miscellaneous Subjects:—	Ha.500		
			? 8	Series B1—Flags (50 × 66 mm.)		—	—
			? 12	Series B3—Regimental Badges (50 × 66 mm.)		—	—
			? 2	Series C1—Flags (65 × 55 mm.)		—	—
			? 1	Series C2—Flags (70 × 65 mm.)		—	—
			? 4	Series C3—Regimental Badges (64 × 77 mm.)		—	—
			? 2	Series C4—Crests of Warships (64 × 77 mm.)		—	—
			? 1	Series D1—Royal Standard (138 × 89 mm.)		—	—
			? 1	Series D2—Shield of Flags (138 × 89 mm.)		—	—
			? 1	Series D3—Regimental Badge (138 × 89 mm.)		—	—

THOMSON & PORTEOUS, Edinburgh

Illus. No.	Size	Printing	Number in set		Handbook ref.	Price per card	Complete set
Pre-1919 Issues							
	D2	C	50	Arms of British Towns		£3.00	£150.00
	A	BW	25	*Boer War Celebrities—"STEW"	H.105	£24.00	—
297	A	C	20	European War Series	H.129	£5.00	£100.00
	A	C	25	*Shadowgraphs	H.44	£20.00	—
	A	C	41	V.C. Heroes:—	H.427		
				Ai. Name on back—Luntin Cigarettes		—	£175.00
				Aii. As above, but No. 6 Type B		£3.50	£150.00
				B. Without Maker's Name		£3.50	£150.00

TOBACCO SUPPLY SYNDICATE, London (T.S.S.)

Illus. No.	Size	Printing	Number in set		Handbook ref.	Price per card	Complete set
Pre-1919 Issue							
	D	C	? 23	*Nautical Expressions	H.174	£60.00	—

TURKISH MONOPOLY CIGARETTE CO. LTD.

Illus. No.	Size	Printing	Number in set		Handbook ref.	Price per card	Complete set
Pre-1919 Issue							
	—	C	? 7	*Scenes from the Boer War (113 × 68 mm., folded in three)	Ha.478	£40.00	—

UNITED KINGDOM TOBACCO CO., London

Illus. No.	Size	Printing	Number in set		Handbook ref.	Price per card	Complete set
Post-1920 Issues							
	A	C	50	Aircraft—"The Greys Cigarettes" (Feb. 1933)	Ha.598	35p	£17.50
	—	U	48	Beautiful Britain—"The Greys Cigarettes" (postcard size, 140 × 90 mm.) (Jan. 1929)		90p	£45.00
	—	U	48	Beautiful Britain—"The Greys Cigarettes" (postcard size, 140 × 90 mm.) Second Series (Oct. 1929)		80p	£40.00
286	A2	C	25	British Orders of Chivalry & Valour (Nov. 1936)—"The Greys Cigarettes"	Ha.599	16p	£4.00
585	A	U	24	Chinese Scenes (Mar. 1933)		13p	£1.75
424	A2	U	32	Cinema Stars—Set 4 (1933)	Ha.515–4	22p	£7.00
	A2	U	50	Cinema Stars—Set 7 (1934):—	Ha.515–7		
				A. Anonymous back		22p	£11.00
				B. Back with firm's name		17p	£8.50
293	A2	C	36	Officers Full Dress (Mar. 1936)		36p	£13.00
	A2	C	36	Soldiers of the King—"The Greys Cigarettes" (Aug. 1937)	Ha.603	30p	£11.00

UNITED SERVICES MANUFACTURING CO. LTD., London

Illus. No.	Size	Printing	Number in set		Handbook ref.	Price per card	Complete set
A. Post-1920 Issues							
	A1	C	50	Ancient Warriors (1938)		50p	£25.00
	A1	BW	50	Bathing Belles (1939)	Ha.592	13p	£6.00
	D	U	100	Interesting Personalities (1935)		70p	£70.00
	D	U	50	Popular Footballers (1936)		£1.10	—
	D	U	50	Popular Screen Stars (1937)		£1.00	—
B. Post-1940 Issue							
	A	C	25	Ancient Warriors (1954)		90p	—

UNITED TOBACCONISTS' ASSOCIATION, LTD.

Illus. No.	Size	Print-ing	Number in set		Handbook ref.	Price per card	Complete set
Pre-1919 Issue							
	A	C	? 9	*Actresses—"MUTA"	H.265/Ha.265	£70.00	—

WALKER'S TOBACCO CO. LTD., Liverpool

Post-1920 Issues							
	C	P	60	*British Beauty Spots	Ha.553	—	—
	D2		28	*Dominoes:—			
		U		A. "W.T.C." Monogram back	Ha.535–2	90p	—
		BW		B. Text back		—	—
417	A2	P	32	Film Stars—"Tatley's Cigarettes" (1936)	Ha.623	—	£20.00
	A2	P	31/32	Film Stars—"Tatley's Cigarettes" (1936)		20p	£6.00
	A2	P	48	*Film Stars—Walker's name at base (1937)	Ha.623	80p	—

WALTERS TOBACCO CO. LTD., London

Post-1920 Issue							
	B	U	6	Angling Information (wording only)	Ha.624	30p	£1.80

E. T. WATERMAN, Coventry

Pre-1919 Issue							
	D	C	30	*Army Pictures, Cartoons, etc.	H.12	—	—

WEBB & RASSELL, Reigate

Pre-1919 Issue							
	A	U	50	War Portraits	H.86	£7.50	—

H. C. WEBSTER ("Q. V. Cigars")

Pre-1919 Issue							
	—	BW	?	*Barnum and Bailey's Circus (60 × 42 mm.)	H.428	£80.00	—

HENRY WELFARE & CO., London

Pre-1919 Issue							
	D	P	? 22	Prominent Politicians (? 1911)	H.429	£50.00	—

WESTMINSTER TOBACCO CO. LTD., London

Post-1920 Issues

Inscribed "Issued by the Successors in the United Kingdom to the Westminster Tobacco Co., Ltd. ..." For other issues see RB21.

Illus. No.	Size	Print-ing	Number in set		Price per card	Complete set
582	A2	P	36	Australia—"First Series" (1932)	13p	£2.00
	A2	P	48	British Royal and Ancient Buildings (1925) (see RB21/200/159–I):—		
				A. Unnumbered, without descriptive text	35p	£17.50
				B. Numbered, with descriptive text	30p	£15.00
	A2	P	48	British Royal and Ancient Buildings—"A Second Series ..." (1926).	30p	£15.00
	A2	P	36	Canada — "First Series" (1927) (see RB21/292–1)	30p	£11.00
	A2	P	36	Canada—"Second Series" (1928) (see RB21/292–2)	30p	£11.00
	A2	P	48	Indian Empire—"First Series" (1926) (see RB21/293/1)	20p	£10.00
	A2	P	48	Indian Empire—"Second Series" (1927) (see RB21/293–2)	25p	£12.50
	A2	P	36	New Zealand—"First Series" (1929) (see RB21/294–1)	30p	£11.00
	A2	P	36	New Zealand—"Second Series" (1930) (see RB21/294–2)	13p	£2.00
	A2	P	36	South Africa—"First Series" (1930) (see RB21/295–1)	30p	£11.00
	A2	P	36	South Africa—"Second Series" (1931) (see RB21/295–2)	23p	£8.00
Not Issued						
	A2	P	36	Australia, Second Series, plain back	13p	£1.75

WHALE & CO.

Pre-1919 Issue							
	A	C	? 2	Conundrums	H.232	—	—

M. WHITE & CO., London

Illus. No.	Size	Printing	Number in set		Handbook ref.	Price per card	Complete set
Pre-1919 Issue							
—		BW	20	*Actresses—"BLARM"	H.23	£45.00	—

WHITFORD & SONS, Evesham

Post-1920 Issue							
	C2	C	20	*Inventors Series	H.213	£3.50	—

WHOLESALE TOBACCO SUPPLY CO., London ("Hawser" Cigarettes)

Pre-1919 Issues							
	A	C	25	Armies of the World	H.43	£45.00	—
	A	C	40	Army Pictures	H.69/Ha.69	£45.00	—

P. WHYTE, England

Pre-1919 Issue							
	D	C	30	*Army Pictures, Cartoons, etc.	H.12	—	—

W. WILLIAMS & CO., Chester

Illus. No.	Size	Printing	Number in set		Handbook ref.	Price per card	Complete set
A. Pre-1919 Issues							
	A	BW	25	*Boer War Celebrities—"STEW"	H.105	£27.00	—
569	A	C	50	Interesting Buildings	H.70	£3.50	£175.00
577	A	BW	12	Views of Chester	H.430	£8.00	£100.00
	A	BW	12	Views of Chester—As It Was:—	H.430		
				A. Toned card		£9.00	£110.00
				B. Bleuté card		£10.00	—
B. Post-1920 Issues							
	A	U	30	Aristocrats of the Turf	Ha.554	£1.50	£45.00
	A	U	36	Aristocrats of the Turf 2nd Series		£6.00	—
	A	C	25	Boxing	H.311	£1.50	£37.50

W. D. & H. O. WILLS, Bristol

Illus. No.	Size	Printing	Number in set		Handbook ref.	Price per card	Complete set
A. Period to 1902—including series issued abroad.							
	A	U	? 45	*Actresses—collotype:—	H.431		
				A. "Wills' Cigarettes"—"4 brands" back		£38.00	—
				B. "Wills' Cigarettes"—"no brands" back		£38.00	—
				C. "Wills' Cigarettes"—plain back		—	—
				D. "Wills' Cigarettes"—"4 brands" back		—	—
				E. "Wills' Cigarettes"—"no brands" back		£45.00	—
				F. "Wills' Cigarettes"—plain back		—	—
	A	C	? 1	*Actresses, brown type-set back	H.432	—	—
472	A	C	52	*Actresses, brown scroll back, with P.C. inset		£9.00	£470.00
470	A	C	52	*Actresses, grey scroll back:—	H.433		
				A. Without P.C. inset		£9.00	£470.00
				B. With P.C. inset		£9.00	£470.00
	A	U		*Actresses and Beauties—collotype, "Three Castles" and "Firefly" front:—	H.434		
			? 30	Actresses		£65.00	—
			? 16	Beauties		£65.00	—
	A	C		*Advertisement Cards:—	H.435		
			?	1888 issue		—	—
			? 1	1889–90 issues		—	—
			? 11	1890–93 issues		—	—
			? 3	1893 issue (various backs)		From £90.00	—
			? 6	1893–94 issue		From £90.00	—
81	A	C	50	*Animals and Birds in Fancy Costumes	H.436/Ha.436	£26.00	£1300.00
	A	U	? 10	*Beauties—collotype:—	H.437		
				A. "W. D. & H. O. Wills' Cigarettes"		£80.00	—
				B. "Firefly" Cigarettes		—	—
	A1	C	? 1	*Beauties ("Girl Studies"), type-set back	H.438	—	—
	A	C		*Beauties, brown backs:—	H.439/Ha.439		
			52	A. With P.C. inset—scroll back		£9.00	£470.00
			10	B. As A, 10 additional pictures		£32.00	—
			? 11	C. "Wills' Cigarettes" front, scroll back		£75.00	—
			? 14	D. "Wills' Cigarettes" front, type-set back		£85.00	—
467	K	C	52	*Beauties, miniature cards, P.C. inset, grey scroll back		£9.00	£470.00
495	A	C	50	Builders of the Empire (1898):—			
				A. White card		£2.80	£140.00
				B. Cream card		£2.80	£140.00
512	A	C	60	Coronation Series (1902):—			
				A. "Wide arrow" type back		£2.00	£120.00
				B. "Narrow arrow" type back		£2.00	£120.00
	A	C	50	*Cricketers (1896)	H.440	£27.00	—
157	A	C		Cricketer Series, 1901:—			
			50	A. With Vignette		£6.00	£300.00
			25	B. Without Vignette		£6.00	£150.00

Illus. No.	Size	Print- ing	Number in set		Handbook ref.	Price per card	Complete set
	A	C		*Double Meaning (1898):—			
			50	A. Without P.C. inset.....................		£4.00	£200.00
			52	B. With P.C. inset........................		£4.00	£210.00
	A	C	50	Japanese Series	H.441/Ha.441	£27.00	—
		C		*Kings and Queens:—	H.442		
	A1		50	A. Short card (1897):			
				(a) Grey back, thin card		£2.20	£110.00
				(b) Grey back, thick card		£2.40	£120.00
				(c) Brown back		£7.50	—
490	A			B. Standard size card (1902):			
			51	(a) Blue-grey back with 5 substitute titles		£2.80	£140.00
			50	(b) Grey back, different design, thinner card............................		£5.00	£250.00
635 etc.	A	C		*Locomotive Engines and Rolling Stock:—	H.443		
			50	A. Without I.T.C. Clause (1901–2)........		£3.20	£160.00
			7	B. As A, 7 additional cards		£10.00	—
				C. With I.T.C. Clause—See B Period.			
	A	C	50	*Medals:—	H.71		
				A. White card..........................		£1.60	£80.00
				B. Toned card		£2.00	£100.00
	A	C	25	*National Costumes........................		£110.00	—
	A	C	20	Our Gallant Grenadiers:—	H.163		
				A. Deep grey on toned card..............		£12.00	£240.00
				B. Blue-grey on bluish card..............		£12.00	£240.00
	A	C	50	Seaside Resorts (1899).....................		£4.50	£225.00
331	A	C		*Ships:—	H.444		
			25	A. Without "Wills" on front (1895):			
				(a) "Three Castles" back		£15.00	£375.00
				(b) Grey scroll back		£15.00	£375.00
			50	B. With "Wills" on front, dark grey back (1896)		£8.00	£400.00
			100	C. Green scroll back on brown card (1898–1902):		—	£1350.00
				i. 1898–25 subjects as A		£13.00	—
				ii. 1898–50 subjects as B		£13.00	—
				iii. 1902–25 additional subjects		£15.00	—
319	A	C		*Soldiers of the World (1895–7):—	H.445		
				A. Without P.C. Inset:			
			100	(a) With "Ld." back, thick card........		£5.50	£550.00
			100	(b) With "Ld." back, thin card........		£6.50	—
			100	(c) Without "Ld." back, thin card......		£5.50	£550.00
			1	Additional card (as c) "England, Drummer Boy"		—	£75.00
			52	B. With P.C. inset......................		£17.00	£900.00
	A	C	50	*Soldiers and Sailors:—	H.446		
				A. Grey back		£30.00	—
				B. Blue back		£30.00	—
239	A	C	50	Sports of All Nations (1900)		£3.20	£160.00
	A	BW		Transvaal Series:—	H.360		
			50	A. With black border (1899)............		£6.00	—
			66	Bi. Without black border (1900–01)		£1.40	£90.00
			?	Bii. Intermediate cards—additions and alternatives (1900–01)		£1.40	—
			66	C. Final 66 subjects, as issued with "Capstan" back (see B Period) (1902) .			
	A	C		"Vanity Fair" Series (1902):—	H.447		
			50	1st Series		£2.00	£100.00
			50	2nd Series		£1.60	£80.00
			50	Unnumbered —43 subjects as in 1st and 2nd, 7 new subjects......................		£1.60	£80.00
79	A	C		Wild Animals of the World:—	H.77		
			50	A. Green scroll back		£2.80	£140.00
			52	B. Grey back, P.C. inset		£5.00	£260.00
B. Period to 1902–1919—Home Issues i.e. series bearing Imperial Tobacco Co. ("I.T.C.") Clause.							
318	A	C	50	Allied Army Leaders (Mar. 1917):—			
				A. Without comma in I.T.C. Clause.......		90p	—
				B. With comma (or stop) in I.T.C. Clause .		85p	£42.50
47	A	C	50	Alpine Flowers (Oct. 1913)		32p	£16.00
592	A	C	50	Arms of the Bishopric (Aug. 1907)		45p	£22.50
591	A	C	50	Arms of the British Empire (Oct. 1910)......		45p	£22.50
594	A	C	50	Arms of Companies (Jul. 1913)		45p	£22.50
597	A	C	50	Arms of Foreign Cities (Jul. 1912):—			
				A. White card..........................		45p	£22.50
				B. Cream card		70p	—
				C. As A, with "Mark"..................		80p	—
362	A	C	50	Aviation (Jan. 1910).......................		90p	£45.00
265	A	C	50	Billiards (May 1909).......................		50p	£25.00
	A	C	50	*Borough Arms (1–50)—from June 1904:—			
				A. Scroll back, unnumbered	H.448	60p	£30.00
				B. Scroll back, numbered on front		£4.50	—
				C. Descriptive back, numbered on back ...		80p	£40.00
				D. 2nd Edition—1–50		40p	£20.00
595	A	C	50	*Borough Arms (51–100):—			
				A. 2nd Series...........................		40p	£20.00
				B. 2nd Edition, 51–100		40p	£20.00

Illus. No.	Size	Print-ing	Number in set		Handbook ref.	Price per card	Complete set
	A	C	50	*Borough Arms (101–150):—			
				A. 3rd Series, Album clause in grey........		40p	£20.00
				B. 3rd Series, Album clause in red.........		40p	£20.00
				C. 2nd Edition, 101–150................		40p	£20.00
	A	C	50	*Borough Arms (151–200), 4th series........		40p	£20.00
	A	C	24	*Britain's Part in the War (Sep. 1917)		80p	£20.00
25	A	C	50	British Birds (May 1917)		50p	£25.00
	A	C	1	*Calendar for 1911 (Dec. 1910)		—	£10.00
	A	C	1	*Calendar for 1912 (Dec. 1911)		—	£5.00
	B	U	25	Celebrated Pictures (Feb. 1916):			
				A. Deep brown back		£1.00	£25.00
				B. Yellow-brown back		90p	£22.50
	B	U	25	Celebrated Pictures, 2nd Series (Nov. 1916)..		90p	£22.50
390	A	C	50	Celebrated Ships (Sep. 1911)...............		70p	£35.00
515	A	C	50	The Coronation Series (May 1911).........		50p	£25.00
158	A	C	50	Cricketers (May 1908):—			
				A. 1–25 "Wills'S" at top front		£2.00	£50.00
				B. 1–50 "Wills's" at top front		£2.00	£100.00
	B	C	25	Dogs (May 1914)		80p	£20.00
	B	C	25	Dogs, 2nd Series (Jun. 1915)		80p	£20.00
	A	C	50	Famous Inventions (Nov. 1915).............		45p	£22.50
	A	C	50	First Aid:—			
				A. Without Album Clause (Apr. 1913)		30p	£15.00
				B. With Album Clause (Jan. 1915)		30p	£15.00
	A	C	50	Fish & Bait (May 1910).....................	H.65	40p	£20.00
169	A	U	66	*Football Series (1902)	H.81	£2.00	£135.00
	A	C	50	Garden Life (Oct. 1914)	H.449	30p	£15.00
562	A	C	50	Gems of Belgian Architecture (Feb. 1915) ...		40p	£20.00
570	A	C	50	Gems of French Architecture (1917):—			
				A. White card........................		90p	£45.00
				B. Bleuté card.......................		£1.00	—
				C. Rough brown card		£1.00	—
559	A	C	50	Gems of Russian Architecture (Feb. 1916)...		45p	£22.50
	A	C	50	Historic Events (Jan. 1912)	H.464	55p	£27.50
415	A	C	50	*Locomotive Engines and Rolling Stock, with I.T.C. Clause		£3.20	£160.00
				For issue without I.T.C. Clause see Period A.			
322	A	C	50	Military Motors (Oct. 1916):—			
				A. Without "Passed by Censor"		60p	£30.00
				B. With "Passed by Censor"..............		60p	£30.00
	A	C	50	Mining (Jun. 1916)......................	H.450	40p	£20.00
523	A	C	50	Musical Celebrities (Apr. 1911)		70p	£35.00
	A	C	50	Musical Celebrities—Second Series (Sep. 1916):—	H.465		
				Set of 50 with 8 substituted cards..........		£1.40	£70.00
				8 original cards (later substituted).........		£100.00	—
335	A	C	50	Naval Dress & Badges (Jul. 1909)	H.172	£1.00	£50.00
343	A	C	50	Nelson Series (Jul. 1905)...................		£1.00	£50.00
56	A	C	50	Old English Garden Flowers (Jun. 1910)		30p	£15.00
	A	C	50	Old English Garden Flowers, 2nd Series (Jan. 1913).................................		30p	£15.00
584	A	C	50	Overseas Dominions (Australia) (Apr. 1915).	H.451	35p	£17.50
581	A	C	50	Overseas Dominions (Canada) (Jun. 1914) ..		35p	£17.50
	A	C	50	Physical Culture (Feb. 1914)...............		40p	£20.00
482	A	U	100	*Portraits of European Royalty (1908):—			
				1–50 (Sept. 1908).....................		55p	£27.50
				51–100 (Dec. 1908)...................		55p	£27.50
	B	U	25	Punch Cartoons (Mar. 1916):—			
				A. Toned card		£2.00	£50.00
				B. Glossy white card		£3.00	—
	B	U	25	Punch Cartoons—Second Series (May 1917)		£7.00	—
298	A	C	12	Recruiting Posters (Apr. 1915)..............	H.452	£2.50	£30.00
42	A	C	50	Roses (Apr. 1912)......................		30p	£15.00
	A	·C	50	Roses, 2nd Series (Aug. 1913).............		30p	£15.00
	A	C	50	School Arms (Nov. 1906).................		50p	£25.00
	A	C	50	Signalling Series (May 1911)	H.453	50p	£25.00
	A	C	50	Time & Money in Different Countries (May 1906)................................	H.454	90p	£45.00
	A	BW	66	Transvaal Series, "Capstan" back (1902)	H.360	£2.25	—
				For other "Transvaal Series" see A Period.			
395	A	C	25	The World's Dreadnoughts (Jul. 1910)		90p	£22.50

C. Post-1920 Issues

Home issues, i.e., series with I.T.C. Clause. For export issues, see RB21.

Illus. No.	Size	Print-ing	Number in set		Handbook ref.	Price per card	Complete set
292	A	C		Air Raid Precautions (Aug. 1938):—	Ha.544		
			50	A. Home issue—adhesive back........		13p	£5.00
			40	B. Irish issue—non-adhesive back........		35p	£14.00
	A	C	48	Animalloys (sectional) (June 1934) (see RB21/200/124)		13p	£6.00
77	B	C	25	Animals and Their Furs (Dec. 1929)........		50p	£12.50
587	B	C	25	Arms of the British Empire—"First Series" (Nov. 1931)...........................		28p	£7.00
	B	C	25	Arms of the British Empire—"Second Series" (Apr. 1932).....................		30p	£7.50
	B	C	42	Arms of Oxford & Cambridge Colleges (Oct. 1922).................................		90p	£37.50
	B	C	25	Arms of Public Schools—"1st Series" (Aug. 1933).................................		26p	£6.50

Illus. No.	Size	Print-ing	Number in set		Handbook ref.	Price per card	Complete set
589	B	C	25	Arms of Public Schools—"2nd Series" (Mar. 1934)		26p	£6.50
588	B	C	25	Arms of Universities (May 1923)		80p	£20.00
181	A	C	50	Association Footballers "Frameline" back (Nov. 1935) (see W/134)		13p	£6.00
	A	C	50	Association Footballers—"No frameline" back (Nov. 1939):—			
				A. Home issue—adhesive back		15p	£7.50
				B. Irish issue—non-adhesive back		20p	£10.00
267	B	C	25	Auction Bridge (July 1926)		70p	£17.50
566	B	C	25	Beautiful Homes (Nov. 1930)		70p	£17.50
4	A	C	50	British Butterflies (June 1927) (see W/156)		18p	£9.00
551	B	C	25	British Castles (Nov. 1925)		75p	£18.50
543	B	C	25	British School of Painting (June 1927)		60p	£15.00
—		BW	48	British Sporting Personalities (66 × 52 mm.) (Mar. 1937)		13p	£5.50
	B	C	40	Butterflies & Moths (Oct. 1938)		33p	£13.00
	B	C	25	Cathedrals (Feb. 1933)		80p	£20.00
418	A	C	25	Cinema Stars—"First Series" (Jan. 1928)		36p	£9.00
419	A	C	25	Cinema Stars—"Second Series (Mar. 1928)		26p	£6.50
	A	U	50	Cinema Stars—"Third Series" (June 1931)		30p	£15.00
	A	C	50	Cricketers, 1928 (Jan. 1928)		30p	£15.00
	A	C	50	Cricketers—"2nd Series" (May 1929)		30p	£15.00
117	A	C	50	Dogs—Light backgrounds (Sep. 1937) (see W/187):—			
				A. Home issue—adhesive back		13p	£6.00
				B. Irish issue—non-adhesive back		20p	£10.00
	A	C		Do You Know (see RB21/200/188):—			
			50	"A Series of 50" (Sep. 1922)		15p	£7.50
654			50	"2nd Series of 50" (May 1924)		15p	£7.50
			50	"3rd Series of 50" (Feb. 1926)		15p	£7.50
			50	"4th Series of 50" (July 1933)		15p	£7.50
681 etc.	A	C	50	Engineering Wonders (Sep. 1927) (see W/193)		16p	£8.00
	A	C	50	English Period Costumes (Aug. 1929) (see W/195)		24p	£12.00
	B	C	25	English Period Costumes (Jan. 1927)		44p	£11.00
532	B	C	40	Famous British Authors (Aug. 1937)		18p	£7.00
	B	C	30	Famous British Liners—"First Series" (June 1934)		£1.10	£33.00
	B	C	30	Famous British Liners—"Second Series" (June 1935)		40p	£12.00
	B	C	25	Famous Golfers (June 1930)		60p	£15.00
	A	C		A Famous Picture ... (sectional) (see RB21/200/210 to 212):—			
			48	Series No. 1—"Between Two Fires" (Mar. 1930)		20p	£10.00
			48	Series No. 2—"The Boyhood of Raleigh" (Aug. 1930)		16p	£8.00
			48	Series No. 3—"Mother and Son" (Feb. 1931)		16p	£8.00
			48	"The Toast" (June 1931):—			
				A. Home issue—Series No. 4		16p	£8.00
				B. Irish issue—Series No. 1		90p	—
			48	"The Laughing Cavalier" (Oct. 1931):—			
				A. Home issue—Series No. 5:—			
				1. No stop after numeral		20p	£10.00
				2. Full stop after numeral		20p	£10.00
				B. Irish issue—Series No. 2		90p	—
			49	Series No. 6—"And When did you Last See Your Father?" (Feb. 1932)		40p	£20.00
602	A	C	25	Flags of the Empire (Nov. 1926 and Mar. 1929) (see W/215)		30p	£7.50
	A	C	25	Flags of the Empire—"2nd Series" (Apr. 1929) (see W/216)		30p	£7.50
68	A	C	50	Flower Culture in Pots (Feb. 1925) (see W/217)		13p	£6.00
73	B	C	30	Flowering Shrubs (Feb. 1935)		40p	£12.00
64	A	C	50	Flowering Trees & Shrubs (July 1924)		15p	£7.50
65	A	C	50	Garden Flowers (Jan. 1933)		13p	£5.00
44	A	C	50	Garden Flowers by Richard Sudell (Jan. 1939) (see W/222):—			
				A. Home issue—four brands quoted at base		13p	£3.25
				B. Irish issue—no brands at base		13p	£5.00
70	B	C	40	Garden Flowers—New Varieties—"A Series ..." (Jan. 1938)		13p	£3.50
	B	C	40	Garden Flowers—New Varieties—"2nd Series ..." (June 1939)		13p	£3.50
	A	C	50	Garden Hints (Jan. 1938) (see W/226):—			
				A. Home issue—Albums "one penny each"		13p	£2.50
				B. Irish issue—Album offer without price		13p	£5.00
	A	C	50	Gardening Hints (Mar. 1923) (see W/227)		16p	£8.00
	B	C	25	Golfing (June 1924)		60p	£15.00
590	B	C	25	Heraldic Signs & Their Origin (May 1925) (see W/230)		65p	£16.00
	A2	P	54	Homeland Events (Feb. 1932)		13p	£6.50
	A	C	50	Household Hints (Jan. 1927) (see W/234)		14p	£7.00
	A	C	50	Household Hints—"2nd Series" (July 1930)		16p	£8.00

Illus. No.	Size	Print-ing	Number in set		Handbook ref.	Price per card	Complete set
	A	C	50	Household Hints (Sep. 1936) (see W/236)....			
				A. Home issue—Albums "one penny each"		13p	£3.25
				B. Irish issue—Album offer without price .		13p	£6.00
237	A	BW	50	Hurlers (July 1927)..........................		22p	£11.00
	A	C	25	Irish Beauty Spots (July 1929)		£2.00	£50.00
	A	C	25	Irish Holiday Resorts (May 1930)...........		£2.00	£50.00
	A	C	50	Irish Industries (Feb. 1937):—			
				A. Back "This surface is adhesive ..."		—	—
				B. Back "Ask your retailer ..."		22p	£11.00
	A	U	25	Irish Rugby Internationals (June 1928)......		£2.00	£50.00
277	A	C	50	Irish Sportsmen (Oct. 1935)..................		50p	£25.00
	B	C	40	The King's Art Treasures (June 1938)		16p	£6.50
254	B	C	25	Lawn Tennis, 1931 (May 1931)		60p	£15.00
324	A	C	50	Life in the Royal Navy (July 1939) (see W/253)..................................		13p	£3.50
	A	C	50	Life in the Tree Tops (Oct. 1925) (see W/254)		17p	£8.50
	A	C	50	Lucky Charms (Oct. 1923) (see W/256)......		15p	£7.50
397	A	C	50	Merchant Ships of the World (Oct. 1924) (see RB21/200/257)		35p	£17.50
	K2	C	53	*Miniature Playing Cards (1932–34) (see W/260):—		40p	£20.00
				A. Home issue, blue back—"narrow 52" (2 printings)			
				B. Home issue, blue back—"wide 52" (4 printings)		40p	£20.00
				C. Home issue, pink back (3 printings)		40p	—
				D. Irish issue, blue back (7 printings)		60p	—
561	B	C	25	Modern Architecture (Aug. 1931)...........		50p	£12.50
	B	U	30	Modern British Sculpture (Sep. 1928)		50p	£15.00
	B	C	25	Old Furniture—"1st Series" (Oct. 1923)....		80p	£20.00
	B	C	25	Old Furniture—"2nd Series" (Feb. 1924)....		80p	£20.00
	B	C	40	Old Inns—"A Series of 40" (July 1936)......		70p	£28.00
563	B	C	40	Old Inns—"Second Series of 40" (Sep. 1939)		30p.	£12.00
	B	C	25	Old London (July 1929)		70p	£17.50
609	B	C	30	Old Pottery & Porcelain (Oct. 1934).........		35p	£11.00
613	B	C	25	Old Silver (Nov. 1924).....................		70p	£17.50
	B	C	25	Old Sundials (Mar. 1938)....................		60p	£15.00
486	A	BW	50	Our King and Queen (Feb. 1937) (see W/286)		13p	£3.50
	B	C	25	Public Schools (Nov. 1927)		50p	£12.50
131	B	C	40	Racehorses & Jockeys, 1938 (Feb. 1939).....		35p	£14.00
	A	C	50	Radio Celebrities—"A Series ..." (Aug. 1934):—			
				A. Home issue—back "This surface ..."		14p	£7.00
				B. Irish issue—back "Note. This surface ..."		50p	—
	A	C	50	Radio Celebrities—"Second Series ..." (July 1935):—			
				A. Home issue—back "This surface ..." ...		14p	£7.00
				B. Irish issue—back "Note. This surface ..."		50p	—
414, 663 etc.	A	C	50	Railway Engines (Jan. 1924) (see RB21/200/303)		45p`	£22.50
410, 807 etc.	A	C	50	Railway Engines (May 1936):—			
				A. Home issue—back "This surface ..." ...		28p	£14.00
				B. Irish issue—back "Note. This surface ..."		30p	£15.00
407, 657 etc.	A	C	50	Railway Equipment (Apr. 1939) (see W/305)		13p	£3.00
409, 664 etc.	A	C	50	Railway Locomotives (Dec. 1930)...........		40p	£20.00
488, 735	A	C	50	The Reign of H.M. King George V (Apr. 1935)...................................		13p	£5.50
	B	C	25	Rigs of Ships (Feb. 1929)		70p	£17.50
	A	C	50	Romance of the Heavens (Aug. 1928) (see W/313):—			
				A. Thin card.............................		30p	£15.00
				B. Thick card		30p	£15.00
	A	C	50	Roses (May 1926) (see W/94)		20p	£10.00
67	B	C	40	Roses (Jan. 1936)		35p	£14.00
	—	BW	48	Round Europe (66 × 52 mm.) (Jan. 1937)....		13p	£5.50
185	A	C	50	Rugby Internationals (Nov. 1929)...........		16p	£8.00
	A	C	50	Safety First (Dec. 1934) (see W/321):—			
				A. Home issue—"This surface ..."........		13p	£5.00
				B. Irish issue—"Note. This surface ..." ...		50p	—
	A	C	50	The Sea-Shore (May 1938) (see W/322):—			
				A. Home issue—special album offer.......		13p	£3.25
				B. Irish issue—general album offer........		13p	£6.00
	A	U	40	Shannon Electric Power Scheme (1931)......		90p	—
399	A	C	50	Ships' Badges (June 1925) (see W/328)		22p	£11.00
677 etc.	A	C	50	Speed (Mar. 1930).........................		45p	£22.50
	A	C	50	Speed (Oct. 1938) (see W/330):—			
714 etc.				A. Home issue—four brands quoted at base		13p	£4.25
				B. Irish issue—no brands at base..........		16p	£8.00
401	A	C	50	Strange Craft (Dec. 1931)...................		14p	£7.00
53	B	C	40	Trees (Feb. 1937)..........................		40p	£16.00
	B	C	25	University Hoods & Gowns (May 1926).....		£1.10	£27.50
39	A	C	50	Wild Flowers (June 1923):—			
				A. With dots in side panels................		13p	£6.50
				B. Without dots in side panels		13p	£6.50

Illus. No.	Size	Print-ing	Number in set		Handbook ref.	Price per card	Complete set
46	A	C	50	Wild Flowers—"Series of 50" (Feb. 1936) (see W/346):—			£3.50
				A. Home issue—back "This surface...",...		13p	
				B. Irish issue—back "Note. This surface ..."		40p	—
	A	C	50	Wild Flowers—"2nd Series ..." (May 1937) (see W/347):—			
				A. Home issue—adhesive back............		13p	£3.00
				B. Irish issue—non-adhesive back.........		13p	£6.50
	A	C	50	Wonders of the Past (Sep. 1926) (see W/348).		30p	£15.00
	A	C	50	Wonders of the Sea (Nov. 1928) (see W/349).		25p	£12.50

D. Post-1940 Issues

708 etc.	—	C	36	World of Speed (70 × 44 mm.) (1981).......		—	—

E. Unissued Series

	A	P	50	Gems of Italian Architecture (photographic reproduction of original series prepared in 1917) (1960)............................		09p	£4.50
	A	C	50	Life in the Hedgerow.....................		60p	£30.00
	A	C	50	Life of King Edward VIII		—	£375.00
	A	C	25	Pond and Aquarium 1st Series.............		—	£10.00
	A	C	25	Pond and Aquarium 2nd Series.............		—	£10.00
	B	C	40	Puppies.................................		—	—
	A	C	50	Waterloo................................		£38.00	—

F. Miscellaneous

			6	Boer War Medallions (see W/18)............		—	—
		C	12	The British Empire (133 × 101 mm.)........		£3.50	£42.00
		C	12	Cities of Britain (133 × 101 mm.)..........		£3.50	—
		C	6	Flags of the Allies (shaped) (see W/67)		£6.00	—
		C	32	Happy Families (non-insert) (91 × 63 mm.) ..		£4.00	—
		C	12	Industries of Britain (133 × 101 mm.)........		£3.50	—
			1	Pinchbeck Medallion (see W/18A)		—	
				Three Castles Sailing Ship Model advertisement cards:—			
	A	C	1	A. View from Stern:—			
				I. Three Castles Cigarettes............		—	£0.80
				II. In the eighteenth century		—	£0.80
	A	C	1	B. View from Bows:—			
				I. Three Castles Filter		—	£0.80
				II. Three Castles Filter magnum		—	£0.80
	A	BW	1	C. Sailing Ship Black Line Drawing.......		—	£0.80
	A	BW	1	D. Three Castles Shield Black Line Drawing.............................		—	£0.80

WILSON & CO., Ely

Pre-1919 Issue

	A	C	50	War Portraits..........................	H.86	£37.00	—

W. WILSON, Birmingham

Pre-1919 Issues

	D	C	30	*Army Pictures, Cartoons, etc................	H.12	—	—
	A	C	50	War Portraits............................	H.86	—	—

A. & M. WIX, London and Johannesburg

Post-1920 Issues

	—	—		Cinema Cavalcade (50 coloured, 200 black and white; sizes—70 small, 110 large, 70 extra-large):—			
			250	"A Series of 250..." ("Max Cigarettes")...		25p	—
			250	"2nd Series of 250..." ("Max Cigarettes").		13p	£32.50
	A2	C	100	Film Favourites—"Series of 100 ..."........	Ha.581–1	—	—
	A2	C	100	Film Favourites—"2nd Series of 100 ..."....	Ha.581–2	70p	—
	A2	C	100	Film Favourites—"3rd Series of 100":—	Ha.581–3		
				A. White card..........................		—	—
				B. Cream card		35p	£35.00
	J1	C	100	*Men of Destiny (folders) (P.O. Box 5764, Johannesburg)........................		£1.50	—
	—	C	250	Speed Through the Ages (171 small, 79 large):—	Ha.583		
				A. Back in English & Afrikaans...........		30p	£75.00
				B. Back in English		30p	£75.00
	—	C	250	This Age of Power & Wonder (170 small, 80 large) ("Max Cigarettes")		22p	£55.00

J. WIX & SONS LTD., London

A. Post-1920 Issues

	C	C	50	Builders of Empire—"Kensitas"............		13p	£3.50
	A2	C	50	Coronation (1937):—			
				A. J. Wix back:—			
				1. Linen finish........................		13p	£3.50
				2. Varnished		13p	£5.00
				B. "Kensitas" back		13p	£3.50
		C		Henry:—	Ha.625		
				"A Series of ..." (1935):—			
	B1		50	A. Large size...........................		18p	£9.00

Illus. No.	Size	Print-ing	Number in set		Handbook ref.	Price per card	Complete set
—			25	B. Extra-large size......................		60p	£15.00
				"2nd Series..." (1936):—			
	B1		50	A. Large size..........................		60p	£30.00
—			25	B. Extra-large size......................		50p	£12.50
	B1		50	3rd Series (1936)......................		30p	£15.00
	B1		50	4th Series (1936)......................		13p	£6.00
	B1		50	5th Series (1937)......................		13p	£2.75
		U	25	Love Scenes from Famous Films—"First Series":—			
442	C2			A. Small size.........................		80p	—
	B1			B. Large size..........................		80p	£20.00
—				C. Extra-large size (127 × 88 mm.)........		£1.40	£35.00
		U		Love Scenes from Famous Films—"Second Series":—			
	C2		25	A. Small size.........................		70p	—
	B1		25	B. Large size..........................		70p	—
—			19	C. Extra-large size, (127 × 88 mm.).......		£1.40	—
	K2	C	53	*Miniature Playing Cards (anonymous):—	Ha.535–3A		
				A. Scroll design:—			
				1. Red back.........................		13p	£5.00
				2. Blue back........................		25p	£12.50
				B. Ship design:—			
				1. Red border—Nelson's "Victory"....		25p	£12.50
				2. Black border—Drake's "Revenge"..		30p	£15.00
		U	25	Scenes from Famous Films—"Third Series":—			
	C2			A. Small size.........................		90p	£22.50
—				B. Extra-large size (127 × 88 mm.)........		£1.40	—

B. Silks

Illus. No.	Size	Print-ing	Number in set		Handbook ref.	Price per card	Complete set
—		C	48	British Empire Flags—"Kensitas" (78 × 54 mm.) (1933):—	Ha.496–4		
				A. Inscribed "Printed in U.S.A."..........		40p	£20.00
				B. Without the above..................		35p	£17.50
—		C	60	Kensitas Flowers—"First Series", small (68 × 40 mm.) (1934):—	Ha.496–1		
				1. Back of folder plain..............		70p	£42.00
				2. Back of folder printed in green:—			
				(a) Centre oval, 19 mm. deep..........		70p	£42.00
				(b) Centre oval, 22 mm. deep..........		70p	£42.00
				(c) As (b), inscribed "Kensitas Flowers are washable..." below number....		70p	£42.00
—		C	60	Kensitas Flowers—"First Series", medium (76 × 55 mm.) (1934):—	Ha.496–1		
				A. Back of folder plain..............		90p	£55.00
				B. Back of folder printed in green........		90p	£55.00
	fl	C	30	Kensitas Flowers—"First Series" extra-large (138 × 96 mm.) (1934):—	Ha.496–1		
				A. Back of folder plain..............		£5.00	—
				B. Back of folder printed in green........		£5.00	—
—		C	40	Kensitas Flowers—"Second Series" (1935):—	Ha.496–2		
				A. Small size, 68 × 40 mm...............		£1.10	£45.00
				B. Medium size, 76 × 55 mm.............		£1.40	—
606	—	C	60	National Flags—"Kensitas" (78 × 54 mm.) (1934)................................	Ha.496–3	33p	£20.00

C. Post-1940 Issues

Illus. No.	Size	Print-ing	Number in set		Handbook ref.	Price per card	Complete set
				Ken-cards (102 × 118 mm):—			
			12	Series 1. Starters/Snacks (1969).............		—	£4.00
			12	Series 2. Main Courses (1969)...............		—	£4.00
			12	Series 3. Desserts (1969)...................		—	£4.00
			12	Series 4. Motoring (1969)..................		—	£4.00
			12	Series 5. Gardening (1969).................		—	£4.00
			12	Series 6. Do It Yourself (1969).............		—	£4.00
			12	Series 7. Home Hints (1969)...............		—	£4.00
			12	Series 8. Fishing (1969)....................		—	£4.00

D. Miscellaneous

Illus. No.	Size	Print-ing	Number in set		Handbook ref.	Price per card	Complete set
—		C	50	Bridge Hands (140 × 105 mm.).............		—	—
			42	Card Tricks by Jasper Maskelyne:—	Ha.535–3B		
				A. Size 70 × 34 mm.		£1.00	—
				B. Size 70 × 48 mm.		£1.00	—
		U		Jenkynisms:—			
				A. "The K4's" Series (75–78 × 65 mm.):			
			101	I. Known as 1st Series..............		50p	—
			50	II. Known as 2nd Series.............		50p	—
			30	III. Known as 3rd Series		50p	—
			1	IV. Known as 4th Series		—	—
				B. The Red Bordered series (2 sizes for each series):			
			17	I. Series of Quotations		60p	—
			? 42	II. "Today's Jenkynisms"		60p	—

WOOD BROS., England

Illus. No.	Size	Print-ing	Number in set		Handbook ref.	Price per card	Complete set
—		BW	28	Dominoes (63 × 29 mm.)		—	—

T. WOOD, Cleckheaton

Illus. No.	Size	Print-ing	Number in set		Handbook ref.	Price per card	Complete set
Pre-1919 issue							
	D	C	30	*Army Pictures, Cartoons, etc..............	H.12	—	—

JOHN J WOODS, London

Pre-1919 Issue							
	A	BW	? 8	*Views of London.........................	H.395	£80.00	

W. H. & J. WOODS LTD., Preston

A. Pre-1919 Issue							
	A	C	25	*Types of Volunteers and Yeomanry.........	H.455	£13.00	£325.00
B. Post-1920 Issues							
	A2	U	25	Aesop's Fables............................	Ha.518	26p	£6.50
375	A2	P	50	Modern Motor Cars		90p	£45.00
	D	C	25	Romance of the Royal Mail		13p	£2.50

J. & E. WOOLFE

Pre-1919 Issue							
	A	U	? 40	*Beauties—"KEWA"	H.139	—	—

M. H. WOOLER, London

Pre-1919 Issue							
	A	—	? 1	Beauties "BOCCA"........................		—	—

T. E. YEOMANS & SONS LTD., Derby

Pre-1919 Issues							
	—	C	72	Beautiful Women (75 × 55 mm.)	Ha.284	—	—
	A	U	50	War Portraits.............................		—	—

JOHN YOUNG & SONS LTD., Bolton

Pre-1919 Issues							
	A2	C	? 4	Naval Skits	H.457/Ha.457	£100.00	—
	A2	C	12	*Russo-Japanese Series.....................	H.456	£27.00	

ANONYMOUS SERIES

A. Pre-1919 Issues. With letterpress on back of card

	A2	C	20	Animal Series: See Hill			
				A. "The cigarettes with which ..." back		—	—
				B. Space at back		—	—
	A	U	? 40	*Beauties—"KEWA," "England Expects ..." back...................................	H.139	—	—
	D	BW	25	*Boxers, green back. See Cohen Weenen		—	—
	A1	C	? 3	*Celebrities—Coloured, 1902 Calendar back ..		—	—
	D	C	39	*Celebrities—"GAINSBOROUGH I", 1902 Calendar back, gilt border to front. See Cohen Weenen...........................	H.90	—	—
	A2	C	20	*Interesting Buildings and Views, 1902 Calendar back	Ha.96		—
	D2	C	20	*Nations, 1902 Calendar back	Ha.97	—	—
	A	C	25	*Types of British Soldiers, "General Favourite Onyx" back	H.144		—
	D	C	25	V.C. Heroes (Nos. 51–75—See Cohen Weenen)...............................		—	—
	A	C	41	V.C. Heroes—"Pure Virginia Cigarettes"— Dobson Molle & Co. Ltd.—Printers	H.427	—	—
	D	U	50	*War Series (Cohen Weenen—Nos. 1–50).....	H.103	—	—
	A	C	41	V.C. Heroes—See Thomson & Porteous	H.427	—	—

B. Pre-1919 Issues. With plain back

	A	U	25	*Actors and Actresses—"FROGA C".........	H.20/Ha.20	—	—
	D2	U	? 5	*Actresses—"Anglo".......................	Ha.185	—	—
		U		*Actresses—"ANGOOD":—	H.187/Ha.187		
			? 13	A. Brown tinted—			
				i. Thick board........................		—	—
				ii. Thin board........................		—	—
			? 1	B. Green tinted		—	—
			? 10	C. Black tinted		—	—
	A1	BW	20	*Actresses—"BLARM"	H.23	£6.00	—
	D	U	20	*Actresses—Chocolate tinted. See Hill........	H.207	—	—
	A	C	? 19	*Actresses—"DAVAN":—	Ha.124		
				A. Portrait in red only		—	—
				B. Portrait in colour		—	—
	D	BW	12	*Actresses—"FRAN". See Drapkin	H.175	—	—
	A	U	26	*Actresses—"FROGA A"	H.20	—	—

249

Illus. No.	Size	Print-ing	Number in set		Handbook ref.	Price per card	Complete set
	A1	BW	? 15	*Actresses—"HAGG B"	H.24/Ha.24	£10.00	—
	A	BW	15	*Actresses—"RUTAN" See Rutter	H.381	—	—
	—	C	50	*Actresses Oval Card (as Phillips)	Ha.324	—	—
	A1	U		*Actresses and Beauties—Collotype (See Ogden)	H.306	—	—
	C	C	20	*Animal Series. See Hill		—	—
	—	C	? 12	*Arms of Cambridge Colleges (17 × 25 mm.). See Kuit	H.458	—	—
	—	C	? 12	*Arms of Companies (30 × 33 mm.). See Kuit	H.459	—	—
	A2	BW	? 13	*Battleships. See Hill	H.208/Ha.208	—	—
	A	C	? 14	*Beauties—"BOCCA"	H.39/Ha.39	£10.00	—
	A		50	*Beauties—"CHOAB":—	H.21		
		U		A. Unicoloured		—	—
		C		B. Coloured		£7.00	—
	A			*Beauties—"FECKSA":—	H.58/Ha.58		
		U	50	A. Plum-coloured front		—	—
		C	? 6	B. Coloured front		£8.00	—
	D2	U	? 18	*Beauties—"FENA"	H.148/Ha.148	—	—
	A2	C	25	*Beauties—"GRACC"	H.59	£8.00	—
	A	C	26	*Beauties—"HOL"	H.192	£10.00	—
	A	U	? 41	*Beauties—"KEWA"	H.139/Ha.139	—	—
	—	C	30	*Beauties—Oval card (36 × 60 mm.) (See Phillips)	H.244	—	—
	A	U	? 17	*Beauties—Collotype	Ha.278	—	—
	D1	U		*Bewlay's War Series:—	Ha.477		
			12	1. Front without captions		—	—
			? 1	2. Front with captions		—	—
	A2	BW	20	*Boer War Cartoons	H.42	—	—
	A	C	? 25	*Boer War and General Interest:—	H.13		
				A. Plain cream back		—	—
				B. Brown Leaf Design back		—	—
				C. Green Leaf Design back		—	—
				D. Green Daisy Design back		—	—
	A2	BW	? 16	*Boer War Celebrities—"CAG"	H.79/Ha.79	—	—
	A		? 8	Boer War Celebrities "RUTTER":—	Ha.382		
		BW		A. Front in Black & White		—	—
				B. Front in light orange & Brown		—	—
	A1	BW	20	*Boer War Generals—"CLAM"	H.61	—	—
	A2	BW	? 12	*Boer War Generals—"FLAC"	H.47	—	—
	D	C	25	*Boxer Rebellion—Sketches (1904)	H.46	£6.00	—
	A	C	54	*British Beauties (Phillips) (1–54)	H.328	—	—
	A	C	54	*British Beauties (Phillips) (55–108) Matt	H.328	—	—
	A	C	12	British Queens	Ha.480	—	—
	A	BW	16	*British Royal Family	H.28	£8.00	—
	A	C	45	*Celebrities—Coloured (Cohen Weenen)	H.89	—	—
	D	C	39	*Celebrities—"GAINSBOROUGH I". See Cohen Weenen	H.90	—	—
	D	BW	?147	*Celebrities—"GAINSBOROUGH II". See Cohen Weenen	H.91	—	—
	A1	P	36	*Celebrities of the Great War (1916). See Major Drapkin & Co.		—	—
	A	BW	? 10	Celebrities of the Great War	Ha.236	—	—
	A	C		*Colonial Troops:—	H.40		
			30	A. Cream card		—	—
			50	B. White card		—	—
	A	BW	20	Cricketers Series	H.29	—	—
	A	C	50	Dogs (as Taddy)	Ha.487	£6.00	—
	A	C	25	*England's Military Heroes. See Player:—	H.352		
				A. Wide card		—	—
				B. Narrow card		—	—
	A	C	25	*England's Naval Heroes. See Player:—			
				A. Wide card		—	—
				B. Narrow card	H.353	—	—
	A	C	20	*The European War Series	H.129	£2.00	—
	A	C		*Flags, Arms and Types of Nations:—	H.115		
			24	A. Numbered		£5.00	—
			? 1	B. Unnumbered		—	—
	A	C		*Flags and Flags with Soldiers:—	H.41		
			30	A. Flagstaff Draped		£4.00	—
			15	B. Flagstaff not Draped (Flags only)		£4.00	—
	A1	C	30	*Flags of Nations. See Cope	H.114	—	—
	A1	C	24	*Girls, Flags and Arms of Countries. See Rutter	H.383	—	—
	A	C	40	*Home and Colonial Regiments:—	H.69		
				20. Caption in blue		—	—
				20. Caption in brown		£7.00	—
	A	C	52	*Japanese Series, P.C. Inset. See Muratti		—	—
	A1	P	? 2	*King Edward and Queen Alexandra	H.460	£15.00	—
	D	C	20	*National Flag Series. See Hill		—	—
	D	C	20	*Nations, gilt border. See Cohen Weenen	H.97	—	—
	D	C	40	*Naval and Military Phrases:—	H.14		
				A. Plain front (no border)		£4.00	—
				B. Front with gilt border		—	—
	—	U	? 1	*Portraits .See Drapkin & Millhoff (48 × 36 mm.)	H.461	—	—
	A	U	? 47	*Pretty Girl Series—"BAGG"	H.45/Ha.45	—	—
	A1	C	20	*Prince of Wales Series. See Hill	H.22	—	—
	D	C	30	*Proverbs	H.15	—	—
	A	BW	19	Russo-Japanese Series	Ha.184	—	—
	A	C	20	Russo-Japanese War Series	H.100	—	—

Illus. No.	Size	Print-ing	Number in set		Handbook ref.	Price per card	Complete set
	A	C	10	Scenes from San Toy. See Richard Lloyd.....	H.462	—	—
	A	C	25	Sports & Pastimes Series No. 1	H.225	£4.00	—
	A	C	25	*Star Girls	H.30	—	—
	A1	BW	? 28	*Statuary (Hill A–D)	H.218	—	—
	A	C	25	*Types of British and Colonial Troops........	H.76	—	—
	A2	C	25	*Types of British Soldiers	H.144	—	—
	—	U	? 21	Views and Yachts (narrow, abt. 63 × 30 mm.) .	Ha.262–2	—	—
	D	BW	12	*Views of the World. See Drapkin	H.176	—	—
	D	BW	8	*Warships. See Drapkin	H.463/Ha.463	—	—
	D			*War Series:—	Ha.103		
		U	? 1	A. Front in brown.........................		—	—
		BW	? 2	B. Front in black and white		—	—

C. Post-1920 Issues. With letterpress on back

		C	25	Cinema Stars—see Teofani:—	Ha.530		
	C2			A. Small size............................			
	—			B. Extra-large size (109 × 67 mm.)........			
	A2	U	50	Cinema Stars—Set 7—see United Kingdom Tobacco Co...........................	Ha.515–7		
	D2	C	25	Cinema Stars—Set 8—see Moustafa........	Ha.515–8		
	A2	C	50	Evolution of the British Navy—see Godfrey Phillips................................			
	A2	BW	40	Famous Film Stars, text in Arabic (two series)—see Hill........................			
	A2	C	50	Famous Footballers—see Godfrey Phillips....			
	A2	C	35	Famous Stars—see Reliance Tobacco Mfg. Co....................................	Ha.572		
	C2	C	20	Great Inventors—see Teofani...............	H.213		
	D2	U	48	Modern Movie Stars and Cinema Celebrities—see Teofani	Ha.569		
	D2	C	25	Pictures of World Interest—see Moustafa....			
	C2	U	24	Well-Known Racehorses—see Teofani	Ha.609		

D. Post-1920 Issues. With Designs on Back

	A	BW	25	Careless Moments		16p	£4.00
	D2	U	28	*Dominoes ("W.T.C." monogram back)—see Walker's Tobacco Co....................	Ha.535–2		
	—	C	53	*Miniature Playing Cards (68 × 42 mm.) (red back, black cat trade mark in centre)—see Carreras.............................	Ha.535–1		
	K2	C	53	*Miniature Playing Cards (blue scroll back)— see Godfrey Phillips			
	K2	C	53	*Miniature Playing Cards—see J. Wix:— A. Scroll design:—	Ha.535–3		
				1. Red back			
				2. Blue back			
				B. Ship design:—			
				1. Red border—Nelson's "Victory"			
				2. Black border—Drake's "Revenge"..			
		C		*Playing Cards and Dominoes—see Carreras:—	Ha.535–1		
		C	52	A. Small size:—			
				1. Numbered			
				2. Unnumbered			
	—		26	B. Large size (77 × 69 mm.):—			
				1. Numbered			
				2. Unnumbered			

E. Post-1920 Issues. With Plain Back

	A2	P	36	Australia, Second Series		13p	£1.75
	A2	P	18	*Beauties—see Marcovitch..................	Ha.627		
	A1	P	60	*British Beauty Spots—see Coudens	Ha.553		
	B1	P	50	*British Castles, Nd. S.J.51–S.J.100—see Pattreiouex	Ha.595–3		
	—	C	108	*British Naval Crests (74 × 52 mm.)..........	Ha.504–4	—	—
	D2	CP	50	*Camera Studies—see Moustafa			
	B1	P	50	*Cathedrals and Abbeys, Nd. S.J.1–S.J.50— see Pattreiouex	Ha.595–3		
	A	C	25	*Charming Portraits—see Continental Cigarette Factory	Ha.549		
	A2	U	30	*Cinema Stars—Set 3	Ha.515–3	—	—
	A2	U	30	*Cinema Stars—Set 6	Ha.515–6	30p	£9.00
	—	C	110	*Crests & Badges of the British Army (74 × 52 mm.):—	Ha.502–2		
				(a) Numbered...........................		—	—
				(b) Unnumbered		—	—
	—	BW	12	*Film Actors and Actresses (56 × 31 mm.)—see Teofani................................	Ha.618		
	A	C	20	*Head Dresses of Various Nations—see Teofani................................	Ha.619–1		
	A	—	20	*Inventors and Their Inventions—see Hill	H.213		
	—	C	? 9	*Irish Views (68 × 67 mm.)—see Lambkin.....	Ha.585		
	—	BW	12	*London Views (57 × 31 mm.)—see Teofani ...	Ha.620		
	A	C	50	*Natives in Costume—see Teofani	Ha.619–2		
	—	P	30	*Photographs (Animal Studies) (64 × 41 mm.) .	Ha.541	£1.00	—
	—	C	? 48	*Regimental Colours II (76 × 70 mm.)........	Ha.502–7	—	—
	—	P	22	*Teofani Gems I—Series of 22 (53 × 35 mm.)— see Teofani	Ha.621–1		
	—	P	28	*Teofani Gems II—Series of 28 (53 × 35 mm.)—see Teofani	Ha.621–2		
	—	P	36	*Teofani Gems III—Series of 36 (53 × 35 mm.)—see Teofani	Ha.621–3		
	A	C	50	*World's Smokers—see Teofani.............	Ha.619–3		

F. Post-1920 Issues. ANONYMOUS SERIES—Silks and Other Novelty Issues

For Anonymous Metal Plaques—see International Tobacco Co.

For Anonymous Metal Charms—see Rothman's.

For Anonymous Miniature Rugs—see Godfrey Phillips.

For Anonymous Lace Motifs—see Carreras.

For Anonymous Woven Silks—see Anstie and J. Wix.

For Anonymous Printed Silks with Blue Borders—see Themans.

Anonymous ordinary printed British silks which are found unbacked are listed below, with cross-reference to issuing firms. Entries marked † are only anonymous when the paper backings are missing, and in these cases the indication applies only to the silks without backings.

Arms of Countries and Territories—see Phillips	Ha.504–12
Battleship Crests I—see Morris†	Ha.504–3
British Admirals—see Phillips	Ha.504–5
British Butterflies and Moths II—see Phillips	Ha.505–6
British Naval Crests II—see Phillips	Ha.504–4
Butterflies I—see Phillips	Ha.505–5
Butterflies and Moths III—see Lea†	Ha.505–7
Clan Tartans—see Phillips	Ha.505–15
Colonial Army Badges—see Phillips	Ha.502–3
County Cricket Badges—see Phillips	Ha.505–8
Crests & Badges of the British Army II—see Phillips and Singleton & Cole†	Ha.502–2
English Flowers—see Morris†	Ha.505–4
English & Foreign Birds I—see Morris†	Ha.505–1
Flags—Set 1—see Gallaher†	Ha.501–1
Flags—Set 2—see Muratti	Ha.501–2
Flags—Set 3—see Muratti†	Ha.501–3
Flags—Set 4—see Phillips	Ha.501–4
Flags—Set 5—see Phillips	Ha.501–5
Flags—Set 6—see Phillips	Ha.501–6
Flags—Set 7—see Phillips	Ha.501–7
Flags—Set 8—see Muratti†	Ha.501–8
Flags—Set 9—see Phillips	Ha.501–9
Flags—Set 10 (7th, 10th and 12th Series)—see Phillips	Ha.501–10
Flags—Set 11 (Fourth to Seventh Series)—see John Sinclair	Ha.501–11
Flags—Set 12 ("Let 'em all come" and Allies grouped Flags)—see Phillips	Ha.501–12
Flags—Set 13—see Phillips	Ha.501–13
Flags—Set 14 (House Flags)—see Phillips	Ha.501–14
Flags—Set 15 (Pilot and Signal Flags)—see Phillips	Ha.501–15
Football Colours—see Phillips	Ha.505–9
Great War Leaders I—see Muratti†	Ha.504–6
Great War Leaders II—see Phillips	Ha.504–7
Great War Leaders III and Warships—see Phillips	Ha.504–10
Great War Leaders IV and Celebrities—see Phillips	Ha.504–11
Irish Patriots—see Phillips	Ha.505–11
Naval Badges of Rank and Military Headdress—see Phillips	Ha.504–9
Old Masters—Set 2—see Phillips	Ha.503–2
Old Masters—Set 3A—see Phillips	Ha.503–3A
Old Masters—Set 3B—see Phillips	Ha.503–3B
Old Masters—Set 4—see Phillips	Ha.503–4
Old Masters—Set 5—see Phillips	Ha.503–5
Old Masters—Set 7—see Phillips	Ha.503–7
Old Pottery—see Lea†	Ha.505–14
Orders of Chivalry I—see Phillips	Ha.504–14
Orders of Chivalry II—see Murray†	Ha.504–15
Pottery Types—see Salmon & Gluckstein† (see RB21/311)	
Regimental Badges I—see Muratti† and John Sinclair†	Ha.502–1
Regimental Colours I—see Muratti†	Ha.502–6
Regimental Colours II—see Phillips and John Sinclair	Ha.502–7
Regimental Colours III—see Phillips	Ha.502–8
Regimental Colours IV—see Morris	Ha.502–9
Regimental Colours V—see Muratti†	Ha.502–10
Regimental Colours & Badges of the Indian Army—see Drapkin†	Ha.502–5
Regimental Crests and Badges III—see Lea†	Ha.502–4
Religious Pictures—see Phillips	Ha.505–10
Victoria Cross Heroes I—see Phillips	Ha.504–1
Victoria Cross Heroes II—see Phillips and Cohen Weenen†	Ha.504–2
War Pictures—see Phillips	Ha.504–8

INDEX OF BRANDS

The following is a list of the cases so far known where cards appear without the name of issuer, but inscribed with a Brand Name or other indication which is the collector's only clue to the identity of issuer.

A. INDEX OF BRANDS and initials found on British issues of cards or silks.

All Arms Cigarettes—see Carreras

B.D.V. Cigarettes—see Godfrey Phillips
Bandmaster Cigarettes—see Cohen Weenen and Drapkin
Big Gun Cigarettes—see Sandorides
Black Cat Cigarettes—see Carreras
Blush of Day Cigarettes—see Robinson & Barnsdale
Broadway Novelties—see Teofani
The Buffs—see Drapkin

Cake Walk Cigarettes—see Pezaro
Casket and Critic Cigarettes—see Pattreiouex
The Challenge Flat Brilliantes—see Gloag
Citamora Cigarettes—see Gloag
Club Member Cigarettes—see Pattreiouex
Club Mixture Tobaccos—see Continental Cigarette Factory
Colin Campbell Cigars—see Robinson & Barnsdale
Crowfoot Cigarettes—see Hill
Cymax Cigarettes—see Coudens

Eldona Cigars—see Drapkin & Millhoff
Erinmore Cigarettes—see Murray
Explorer Cigars—see Drapkin & Millhoff

The Favourite Magnums Cigarettes—see Teofani
The Flor de Dindigul Cigar—see Bewlay
Forecasta—see B. Morris
Fresher Cigarettes—see Challis

G.P.—see Godfrey Phillips
Gainsborough Cigarettes—see Cohen Weenen
Gala Cigarettes—issuers unknown, see under Miscellaneous
General Favourite Onyx—issuers unknown, see under Anonymous
Gibson Girl Virginia, Madrali Turkish and Hungarian—see Hill
Gold Flake Cigarettes—see Hill

Gold Flake, Honeydew and Navy Cut Medium Cigarettes—see Hill
The Greys Cigarettes—see United Kingdom Tobacco Co.

Hawser, Epaulet and Honey Flake Cigarettes—see Wholesale Tobacco Supply Syndicate
Heart's Delight Cigarettes—see Pritchard & Burton

Jersey Lily Cigarettes—see Wm. Bradford
Cigarette Job—see Societe Job
Junior Member Cigarettes—see Pattreiouex

Kensitas Cigarettes—see J. Wix

Leon de Cuba Cigars—see Eldons
Levant Favourites—see B. Morris
Life Ray Cigarettes—see Carreras
Lucana Cigarettes—see Sandorides

Matossian's Cigarettes—see Henly & Watkins
Max Cigarettes—see A. & M. Wix
Mayblossom Cigarettes—see Lambert & Butler
Mills—see Amalgamated

New Orleans Tobacco—see J. & T. Hodge

Oracle Cigarettes—see Tetley

Pibroch Virginia—see Fryer
Pick-Me-Up Cigarettes—see Drapkin & Millhoff
Pinnace—see Godfrey Phillips
Pioneer Cigarettes—see Richmond Cavendish
Polo Mild Cigarettes—see Murray
Private Seal Tobacco—see Godfrey Phillips

Q.V. Cigars—see Webster

R.S.—see Robert Sinclair

Reina Regenta Cigars—see B. Morris
De Reszke Cigarettes—see Millhoff and Godfrey Phillips
Ringers Cigarettes—see Edwards, Ringer & Bigg
Roseland Cigarettes—see Glass

Senior Service Cigarettes—see Pattreiouex
Spinet Cigarettes or The Spinet House—see Hill
The Spotlight Tobaccos—see Hill
Star of the World Cigarettes—see J.L.S.
State Express Cigarettes—see Ardath

Summit—see International Tobacco Co.
Sunripe Cigarettes—see Hill
Sweet Alva Cigarettes—see Drapkin

T.S.S.—see Tobacco Supply Syndicate
Tatley's Cigarettes—see Walker's Tobacco Co.
Three Bells Cigarettes—see J. & F. Bell
Tipsy Loo Cigarettes—see H. C. Lloyd
Topsy Cigarettes—see Richards & Ward
Trawler, Critic and King Lud Cigarettes—see Pattreiouex

W.T.C.—see Walker's Tobacco Co.

B. INDEX OF INSCRIPTIONS found on British issues of cards

'The Cigarettes with which these Picture Cards are issued are manufactured in England and are Guaranteed Pure'—see Hill.
'England expects that Every Man will do his duty—By Purchasing these Cigarettes you are supporting British labour'—issuers unknown, see Anonymous
'Issued with these Famous Cigarettes'—see Teofani
'Issued with these Fine Cigarettes'—see Teofani
'Issued with these High Grade Cigarettes'—see Teofani
'Issued with these Well-known Cigarettes'—see Teofani
'Issued with these World Famous Cigarettes'—see Teofani
'Presented with these well-known choice cigarettes'—see Teofani
'Smoke these cigarettes always'—see Teofani
'These Cigarettes are Guaranteed Best British Manufacture'—see Hill.

C. INDEX OF OTHER INDICATIONS found on British Tobacco Issues

THE B.I. Co.—see Burstein Isaacs
Chantler & Co., Bury—see Lea
'Eagle, Cork'—see Lambkin
Agnes D. Eld, Dudley—see Lea
L. & Y. Tobacco Co.—see Lancs. and Yorks. Tobacco Manufacturing Co.
Orient Line Steamships—see Singleton & Cole
P. O. Box 5764, Johannesburg—see A. & M. Wix
S. C. Peacock Sales Co.—see Lea

HOW TO ORDER CARDS

Availability

We have the world's largest stocks of cigarette cards and the chances are that we will be able to supply your requirements for most series at the prices shown in the catalogue. However, certain odd cards, particularly from rarer series, may not be available in top condition and in such cases it is helpful if you indicate whether cards of a lower standard are acceptable at reduced prices. If a complete set is not in stock, we may be able to offer a part set, with one or two cards missing, at the appropriate fraction of full catalogue price. In some instances we can supply sets on request in fair to good condition at half catalogue price. If in doubt, please write for a quotation, enclosing a stamped, self-addressed envelope.

End Numbers

When ordering odd cards, please allow treble price for end numbers, for example, numbers 1 and 50 of a set of fifty, because these are the cards most frequently damaged in collections and consequently are more difficult to obtain in top condition.

Postage, Packing and VAT

An extra charge for postage and packing is made on all orders for cards, based on current postal rates and depending on the weight of the package. Please allow for this in your remittance. Any difference will be invoiced as a debit or credit to be carried forward to the next order. Cards are zero-rated for VAT at the time of publication, but postage and packing is classed as a service and is subject to VAT at the current rate.

Ordering

Please ensure that your name and full address are clearly shown. State the maker's name and the set title required (with 'first series', 'second series', date of issue, etc. as appropriate). For odds, please list each individual number wanted. Make your crossed cheque or postal order payable to The London Cigarette Card Company Limited and enclose with order. Notes and coins should be registered. Foreign remittances will be credited after conversion and deduction of bank charges. Please allow 14 days for delivery. Send your order to:

> The London Cigarette Card Co. Ltd.
> Sutton Road
> Somerton
> Somerset TA11 6QP

Guarantee

In the unlikely event that you, the collector, are not satisfied with the cards supplied, we guarantee to replace them or refund your money, provided the goods are returned within 14 days of receipt. This guarantee does not affect your statutory rights.

BOOKS FOR THE COLLECTOR

Catalogues and Handbooks

The Catalogue of British Cigarette Cards, 1983 Edition
Catalogue of British cigarette card issues from 1888 to 1983. Gives selling prices for odd cards and sets in first class condition from our extensive stocks. Details of over 4,000 series .... £5.00 post free

The Complete Illustrated Catalogue of British Cigarette Cards, 1983 Edition
A highly readable history of cigarette cards from their origins to the present day, with special chapters on collecting. Full size coloured illustrations of cards from more than 600 series plus a special pictorial feature on railways. The book includes the *Catalogue of British Cigarette Cards from 1888 to 1983* (as detailed above).. £12.95
plus £1.80 post

The International Catalogue of Cigarette Cards
With over 200 colour illustrations, this companion volume to the above book, contains sections on the history and development of international cards. Details of over 2000 series.................. £7.95
plus £1.20 post

Trade Card Catalogue (1983 edition). Gives selling prices for odd cards and sets in first-class condition from our extensive stocks. Details of over 4000 series .... £3.50 post free

Handbook Part I ('H' reference). British cigarette card issues 1888 to 1919. 172 pages of listings of un-numbered series, illustrations, etc... £4.50 post free

Handbook Part II ('Ha' reference). British cigarette card issues 1920 to 1940, plus amendments and additions to Part I. 164 pages of listings of un-numbered series, illustrations, etc............... £4.50 post free

Other reference books

Collecting Cigarette Cards and other Trade Issues by Dorothy Bagnall. An illustrated paperback	£3.50 post free
Directory of British Issuers	£1.50 post free
Glossary of Cartophilic Terms	£1.50 post free
Issues of Abdulla/Adkin/Anstie	£1.50 post free
Issues of Ardath	£1.50 post free
Issues of Churchman	£1.50 post free
Issues of Faulkner	£1.50 post free
Issues of Gallaher	£1.50 post free
Issues of Hill	£1.50 post free
Issues of Lambert & Butler	£1.50 post free
Issues of Godfrey Phillips	£1.50 post free
Issues of Player	£1.50 post free
Issues of Taddy	£1.50 post free
Wills Reference Book	£5.00 post free
Ogdens and Guinea Gold Reference Book	£10.00 post free
B.A.T. and Tobacco War Reference Book	£10.00 post free
British Trade Index Part I (pre-1945 issues)	£7.00 post free
World Tobacco Index Part I	£10.00 post free
World Tobacco Index Part II	£10.00 post free
World Tobacco Index Part III	£10.00 post free
Guide Book No 1 — Ty-Phoo Tea Cards	£1.50 post free
Guide Book No 2 — F. & J. Smith Cards	£2.00 post free
Guide Book No 3 — A. & B. C. Gum Cards	£2.75 post free

All the above books are available from
THE LONDON CIGARETTE CARD COMPANY LTD.,
SUTTON ROAD, SOMERTON, SOMERSET, TA11 6QP
Tel. Somerton (0458) 73452